D1263369

METHODS IN VIROLOGY

VOLUME IV

METHODS IN VIROLOGY
Advisory Board

METHODS IN VIROLOGY

EDITED BY

KARL MARAMOROSCH

BOYCE THOMPSON INSTITUTE FOR PLANT RESEARCH
YONKERS, NEW YORK

AND

HILARY KOPROWSKI

THE WISTAR INSTITUTE OF ANATOMY AND BIOLOGY
PHILADELPHIA, PENNSYLVANIA

Volume IV

ACADEMIC PRESS   New York San Francisco London   1968
A Subsidiary of Harcourt Brace Jovanovich, Publishers

ACADEMIC PRESS INC.
111 Fifth Avenue, New York, New York 10003

United Kingdom Edition published by
ACADEMIC PRESS, INC. (LONDON) LTD.
24/28 Oval Road, London NW1

LIBRARY OF CONGRESS CATALOG CARD NUMBER: 66–30091

PRINTED IN THE UNITED STATES OF AMERICA

List of Contributors

Numbers in parentheses indicate the pages on which the authors' contributions begin.

*ANDREWES, C. H., Common Cold Research Unit, Salisbury, England (593).

BACHRACH, HOWARD L., Plum Island Animal Disease Laboratory, Animal Disease and Parasite Research Division, Agricultural Research Service, U. S. Department of Agriculture, Greenport, New York (351).

BREESE, SYDNEY S., JR., Plum Island Animal Disease Laboratory, Animal Disease and Parasite Research Division, Agricultural Research Service, U. S. Department of Agriculture, Greenport, New York (351).

BROWN, ARTHUR, Biological Sciences Laboratory, Fort Detrick, Frederick, Maryland (531).

CALLIS, JERRY J., Plum Island Animal Disease Laboratory, Greenport, New York (465).

CAMPBELL, ALLAN M., Biology Department, University of Rochester, Rochester, New York (279).

COTTRAL, GEORGE E., Plum Island Animal Disease Laboratory, Greenport, New York (465).

GINOZA, WILLIAM, Department of Biophysics, The Pennsylvania State University, University Park, Pennsylvania (139).

†HANAFUSA, HIDESABURO, Collège de France, Laboratoire de Médicine Expérimentale, Paris, France (321).

KLECZKOWSKI, A., Rothamsted Experimental Station, Harpenden, Herts, England (93, 615).

LEVY, ALLAN H., The Biomathematics Research Facility, Baylor University College of Medicine, Houston, Texas (1).

* Present address: Overchalke, Coombe Bissett, Salisbury, England.

† Present address: The Public Health Research Institute of the City of New York, Incorporated, New York, New York.

v

LINK, FRANTIŠEK, Swiss Serum and Vaccine Institute, Berne, Switzerland (211).

*MARKHAM, ROY, Agricultural Research Council's Virus Unit, Cambridge, England (503).

McKINNEY, HAROLD H., Crops Research Division, Agricultural Research Service, U. S. Department of Agriculture, Beltsville, Maryland (491).

OFFICER, JULIUS E., Biological Sciences Laboratory, Fort Detrick, Frederick, Maryland (531).

**OZEKI, HARUO, Department of Chemistry, National Institute of Health of Japan, Shinagawa-ku, Tokyo, Japan (565).

POTASH, LOUIS, Flow Laboratories Incorporated, Rockville, Maryland (371).

†SILBER, GUSTAVE, Crops Research Division, Agricultural Research Service, U. S. Department of Agriculture, Beltsville, Maryland (491).

‡SMITH, THOMAS J., Department of Microbiology, The Johns Hopkins University School of Medicine, Baltimore, Maryland (1).

¶WAGNER, ROBERT R., Department of Microbiology, The Johns Hopkins University School of Medicine, Baltimore, Maryland (1).

WARD, THOMAS G., Department of Virus Research, Microbiological Associated, Washington, D. C. (481).

WASSERMANN, FELIX E., Department of Microbiology, New York Medical College, New York, New York (53).

* Present address: John Innes Institute, Norfolk, England.
** Present address: Department of Biology, Faculty of Science, Osaka University, Toyonaka, Osaka, Japan.
† Present address: Division of Research Grants, National Institutes of Health, Public Health Service, U.S. Department of Health, Education, and Welfare, Bethesda, Maryland.
‡ Present address: Department of Virus Diseases, Walter Reed Army Institute of Research, Walter Reed Army Medical Center, Washington, D. C.
¶ Present address: Department of Microbiology, University of Virginia School of Medicine, Charlottesville, Virginia.

Preface

Tanto sa Ciascuno Quanto Opera*
St. Francis

Virology is a scientific discipline which operates far beyond the narrow confinement of its goals. Hence, descriptions of methods used to study viruses are scattered throughout articles dealing with all imaginable branches of the life sciences. The search for a particular technique may occupy as much of the scientist's time as the completion of experiments based on that technique.

It was to correct this unfortunate situation that the idea of "Methods in Virology" was first conceived. The editors felt that, in view of the steadily increasing interest in the field of virology, publication of a comprehensive and authoritative treatise on methods used in the study of human, animal, plant, insect, and bacterial viruses would be welcomed by their colleagues. This work will enable virologists, graduate students, and prospective students of virology to appreciate the diversity and scope of the methods currently being used to study viruses, and, most important, to evaluate the advantages, limitations, and pitfalls of these methods.

The contributors were chosen on the basis of their outstanding knowledge of a given method, either as creators of new techniques, or as recognized authorities in their specialized fields. Other than clarity of expression and limitations on the length of presentations, no restrictions were imposed on the contributors. For example, the form of presentation of each chapter was the prerogative of its author. Some chapters follow the time-proven outline of recipes found in cookbooks, others are written in a highly original—even controversial—and sophisticated style.

It was the editors' intent to provide readers interested in one particular technique with a self-contained chapter describing this technique. As a result of this decision, it was sometimes impossible to avoid overlap of information in some chapters. The editors felt that completeness of description warranted this occasional duplication.

The first four volumes of "Methods in Virology" have been published in rapid succession. As new methods of study of viruses develop, their descriptions will be included in future volumes.

* Everybody knows as much as he works.

The editors wish to take this opportunity to thank their Board of Advisors—F. C. Bawden, Sven Gard, George K. Hirst, S. E. Luria, André Lwoff, Roy Markham, K. F. Meyer, George E. Palade, C. Vago, and Robley C. Williams—for invaluable assistance provided in the preparation of this work. They are confident that these efforts were not made in vain, since they will provide virologists everywhere with new and valuable tools to facilitate their quests for new discoveries.

January, 1968

KARL MARAMOROSCH
HILARY KOPROWSKI

Table of Contents

List of Contributors .... **v**

Preface .... **vii**

Contents of Other Volumes .... **xv**

Chapter 1—**Techniques for the Study of Interferons in Animal Virus-Cell Systems**
ROBERT R. WAGNER, ALLAN H. LEVY, AND THOMAS J. SMITH

I. General Considerations	2
II. Production of Interferons	5
III. Bioassay	17
IV. Biologic Tests for Identification of Interferons	25
V. Effect of Physical and Chemical Agents	28
VI. Physical Properties and Purification	31
VII. Methods for Studying Interferon Biosynthesis	40
VIII. Methods for Studying Action of Interferons	45
Addendum	48
References	48

Chapter 2—**Methods for the Study of Viral Inhibitors**
FELIX E. WASSERMANN

I. Introduction	53
II. Specific Inhibition of Virus Infections	55
III. Nonspecific Inhibition of Virus Infections	60
References	91

Chapter 3—**Methods of Inactivation by Ultraviolet Radiation**
A. KLECZKOWSKI

I. Sources of Radiation	94
II. Methods of Exposure	98
III. Absorption of Radiation Energy	99
IV. Measurement of Radiation Intensity	118
V. Progress of Inactivation	129
References	138

Chapter 4—Inactivation of Viruses by Ionizing Radiation and by Heat

WILLIAM GINOZA

I. Introduction 139
II. Ionizing Radiation 140
III. Thermal Inactivation of Viruses 180
   References 205

Chapter 5—Methods for Testing Antiviral Agents

FRANTIŠEK LINK

I. Introduction: Principles of Prophylactic and Therapeutic
   Assays in Virology 211
II. Experiments in Animals 215
III. Experiments in Eggs 255
IV. Experiments in Tissue Cultures 263
V. Conclusion: Comments on Statistical Evaluation of the Experiment ... 274
   References 277

Chapter 6—Techniques for Studying Defective Bacteriophages

ALLAN M. CAMPBELL

I. Induction and Detection of Defective Lysogenic Bacteria 279
II. Detection and Properties of Defective Virus Particles 297
III. Genetic Localization of the Defect 305
IV. Complementation 311
V. Definition of the Physiological Block(s) 312
   References 319

Chapter 7—Methods for the Study of Defective Viruses

HIDESABURO HANAFUSA

I. Introduction 321
II. Defectiveness of Rous Sarcoma Virus 322
III. Experiments with Defective RSV 332
IV. Defective Plant Viruses 344
   Addendum 348
   References 348

Chapter 8—Cell Cultures and Pure Animal Virus in Quantity

HOWARD L. BACHRACH AND SYDNEY S. BREESE, JR.

I. Introduction 351
II. Production and Purification of Centigram Quantities of FMDV 352
III. Large-Scale Purification of Other Animal Viruses 366
    References 368

Chapter 9—Methods in Human Virus Vaccine Preparation

LOUIS POTASH

I. Introduction 372
II. Historical Development of Human Viral Vaccines 373
III. Virus Vaccine Manufacturing Standards 393
IV. Killed Virus Vaccine Production—Licensed Biologicals 402
V. Live Virus Vaccine Production—Licensed Biologicals 416
VI. Virus Vaccines—General Considerations 429
VII. Production of Experimental Vaccines—General Principles 443
VIII. Vaccine Production—Special Problems 451
IX. Summary 458
    References 458

Chapter 10—Methods for Containment of Animal Pathogens at the Plum Island Animal Disease Laboratory

JERRY J. CALLIS AND GEORGE E. COTTRAL

I. Introduction 465
II. General Features of a Microbiological Safety Program 466
III. Laboratory Location, Design, and Operation 472
IV. Animal Facilities 476
V. Laboratory Techniques 478

Chapter 11—Methods of Storage and Preservation of Animal Viruses

THOMAS G. WARD

I. Introduction 481
II. Principles 482
III. Glycerol Storage and Shipping 484
IV. Refrigeration 485
V. Freezing 486
VI. Lyophilization and Freeze-Drying 488
    References 489

Chapter 12—**Methods of Preservation and Storage of Plant Viruses**

HAROLD H. MCKINNEY AND GUSTAVE SILBER

I. Introduction 491
II. Laboratory Methods of Preservation 492
References 501

Chapter 13—**The Optical Diffractometer**

ROY MARKHAM

I. The Apparatus 504
II. The Alignment of the Optical System 507
III. Experimental Procedure 510
IV. The Use of the Optical Diffractometer 511
V. Other Methods for Examining Diffraction Patterns 527
References 529

Chapter 14—**Contamination of Cell Cultures by Mycoplasma (PPLO)**

ARTHUR BROWN AND JULIUS E. OFFICER

I. Introduction 531
II. Properties of Mycoplasma 532
III. Sources of Mycoplasma Contamination 533
IV. Procedures for Detection, Elimination, and Prevention and
Control of Mycoplasma Contamination 535
V. Summary 561
References 561

Chapter 15—**Methods for the Study of Colicine and Colicinogeny**

HARUO OZEKI

I. Introduction 565
II. Detection of Colicinogenic Strains 567
III. Genetic Transfer of Colicinogenic Properties 574
IV. Production of Colicine 581
V. Mode of Action 588
References 591

Chapter 16—**Methods of Virus Classification**

C. H. ANDREWES

I. Introduction 593
II. Fundamental Characters Useful for Defining Major Groups 595

III. Characters Used for Defining Groups at Lower Levels 599
IV. Characters of the Main Groups of Viruses 603
  V. Discussion 610
     References 612

Chapter 17—Experimental Design and Statistical Methods of Assay

A. KLECZKOWSKI

     The Summation Symbol 616
  I. Introduction 617
 II. Experimental Design 625
III. Probability 638
 IV. Frequency Distributions 642
  V. Tests of Significance 667
 VI. Estimation of Virus Concentration 705
     Appendix: Simple Derivations of Some Properties of the
       Mean and of the Variable 724
     References 730

Author Index 731

Subject Index 747

Contents of Other Volumes

Volume I

Natural Ecology
  Harald Norlin Johnson

Virus Hosts and Genetic Studies
  A. G. Dickinson and J. M. K. Mackay

Methods for the Study of Mosquitoes
  as Virus Hosts and Vectors
  Roy W. Chamberlain and W. Daniel
  Sudia

Methods of Studying Ticks and Mites
  as Virus Hosts and Vectors
  Cornelius B. Philip

Methods of Studying Plants as Virus
  Hosts
  L. Bos

Laboratory Methods of Virus Transmission in Multicellular Organisms
  D. Blaškovič and B. Styk

Mechanical Transmission of Plant Viruses
  C. E. Yarwood and R. W. Fulton

Plant Virus Transmission by Insects
  K. G. Swenson

Nematode Transmission
  D. J. Raski and W. B. Hewitt

Methods for Experimenting with Mite
  Transmission of Plant Viruses
  J. T. Slykhuis

Fungus Transmission of Plant Viruses
  D. S. Teakle

Plant Viruses: Transmission by Dodder
  C. W. Bennett

Graft Transmission of Plant Viruses
  L. Bos

Insect Pathogenic Viruses
  Kenneth M. Smith

Bacteriophage Techniques
  A. Eisenstark

Animal Tissue Culture
  J. S. Porterfield

Plant Tissue Culture
  B. Kassanis

Invertebrate Tissue Cultures
  C. Vago

AUTHOR INDEX—SUBJECT INDEX

Volume II

The Ultracentrifuge
  Roy Markham

Equilibrium Ultracentrifugation
  H. M. Mazzone

Density-Gradient Centrifugation
  Myron K. Brakke

Miscellaneous Problems in Virus Purification
  Myron K. Brakke

New Centrifugal Methods for Virus
  Isolation
  N. G. Anderson and G. B. Cline

Chromatography and Membrane Separation
  Lennart Philipson

Water–Organic Solvent Phase Systems
  Lennart Philipson

Virus Concentration by Ultrafiltration
  Karl Strohmaier

Diffusion
  Roy Markham

Two-Phase Separation of Viruses
  Per-Åke Albertsson

Volume II (*Continued*)

Purification of Virus by Adsorption on Cells and Elution
Felix E. Wassermann

Molecular Sieve Methods
G. K. Ackers and R. L. Steere

Filtration Techniques
Vernon P. Perry and Monroe M. Vincent

Electrophoresis of Viruses
A. Polson and B. Russell

Labeling of Viruses with Isotopes
Claudia Henry

Separation of Viruses into Components
R. K. Ralph and P. L. Bergquist

Methods of Degrading Nucleic Acids and Separating the Components
T. H. Lin and R. F. Maes

Assay of Infectivity of Nucleic Acids
S. Sarkar

AUTHOR INDEX—SUBJECT INDEX

Volume III

Analysis of Protein Constituents of Viruses
H. Fraenkel-Conrat and R. R. Rueckert

Analysis of Lipid Components of Viruses
David Kritchevsky and Irwin L. Shapiro

RNA Virus RNA Polymerase: Detection, Purification, and Properties
J. T. August and Lillian Eoyang

Immunological Techniques for Animal Viruses
Jordi Casals

Serological Techniques for Plant Viruses
R. E. F. Matthews

The Plaque Assay of Animal Viruses
Peter D. Cooper

Transformation Assays
M. G. P. Stoker and I. A. Macpherson

Methods for Selecting RNA Bacteriophage
Mamoru Watanabe and J. T. August

Structural Studies of Viruses
J. T. Finch and K. C. Holmes

Microscopic Techniques
Rex S. Spendlove

Electron Microscopy of Isolated Virus Particles and Their Components
Robert W. Horne

The Application of Thin Sectioning
C. Morgan and H. M. Rose

Autoradiographic Methods for Electron Microscopy
Nicole Granboulan

AUTHOR INDEX—SUBJECT INDEX

METHODS IN VIROLOGY

VOLUME IV

1 Techniques for the Study of Interferons in Animal Virus–Cell Systems

Robert R. Wagner, Allan H. Levy, and Thomas J. Smith

I.	General Considerations	2
	A. Definition of Interferon	2
	B. Interferon-Mediated versus Direct Viral Interference	3
II.	Production of Interferons	5
	A. Principles and Problems	5
	B. Choice of Inducing Virus	6
	C. Inducible Cells	11
	D. Interferon Production in Animals	13
	E. Other Inducing Agents	14
	F. Representative Systems	14
III.	Bioassay	17
	A. Choice of Cell System	18
	B. Choice of Indicator Virus	19
	C. Titration Methods	20
IV.	Biologic Tests for Identification of Interferons	25
	A. Lack of Antiviral Specificity	26
	B. Lack of Direct Antiviral Action	26
	C. Lack of Effect of Antiviral Antibody	26
	D. Other Negative Tests of Biologic Activity	26
	E. Adsorption of Interferon	27
	F. Species Specificity	27
	G. Antigenicity of Interferons	28
V.	Effect of Physical and Chemical Agents	28
	A. pH	28
	B. Heat	29
	C. UV Irradiation	29
	D. Enzymes	30
	E. Other Chemicals	30
	F. Storage	31
VI.	Physical Properties and Purification	31
	A. Precipitation	32
	B. Chromatography	33
	C. Electrophoresis	34
	D. Centrifugation	35
	E. Molecular Sieve Filtration	38

VII. Methods for Studying Interferon Biosynthesis 40
    A. Current Working Hypotheses 40
    B. Model Systems 43
VIII. Methods for Studying Action of Interferons 45
    A. Current Working Hypotheses 45
    B. Key Experiments 46
    Addendum 48
    References 48

I. General Considerations

A. DEFINITION OF INTERFERON

Interferons are a physically heterogeneous, but biologically related, class of cellular proteins that have one physiologic function in common: they interact with cells of the same or related animal species as the cells from which they are derived and, in so doing, set off a complex series of events that results in generalized resistance to viral infection. The first interferon was described by Isaacs and Lindenmann (1957) and was so named because the original observation was made during the course of studies on the phenomenon of viral interference (reviewed by Schlesinger, 1959; Wagner, 1960). The prototype experiment consisted of exposing Maitland-type cultures of chick embryo chorioallantois to influenza virus inactivated by heat or UV irradiation. Not only does this tissue become resistant to superinfection with infectious influenza virus (classical interference), but it releases a "soluble" inhibitor that can transfer the resistance to other chorioallantoic tissues. The resistance-promoting factor was quickly identified as a nonviral protein, or protein-containing compound, that was active in inhibiting replication of other animal viruses as well as the virus that induced its formation. It has been learned since this time that virtually every class of animal viruses is capable of inducing the formation of interferons that are active against heterologous as well as homologous viruses (reviewed by Ho, 1962; Isaacs, 1963). Both replicating and nonreplicating viruses may induce interferon formation by cells derived from different tissues and many animal species. Interferons have not been conclusively demonstrated for plant or bacterial viruses. An inhibitor with some of the properties of interferon has been found in plant tissues infected with tobacco mosaic virus, but the active principle appears to be RNA rather than protein (Sela *et al.*, 1966).

Recent studies indicate that viruses are not essential for inducing interferon synthesis by animal cells (reviewed by Glasgow, 1965). Bacteria and a variety of macromolecular compounds, most of them containing polysaccharides of microbial origin, stimulate the production of interferon in intact animals (Youngner and Stinebring, 1964; Ho, 1964b), sometimes in tissue culture (Kleinschmidt *et al.*, 1964) and leukocyte suspensions (Wheelock, 1965). These interferons are biologically similar to those induced by viruses but generally differ in physical properties (Youngner *et al.*, 1965). The physical differences may owe as much to the producing cell type as to the inducing agent.

B. INTERFERON-MEDIATED VERSUS DIRECT VIRAL INTERFERENCE

Interference in animal virus–cell systems (Schlesinger, 1959) can be conveniently divided into two types: *heterologous interference* denotes unilateral or reciprocal inhibition between completely unrelated viruses, and *homologous interference* is a term suggested for antagonism between closely related virus pairs. *Autointerference* appears to be a special case of homologous interference that occurs under conditions of high multiplicity infection with a population of antigenically homogeneous virus particles.

Interferon production is almost undoubtedly the most important, and possibly the only, factor in heterologous interference. The most striking example of this type is the remarkable resistance to infection with equine encephalitis viruses caused by prior infection with avirulent influenza virus (Henle and Henle, 1945; Vilches and Hirst, 1947). Evidence has been presented that the degree of interference is related to the capacity of influenza virus to induce the synthesis of interferon (Wagner, 1960, 1961). An extensive older literature (reviewed by Henle, 1950; Schlesinger, 1959) also contains many examples of homologous interference among influenza viruses, which are at least partially attributable to interferon production in infected tissues or cell cultures (see Isaacs, 1963). It has been shown that replication of influenza virus in the chick embryo allantois ceases at about the time that interferon synthesis begins in the same tissue (Wagner, 1963a). Baron (1963) and Wagner (1963b,c) reviewed the evidence for the role of endogenous tissue interferon as an intrinsic host mechanism for recovery from viral infections of various kinds. The universality of this phenomenon remains to be proved, but current evidence indicates that nonspecific resistance to viral infection often results from infection with homologous or heterologous viruses that induce interferon formation.

Interference by rubella virus with growth of Newcastle disease virus in cercopithicus monkey kidney cells, determined by the hemadsorption-negative plaque test (Marcus and Carver, 1965), may be an exception to the general rule that heterologous interference is mediated by interferon. The same rubella-infected cells are susceptible to the cytopathic action of ECHO virus type 11 and other heterologous viruses. However, rubella virus does induce interference with ECHO virus 11 in these cells after prolonged incubation (Parkman *et al.*, 1962) and does induce interferon production in human amnion cells (Neva and Weller, 1964) and monkey kidney cells (Parkman *et al.*, 1966).

The avalanche of research on interferon has tended to obscure the fact that homologous interference can also occur by direct competition or interaction between two viruses without the necessity for invoking cellular interferon as the mediator. The issue is further complicated by evidence that certain viruses, such as the Rous inhibitory factor (RIF) and herpesvirus, can interfere directly with homologous viruses (Rubin, 1960; Roizman, 1965) and can also induce the formation of interferon (Bader, 1962; Aurelian and Roizman, 1965). Two forms of direct viral interference can be recognized. In one, the homologous interfering virus destroys or preempts the cytoplasmic membrane receptors for attachment of the second or superinfecting virus (Baluda, 1959; Crowell, 1966). However, more commonly, direct interference occurs by competitive inhibition of the interfering virus pairs at an intracellular site. Cords and Holland (1964) showed that mixed enterovirus infection results in inhibition of RNA synthesis of the superinfecting virus under restricted conditions of multiplicity and timing. This interfering activity is reversed by guanidine, which suggests the requirement for unimpaired synthesis of interfering viral RNA, but guanidine also blocks interferon synthesis induced by poliovirus (Johnson and McLaren, 1965). Pohjanpelto and Cooper (1965) described a different type of direct interference between a heat-defective mutant of poliovirus and a homotypic wild type, which does not appear to depend on RNA synthesis of the interfering virus. Roizman (1965) presented another hypothesis for direct interference between homologous viruses, which deserves particular attention. He showed that infection of nonpermissive cells with a conditional lethal mutant of herpesvirus results in interference with a simultaneously infecting virulent mutant. He attributes this interference to the formation in nonpermissive cells of nonfunctional subunits coded for by the defective virus. There is still another potential mechanism of viral interference in animal cells exemplified by the transmissible interfering factor (T) of vesicular stomatitis virus, which was originally described by Cooper and Bellett

(1959). Huang and Wagner (1966) recently showed that T is a defective, truncated form that specifically interferes with homologous virus in a manner that suggests a viral coding error in the ordering of protein synthesis. Undoubtedly, more examples will come to light of direct interference caused by defective viruses, which will require particular care in distinguishing the effects from viral interference caused by interferon.

II. Production of Interferons

A. PRINCIPLES AND PROBLEMS

The capacity to synthesize interferon is a latent cellular function that is induced by viral infection or by other stimuli. The mechanisms and kinetics of interferon formation in model systems are considered in Section VII. Virtually all classes of viruses can serve as inducing agents, and all species and types of vertebrate cells seem to be capable of synthesizing interferon under certain conditions. By and large, the interferon-synthesizing efficiency of the virus–cell system can be determined only empirically. The only predictable factor is that viruses highly virulent for a specific cell type will usually fail to induce formation of significant quantities of interferon in that system. Conversely, cells completely resistant to infection, owing to failure of attachment or penetration of a specific virus, are also probably incapable of producing interferon. It seems likely that cells must undergo the initial stages of infection as a minimal requirement for viral induction of interferon synthesis, although the stages have not been studied in detail. The finding by Johnson and McLaren (1965) that guanidine hydrochloride blocks interferon synthesis by human amnion cells infected with poliovirus suggests that early expression of the viral genome is essential for interferon induction. However, few detailed analyses have been made of the critical factors and sequence of events leading to interferon induction. Nor have virus–cell systems been investigated systematically for their efficiency in producing interferon. Most investigators have chosen a system that works sufficiently well for them without standardizing the conditions for maximal reproducibility. Hence, there may be considerable variation from laboratory to laboratory as well as periods of lack of reproducibility in the same laboratory.

It is not possible at the present time to make quantitative comparisons of interferon yields obtained in different laboratories. In addition to variations in procedures for interferon production, the methods of titration and the test viruses used for assay are not uniform.

Each investigator has varied his techniques to suit his own needs and interests. A movement is now afoot to create international reference standards and titration procedures but, until such time as these become available and universally acceptable, quantitative comparisons of different systems have little validity. Therefore, the data from different laboratories recorded in this section afford only a relative comparison of the efficiency of interferon-producing systems. To complicate matters still further, animal tissues and cell cultures often contain antiviral substances, usually in low titer, that do not fulfill the criteria of interferons (see Section IV).

B. CHOICE OF INDUCING VIRUS

Tables I and II list some of the viruses that have been used to induce interferon production in cell cultures and animals. As noted, these include both DNA and RNA viruses, which range in size from the large poxviruses to the small picornaviruses (see earlier reviews by Ho, 1962; Isaacs, 1963). By and large the DNA viruses as a class are less efficient inducers, but they have not been as thoroughly screened. The myxoviruses and arboviruses are the best inducers of interferon synthesis in a wide variety of cell types. In contrast, the picornaviruses are generally less efficient inducers, although respectable interferon yields have been obtained from calf kidney cells infected with foot-and-mouth disease virus (Dinter and Philipson, 1962), from human amnion cells infected with poliovirus (Johnson and McLaren, 1965), and from mice infected with coxsackie B virus (Heineberg et al., 1964). It must be remembered that these and the following generalizations are based on studies of relatively few cell types. Choice of cell type and the virus–cell system used for assay is equal in importance to the choice of inducing virus. Simian virus 5, for example, has no capacity to stimulate interferon synthesis in rhesus (Choppin, 1964) or cercopithecus (Smith, 1966) kidney cells, whereas the same agent induces interferon production in hamster embryo (Choppin, 1966) and rabbit kidney cells (Smith, 1966).

A number of viruses appear to be incapable of inducing interferon synthesis, although they have been studied in only a limited number of cell types. Evidence for the presence of interferon in cultures infected with adenoviruses is not convincing, although an interferonlike inhibitor is released from cells exposed to boiled adenovirus (Khoobyarian and Fischinger, 1965). Careful studies with mouse cytomegalovirus in mouse embryo cultures, L cells, and intact mice have also failed to reveal interferon production (Osborn and Medearis, 1966). Con-

TABLE I

VIRAL INDUCTION OF INTERFERON SYNTHESIS IN CELL CULTURES (REPRESENTATIVE SYSTEMS)

Virus group	Inducing virus	Animal species	Cell type [(P)rimary or (S)table]	Interferon yield[a]	Key reference
Poxvirus	Vaccinia	Mouse	Fibroblast (S)	48	Glasgow and Habel (1962)
Herpesvirus	Herpes simplex	Chick	Fibroblast (P)	50	Lampson et al. (1965)
Adenovirus		Dog	Kidney (S)	8	Aurelian and Roizman (1965)
	Type 2 (heated)	Rabbit	Heart (S)	?	Khoobyarian and Fischinger (1965)
Papovavirus	Polyoma	Mouse	Fibroblast (P)	16	Allison (1961)
Myxovirus	NDV	Many	Many (P and S)	1,000±	—
	NDV	Rabbit	Kidney (P)	10,000	Smith and Wagner (1967a)
	Parainfluenza	Calf	Kidney (P)	32	Hermodsson (1964)
		Man	KB (S)	?	Chany (1961)
		Tortoise	Kidney (P)	64	Falcoff and Fauconnier (1965)
	Measles	Man	HeLa (S)	32	De Maeyer and Enders (1961)
	Rubella	Man	Amnion (P)	8	Neva and Weller (1964)
		Monkey	Kidney (P)	?	Parkman et al. (1966)
	Rous	Chick	Fibroblast (P)	Low	Bader (1962)
Arbovirus A	Sindbis	Chick	Fibroblast (P)	32	Ho and Breinig (1962)
	Chikungunya	Chick	Fibroblast (P)	600	Heller (1963)
	EEE	Mouse	L-929 (S)	32	Wagner (1963a)
	WEE	Mouse	L-929 (S)	50	Lockart (1963)
Arbovirus B	Tick-borne	Chick	Fibroblast (P)	128	Vilček (1963)
Picornavirus	Polio	Man	Amnion (P)	16	Johnson and McLaren (1965)
	Foot-and-mouth	Calf	Kidney (P)	16	Dinter and Philipson (1962)

[a] Interferon yields are in approximate units owing to great variation in assay procedures.

TABLE II
Interferon Production in Vivo (Representative Systems)

Animal	Inducing agent	Route[a]	Dose	Tissue	Peak time	Titer[b]	Key reference
Chick embryo	Influenza A (WS-E)	Allantoic	10^5 ID$_{50}$	Allantoic fluid	3 days	128+	Wagner (1961)
	Influenza B (Lee)	Allantoic	10^5 ID$_{50}$	Allantoic fluid	3 days	1,024	Cantell et al. (1965)
	NDV	Allantoic	10^5 ID$_{50}$	Allantoic fluid	3 days	128+	Cantell et al. (1965)
	Parainfluenza 1	Allantoic	10^5 ID$_{50}$	Allantoic fluid	5 days	30	Cantell et al. (1965)
Duck embryo	Influenza A (WS-E)	Allantoic	10^5 ID$_{50}$	Allantoic fluid	3 days	8	Wagner (1961)
Chicken	Powassan	iv	10^{10} LD$_{50}$	Blood	2–4 days	96	Larke (1965)
	Brucella abortus	iv	10^{10}	Blood	6–12 hours	128	Youngner and Stinebring (1964)
Mouse	NDV	iv	10^7 pfu	Blood	4 hours	100	Baron and Buckler (1963)
	Sindbis	iv	10^8 pfu	Blood	4 hours	27	Baron and Buckler (1963)
	Influenza A (PR8)	in	100 ID$_{50}$	Lung	3–5 days	32	Baron et al. (1964)
	West Nile	ic	600 LD$_{50}$	Brain	3–4 days	9,500[c]	Finter (1964, 1965)
	Coxsackie B1	ip	300 LD$_{50}$	Many	4 days	1,000	Heineberg et al. (1964)
	Sindbis	ic	500 pfu	Brain	2 days	1,024[d]	Vilček (1964)
	Endotoxin	ic	500 µg	Blood	2 hours	500	Youngner and Stinebring (1965)
Rabbit	Sindbis	ic	10^{10} pfu	Blood	7 hours	10,000	Kono and Ho (1965)
	NDV	iv	10^8 pfu	Blood	6 hours	10,000	Smith and Wagner (1967a)
	Endotoxin	iv	2 µg+	Blood	2 hours	128	Ho (1964b)
Man	Measles	sc	Vaccine	Blood	7–11 days	50	Petralli et al. (1965)
	Yellow fever	sc	Vaccine	Blood	6 days	180[d]	Wheelock and Sibley (1965)

[a] iv = intravenous; in = intranasal; ic = intracerebral; sc = subcutaneous.
[b] Titers are only approximate owing to variations in assay methods. Most are based on inhibition of pfu in PDD$_{50}$/ml.
[c] Quantitative hemadsorption titration.
[d] Inhibition of cytopathogenicity.

certed attempts to stimulate interferon production in chick, mouse, and rabbit cells infected with infectious or inactivated vesicular stomatitis virus were also unsuccessful (Wagner, 1966), presumably owing to the virulence of this agent (Wagner and Huang, 1966). A somewhat less virulent small-plaque variant has been reported to induce the formation of very low yields of interferon (Wagner et al., 1963). Failure to induce interferon formation may be related to the capacity of a virus to inhibit RNA synthesis in infected cells (Wagner and Huang, 1966), but this is not likely to be the only factor.

Newcastle disease virus (NDV) is by far the most useful agent for producing interferons in high yield. Only in its most susceptible host, the chick embryo, does NDV sometimes induce only moderate amounts of interferon (Baron, 1964). Mammalian cells respond to infection with the highest titers of interferon recorded for any virus–cell system. High yields are produced within 8–12 hours after infection with NDV of primary cultures of mouse embryo fibroblasts (A. H. Levy, 1966), L cells (Wagner, 1964), rabbit kidney cells (Smith, 1966), calf kidney cells (Hermodsson, 1963), and, undoubtedly, many others. NDV does not ordinarily undergo a complete cycle of replication in these cells, although noninfectious hemagglutinin may be formed, and the cells frequently survive the infection. In addition, high titers of interferon appear in the blood of mice (Baron and Buckler, 1963), rabbits (Ho, 1964b), and chickens (Youngner and Stinebring, 1964) after intravenous injection of NDV.

Other factors also determine the interferon-inducing activity of viruses. Among these are the following:

1. *Multiplicity*

In general, relatively high inputs of infecting virus are required for rapid induction of interferon synthesis. However, few systematic studies have been made on the relationship of infecting dose to interferon yield. The infecting dose appears to be more critical for those viruses that multiply poorly or not at all in a particular cell type. In the case of NDV we have found that an input ratio of ~5 plaque-forming units (pfu)/cell is optimal for producing high yields and that higher multiplicities are not necessary (Wagner, 1966). Chikungunya virus is reported to be a better inducer when chick embryo cells are infected at low multiplicity, i.e., 0.06 pfu/cell (Gifford, 1963), but we have had better results at inputs of 1 pfu/cell (Wagner, 1966). Aurelian and Roizman (1965) found that nonreplicating herpesvirus induced maximal interferon yields in cultures of nonpermissive DK cells infected at a multiplicity of 10. Higher or lower multiplicities resulted in no interferon production or reduced yields. Viruses that replicate in and cross-infect cells can, of course, reach a mass sufficient to induce interferon synthesis even when infection is initiated at low multiplicity. However, earlier production and higher titers can be expected when the inoculum contains sufficient virus to infect most of the cells in a culture without causing cytotoxicity. Hence, we have usually aimed for an input ratio of ~5 pfu/cell to test the interferon-inducing activity of a virus in an unknown system. It is also wise to remember to sample the cultures within 6 hours of infection, when the titers may be maximal, as well as at 24 hours.

2. *Strain Variation of Inducing Viruses*

A number of attempts have been made to compare the interferon-inducing activities of different strains of the same virus. Baron (1964) examined eight NDV strains of varying virulence for chickens and made the surprising observation that chick embryos infected with strains of low virulence produced no interferon. However, the yields in allantoic fluid after infection with virulent viruses were very low. We have compared three NDV strains in L and Krebs-2 mouse cells and found slightly higher interferon yields on induction with an avirulent vaccine strain, but the differences were not consistent (Wagner, 1966). More significant differences in interferon-inducing activity can be demonstrated with large- and small-plaque mutants of Western equine encephalitis virus (Lockart, 1963). In addition, Friedman *et al.* (1963) found that a strain of polyomavirus of low oncogenicity induced somewhat more interferon in mouse embryo cultures than did a large-plaque strain of high oncogenicity. More striking differences have been noted between virulent and avirulent strains of herpes simplex and parainfluenza viruses. The host-range herpes mutant studied by Aurelian and Roizman (1965) was incapable of inducing interferon synthesis in dog kidney cells, whereas a conditional lethal herpes mutant did induce interferon formation in nonpermissive cells. Strain variation has been best demonstrated with parainfluenza 3 virus; strains of human origin induce abundant interferon production in calf kidney cells, whereas infection with virulent bovine strains results in no detectable interferon synthesis (Hermodsson, 1964).

3. *Inactivated Virus*

Early studies by Lindenmann *et al.* (1957) revealed that influenza virus inactivated by heat or UV irradiation retains its capacity to induce interferon synthesis (reviewed by Isaacs, 1963). This appears to be a general property of myxoviruses; similar findings have been reported by Paucker *et al.* (1962) for NDV and by Hermodsson (1964) for parainfluenza 3 virus. In fact, higher interferon yields can sometimes be obtained by prior irradiation of inducing virus. Excessive heating or irradiation will, of course, destroy interferon-inducing activity. Heat-inactivated Rous sarcoma virus also induces interferon production (Bader, 1962). In contrast, interferon-inducing activity of arboviruses and, possibly, picornaviruses appears to be far more labile. Inactivation of the infectivity of poliovirus (Ho and Enders, 1959). Russian tick-borne virus (Vilček, 1963), Sindbis virus (Ho and Breinig, 1962), and Western equine encephalitis virus (Lockart, 1963) results in loss of interferon-inducing activity. However, heat-inactivated chikungunya virus does induce interferon production by chick embryo cells (Gifford and Heller, 1963). Systematic analysis of heat and UV dose–response curves of infectivity versus interferon-inducing activity could shed more light on the nature of the interferon response to different classes of viruses.

It is also evident that interferon induction is dependent on the input of inactivated virus. Burke and Buchan (1965) showed that infection of chick embryo cell cultures with 80 hemagglutinating units of UV-irradiated Mel. influenza virus (7.25×10^5 ergs/cm^2) results in 10 times more interferon production than does infection with 20 hemagglutinating units of the same irradiated virus.

4. *Reinduction*

Lindenmann *et al.* (1957) showed that heat-inactivated influenza virus can repeatedly induce interferon formation in the same culture of suspended chick chorioallantoic cells. The second crop was obtained in as good yield as the first. The failure of Burke and Buchan (1965) to induce a second crop of interferon by reinfection of chick fibroblast cultures with NDVuv may have owed to the cytotoxic effect of the first infection. Although heated Sindbis virus does not stimulate interferon production, it seems to serve as a primer for interferon production induced by infectious virus (Ho and Breinig, 1962). In fact, Friedman (1966) found evidence that interferon itself may be a primer that facilitates more interferon production.

C. INDUCIBLE CELLS

1. *Primary Tissue Cultures*

Table I indicates that interferon is produced by cells of vertebrate species ranging from man to the tortoise and fish. In addition to those species listed, interferons have been induced by viral infection of cells cultured from tissues of rats, guinea pigs, hamsters, ferrets, sheep, pigs, and monkeys (see Isaacs, 1963). Not much is known about comparative efficiencies of cells from different organs to synthesize interferon. Owing to convenience in their preparation, primary (or secondary) cultures of renal epithelium or fibroblasts from preparations of embryonic skin and muscle have been most extensively tested and found to be quite satisfactory in general. Primary human amnion cultures also have provided an available source of cells for interferon production.

In our experience rabbit renal epithelium provides the most reliable tissue for rapid production of interferon in high yield, particularly when NDV is used as the inducing virus (Smith, 1966).

2. *Continuous Cell Lines*

Cells derived from tumors or transformed *in vitro* were once thought to be generally inferior to primary or secondary tissue cultures as producers of interferon, but this is not necessarily the case. In fact, Gresser and Enders (1962) showed that a stable line of human amnion cells produced enough interferon in response to infection with Sindbis virus to protect primary amnion cells in mixed cultures. Some confusion arose in early studies because interferons induced in cultures of continuous cell lines were tested in cultures of the same tumor cells, which are, generally, less sensitive to interferon action (see Section III). Titers are usually much higher when tested on primary cell cultures of the same species regardless of the tissue source. However, some variation in interferon-synthesizing capacity has been noted among clones of HeLa cells (Cantell and Paucker, 1963) and of mouse L cells (Lockart, 1965). Interesting differences in interferon synthesis have also been reported to occur among lines of hamster cells transformed with carcinogenic hydrocarbons (Rotem *et al.*, 1964). In our experience, one of the most satisfactory systems for studying interferon synthesis is the highly malignant, ascitic form of the Krebs-2 mouse carcinoma (Wagner and Huang, 1966). Krebs-2 cells in suspended culture produce abundant amounts of interferon when stimulated with NDV; this interferon does not inhibit virus replication in Krebs-2 cells but can be assayed on L cells.

3. *Leukocytes*

Gresser (1961) originally described the production of interferon by human leukocytes in response to viral infection. Leukocytes, predominantly of mononuclear type, present in peritoneal exudates of mice also produce interferon after infection with vaccinia virus (Glasgow and Habel, 1963; Glasgow, 1966) and NDV or influenza virus (Lackovič and Borecky, 1966). In an important experiment, Wheelock (1965) demonstrated that human blood leukocytes can produce two kinds of interferon: one formed in response to infection with NDV was typically stable to heat and low pH, while the other, induced by exposure to phytohemagglutinin (extract of kidney bean), was relatively labile. Smith and Wagner (1967a) found that macrophages are the interferon-producing cells in peritoneal exudates of rabbits. These cells "spontaneously" release at 37°C a labile species of interferon, but can also be induced by NDV infection to synthesize extremely large quantities of stable interferon.

D. INTERFERON PRODUCTION IN ANIMALS

Table II summarizes selected data on the appearance of interferons in the tissues and body fluids of animals injected with viruses, bacteria, or bacterial products. At least three kinds of interferon responses can be distinguished. Infection of chick embryo allantois or mouse brain, for example, results in viral multiplication and delayed appearance of interferon, which reaches peak titers only after several days. In many animals, the appearance of circulating interferon coincides with the viremic phase of infection (Baron et al., 1966a). The second type of response is the appearance of interferon within 2 hours after intravenous injection of massive doses of virus. Third, intravenous injection of bacteria or bacterial endotoxin induces an even more rapid appearance of interferon in blood serum or plasma. The interferon response to intravenous injection of either viruses or bacterial products is transitory; peak titers are achieved in 2–6 hours, and the viral inhibitor largely disappears by 24 hours.

Recent experiments indicate that circulating interferons may be of several different molecular species, depending, apparently, on whether the inducing agent is of viral or bacterial origin. Endotoxin-induced interferons also tend to be more readily inactivated by heat or low pH. Studies of molecular weight of different mouse interferons (Hallum et al., 1965) estimated by filtration through Sephadex G-100 (see Section VI) gave the following results: NDV-induced $\cong$ 25,000; endotoxin-induced $\cong$ 85,000–89,000; brucella-induced $\cong$ 77,000 and 54,000 (two peaks). To complicate matters, Lampson et al. (1966) claim to have found in mouse serum after NDV induction two different interferons with molecular weights of 38,000 and 23,500, and isoelectric points at pH 7.4 and 7.7, respectively. However, the resolving power of their Sephadex column is not convincing.

E. OTHER INDUCING AGENTS

Interferon production can also be induced by substances other than those of viral or bacterial origin. The most interesting of these is statolon, a complex polyanionic polysaccharide obtained from the mold *Penicillium stoloniferum* (Kleinschmidt et al., 1964). This inducer could be classified among the bacterial endotoxins except for the observations that it induces interferon synthesis in mouse tissue culture, which endotoxin does not, as well as in mice (Kleinschmidt and Murphy, 1965). Smith (1966) confirmed these findings in experiments with cultures of rabbit kidney cells and leukocytes. Merigan and Kleinschmidt (1965) found that statolon induces both an 85,000 molecular weight species of interferon in the serum of mice and a 30,000 molecular weight species in mouse spleen or L cells. Merigan (1967) also found that phytohemagglutinin induces in human leukocytes the formation of still another interferon of 18,000 molecular weight. Helenine, a product of the mold *Penicillium funiculosum*, resembles statolon in its capacity to induce interferon formation in mice and in cultures of mouse L cells (Rytel et al., 1966).

The question whether foreign or denatured nucleic acid can stimulate interferon production (Isaacs et al., 1963) is still in abeyance. Preparations of nucleic acids are themselves virucidal, and the levels of antiviral activity in RNA-treated cell cultures are very low.

F. REPRESENTATIVE SYSTEMS

1. *Chick Embryo-Influenza Virus* (Wagner, 1960, 1961, 1963a; Cantell et al., 1965)

This system is one of the simplest and most reliable methods for bulk production of interferon. No special precautions are required to obtain consistently high-titered preparations in large volumes. Commercial laboratories can readily manufacture liter quantities as a by-product of influenza vaccine production. The variations in titer from egg to egg should be less than 10-fold; the complete absence of interferon in any one allantoic fluid can usually be attributed to improper inoculation of virus. Attention to a few simple details should insure consistently optimal yields.

a. *Choice of Virus.* The WSE strain of influenza A and the Lee strain of influenza B are somewhat superior to PR8 (A), A_2 strains, NDV, and mumps, and far superior to Sendai (parainfluenza 1).

b. *Dose of Inoculum.* 10^4-10^5 EID_{50} (50% egg-infective dose).

c. *Route of Inoculation.* Allantoic.

d. *Age of Embryo.* Ten to 11 days.

e. *Time of Incubation.* Sixty to 72 hours.

f. *Temperature of Incubation.* Depending on the virus, 37°–40°C.

g. *Harvesting of Allantoic Fluid.* It is advisable but not essential to chill the embryo before removing the allantoic fluid.

h. *Procedures Recommended for Processing Allantoic Fluids.* Three 1-hour cycles of centrifugation at 50,000–100,000 g should remove all hemagglutinin and reduce infectivity to less than 10^3 EID_{50}. The final supernatant should be dialyzed against large volumes of 0.01–0.1 M HCl for 24 hours at 4°C, followed by overnight dialysis at 4°C against 2 liters of Earle's buffered saline solution containing phenol red (pH 7.2). Influenza virus can also be removed from the fluids by adsorption at 4°C on 10% packed chicken erythrocytes. The titer of crude interferon should remain constant for several weeks at 4°C and for several months at −20°C. Purified chick interferon is much more labile (Lampson *et al.*, 1963). Frequent freezing and thawing should be avoided.

2. *Virus-Infected Cell Cultures* (Paucker *et al.*, 1962; Heller, 1963; Wagner, 1964; Wagner and Huang, 1965)

Surprisingly few detailed analyses of the kinetics of interferon formation have been made under optimal experimental conditions. The results of many studies are unreliable because interferon titers were determined by percent plaque inhibition at one or just a few dilutions (see Section III). In others, little attention has been paid to cell concentration, multiplicity of infection, state of the cells and virus, medium, temperature, pH, etc. The model systems described here are those with which we have had some experience. Certain parameters could have been better controlled, but, in general, all factors known to influence interferon formation and assay have been considered. The systems best studied to date are chick cell–arbovirus A, L cell–NDV, and Krebs-2 ascites cell–NDV. More consistently higher interferon yields [5000 plaque-depressing doses (PDD_{50})] can be obtained by NDV infection of rabbit kidney (Smith, 1966) cells. Rabbit interferon has the additional advantage of being more stable on storage than is mouse interferon.

a. Chick Cell Monolayers Infected with Chikungunya Virus. About 10^7 cells from trypsinized suspensions of 10-day-old chick embryos in 10 ml of 0.25% lactalbumin hydrolyzate in Earle's buffered saline solution or medium 199 supplemented with 4–5% calf serum are seeded into screw-capped milk-dilution bottles (surface $\cong 40$ cm^2). By 24 hours at 37°C the monolayer should be confluent and contain approximately 1–2×10^7 cells, predominantly fibroblasts. After removing the medium and washing the cells with phosphate-buffered saline (PBS), chickungunya virus in a volume of 0.5–1 ml is added to the drained cell layer and adsorption permitted for 30–60 minutes at 37°C. The optimal multiplicity of infection must be determined by trial and error; we have had satisfactory results at an input ratio of 1–5 pfu/cell. After infection the cell layer may be washed, although this is not necessary, and the monolayer covered with lactalbumin hydrolyzate or medium 199 containing 2% serum. The cells should be incubated at 37°C in a relatively high CO_2 atmosphere. Isaacs (1962) reported greater interferon yields at an incubation temperature of 39°C or higher. Interferon can be detected in the medium within 4 hours after the end of adsorption. The increase in titer is linear and reaches a peak at 12–18 hours after infection. Care must be taken to rid the medium of virus by centrifugation at 100,000 g and acidification to pH 2. Maximal interferon titers should range from 100 to 600 PDD$_{50}$/ml for chick embryo cells using vesicular stomatitis or chikungunya as the test viruses.

b. L Cell Monolayers Infected with NDV. About 3–4×10^6 L cells in 10 ml of medium 199 supplemented with 20% calf serum are seeded into screw-capped milk-dilution bottles. By 24–48 hours at 37°C, confluent monolayers contain 6–8×10^6 cells. After draining the medium the cell layer is infected with 1 ml of NDV at an input ratio of 5 pfu/cell and adsorption permitted for 30–60 minutes at 37°C. The cells are then washed twice with 20 ml of PBS and covered with medium 199 with $NaHCO_3$ but without added serum. After incubation at 37°C in high CO_2, interferon should appear in the medium 2–4 hours after the end of virus attachment and should increase linearly to a peak at 12–18 hours. Maximal titers range from 250 to 500 PDD$_{50}$/ml when assayed on L cells (the yL line; Wagner, 1965) or mouse embryo monolayers using encephalomyocarditis or vesicular stomatitis as the test viruses. It is essential to process the interferon-containing medium by three cycles of centrifugation at 100,000 g followed by acidification to pH 2 in order to rid the medium of residual interfering NDV. There is no advantage in disrupting the cells, because interferon is released very rapidly after its formation. In our experience higher interferon yields are obtained from cells infected with a vaccine strain of NDV rather than with more virulent strains. We have noted lower yields in suspensions of infected L cells. Entirely comparable or slightly higher interferon titers can be obtained from NDV-infected monolayers of primary mouse embryo cultures.

c. *Suspensions of Krebs-2 Ascites Cells Infected with NDV.* These cells are ideal for short-term experiments that call for suspended cell cultures. They are readily available in abundant quantities when maintained by weekly intraperitoneal passage in ordinary Swiss mice injected with ascitic fluid diluted 10^{-1} to 10^{-3}. The ascitic fluid is aspirated just prior to use, the cells sedimented by centrifugation at ~400 rpm, counted in a hemacytometer, and washed twice with PBS. The pelleted cells are infected with 1 ml of NDV at an input ratio of 5 pfu/cell. Adsorption is carried out in a 12-ml conical centrifuge tube that is submerged and shaken constantly in a water bath maintained at 37°C. The cells are then washed twice more with 10 ml of cold PBS to remove unattached virus. The infected cells are suspended in medium 199 to a final concentration of 2×10^6 cells/ml and transferred in 10-ml (or 20-ml) volumes to siliconized 125-ml Erlenmeyer flasks. Krebs-2 cultures need not be gassed with CO_2 because of their high rate of glycolysis and evolution of CO_2. Flasks should be tightly stoppered with screw caps or silicone stoppers. The cells are kept in suspension by gentle agitation on a rotary shaker (about 60 cycles/minute), with the flasks submerged in a water bath maintained at the desired temperature (usually 37°C). At intervals after infection, aliquots of suspended Krebs-2 cells can be removed, sedimented, and the supernatant medium assayed for interferon content after removing residual NDV by sedimentation and acidification. Interferon appears in the medium in this system by 3–4 hours, and the titer increases linearly to a peak of 160–320 PDD_{50}/ml by 8–14 hours after NDV infection. This method should be equally adaptable to other virus–cell systems and is particularly advantageous for correlating studies of interferon synthesis with viral replication and biochemical alterations.

III. Bioassay

The bioassay of all interferons depends ultimately on protection afforded cells against one or more manifestations of viral infection. Interferons inhibit viral replication within protected cells and prevent or delay those events associated with viral replication. Thus, depending on the virus–cell system, titrations of interferons can be based on decreased yield of infectious virus or of viral products (such as hemagglutinin and antigen), as well as decreased cytopathic effects, hemadsorption, immunofluorescence, and, in the case of tumor viruses, cytologic transformation or synthesis of T antigen. No practical methods have been devised for assaying interferons by their inhibitory effects on early biochemical events in viral infection (see Section VIII).

The *precision* of interferon quantitation largely depends on the precision attainable in measuring the particular viral effect whose inhibition is used to mark the action of interferon. Assays based on inhibition of hemagglutinin formation, for example, are subject to considerable error because of inherent variations in yield and of titration errors in the range of 50%. On the other hand, interferon assays based on inhibition of plaque formation can be refined to reduce the error to 10% or less, equivalent to the sampling error of plaque assays.

The *sensitivity* of interferon assays depends on the susceptibility to interferon of both the test cell system and the indicator virus. Ideally, the investigator should choose cells and viruses of maximal susceptibility, but factors such as expense, technical ease in handling, and reproducibility must also be taken into consideration in selecting an assay procedure.

A. Choice of Cell System

Cell cultures selected for interferon assay are restricted to the species of origin of the particular interferon preparation. In addition, with some notable exceptions (Cantell and Paucker, 1963), primary cell cultures are generally far more susceptible to interferon action than continuous cell lines derived from neoplastic tissues. Differences in susceptibility to interferon may also be present among cells from different tissues of the same animal. In fact, different clones of the same cell line may exhibit varying degrees of interferon sensitivity. For example, Lockart (1965) and Wagner (1965) found considerable variation in titers of the same interferon preparation assayed on different sublines of the L-929 line of mouse fibroblasts.

No information is available on the mechanisms determining these cellular differences in sensitivity, but they are at least partially genetically determined. It is unlikely that different rates of interferon adsorption are responsible factors, particularly in view of the observation (Merigan, 1964) that adsorption of inactive interferon from a heterologous species is similar to that of homologous interferon. Cellular sensitivity may be related in part to the maturity of the tissues used to prepare cell cultures; Isaacs and Baron (1960) found that allantoic membranes of young chick embryos are less susceptible to interferon action than membranes of older embryos. However, no apparent differences in titers of mouse interferon are detectable when assayed on primary mouse embryo cells compared with older secondary cultures (A. H. Levy, 1966). Nor does the metabolic state of the cultured cells appear to influence interferon titration, although there is some evidence that dividing cells are less sensitive than contact-inhibited cultures.

We have found the following monolayer cultures suitable for assay of homologous interferons by plaque inhibition: primary or secondary fibroblast cultures from 10- or 11-day-old chick embryos, primary or secondary fibroblast cultures from 16–18-day-old mouse embryos, L cells, and renal epithelium of 3-week-old rabbits. Other types of cultures in wide use are primary human amnion, diploid cell lines, calf kidney, and rat embryo.

B. Choice of Indicator Virus

A wide variety of viruses has been employed in the bioassay of interferons. Although vaccinia virus has been used extensively and with excellent reproducibility (Lindenmann and Gifford, 1963), DNA viruses in general appear to be less susceptible than RNA viruses. The arboviruses, particularly those of group A, have been quite popular because of their high degree of sensitivity to interferon and their ability to form plaques rapidly on chick embryo and other cell types. Studies with Eastern (Wagner, 1961) and Western (Lockart, 1963) equine encephalitis viruses have given reproducible results of high sensitivity and reliability. However, they have been largely supplanted by other arboviruses that are less dangerous for routine laboratory use. Burke and Buchan (1965) found that chikungunga and Bunyamwera viruses were about 4 times more sensitive than Semliki Forest virus. Many investigators have favored the use of Sindbis virus because of its sensitivity to interferon and reliable plaque formation on chick embryo cells. The myxoviruses have not been widely used because of delayed plaque formation and relative resistance of some types to interferon. However, Finter (1964) described an extremely sensitive assay procedure for calf, mouse, chick, and rabbit interferons by the quantitative hemadsorption (QH) method with Sendai and influenza A as the test viruses. We have found encephalomyocarditis virus to be very satisfactory for interferon assays on mouse embryo or L cells.

In recent years, vesicular stomatitis (VS) virus has gradually replaced most other indicator viruses in interferon assays. This virus has the great advantage of producing plaques or cytopathic effects on virtually all vertebrate cell monolayers in 1 or 2 days and is invariably susceptible to interferon. In addition, it is stable on storage, easy to prepare in high-titered stocks, and the plaques are easy to score. In our experience interferon titers with VS virus as the test virus are comparable to those obtained with Eastern equine encephalitis in chick cells or encephalomyocarditis virus in mouse cells. A small-plaque variant of VS virus was found to be slightly, but consistently, more sensitive than the large-plaque parent (Wagner *et al.*, 1963), and the Indiana serotype is slightly more sensitive than the New Jersey serotype, but the differences are not great.

C. TITRATION METHODS

1. *Inhibition of Virus Yield*

A yield-inhibition assay is a two-part test. In the first part, dilutions of interferon in maintenance medium are incubated with a series of cell cultures (usually for 4–24 hours at 37°C), following which the interferon-containing medium is removed and the cells challenged with a standard inoculum of the indicator virus. The fluids are harvested after further incubation of the interferon-treated cultures for a period of time sufficient to produce maximal yields of virus in appropriate controls. In the second part of the test, virus yields from each culture are measured either by plaque titration, cytopathic effect [50% tissue culture infective dose ($TCID_{50}$)], animal inoculation, hemagglutination, or other suitable quantitative procedure. The interferon titer is taken at some arbitrary end point, such as the reciprocal of the dilution that inhibits virus yield by 90%.

Although assays based on inhibition of virus yield have the advantage of relatively high sensitivity (Hermodsson and Philipson, 1963) and are widely applicable, these procedures are not recommended for routine use because they are cumbersome and subject to wide variations inherent in a two-part test. Only plaque assay of virus yield offers sufficient accuracy, but yields must be determined for each interferon dilution. All other procedures for measuring inhibition of virus replication are laborious and difficult to control, with the possible exception of hemagglutinin (HA) production by myxoviruses.

The original procedure of Isaacs and Lindenmann (1957) for assaying chick interferon consisted of measuring reduction in HA yields from suspended fragments of chick chorioallantoic membranes exposed to interferon prior to infection with influenza virus. The method is simple, can be readily applied to other cell systems, and is useful for titrations that do not call for precise quantitation. One modification (Burke, 1961) consists of incubating interferon or interferon dilutions at 37°C (usually overnight) with a series of cell cultures in any suitable medium. The tubes are then decanted and infected with the test myxovirus (e.g., PR8 strain of influenza A, 10^4 EID_{50}) at an input sufficient to produce optimal HA yields in 24–48 hours. Titers of interferon can be expressed as percentage reduction in HA yields based on HA titers in control cultures not treated with interferon or as the reciprocal of the dilution that reduces HA yields by 4 log_2 units.

Attempts to measure interferon potency at a single dilution usually lead to erroneous results, because the assumption of inverse proportionality between interferon concentration and virus yield probably holds only over a limited range. Clearly, the preferable procedure is to test each interferon sample at various dilutions along with a standard reference preparation. Isaacs (quoted by Lindenmann and Gifford, 1963) noted a linear response when the logarithm of interferon dilutions is plotted against the percentage reduction in HA yields. As in other biologic systems, logarithmic transformation appears to normalize the dose-response curve. By the use of such a calibration curve, it is possible to express interferon activity as the reciprocal of the dilution that reduces HA yield to 50% of controls. However, even with carefully constructed curves, the accuracy of the method is still suspect because of other critical factors such as heterogeneity in membrane fragments or cell cultures and variability in HA titrations.

Similar variability also applies to other assay procedures based on yield of infectious virus. The vagaries of such methods are emphasized by the studies of Gauntt and Lockart (1966), who found that interferon concentrations ranging from 220 to 3 units inhibited yields of Mengo virus in L cells by the same 80–90%. This inhibitory effect was no longer apparent at interferon concentrations of 1–0.1 units.

2. Inhibition of Cytopathic Effect (CPE)

This test is also based, indirectly, on inhibition of virus yield, which results in reduced and delayed cross-infection of cells with a cytopathogenic virus. The method is widely employed and is similar to titration of antibody by neutralization of virus-induced CPE in tube cultures. Series of cell cultures should, of course, be pretreated with interferon dilutions for some standard period of time (most investigators prefer 12–24 hours) prior to challenge with a standard dose of virus in the range of 10–100 $TCID_{50}$. The end point of the titration is usually taken as the dilution at which half the cultures are protected to some predetermined degree (e.g., 50% CPE) at a time when 90–100% CPE is noted in control cultures. Sreevalsan and Lockart (1962) found that the sensitivity of this method compared favorably with that of plaque inhibition and reduction in yield of Western equine encephalitis virus.

High concentrations of interferon may completely prevent CPE, but this effect can be overcome by higher inputs of challenge virus (or at lower interferon concentrations), thus resulting in delayed appearance of CPE. In addition to dose of test virus, particular attention must be paid to uniformity in cell numbers in each culture, conditions for cell maintenance, and the time at which end points are recorded.

3. Inhibition of Transformation

The capacity of interferon to prevent transformation of cells infected with tumor viruses can be made the basis of a useful assay. Bader (1962) showed that chick interferon blocks the formation of transformed foci induced by Rous sarcoma virus in monolayers of chick embryo cells. The procedure is essentially a variation of the plaque-inhibition assay and is subject to the same analytical considerations.

4. Plaque-Inhibition Assay

This technique (Wagner, 1961) is potentially the most precise procedure for titration of all interferons. Although its sensitivity for detecting small amounts of interferon is somewhat lower than virus-yield assays, this disadvantage is greatly outweighed by its simplicity and reproducibility. Conceptually, the plaque-inhibition assay for interferon is similar to the plaque-neutralization technique for assay of antibody potency (Dulbecco et al., 1956), with the obvious exception that interferons interact with test cells rather than indicator virus. Resistance of cell monolayers is manifested by a reduced number of plaques and a reduced size of those plaques that appear at higher interferon dilutions.

a. General Description of Procedure. The plaque-inhibition assay is applicable to any type of cell culture that readily forms confluent monolayers. Primary or secondary cultures are generally preferable because their sensitivity to interferons is usually greater than that of continuous cell lines. Any interferon-sensitive virus can be used provided that plaques form rapidly and consistently on the cell type under study. In practice, vesicular stomatitis virus can be used in almost all systems.

We have obtained the most satisfactory results with the following most recently modified procedure: Serial or, more preferably, parallel 2-fold dilutions of the putative interferon are prepared in medium 199 with 2% calf serum or in any other suitable maintenance medium. Two-milliliter aliquots of each dilution are then added to two or three drained replicate monolayers in 60-mm plastic plates and incubated for 4–6 hours at 37°C. Slightly higher titers can sometimes be obtained by overnight incubation with 2–4 ml of each dilution, but this is not usually essential. After interaction with the cell sheet, residual interferon is removed by aspiration, and each monolayer is infected with 0.2 ml of virus estimated to produce 50–100 plaques. Smaller numbers of plaques introduce too great a sampling error; larger numbers are more difficult to score accurately and often result in lower titers, although the end points are theoretically independent of input pfu (Lindenmann and Gifford, 1963). Ideally, the dilutions of interferon should encompass the full anticipated activity of the preparation, ranging from low dilutions that will completely inhibit plaque formation to high dilutions in which plaque numbers and size are indistinguishable from those in controls. At least three control plates previously exposed to medium alone should be included in each titration series. After allowing 1 hour at 37°C for virus adsorption, the cell sheets are covered with agar (or other overlay) without washing the monolayers or removing the residual virus inoculum. We usually incorporate neutral red in the overlay for chick embryo cultures but stain other cells several hours to a day before scoring the plaques. The titration is read at the earliest time, about 40 hours with VS virus, when a full or nearly full complement of small plaques appears in the control plates.

b. *Scoring.* Interferon reduces both the total number of plaques and their size. It is possible, therefore, to score the results in terms of both parameters. In fact, reduction in plaque size is frequently noted several 2-fold dilution steps beyond the point at which total numbers are significantly reduced. In practice, however, it is difficult to obtain consistent results using total plaque area as the criterion of interferon activity even by photographic reproduction and measuring devices. Hence, we have routinely based our titrations solely on plaque number without reference to plaque size. Although this mode of scoring undoubtedly wastes some of the information in the assay procedure, it provides a simple level of consistency (a plaque is visible or not at the time of reading). The end point of the titrations is expressed as that dilution of interferon at which the plaque number is reduced to 50% of the control count. Most investigators record their results as the 50% plaque-depressing dose (PDD_{50}).

Lindenmann and Gifford (1963) made a comprehensive analysis of the plaque-scoring procedure for interferon assays in which they used vaccinia as the test virus in chick embryo monolayers with a fluid overlay. They first observed the normal course of vaccinia plaque formation and found that the rate at which plaques emerged into visibility could be described by a normal sigmoid curve that reaches a maximum asymptotically. At any time from 18 hours after infection, the distribution of plaque diameters could be approximated by a gaussian curve. The kinetics of plaque development was best explained by assuming that a variable number of "infraplaques" are hidden below the threshold of visibility. The existence of these infraplaques makes it important to keep assay conditions constant in order to minimize variations in proportion of infraplaques to visible plaques. In interferon-treated cultures plaques emerge into visibility at a rate slower than that in untreated cultures and take a longer time to reach a maximum. Therefore, titers of interferon will appear to be lower when visible plaques are scored late after infection. However, some plaques in interferon-treated cultures are permanently inhibited even after prolonged incubation.

c. Statistical Evaluation of Plaque-Inhibition Assays. If the sole source of error in a plaque-inhibition assay arose from the variation inherent in random sampling, the predicted variance calculated from a Poisson distribution would be equal to the mean. Lindenmann and Gifford (1963) found that the variance of the vaccinia virus assay itself as well as the interferon plaque-inhibition assay is approximately twice that of the mean. They interpreted these findings to indicate that other factors were operative in addition to those resulting from sampling. Inhomogeneity of biologic responses of the cell monolayers to interferon or to challenge virus could be a source of this greater than predicted error. Such variability seems to delimit the biologic boundaries of the system but is neither cause nor justification for abandoning efforts to control its precision within these limits.

By using three or four replicate plates at each dilution, Lindenmann and Gifford (1963) were able to achieve a coefficient of variation of 19% in their titrations of stock vaccinia virus or of plaque inhibition by interferon. They also employed dilutions that would ensure data encompassing the range of 20–80% plaque inhibition with each titration. The most useful way of expressing the results is a probit transformation. A straight line can be obtained if the probit of plaque inhibition is plotted against sample dilution. When the data obtained from assays of two separate interferon preparations are plotted in this manner, the antilog of the distance between the two lines measured parallel to the x axis (dilution) is a measure of relative interferon potency.

Lindenmann and Gifford (1963) also established the reproducibility of their vaccinia plaque-inhibition titration procedure. In a series of six separate assays of the same interferon preparation titrated in three dilution steps with three replicate plates at each step, the mean interferon concentration was found to be 33.5 $PDD_{50}/\mu l$ with a range of 20–74 and a standard error of 20.1. Thus, it appears that an assay with three replicates can discriminate between interferons with somewhat less than 2-fold differences in potency. Although this precision may not seem to be impressive, it is wise to remember that even this level of quantitation is achieved only with replicate determinations.

IV. Biologic Tests for Identification of Interferons

A major pitfall in interferon research is the frequent contamination of crude preparations with other antiviral substances. Ho (1964a) described in detail the problem he encountered in identifying a viral inhibitor present in homogenates of "normal" chick embryo cells, which had some of the properties of interferon. Buckler and Baron (1966) found similar acid-stable inhibitors of vaccinia virus in normal mouse serum and lung extracts, as well as uninfected allantoic fluid of chick embryos. A related potential difficulty is the presence in animal tissues of masked or latent viruses that can interfere with replication of the test virus used for assay of interferon. Presumably, similar viruses or mycoplasmas contaminating continuous cell lines would pose the same problem, although Yershov and Zhdanov (1965) detected no interferon in mycoplasma-infected cultures. The greatest danger, however, is failure to rid putative interferon preparations of the inducing virus or its noninfectious products. We have encountered this problem, particularly with NDV, which retains interfering activity even after prolonged exposure to acid. Under most circumstances, therefore, it is unsafe to assume that an antiviral substance is an interferon unless it has been at least partially purified by differential centrifugation or precipitation. Even then, it must fulfill certain physicochemical criteria (see Section V) and exhibit at least some of the biologic properties listed below.

A. Lack of Antiviral Specificity

Interferons are not virus specific (Ho, 1962). Therefore, all candidate interferons should be tested initially against two or more unrelated viruses.

B. Lack of Direct Antiviral Action

Interferons are not virucidal but exert their effect on the virus-infected cell (Wagner, 1961). Therefore, infectivity should be completely recovered from a mixture of virus and interferon that is diluted beyond the effective interferon concentration. Another and more critical test is to incubate the undiluted interferon preparation with ~100 pfu of test virus and plate the mixture directly on a monolayer of cells from an animal species heterologous to the one used for preparing the interferon. If the plaque count is the same as that in an appropriate control, then the preparation presumably does not contain inhibitors other than interferon.

C. Lack of Effect of Antiviral Antibody

Interferons are cellular rather than viral products. As expected, therefore, their activity is not neutralized by specific antibody directed against the viruses used to induce their formation (Isaacs and Lindenmann, 1957). This observation provides an important and simple means for distinguishing the antiviral activity of interferon from that of contaminating virus. Evidence for the presence of interferon is incomplete unless its antiviral activity is shown to be unaffected by potent viral antibody. Some investigators have used antiserum routinely to rid interferon preparations of inducing virus, but this method alone may not be entirely reliable because of the unneutralized virus fraction always present in virus–antibody mixtures.

D. Other Negative Tests of Biologic Activity

Crude preparations of interferons have been reported to affect many cellular functions. These effects almost undoubtedly result from contaminants. Purified interferons appear to have no influence on virus attachment, cell division, aerobic glycolysis, or synthesis of cellular RNA, DNA, and protein (Baron et al., 1966b; H. B. Levy and Merigan, 1966).

E. ADSORPTION OF INTERFERON

Several investigators have presented data purporting to demonstrate uptake of interferon by cell layers (see Wagner, 1961); others have disputed these claims. If, as we believe, interferon does attach to cells irreversibly, the process is slow and inefficient. Moreover, interferon prepared from cells of one animal species shows no selective affinity for attachment to the same cells. Purified chick and mouse interferons adsorb equally well on cells of the heterologous species or even on wettable glass surfaces (Lampson *et al.*, 1963; Merigan, 1964). In our experience the chances of demonstrating interferon adsorption are considerably enhanced by applying small volumes ($\sim$0.1 ml) of moderately high-titered interferon to a large number (6–10) of cell monolayers. After incubation for 1 hour at 20°–37°C, the fluids are aspirated, pooled, and 0.1-ml aliquots transferred to a second series of monolayers (necessarily fewer, owing to evaporation), thence to a third, and so on. Directly after removing the interferon inocula, each monolayer is challenged with an estimated 100 pfu of a test virus and covered with agar (or other overlay). The decline in plaque-reducing activity of interferon on serial transfer can be plotted as a function of interferon adsorption.

F. SPECIES SPECIFICITY

This interesting biologic property is an important criterion of interferon activity. In recent years, virtually all investigators have agreed that the action of interferon produced by cells of one animal species is highly specific for cells of the same species. Several studies appear to show minor degrees of cross-reactivity among presumably related species, e.g., the action of monkey interferon on human cells (Sutton and Tyrrell, 1961) and duck interferon on chick cells (Wagner, 1961). A careful, quantitative study of mouse serum interferon showed about 5% activity when titrated on rat and hamster cells and less than 0.1% on chick and monkey cells when compared with plaque inhibition of vesicular stomatitis virus on mouse cells (Buckler and Baron, 1966). However, only crude interferons were used in these studies. Purified and concentrated interferons prepared from chick, mouse, human, or rabbit cells have no activity (<0.1%) when tested on heterologous cells of unrelated or distantly related species (Lampson *et al.*, 1963; Merigan, 1964). Until proved otherwise, an antiviral substance should not be considered an interferon unless its antiviral activity is found to be restricted to cells of its species of origin.

G. Antigenicity of Interferons

After abortive attempts by other investigators, Paucker (1964) finally succeeded in demonstrating unequivocally that mouse (L cell) and chick interferons induce specific antiinterferon antibodies in guinea pigs and rabbits. The immunization procedure consisted of weekly intramuscular injections of guinea pigs with 1 ml (or weekly intraperitoneal injections of rabbits with 2 ml) of interferons at a concentration of 1000 PDD_{50}/ml. Antibody appeared in the serum at about 10 weeks and reached respectable levels at 18–20 weeks. These antisera showed relatively weak, but definite, capacity to neutralize the inhibitory effect of interferon on plaque formation by VS virus plated on homologous cells. The sensitivity was enhanced about 10-fold by reducing the amount of interferon and the number of cells used in the antiinterferon assay. For this purpose Paucker adapted the phenol red color test as the indicator of VS virus replication, as well as inhibition of virus replication by interferon and neutralization of interferon inhibition of virus replication by antiserum against interferon. In this way he demonstrated that the active molecular sites of mouse, chick, and human interferons are antigenically unrelated, confirming in an elegant manner their species specificity. Low levels of antiviral activity of interferon preparations titrated on cells of heterologous species were not neutralized by specific antiinterferon serums. Immunologic tests of this type provide a critical basis for identification of interferons, but they are not recommended for routine use.

V. Effect of Physical and Chemical Agents

Interferons can be further characterized and identified on the basis of inactivation by physical and chemical agents. Reactivity can be measured only by loss of biologic activity, preferably by assay of plaque-reducing capacity before and after treatment. Compared with most proteins, interferons are relatively resistant to inactivation, although some, such as virus-induced mouse interferon and all nonviral-induced interferons, appear to be more labile. Few detailed analyses have been made of inactivation kinetics to derive physical constants that would provide data on molecular structure. Nevertheless, the following crude tests afford useful criteria for classification.

A. pH

Resistance to inactivation by acid (and alkali) is characteristic of all interferons; hence, this property qualifies as part of the definition of interferon. Wagner (1963a) and others showed that crude virus-induced chick interferon is stable at 4°C for 48 hours over a pH range of 1–11; more than 75% of the activity is lost at pH 12.6. Lampson *et al.* (1963) reported no loss in titer of purified chick interferon held at pH 2–10 for 1 hour at 25°C, and only partial reduction in titer at pH 1 or 11. The same authors (1966) reported virtually identical results with virus-induced mouse serum interferon. Similar degrees of stability in acid or alkali have been reported for virus-induced interferons prepared from other animal species. However, endotoxin-induced interferons of higher molecular weight are more labile (Ho, 1964b). Interferon induced in human leukocytes by phytohemagglutinin is also unstable at a pH below 3 or above 9 (Wheelock, 1965). We have also examined an interferon "spontaneously" produced by rabbit macrophages and found 90% loss in its activity after exposure to pH 2 for 48 hours (Smith and Wagner, 1967b).

The procedure we have favored to test the pH stability of an interferon is to dialyze it against large volumes of normal saline (or KCl–HCl buffer) adjusted with HCl or NaOH to the desired pH. After 24–48 hours at 4°C, the preparation is redialyzed to neutrality against Earle's buffered saline containing phenol red as indicator. Other investigators have found it more convenient to add concentrated HCl or NaOH directly to the interferon sample. In most cases, it is sufficient to test the stability of interferon at pH 2.

B. HEAT

Heat stability is a more variable property among interferons than is pH stability. Virus-induced chick interferons, either crude (Wagner, 1963a) or purified (Lampson *et al.*, 1963; Merigan, 1964), show little reduction in titer after exposure to 65°C for 1 hour and only 50% reduction at 75°C. Complete inactivation occurs only at temperatures of 85°–100°C. Purified virus-induced mouse interferon, on the other hand, is almost completely destroyed at 65°C (Merigan, 1964). Virus-induced rabbit and human interferons resemble chick interferon in their heat stability. In contrast, endotoxin-induced and leukocyte interferons of rabbit origin are rapidly inactivated at 56°C (Ho, 1964b; Smith and Wagner, 1967b), despite the presence of protective inert proteins in crude preparations.

C. UV IRRADIATION

Purified chick interferon is completely inactivated by UV light ($\lambda = 2537$ Å) when exposed for 4 minutes at a distance of 7 inches

(Lampson *et al.*, 1963). The failure of other investigators to detect loss of interferon activity after UV irradiation (Lindenmann *et al.*, 1957) probably arises from the protection afforded by contaminating protein and other substances in their crude preparations.

D. ENZYMES

The biologic activity of all interferons that have been studied is destroyed by proteolytic enzymes. Lampson *et al.* (1963) reported loss of antiviral activity varying from 75 to 94% when purified chick interferon was incubated for 1–4 hours at 37°C with trypsin, chymotrypsin, pepsin, or papain. The following enzymes have no effect on chick interferon activity: leucine aminopeptidase, carboxypeptidase, α-amylase, lipase, DNase, RNase, and neuramindase (RDE) (Lampson *et al.*, 1963; Lindenmann *et al.*, 1957). These data are consistent with the preliminary chemical analysis by Lampson *et al.* (1963), who found that purified chick interferon contained only protein (perhaps a trace of carbohydrate).

Susceptibility to proteolytic enzymes is sufficiently consistent to constitute an additional test for identification of interferons. Our procedure is to add 100 μg of crystalline trypsin (3 × crystallized, Worthington Biochemical Corporation) to 1 ml of interferon that titers 160–320 PDD_{50}. After incubation for 1 hour at 37°C, the enzyme reaction is stopped by adding 200 μg of purified soybean inhibitor. Residual interferon is assayed by plaque inhibition along with a control containing interferon and soybean inhibitor. Treatment with trypsin should reduce the titer by at least 90%.

E. OTHER CHEMICALS

Few systematic studies have been made to determine the effects of organic solvents or oxidizing and reducing agents. Lindenmann *et al.* (1957) reported that chick interferon is destroyed by ether, but Chany (1961) found that interferon from KB cells was not. Lindenmann *et al.* (1957) also noted slight reduction in activity of chick interferon after exposure to 6 M urea but not to 0.001 M $NaIO_4$. Hallum *et al.* (1965) found that dialysis for 48 hours against 8 M urea caused no loss in titer of chick interferon but resulted in complete inactivation of virus-induced and endotoxin-induced mouse interferons. Merigan *et al.* (1965) reported about 80% inactivation of purified chick interferon after treatment with 10^{-1} M β-mercaptoethanol and suggested that its structure was that of a covalently bonded protein with one or more polypeptide chains. An attempt to reconstitute the activity of reduced interferon by air oxidation was unsuccessful. Similar susceptibility of virus-induced and endotoxin-induced mouse interferons was reported by Hallum *et al.* (1965). Diisopropyl fluoroacetate (5×10^{-3} M, 1 hour, 38°C, pH 8) had no effect on the biologic activity of purified chick interferon, suggesting absence of esterase activity (Merigan *et al.*, 1965). Schonne (1966) tested the effect of a large number of chemicals on Sindbis virus-induced rat interferon and found significant inactivation caused by the following: 4 M urea; 0.05 M cysteine; 1 M sodium thioglycollate (but not 0.142 M β-mercaptoethanol); 0.05 M sodium periodate; 0.01 M fluorodinitrobenzene; and 0.01 M phenyl isothiocyanate. Activity of rat interferon was unchanged after treatment with cyanate, p-chloromercuribenzoate, iodoacetamide, acetic anhydride, and acetimide.

F. STORAGE

The virus-induced interferons of low molecular weight are very stable on storage except for those produced in mouse cell cultures or tissues. We have stored crude chick interferon for 1 year at −20°C or for several months at 4°C without appreciable loss in titer. Lyophilized interferon is at least equally stable. Similar results have been obtained with purified interferons; however, considerable loss in titer occurs by adsorption onto glass surfaces, which can be prevented by adding 0.05% bovine serum albumin with or without 20 μg/ml of Tween 80 (Lampson *et al.*, 1963). Mouse interferons are much less stable (Merigan, 1964) and in our experience must be used within a week or so after preparation. We have also found that interferons produced spontaneously by rabbit leukocytes can be stored for several weeks, whereas virus-induced rabbit interferon retains its titer for several months at 4°C. Repeated freezing and thawing can cause considerable loss in biologic activity of all interferons. Therefore, it has been our practice to store our interferon preparations at 4°C (without preservatives) if they are to be used within several weeks, or at −20°C if aliquots of large pools are required for repeated studies.

VI. Physical Properties and Purification

The techniques for molecular characterization of interferons do not differ in essential details from those used for studying the physicochemical properties of other proteins. However, all published values for physical constants of interferons must be considered tentative because of intrinsic inaccuracies of the bioassay procedures (see Section III), which form the bases for all analyses of physical properties. Nevertheless, the data obtained from studies of virus-induced interferons are consistent with the properties of neutral proteins ranging in molecular weight from 18,000 to 45,000 daltons, depending on the animal species of origin. The endotoxin-induced interferons are generally of higher molecular weight, 90,000 or greater, but have been studied less thoroughly. Purification procedures presented here are based on the physical properties of only a few virus-induced interferons. At any stage in the purification procedures, the interferon preparation can be concentrated without loss in activity by pervaporation, pressure dialysis, lyophilization, or ultrafiltration.

A. Precipitation

1. *Ammonium Sulfate*

Interferons can be salted out. The method we havé used for chick interferon (Wagner, 1963a) is to add saturated ammonium sulfate to aliquots of interferons to give the desired percent saturation. After standing for 24 hours at room temperature, each precipitate is separated from its supernatant by centrifugation at 2000 rpm. The precipitates are dissolved in distilled water and reconstituted to their original volume or a smaller volume. Ammonium sulfate is removed from supernatants and redissolved precipitates by dialysis against running tap water for 72 hours, tested for residual sulfate with barium chloride, and redialyzed to isotonicity against Earle's buffered salt solution. At 70% saturation with ammonium sulfate all interferon activity is recovered in the precipitate, which provides an efficient method of concentration by redissolving the precipitate in a small volume. At 30 ánd 50% saturation about 10 and 50%, respectively, of interferon activity is precipitated.

2. *Acid*

The acid stability of virus-induced interferons (see Section V) and their relatively high isoelectric points provide another means for differential precipitation and partial purification. Lampson *et al.* (1963) found that dropwise addition of 2 N perchloric acid (PCA) to chick interferon at 5°C to a final concentration of 0.15 N results in precipitation of contaminating protein (90% or less). All the interferon activity remains in the supernatant after centrifugation at 1500 rpm for 30 minutes. Most investigators have used this procedure as the initial step for purification of interferons of all animal species.

3. Zinc Acetate

Precipitation with zinc acetate, 0.02 M final concentration, pH 6, is an efficient method for concentration of crude interferon and for slight purification (Lampson et al., 1963). The zinc-precipitated interferon is sedimented by centrifugation at 1500 rpm for 1 hour and the supernatant discarded. The precipitate is then dissolved by adding 0.2 N HCl to a pH of 2.5 at 5°C and dialyzed for 24 hours against buffered saline at pH 6 or higher. Finally, particulate matter is removed by centrifugation at 2000 rpm. The yields should be 50–100%. Lampson et al. (1963) used two cycles of zinc acetate precipitation before and one cycle after chromatography on carboxymethyl cellulose, but Merigan et al. (1965) reported satisfactory results and 10-fold purification with a single cycle after acidification with PCA. Poor results are obtained with zinc precipitation of purified interferon.

4. Acetone and Alcohol

Žemla and Vilček (1961) reported considerable purification of crude chick interferon by precipitation with 4 volumes of acetone added dropwise with constant stirring at —10° to —15°C. The resulting precipitate is collected on filter paper, washed with a small amount of cold acetone, and dried. The white powder is dissolved in water or saline to the concentration desired and clarified by low-speed centrifugation. The recovery of biologic activity should be 70–90% and the purification about 80-fold with respect to original nitrogen concentration. Fantes et al. (1964) found that ethanol or methanol at neutral pH also precipitates chick interferon. In an interesting refinement of this procedure, Fantes (1966) showed that the addition of 5 volumes of methanol at pH 2 resulted in precipitation of extraneous proteins but not interferon. When the supernatant is adjusted to pH 7.5, the interferon precipitates, apparently affording a considerable degree of purification.

B. CHROMATOGRAPHY

1. Carboxymethyl (CM) Cellulose

Lampson et al. (1963) achieved considerable additional purification of PCA–zinc precipitated chick interferon by two chromatographic cycles through a CM-cellulose column equilibrated with 0.01 M phosphate buffer at pH 6.0. The bulk of extraneous protein passes through the column, whereas the interferon is completely adsorbed. Interferon is retained on the column after successive elution with 0–0.1 M NaCl in 0.01 M phosphate at pH 6.0 and elutes as a sharp peak with 0.1 M NaCl–0.01 M phosphate at pH 8.0.

2. Carboxymethyl-Sephadex

Merigan et al. (1965) found CM-Sephadex (C-25) to be even more satisfactory than CM-cellulose for chromatographic studies of chick and mouse interferons. They used a 15 × 0.5 cm column equilibrated with 0.1 M sodium phosphate, pH 6.0. Interferon is retained at this pH and is eluted by a pH gradient, appearing in the effluent as a fairly sharp peak at pH 6.3–6.8 with about 10% trailing at higher pH. The overall recovery is about 35%, and total purification (including PCA–zinc precipitation steps) is approximately 6500-fold.

Lampson et al. (1965, 1966) used pH gradient elution from CM-Sephadex (C-50) for determining the isoelectric points of various interferons. By this method, chick interferon, induced either by influenza or herpesvirus, had an isoelectric point at pH 6.9–7.1 ± 0.4. The elution peaks of virus-induced mouse and rabbit interferons were slightly higher, ranging from ρH 7.0 to 7.4.

3. Other Methods

The resin Amberlite XE-64 proved to be satisfactory for chromatography of chick and mouse interferons (Merigan et al., 1965). Interferon adsorbs quantitatively on an Amberlite column equilibrated at pH 5 and elutes in good yield through a rising pH gradient produced with sodium succinate (0.5 M). Micronized alumina silicates (Doucil, Alusil) were also useful in the hands of Fantes et al. (1964; Fantes, 1966), who found that chick interferon absorbs at pH 5.5 and can be eluted with 0.5 M KSCN, pH 7.5. Wagner (1960) reported that chick interferon adsorbs completely on bentonite but less than 25% can be eluted with pyridine in a rising pH gradient to pH 9.

C. ELECTROPHORESIS

Electrophoresis has not proved to be as useful as chromatography for characterization and purification of interferons. Lampson et al. (1963) first reported that zone electrophoresis of chick interferon in

Pevikon as the supporting medium gave moderate further purification of PCA–zinc precipitated and chromatographed chick interferon. Electrophoresis was carried out in 0.03 M borate buffer at pH 8.9, and interferon was extracted from the gel with 0.05 N acetic acid in 0.9% NaCl. Other investigators have eliminated this step from purification procedures because of low recovery (less than 5–10%). Lampson et al., (1965) recently used cellulose acetate paper for ionophoresis studies and were unable to fix the isoelectric point of interferon at values more accurately than pH 6–8. More promising results and 5-fold purification were obtained by Merigan et al. (1965) by electrophoresis in a poly-acrylamide gel with β-alanine–acetate buffer and elution of biologic activity by incubation of 1-mm slices of gel in culture medium. It is unlikely that the protein bands visible after staining with amido black correspond to biologic activity.

The validity of electrophoretic methods for purification and char-acterization of interferons must be established by more refined tech-niques, preferably using preparative polyacrylamide disc electrophore-sis, which offers advantages of separation by filtration properties of the stacked gel as well as by electrical charge (Jovin et al., 1964).

D. CENTRIFUGATION

Centrifugation in a water solvent provides a useful method for clari-fication of crude interferons. The routine procedure we have favored (Wagner, 1961) is to subject our preparations to three cycles of centrifugation of 1–2 hours each at 50,000–100,000 g. Most of the in-ducing virus and other particulate matter is pelleted, and 100% of biologic activity remains in the supernatants. Prolonged centrifugation (72 hours) at 105,000 g may result in sedimentation of about 75% of biologic activity (Jovin, 1964), as does centrifugation in water for 2 hours at 254,000 g in the Spinco Model E analytical ultracentrifuge. It is of interest that this latter procedure, coupled with the use of a Fantus separation cell, enabled us to make a reasonably accurate esti-mate of 2 S for the sedimentation coefficient of chick interferon (Wag-ner and Levy, 1960). However, reliable determinations of the densities, sedimentation coefficients, and molecular weights of various interferons can be made at present only by density-gradient centrifugation. The use of the analytical ultracentrifuge is of no value because interferons cannot at present be prepared in sufficient concentration for direct observations of migrating boundaries by optical or UV absorption methods.

1. *Equilibrium (Isopycnic) Sedimentation*

This technique is based on establishment of an equilibrium zone of a macromolecular species in a centrifugal field where the density of the macromolecule is equivalent to that of the solvent. Interferons appear to behave in the same manner as other proteins. Linear gradients can be made satisfactorily with sucrose or cesium chloride, but any of the other common supporting media would presumably serve. One method that could be used is to layer high-titered interferon over a linear sucrose gradient in the usual manner and centrifuge at top speed for at least 48 hours in the Spinco SW-39 rotor head.

A useful and relatively simple procedure for determining the density of crude interferon is to permit a gradient of CsCl to form during centrifugation (Kreuz and Levy, 1965). Sufficient CsCl is added to 4.5 ml of interferon to give an initial density of 1.30–1.32 as determined by weighing in a 50-lambda pipet or by refractometer measurements. The required amount of CsCl will vary, depending on the degree of hydration of the particular lot. The CsCl–interferon mixtures are then centrifuged at 39,000 rpm in the Spinco SW-39 rotor for 48 hours, which approaches equilibrium. Two-drop fractions are collected from the bottom of the tube, 50-lambda aliquots weighed to determine density, the volumes adjusted to 0.5 ml, dialyzed to remove CsCl, and assayed by plaque inhibition using closely spaced dilutions which encompass the range of 30–70% plaque inhibition (see Section III).

In several such equilibrium sedimentation analyses of chick interferon, Kreuz and Levy (1965) showed that the curve of plaque inhibition is gaussian, with a peak corresponding to a solvent density of 1.30. This evidence of density homogeneity indicates that chick interferon is a discrete molecular species. It is also possible from these data to estimate the molecular weight of interferons by the formulation originally applied to DNA by Meselson *et al.* (1957), who showed that the standard deviation of the distribution curve for a given macromolecular species in a linear density gradient is inversely proportional to the square root of the molecular weight. The calculations for chick interferon are presented in the paper by Kreuz and Levy (1965).

2. *Zonal-Rate Centrifugation*

The sedimentation velocities of interferons can be determined by centrifugation in gradient solutions of varying densities along with marker macromolecules. Sedimentation coefficients based on centrifugation for one specified period of time can be calculated from such data;

quite obviously, the values are far less reliable than those obtained by conventional optical measurements with readings at multiple time points in the analytical ultracentrifuge. Using sucrose-gradient centrifugation, Rotem and Charlwood (1963) compared the behavior of chick and mouse interferons with that of a marker protein, lysozyme. They noted that the rate of sedimentation of the interferons and the lysozyme was similar, thus suggesting that the sedimentation coefficients of both interferons were roughly equivalent to the 1.9-S value for lysozyme. Molecular weight can be estimated by adapting the procedure originally applied by Martin and Ames (1961) for determining the sedimentation behavior of enzymes.

Kreuz and Levy (1965) devised another method for calculating the sedimentation coefficients of interferons that is probably more reliable than simple extrapolation between the sedimentation coefficients of bracketing marker proteins. It can be demonstrated that an appropriate combination of gradient and force of centrifugation provides conditions in the sedimentation tube such that the velocity of each molecular species can be made approximately constant; i.e., no significant acceleration of reference protein or interferon occurs during sedimentation. Under such conditions, the following equation represents a good approximation of the sedimentation coefficient:

$$s^{\circ}_{20,w}(\text{int}) = \frac{\Delta X_{\text{int}}}{\Delta X_{\text{ref}}} s^{\circ}_{20,w}(\text{ref}) \tag{1}$$

where ΔX_{int} and ΔX_{ref} are the distances moved by interferon and the reference molecule, respectively, and $s^{\circ}_{20,w}$ is the standard sedimentation coefficient (water as solvent at 20°C) of interferon (int) and the reference molecule (ref).

To achieve conditions of constant velocity, Kreuz and Levy (1965) employed the following system: Centrifuge tubes are filled with 4.8 ml of a solution of CsCl dissolved in PBS to provide a starting specific gravity of 1.13. Density gradients are formed by centrifugation of the uncharged tubes at 39,000 rpm in the Spinco SW-39 rotor head for 48 hours at 4°C. The tubes are removed with as little convection disturbance as possible (which is a greater problem with CsCl than with sucrose gradients). Interferon samples of 0.1 ml, to which had been added human serum albumin labeled with [125]I (^{125}I-HSA, 12,000 counts/minute), are then layered above the preformed density gradients. The tubes are next centrifuged for 10–12 hours, following which 3-drop fractions are removed from the bottom of each tube through a hole made with a hot 22-gage needle. The radioactivity of each sample is determined in a well-type crystal scintillation counter and specific gravity determined by weighing. Samples are then dialyzed and assayed for interferon content by plaque inhibition.

A plot of macromolecular concentration versus distance of migration in the centrifugal field was made for both chick interferon and the marker ^{125}I–HSA (Kreuz and Levy, 1965). The HSA moved approximately twice the distance moved by the interferon in the same time interval. By application of Eq. (1), the sedimentation coefficient of chick interferon was calculated to be 2.3 S. Although the method is relatively tedious, primarily due to the need for dialysis of each sample, the results are reproducible and probably more precise than other procedures that have been described.

E. MOLECULAR SIEVE FILTRATION

Filtration through Sephadex gels has been the most frequently employed and most useful method for estimating the molecular weights of interferons (Jungwirth and Bodo, 1964; Phillips and Wood, 1964; Kreuz and Levy, 1965; Merigan et al., 1965; Hallum et al., 1965; Lampson et al., 1966). The procedure can be expected to afford only 10-fold purification and recovery rates of 50–90% (Merigan et al., 1965); it also has been used to confirm molecular weight determinations estimated by centrifugation and to determine the diffusion coefficient for chick interferon, which was estimated to be 9.5×10^{-7} cm^2 sec^{-1} (Kreuz and Levy, 1965). The methods in general use appear to be fairly reliable but reported values for the molecular weight of chick interferon range from 26,000 to 45,000. Judging by the published reports, the variability from laboratory to laboratory may be attributable to various factors: (1) most columns have been too small; (2) the elution peaks are too broad; (3) internal marker proteins are too few in number; (4) the fraction volumes are too large for the size of the column; and, most important, (5) the assay procedures for interferon are insufficiently accurate and not standardized. Although few procedural details have been reported in the literature, the molecular weight determinations in many instances appear to be based on three to five widely spaced points that often show differences in titers well within the error of the assay method. We have also had similar difficulty in fixing the molecular weight of rabbit interferons. The following detailed procedure for use of a Sephadex G-100 column (Smith, 1966; Smith and Wagner, 1967b) is presented as a proposed standard method for estimating the molecular weights of virus-induced interferons (molecular weight $\leq 50,000$) in the hope that it will minimize the errors and variability inherent in the method. Sephadex G-150 or G-200 should be used for interferons of higher molecular weight.

We employ a column with an internal diameter of 3.35 cm and a bed height of 110 cm to provide a bed volume of ~974 ml. Powdered Sephadex G-100, 65 gm, is allowed to swell in an excess of PBS at pH 7.4 for 24 hours. The swollen gel is sterilized by autoclaving at 110°C for 40 minutes to minimize bacterial contamination. The column is packed at room temperature under sterile conditions, placed at 4°C, and connected to a reservoir of sterile PBS under a constant hydrostatic pressure head. Flow rate is regulated to 20 ml/hour by a stopcock at the bottom of the column.

Samples up to 2 ml in volume are appropriate for a column of these dimensions and are carefully layered between the eluant and the top of the gel bed by means of a peristaltic pump. Small-bore ($\frac{1}{16}$ inch internal diameter) autoclavable Tygon tubing (U.S. Stoneware Company) is convenient for loading the column. Effluent from the column is collected in 4-ml fractions by means of a volume-operated fraction collector. The exclusion volume of the column is fraction 70 (280 ml), and the peak of cytochrome c elution is fraction 165 (660 ml).

Various protein markers of known molecular weight are available for use as internal reference standards for Sephadex columns; a recent report by Andrews (1964) is an excellent reference for complete information on this subject. We have found the following proteins particularly useful as standard markers for determining the molecular weight of virus-induced interferon: bovine serum albumin, monomer (molecular weight, 67,000) and dimer (molecular weight, 134,000) (Armour Pharmaceutical Company); ovalbumin (molecular weight, 45,000) (Nutritional Biochemical Corporation); soybean trypsin inhibitor (molecular weight, 21,500) (Worthington Biochemical Corporation); and cytochrome c (molecular weight, 13,000) (Nutritional Biochemical Corporation). Each of these proteins is dissolved in PBS (35 mg/ml), filtered through a 0.45-μ Millipore filter, and 0.1 ml (3.5 mg) of each is incorporated into the column sample. Protein concentrations in the effluent fractions are determined spectrophotometrically at a wavelength of 215 mμ. Cytochrome c can also be read at 412 mμ. Blue dextran (0.2%, Pharmacia, Uppsala, Sweden), is used as an additional marker to determine the exclusion volume of the column and is read at either 215 or 625 mμ. Blue dextran and cytochrome c serve the additional purpose of evaluating column packing and efficiency of sample loading by observing for skewness and spread of the colored bands. Phenol red in culture medium of interferon samples serves similar purposes. The total recovery of all markers should be at least 70–90%.

Optical density on the abscissa is plotted against effluent fraction on the ordinate; the reference point for the molecular weight of each standard is designated either as the peak fractions (Andrews, 1964) or, even more accurately, as that fraction on the upslope of the absorbance curve that contains 50% of the optical density of the peak fraction. When these reference points for molecular weight, expressed as V_e (elution volume in milliliters)/V_t (total column volume in milliliters), are plotted against the log of the known molecular weights of the standards, a straight line should obtain over a molecular weight range of 13,000–67,000. The elution peaks should not vary by more than one fraction on repeated runs. After the column is carefully calibrated, it is our practice to incorporate only cytochrome c into the interferon sample to be chromatographed, because cytochrome c forms a visible band and its elution volume is well behind that of interferons and serum proteins.

Aliquots of effluent fractions are also assayed for interferon activity by the plaque-inhibition technique (see Section III). When high-titered interferons are placed on the column and fractions are tested at low dilution, the elution zone of interferon activity is considerably broader than that observed for the various protein standards, presumably owing to greater sensitivity of the bioassay. Interferon concentrations are, of course, always too low for spectrophotometric analysis. In our experience, the standard 2-fold dilution technique for interferon assay is not sufficiently accurate to determine exact elution peaks. Closely spaced dilutions made in parallel rather than in series will improve the accuracy of the titrations. As an additional refinement, after the zone of interferon activity has been determined, dilution of the highest titered fractions can be made such that plaque reduction is in the range of 20–80%. By testing each fraction on quadruplicate plates, the relative interferon concentration of the peak fraction can be read as the highest percentage plaque reduction.

The molecular weight of the interferon is read from the curve of V_e/V_t against log molecular weight as determined for the standard reference proteins.

VII. Methods for Studying Interferon Biosynthesis

A. Current Working Hypotheses

The present state of the art does not permit presentation of a unified concept of the mechanism of interferon biosynthesis. However, certain general principles (reviewed by Wagner, 1965) have emerged from a large body of literature, which provide essential bases for future experimental design in any system that involves interferon production. One major problem is the physical differences among interferons derived from cells of different animal species as well as from the same animal species after different modes of induction. In fact, the capacity of the same cells to make two (or more) kinds of interferon has not been excluded. For convenience, the interferons from all animal species can be divided into two general classes: the stable interferons of relatively low molecular weight, which are induced by viral infection (or statolon), and the labile interferons of higher molecular weight, which are induced by bacterial endotoxins or other nonviral substances. These two classes of interferons appear to be formed by different mechanisms.

1. Virus-Induced Interferons

The sequence of events in cellular synthesis of virus-induced interferons has been adduced almost entirely from experiments with specific inhibitors of macromolecular synthesis. Some of the systems used in various laboratories have been chick embryo cell cultures infected with chikungunya virus (Heller, 1963) or with UV-irradiated NDV (Ho, 1964a) and mouse L cells or Krebs-2 ascites cells infected with NDV (Wagner, 1964; Wagner and Huang, 1965). Except for time differences, the data are comparable in each system.

The following interpretation of the available data on interferon synthesis seems reasonable at the present writing. Studies with actinomycin indicate that within 2 hours after interaction with virus the cells begin to synthesize an interferon-specific messenger RNA, which is presumably transcribed in response to some derepression mechanism. The genetic information for this function is almost undoubtedly encoded in cellular DNA and, from data obtained by UV-inactivation kinetics, is likely to be represented in L cells by a single cistron (Cogniaux-Le Clerc et al., 1966). However, cellular DNA synthesis does not seem to be required for optimal interferon production (Burke and Morrison, 1966). In the NDV–Krebs-2 system, the messenger continues to be transcribed between 2 and 6 hours after induction, even if cellular protein synthesis is blocked by puromycin (Wagner and Huang, 1965). The messenger is stable for at least 8 hours. The translational event, evidenced by detection of interferon, begins about 3 hours after virus induction and continues for 6–10 hours. Inhibitors of protein synthesis, such as puromycin, when introduced into the system at any stage, immediately shut off interferon production, which resumes when the inhibitor is withdrawn. The titer of interferon in the medium is always higher than it is in the cells, which is taken as evidence for rapid release after synthesis. The lag period from the time of NDV induction to the onset of interferon synthesis is about 8 hours in chick embryo cells (Ho, 1964a), about 3 hours in Krebs-2 or L cells (Wagner, 1964), and about 1 hour in primary rabbit kidney cells (Smith and Wagner, 1967a).

The experiments cited above appear to exclude the possibility that interferons exist in cells as inactive precursors and that viruses merely facilitate their activation and release. An alternative hypothesis, first proposed by Youngner (1966, personal communication), is that viral inducers may promote the synthesis of a cellular product other than interferon, which then converts an omnipresent interferon precursor into a biologically active form. Such an hypothesis may serve to reconcile the virus-induced and endotoxin-induced mechanisms of interferon formation. However, it also introduces an additional complex step, for which there is no evidence, and which is not readily amenable to experimental testing. Among other things, studies of this kind would seem to require the use of cell-free systems, which are not feasible at the present time for studying interferon formation.

2. *Endotoxin-Induced Interferons*

The relatively few studies of virus-induced synthesis of interferons in animals do not suggest a mechanism different from the one proposed for cell cultures. Ho and Kono (1965) found that actinomycin treatment of rabbits suppresses the appearance of circulating interferon after intravenous injection of NDV. Although Youngner *et al.* (1965) could not confirm this effect of actinomycin in mice, they did note that inhibition of protein synthesis in mice treated with puromycin or cycloheximide did reduce considerably the interferon response to injection of NDV or brucellae. Both groups of investigators agree that inhibitors of RNA and protein synthesis do not influence interferon formation induced in rabbits or mice by intravenous injection of bacterial endotoxins. From these observations they conclude that the labile interferons of high molecular weight are likely to be preformed and that endotoxins merely facilitate their release. This conclusion may well be correct, but we have found recently that "spontaneous" production of heat-labile interferon by cultures of rabbit mononuclear leukocytes is effectively prevented by actinomycin or puromycin (Smith and Wagner, 1967a).

Little is known about which cells produce interferon after intravenous injection of endotoxin. However, Ho and Kono (1965) noted that a state of tolerance develops within 1 day after a single injection of endotoxin or virus. In fact, prior injection of endotoxin markedly reduces the interferon response of a rabbit to a second injection of either endotoxin or virus. The tolerant state can be abolished with thorotrast, perhaps implicating the reticuloendothelial system (Kono and Ho, 1965). However, the tolerance mechanism is undoubtedly very complex, including the presence of inhibitors in the serum that inactivate the interferon-inducing capacity of endotoxin.

B. MODEL SYSTEMS

1. *Interferon Formation in Cell Cultures*

Although many different virus–cell systems can be used to study the mechanisms of interferon formation, we have found that the results are often erratic and difficult to reproduce from day to day. Ideally, experiments of this type call for systems in which interferon is synthesized rapidly after a short lag period. Only under these conditions can specific inhibitors be tested with any degree of confidence that the effects noted are not due to secondary alterations of multiple cellular functions. Frequently there is loss in integrity of the cytoplasmic membrane, resulting in cell death, before the observations can be completed. We recommend the following systems, not to the exclusion of others, but only because we have had firsthand experience with them.

a. Suspensions of Krebs-2 Cells (see Section II). This system is ideal for frequent sampling of cells and media, for periodic introduction or withdrawal of metabolic inhibitors, and for labeling with radioactive precursors of DNA, RNA, and protein. Aliquots of cells can also be removed for counts and histologic examination. After infection with NDV, the integrity of the cytoplasmic membrane should not be impaired for at least 12 hours, as determined by exclusion of the dye eosin.

b. Monolayer Cultures of Primary Rabbit Kidney Cells. In our experience these cultures produce the highest yields of interferon in the shortest period of time. After infection with NDV at a multiplicity of 5, interferon is first detected after a lag period of about 1 hour and reaches a titer of approximately 5000 PDD_{50}/ml (assayed against VS virus on homologous cells) in about 6 hours. Equivalent yields have been reported in cultures of calf kidney, human fibroblasts, and L cells after induction with NDV. Rabbit kidney cells (and L cells) are also suitable for studies of interferon formation after induction with statolon.

2. Interferon Formation in Animals

a. *Intravenous Injection.* As described by Baron and Buckler (1963), interferon appears in the serum of mice 1–2 hours after injection of NDV (10^8–10^9 pfu) into the tail vein. Maximal titers of 80–160 PDD_{50}/ml (versus EMC or VS virus on mouse embryo or L cells) are found in 4–6 hours. Interferon titers of 20,000 PDD_{50}/3 ml reported by Youngner et al. (1965) are probably due to differences in the assay procedure. We have found the rabbit to be a more satisfactory animal for most studies. After injection of 10^8–10^9 pfu into an ear vein, interferon appears in 2 hours and reaches titers of approximately 5000 PDD_{50}/ml in 6 hours. By 24 hours, the titers of circulating interferon fall to very low levels.

Both rabbits and mice make suitable hosts for studying interferon formation in response to intravenous injection of bacterial endotoxin or statolon. Rabbits appear to respond to smaller doses and can be bled more frequently.

b. *Other in Vivo Systems* (see Section II). Two additional systems for studying interferon formation in animals are allantoic infection of chick embryos with influenza virus (Wagner, 1963a) and intracerebral injection of mice with West Nile virus (Finter, 1964).

3. Inhibitors of Interferon Formation

a. *Actinomycin.* This antibiotic at doses of 1–2 μg/ml, or less, effectively blocks cellular RNA and interferon synthesis in the early stages of viral induction in cell cultures (Wagner and Huang, 1965, 1966). It is, of course, not suitable for use with sensitive DNA viruses, reovirus, or influenza virus. Its chief limitation is inability to reverse the effects.

b. *Inhibitors of Protein Synthesis.* Puromycin (10^{-5} M) completely inhibits interferon synthesis in Krebs-2 cells after induction with NDV (Wagner and Huang, 1965). The recommended dose for most tissue culture studies is 50 μg/ml (9.2×10^{-5} M). Puromycin is active at all stages of the cycle of interferon synthesis, and its effect can be completely reversed by washing the cells. Interferon synthesis by chick embryo cells is somewhat less well inhibited by p-fluorophenylalanine at doses of 25 μg/ml (Buchan and Burke, 1965); the inhibitory effect is rapidly reversed by equimolar concentrations of phenylalanine. Cycloheximide and acetoxycycloheximide are also, in our limited experience, extremely effective inhibitors of interferon synthesis *in vitro.*

c. Steroid Hormones. All investigators agree that the cortisones inhibit interferon formation, but the effects are relatively slight and somewhat inconsistent. Cortisone inhibits interferon production and increases virus yield slightly in chick embryos infected with influenza viruses (Kilbourne *et al.,* 1961; Reinicke, 1964; Smart and Kilbourne, 1966). However, relatively large doses (50 μg/ml) of hydrocortisone are required to suppress interferon formation in cultures of chick embryo cells infected with influenza virus (Reinicke, 1965). More potent steroids are effective inhibitors at smaller doses in rat embryo (De Maeyer and De Maeyer, 1963) and mouse cell cultures (Mendelson and Glasgow, 1966). The mechanism of action of cortisones is not known. Carcinogenic hydrocarbons have the same inhibitory effect on interferon synthesis (De Maeyer and De Maeyer, 1964) as does the androgen $\Delta',17\alpha$-methyltestosterone, which enhances protein synthesis rather than suppressing it (De Maeyer and De Maeyer, 1963).

Pretreatment of 34–38 gm mice with 5–10 mg of cortisone also results in 8–16-fold reduction in interferon titers of blood and spleen after induction by NDV administered intravenously (Rytel and Kilbourne, 1966). These effects may be related to steroid effects on lymphoid tissues.

VIII. Methods for Studying Action of Interferons

A. CURRENT WORKING HYPOTHESES

Only virus-induced interferons have been studied for their mechanism of action, and almost all experiments have been performed with chick embryo or mouse cells. There is no reason to believe, however, that other interferons and cell systems will be found to behave differently. It is clear that interferons interact directly with cells rather than with virus or viral constituents. The process is relatively slow and inefficient, and probably results in irreversible binding of at least a fraction of the interferon. Cells treated with interferon become increasingly resistant to infection with challenge viruses over a period of 4 hours or longer (Wagner, 1961), but the kinetics of the reaction have not been worked out in detail. It is known, however, that prolonged incubation of cells with interferon does not significantly augment the antiviral effect, as would be expected if the reaction were a simple linear function. On the other hand, there is some evidence from dose-response curves of plaque reduction (Ho, 1963) and inhibition of Rous focus-forming units (Bader, 1962) that the action of interferon simulates a first-order response over a narrow dose range.

A satisfactory mechanistic model of the antiviral action of interferons must take into account the following salient features of their biologic activity: lack of direct action on virus or viral RNA, lack of viral specificity, cell species specificity, and variation among cells of the same species (see Section IV). Interferons have been reported to affect a variety of cellular and viral functions, but many of these observations can be attributed to impurities in crude interferon preparations. A list of negative or negligible direct effects of interferon includes: rates of cell division, aerobic glycolysis, uncoupling of oxidative phosphorylation, total synthesis of cellular RNA and other macromolecules, and function of viral RNA synthetase (replicase) in a cell-free system. The only well-documented biochemical effects of interferons are inhibition of viral RNA synthesis and, probably, inhibition of early messenger functions of parental viral RNA.

Only one general hypothesis fits all the available experimental data on the mechanism of interferon action. Apparently, when an interferon interacts with a competent cell, it induces the formation of one or more new RNA messengers that are transcribed from cellular DNA. There then follows a translational event that results in synthesis of one or more new proteins, which are the true inhibitors of viral nucleic acid functions rather than interferon itself. These postulates are based on indirect evidence obtained by the use of specific metabolic antagonists of cellular RNA and protein synthesis. No investigators have reported serious attempts to isolate the hypothetical interferon-induced mRNA or the antiviral protein.

B. Key Experiments

1. Effect of Actinomycin on Interferon Action

Taylor (1964, 1965) performed the critical experiments that provide the basis for further study of the mechanism of interferon action. First, she demonstrated that replication of Semliki Forest virus and synthesis of its viral RNA were markedly inhibited in chick embryo cells pretreated with semipurified interferon. The inhibitory effect on viral RNA synthesis was measured by incorporation of adenosine-^{3}H into Schmidt-Thannhauser extracts of RNA. Other labeled nucleoside precursors would be suitable, and phenol extraction should be superior. In these experiments cellular RNA synthesis was blocked by the addition to the medium of actinomycin (1 μg/ml) *after* the cells were treated with interferon. Optimal times and doses were not worked out. However, when cells were first exposed to actinomycin and then treated with interferon, viral RNA synthesis was not inhibited. This experiment tells us that the action of interferon depends on intact capacity of the cells to transcribe RNA. A subsequent study by Lockart (1964) revealed that several hours are required for interferon to exert its optimal action, during which time the antiviral effect can be partially reversed by actinomycin. However, no detailed studies have been made on the kinetics of interferon-induced mRNA synthesis.

2. Effect of Inhibitors of Protein Synthesis

Puromycin (Lockart, 1964; S. Levine, 1964) and p-fluorophenylalanine (Friedman and Sonnabend, 1964) also inhibit the antiviral action of interferon. Dose and time relationships have not been studied in detail.

3. Viral RNA Synthesis

Gordon et al. (1966) made the most comprehensive analysis of the inhibitory action of interferon on viral RNA synthesis. They examined by zonal sucrose-density centrifugation all species of mengovirus RNA made in L cells treated with actinomycin. Their experiments show that interferon prevents incorporation of uridine-^{14}C into both the RNase-sensitive viral RNA that bands in the 40–60-S region and the RNase-resistant viral RNA that bands in the 16–22-S region. Moreover, these inhibitory effects could be reversed by exposing the cells to actinomycin prior to interferon. From these experiments they concluded that interferon (or, more precisely, an interferon-induced antiviral protein) interrupts viral replication at the early stage of formation of the template "minus" strand, thus precluding synthesis of both double- and single-stranded viral RNA. In addition, no partially polymerized viral RNA products could be detected under conditions of interferon inhibition.

4. Other Viral Functions

H. B. Levy and his associates (1966; H. B. Levy, 1964) found that interferon partially blocks the inhibition by mengovirus of RNA synthesis in L cells and the inhibition by Sindbis virus of RNA synthesis in chick embryo cells. These viral effects on cellular RNA synthesis are generally attributed to an inhibitory protein coded for by the viral genome; the supposition follows that interferon blocks this early viral product. However, similar interferon reversal of the viral inhibitor of cellular protein synthesis has not been noted. Oxman and Black (1966) showed that interferon profoundly inhibits malignant transformation of and T antigen synthesis in the 3T3 continuous line of mouse cells infected with the DNA-containing SV40 virus. The inhibition of T antigen formation, as determined by specific immunofluorescence, is most pronounced in cells pretreated with interferon; however, definite inhibition is still noted even when interferon is added 2 hours after SV40 infection, but not at 4 hours. If, as is thought, T antigen represents nonstructural viral protein(s), then interferon appears to inhibit synthesis of early viral proteins.

ADDENDUM

Since this manuscript was prepared about two years ago, much of the data and references on interferon production and action are considerably out of date. In particular, the studies by Marcus and Salb, 1966, and those of Joklik and Merigan, 1966, have revolutionized the biochemical approach to investigation of interferon action. Also, the interferon-inducing factor extracted from cultures of *Penicillium funiculosum* (helenine) was shown to be double-stranded RNA, the action of which could be mimicked by annealed, synthetic oligonucleotides (Lampson *et al.*, 1967). Much more data have also come to light on purification and physical properties of interferons, some of which are published in a book edited by N. B. Finter, 1966.

REFERENCES

Allison, A. C. (1961). *Virology* 15, 47.
Andrews, P. (1964). *Biochem. J.* 91, 222.
Aurelian, L., and Roizman, B. (1965). *J. Mol. Biol.* 11, 539.
Bader, J. P. (1962). *Virology* 16, 436.
Baluda, M. (1959). *Virology* 7, 315.
Baron, S. (1963). *Advan. Virus Res.* 10, 39.
Baron, S. (1964). *In* "Newcastle Disease Virus, an Evolving Pathogen" (R. P. Hanson, ed.), pp. 205–220. Univ. of Wisconsin Press, Madison, Wisconsin.
Baron, S., and Buckler, C. E. (1963). *Science* 141, 1061.
Baron, S., DuBuy, H. G., Buckler, C. E., and Johnson, M. L. (1964). *Proc. Soc. Exptl. Biol. Med.* 117, 338.
Baron, S., Buckler, C. E., McCloskey, R. V., Kirchstein, R. I., and Friedman, R. M. (1966a). *J. Immunol.* 96, 12, 17.
Baron, S., Merigan, T. C., and McKerlie, M. L. (1966b). *Proc. Soc. Exptl. Biol. Med.* 121, 50.
Buchan, A., and Burke, D. C. (1965). *Biochem. J.* 94, 9.
Buckler, C. E., and Baron, S. (1966). *J. Bacteriol.* 91, 231.
Burke, D. C. (1961). *Biochem. J.* 78, 556.
Burke, D. C., and Buchan, A. (1965). *Virology* 26, 28.
Burke, D. C., and Morrison, J. M. (1966). *Virology* 27, 108.
Cantell, K., and Paucker, K. (1963). *Virology* 19, 81.

Cantell, K., Valle, M., Schakir, R., Sukkonen, J. J., and Uroma, E. (1965). *Ann. Med. Exptl. Biol. Fenniae* **43,** 125.

Chany, C. (1961). *Virology* **13,** 485.

Choppin, P. W. (1964). *Virology* **23,** 224.

Choppin, P. W. (1966). Personal communication.

Cogniaux-Le Clerc, J., Levy, A. H., and Wagner, R. R. (1966). *Virology* **28,** 497.

Cooper, P. D., and Bellett, A. J. D. (1959). *J. Gen. Microbiol.* **21,** 485.

Cords, C. E., and Holland, J. J. (1964). *Virology* **22,** 226.

Crowell, R. L. (1966). *J. Bacteriol.* **91,** 198.

De Maeyer, E., and De Maeyer, J. (1963). *Nature* **197,** 724.

De Maeyer, E., and De Maeyer, J. (1964). *J. Natl. Cancer Inst.* **32,** 1317.

De Maeyer, E., and Enders, J. F. (1961). *Proc. Soc. Exptl. Biol. Med.* **107,** 573.

Dinter, Z., and Philipson, L. (1962). *Proc. Soc. Exptl. Biol. Med.* **109,** 893.

Dulbecco, R., Vogt, M., and Strickland, A. G. R. (1956). *Virology* **2,** 162.

Falcoff, E., and Fauconnier, B. (1965). *Proc. Soc. Exptl. Biol. Med.* **118,** 609.

Fantes, K. H. (1966). *In* "Interferons" (N. B. Finter, ed.). pp. 119–180. North Holland Publishing Co., Amsterdam.

Fantes, K. H., O'Neill, C., and Mason, P. J. (1964). *Biochem. J.* **91,** 20P.

Finter, N. B. (1964). *Virology* **24,** 589.

Finter, N. B. (1965). *Nature* **206,** 597.

Finter, N. B. (1966). *In* "Interferons" (N. B. Finter, ed.), North Holland Publishing Co., Amsterdam.

Friedman, R. M. (1966). *J. Immunol.* **96,** 872.

Friedman, R. M., and Sonnabend, J. A. (1964). *Nature* **203,** 366.

Friedman, R. M., Rabson, A. S., and Kirkham, W. R. (1963). *Proc. Soc. Exptl. Biol. Med.* **112,** 347.

Gauntt, C. J., and Lockart, R. Z., Jr. (1966). *J. Bacteriol.* **91,** 176.

Gifford, G. E. (1963) *Nature* **200,** 91.

Gifford, G. E., and Heller, E. (1963). *Nature* **200,** 50.

Glasgow, L. A. (1965). *J. Pediat.* **67,** 104.

Glasgow, L. A. (1966). *J. Bacteriol.* **91,** 2185.

Glasgow, L. A., and Habel, K. (1962). *J. Exptl. Med.* **115,** 503.

Glasgow, L. A., and Habel, K. (1963). *J. Exptl. Med.* **117,** 149.

Gordon, I., Chenault, S., Stevenson, D., and Acton, J. (1966). *J. Bacteriol.* **91,** 1230.

Gresser, I. (1961). *Proc. Soc. Exptl. Biol. Med.* **108,** 799.

Gresser, I., and Enders, J. F. (1962). *Virology* **16,** 428.

Hallum, J. V., Youngner, J. S., and Stinebring, W. R. (1965). *Virology* **27,** 429.

Heineberg, H., Gold, E., and Robbins, F. C. (1964). *Proc. Soc. Exptl. Biol. Med.* **115,** 947.

Heller, E. (1963). *Virology* **21,** 652.

Henle, W. (1950). *J. Immunol.* **64,** 203.

Henle, W., and Henle, G. (1945). *Am. J. Med. Sci.* **210,** 362.

Hermodsson, S. (1963). *Virology* **20,** 333.

Hermodsson, S. (1964). *Acta Pathol. Microbiol. Scand.* **62,** 133 and 224.

Hermodsson, S., and Philipson, L. (1963). *Proc. Soc. Exptl. Biol. Med.* **114,** 574.

Ho, M. (1962). *New Engl. J. Med.* **226,** 1258, 1313, and 1367.

Ho, M. (1963). *Proc. Soc. Exptl. Biol. Med.* **112,** 511.

Ho, M. (1964a). *Bacteriol. Rev.* **28,** 367.

Ho, M. (1964b). *Science* **146,** 1472.

Ho, M., and Breinig, M. K. (1962). *J. Immunol.* **89,** 177.
Ho, M., and Enders, J. F. (1959). *Virology* **9,** 446.
Ho, M., and Kono, Y. (1965). *Proc. Natl. Acad. Sci. U.S.* **53,** 220.
Huang, A. S., and Wagner, R. R. (1966). *Virology* **30,** 173.
Isaacs, A. (1962). *Cold Spring Harbor Symp. Quant. Biol.* **27,** 343.
Isaacs, A. (1963). *Advan. Virus Res.* **10,** 1.
Isaacs, A., and Baron, S. (1960). *Lancet* **II,** 946.
Isaacs, A., and Lindenmann, J. (1957). *Proc. Roy. Soc.* **B147,** 285 and 268.
Isaacs, A., Cox, R. A., and Rotem, Z. (1963). *Lancet* **II,** 113.
Johnson, T. C., and McLaren, L. C. (1965). *J. Bacteriol.* **90,** 565.
Joklik, W. K., and Merigan, T. C. (1966). *Proc. Natl. Acad. Sci. U.S.* **56,** 558.
Jovin, T. (1964). Unpublished data.
Jovin, T., Chrambach, A., and Naughton, M. A. (1964). *Anal. Biochem.* **9,** 351.
Jungwirth, C., and Bodo, G. (1964). *Biochem. Z.* **339,** 38.
Khoobyarian, N., and Fischinger, P. J. (1965). *Proc. Soc. Exptl. Biol. Med.* **120,** 533.
Kilbourne, E. D., Smart, K. M., and Pokorny, B. A. (1961). *Nature* **190,** 650.
Kleinschmidt, W. J., and Murphy, E. B. (1965). *Virology* **27,** 484.
Kleinschmidt, W. J., Cline, J. C., and Murphy, E. B. (1964). *Proc. Natl. Acad. Sci. U.S.* **52,** 741.
Kono, Y., and Ho, M. (1965). *Virology* **25,** 162.
Kreuz, L. E., and Levy, A. H. (1965). *J. Bacteriol.* **89,** 462.
Lackovič, V., and Borecky, L. (1966). *Acta Virol. (Prague)* **10,** 365.
Lampson, G. P., Tytell, A. A., Nemes, M. M., and Hilleman, M. R. (1963). *Proc. Soc. Exptl. Biol. Med.* **112,** 468.
Lampson, G. P., Tytell, A. A., Nemes, M. M., and Hilleman, M. R. (1965). *Proc. Soc. Exptl. Biol. Med.* **118,** 441.
Lampson, G. P., Tytell, A. A., Nemes, M. M., and Hilleman, M. R. (1966). *Proc. Soc. Exptl. Biol. Med.* **121,** 377.
Lampson, G. P., Tytell, A. A., Field, A. K., Nemes, M. M., and Hilleman, M. R. (1967). *Proc. Natl. Acad. Sci. U.S.* **58,** 782.
Larke, R. P. B. (1965). *Proc. Soc. Exptl. Biol. Med.* **119,** 1234.
Levine, S. (1964). *Virology* **24,** 586.
Levy, A. H. (1966). Unpublished data.
Levy, H. B. (1964). *Virology* **22,** 575.
Levy, H. B., and Merigan, T. C. (1966). *Proc. Soc. Exptl. Biol. Med.* **121,** 53.
Levy, H. B., Snellbaker, L. F., and Baron, S. (1966). *Proc. Soc. Exptl. Biol. Med.* **121,** 630.
Lindenmann, J., and Gifford, G. E. (1963). *Virology* **19,** 283, 294, and 302.
Lindenmann, J., Burke, D. C., and Isaacs, A. (1957). *Brit. J. Exptl. Pathol.* **38,** 551.
Lockart, R. Z., Jr. (1963). *J. Bacteriol.* **85,** 556.
Lockart, R. Z., Jr. (1964). *Biochem. Biophys. Res. Commun.* **13,** 513.
Lockart, R. Z., Jr. (1965). *J. Bacteriol.* **89,** 117.
Marcus, P. I., and Carver, D. A. (1965). *Science* **149,** 983.
Marcus, P. I., and Salb, J. M. (1966). *Virology,* **30,** 502.
Martin, R. G., and Ames, B. N. (1961). *J. Biol. Chem.* **236,** 1372.
Mendelson, J., and Glasgow, L. A. (1966). *J. Immunol.* **96,** 345.
Merigan, T. C. (1964). *Science* **145,** 811.
Merigan, T. C. (1967). *New Engl. J. Med.* **276,** 913.

Merigan, T. C., and Kleinschmidt, W. J. (1965). *Nature* **208,** 667.

Merigan, T. C., Winget, C. A., and Dixon, C. B. (1965). *J. Mol. Biol.* **13,** 679.

Meselson, M., Stahl, F. W., and Vinograd, J. (1957). *Proc. Natl. Acad. Sci. U.S.* **43,** 581.

Neva, F. A., and Weller, T. H. (1964). *J. Immunol.* **93,** 466.

Osborn, J., and Medearis, D. N., Jr. (1966). *Proc. Soc. Exptl. Biol. Med.* **121,** 819.

Oxman, M. N., and Black, P. H. (1966). *Proc. Natl. Acad. Sci. U.S.* **55,** 1133.

Parkman, P. D., Buescher, E. L., and Artenstein, M. S. (1962). *Proc. Soc. Exptl. Biol. Med.* **111,** 225.

Parkman, P. D., Hopps, H. E., Bernheim, B. C., and Meyer, H. M., Jr. (1966). *Federation Proc.* **25,** 491.

Paucker, K. (1964). *J. Immunol.* **94,** 371.

Paucker, K., Skurska, Z., and Henle, W. (1962). *Virology* **17,** 301.

Petralli, J. K., Merigan, T. C., and Wilbur, W. R. (1965). *New Engl. J. Med.* **273,** 198.

Phillips, A. W., and Wood, R. D. (1964). *Nature* **201,** 819.

Pohjanpelto, P., and Cooper, P. D. (1965). *Virology* **25,** 350.

Reinicke, V. (1964). *Acta Pathol. Microbiol. Scand.* **60,** 528.

Reinicke, V. (1965). *Acta Pathol. Microbiol. Scand.* **64,** 339.

Roizman, B. (1965). *Virology* **27,** 113.

Rotem, Z., and Charlwood, P. A. (1963). *Nature* **198,** 1066.

Rotem, Z., Berwald, Y., and Sachs, L. (1964). *Virology* **24,** 483.

Rubin, H. (1960). *Proc. Natl. Acad. Sci. U.S.* **46,** 1105.

Rytel, M. W., and Kilbourne, E. D. (1966). *J. Exptl. Med.* **123,** 767.

Rytel, M. W., Shope, R. E., and Kilbourne, E. D. (1966). *J. Exptl. Med.* **123,** 577.

Schlesinger, R. W. (1959). *In* "The Viruses" (F. M. Burnet and W. M. Stanley, eds.), Vol. 3, pp. 157–189. Academic Press, New York.

Schonne, E. (1966). *Biochim. Biophys. Acta* **115,** 429.

Sela, I., Harpaz, I., and Birk, Y. (1966). *Virology* **28,** 71.

Smart, K. M., and Kilbourne, E. D. (1966). *J. Exptl. Med.* **123,** 299 and 309.

Smith, T. J. (1966). Unpublished data.

Smith, T. J., and Wagner, R. R. (1967a). *J. Exptl. Med.* **125,** 559.

Smith, T. J., and Wagner, R. R. (1967b). *J. Exptl. Med.* **125,** 579.

Sreevalsan, T., and Lockart, R. Z., Jr. (1962). *Virology* **17,** 207.

Stinebring, W. R., and Youngner, J. S. (1964). *Nature* **204,** 712.

Sutton, R. N. P., and Tyrrell, D. A. J. (1961). *Brit. J. Exptl. Pathol.* **42,** 99.

Taylor, J. (1964). *Biochem. Biophys. Res. Commun.* **14,** 447.

Taylor, J. (1965). *Virology* **25,** 340.

Vilček, J. (1963). *Acta Virol. (Prague)* **7,** 107.

Vilček, J. (1964). *Virology* **22,** 651.

Vilches, A., and Hirst, G. K. (1947). *J. Immunol.* **57,** 125.

Wagner, R. R. (1960). *Bacteriol. Rev.* **24,** 151.

Wagner, R. R. (1961). *Virology* **13,** 323.

Wagner, R. R. (1963a). *Virology* **19,** 215.

Wagner, R. R. (1963b). *Ann. Rev. Microbiol.* **17,** 285.

Wagner, R. R. (1963c). *Bacteriol. Rev.* **27,** 72.

Wagner, R. R. (1964). *Nature* **204,** 49.

Wagner, R. R. (1965). *Am. J. Med.* **38,** 726.

Wagner, R. R. (1966). Unpublished observations.

Wagner, R. R., and Huang, A. S. (1965). *Proc. Natl. Acad. Sci. U.S.* **54,** 1112.

Wagner, R. R., and Huang, A. S. (1966). *Virology* **28**, 1.
Wagner, R. R., and Levy, A. H. (1960). *Ann. N.Y. Acad. Sci.* **88**, 1308.
Wagner, R. R., Levy, A. H., Snyder, R. M., Ratcliff, G. A., and Hyatt, D. F. (1963). *J. Immunol.* **91**, 112.
Wheelock, E. F. (1965). *Science* **149**, 310.
Wheelock, E. F., and Sibley, W. A. (1965). *New Engl. J. Med.* **273**, 194.
Yershov, F. I., and Zhdanov, V. M. (1965). *Virology* **27**, 451.
Youngner, J. S. (1966). Personal communication.
Youngner, J. S., and Stinebring, W. R. (1964). *Science* **144**, 1022.
Youngner, J. S., and Stinebring, W. R. (1965). *Nature* **208**, 456.
Youngner, J. S., Stinebring, W. R., and Taube, S. E. (1965). *Virology* **27**, 541.
Žemla, J., and Vilček, J. (1961). *Acta Virol. (Prague)* **5**, 129.

2 Methods for the Study of Viral Inhibitors

Felix E. Wassermann

I. Introduction 53
II. Specific Inhibition of Virus Infections 55
  A. Antibody to the Virus 55
  B. Antibody to the Host Cell 58
III. Nonspecific Inhibition of Virus Infection 60
  A. Introduction 60
  B. α-(Neuraminic Acid) Inhibitors of Myxoviruses 61
  C. γ-Inhibitors of Myxoviruses 66
  D. Mucopolysaccharide Inhibitor of Theiler's Virus (GD
    VII) 68
  E. Mucoid Inhibitors of Mumps Virus and Pneumonia
    Virus of Mice (PVM) 69
  F. Mucoid Inhibitors of Bacteriophages 72
  G. Lipid Inhibitors in Normal Sera 72
  H. Nonlipid Inhibitors in Normal Sera 74
  I. Inhibitors in the Overlay Plating Agar 78
  J. Nonspecific Inhibitor of Bacteriophage T2 (Sagik) ... 85
  K. Host-Induced Modification 85
  L. Mycoplasma (PPLO) Contamination of Tissue Culture
    Cells 86
  M. Inapparent and Latent Infections 87
  N. Miscellaneous Factors in the Tissue Culture System .. 88
  O. Virus Inactivation following Virus–Cell Interaction .. 89
  P. Inhibition of Plant Viruses 89
  References 91

I. Introduction

This chapter is concerned with substances and conditions that are capable of impeding the successful growth of viruses in host cells under laboratory conditions. It is clear that innumerable chemical compounds may have profound effects on the outcome of viral infection either because of their toxic properties or their mere presence in excessive amounts. We shall limit the discussion to those substances and conditions that are likely to be encountered during conventional laboratory procedures used for virus cultivation. The concern here, therefore, will not be with compounds specifically added to a system in order to interfere with viral growth. Such compounds include chemotherapeutic agents, halogenated purine and pyrimidine bases, nucleic acid and amino acid analogs, and other specific synthetic inhibitors of protein or nucleic acid synthesis.

Inhibition of virus infection is commonly divided into specific and nonspecific effects. Specific inhibition refers to effects on a particular virus to the exclusion of all others; thus by convention specific inhibition is generally considered to be the consequence of inactivation of viral infections by specific homologous antibody, whereas nonspecific inhibition is not produced by antibody and may operate against several viruses. It may be argued that the division into specific and nonspecific effects might equally well be applied to the mode of action of the inhibitors. We shall employ the conventional usage, however, because it avoids the need for frequent reclassification of inhibitors from "nonspecific" to "specific," as would be required each time investigation revealed the precise mode of action or site of attack of a particular substance.

An attempt is made in this chapter to discuss as many examples of inhibition with different viral infections as possible, together with pertinent detail regarding occurrence, mode of action, properties, and purification of the inhibitors. Of necessity, therefore, some of the material is repetitive. Since a large proportion of the work is still only partially understood and many claims are based on single, unconfirmed reports, much of the presentation gives the impression of undigested observations. The reason for including such material is predicated on the assumption that the reader who is faced with the problem of viral inhibition for the first time, and whose familiarity with virologic methodology is limited, has a need for examples as close to his own situation as possible. The references to the literature, however, have been kept to a minimum in order to achieve the maximum relevance. The expert reader may, therefore, discern unsubstantiated statements that he will surely be able to credit to the proper authority.

Although it is not specifically cited anywhere in the text, every reader should be aware of the eminently useful and meticulous book on virological procedures edited by Lennette and Schmidt (1964). All workers in the field owe these authors a great debt.

II. Specific Inhibition of Virus Infections

A. ANTIBODY TO THE VIRUS

In order to grow, tissue cultures require certain essential nutrients. These are usually supplied to the medium in the form of normal sera of several animal species. However, many so-called normal sera contain inhibiting substances that can interfere with the infectivity of the viruses. In this section only specific antibody directed against the viral agent will be considered, although many of the inhibitors encountered in normal sera are of a different nature and will be discussed later.

Methods to Differentiate Antibody from Other Inhibitors

a. *Heat Treatment.* Probably the principal and also the simplest method of determining whether interference with the infectivity of a virus preparation is caused by specific antiviral components in the serum is to heat the preparation at 56°C for 30 minutes. Antibody is stable and survives the heat treatment. It should be pointed out, however, that not all heat-stable inhibitors are antibody. This subject will be further considered in a later section.

b. *Kinetics of Inactivation.* A second and more quantitative method used to determine the antibody content of a serum makes use of the fact that virus–antibody reactions are not instantaneous, but rather proceed at a rate dependent on the concentration of both the virus and the antibody, as well as on the temperature. This relationship can be expressed by the equation

$$P/P_0 = e^{-\frac{Kt}{D}}$$

where P_0 is the virus concentration at the start of the interaction with antibody, P is its concentration at time, t minutes, and D is the final dilution of the serum in the reaction mixture. Solving for K, the velocity constant, assigns a value to this serum that is characteristic of it with respect to a particular virus. In order to perform such a test, it is necessary to have a sensitive assay system for the virus, preferably a plaque assay. With low antibody concentration, the drop in infectivity per time period is often less than 50%. Therefore, if the error inherent in the assay procedure is not significantly smaller than this, little useful information can be gained.

A tube containing virus-diluting fluid and the appropriate dilution of serum are incubated in a water bath to reach the temperature at which the inactivation kinetics are to be measured. This is commonly 37°C or lower, depending on the nature of the virus and the condition of the experiment. After equilibration, the virus is added and mixed thoroughly in the serum tube. It is advisable to add the virus contained in as small a volume as possible in order to avoid any change in temperature in the equilibrated tube. Small samples are withdrawn at the appropriate times and diluted rapidly into chilled diluent in order to stop the interaction between virus and antibody. The assay of virus survivors may then conveniently take place after all the samples have been collected.

Since the K value is valid only when antibody is at all times in excess, the virus concentration to be added to the reaction is critical, in that antibody exhaustion must be avoided. For the purposes of this determination, the reaction is considered to be pseudomonomolecular, or approaching first order, because in the presence of excess antibody it depends only on the concentration of the virus. There should be enough virus present in the reaction mixture at the onset that at the desired time intervals a sufficiently large dilution may be made away from the serum in order to avoid continued serum action in the assay system. For instance, the addition of 10^7 plaque-forming units (pfu) to a final volume of 5 ml in a tube gives an initial titer of 2×10^6 pfu/ml. Permitting a 100-fold dilution out of the reaction mixture at each time interval, one finds that this method can reliably measure survival of 0.5%, or 1×10^2 pfu/ml. Lower survival than this can be determined, but since the expected number of plaques per plate will be low, more plates are required for accurate assay of survivors. It is essential to determine the viral input independently, because in many instances the serum action is rapid enough to inactivate a large proportion of the input virus before the first sample can be taken and processed. Equally important is the necessity of taking sufficient samples to determine the shape of the survivor curve. The velocity constant is calculated from the initial linear portion of the inactivation curve. If insufficient samples are assayed, the result may often be an underestimation of the true inactivation rate. The reason for this is that frequently an inactivation curve will assume asymptotic shape soon after onset of serum action, and, if frequent samples are not taken, the linear portion cannot be defined. A convenient sampling schedule to follow might be 1, 2, 4, 8, 16, etc., minutes. If the inactivation of the virus appears too rapid to measure, further dilution of the serum is recommended.

Since other inhibitors present in serum could mimic the behavior of a specific antibody, some confirmatory experiments are often desirable. One of these makes use of viruses serologically related to the one used in the neutralization test. If a related virus is exposed to the serum, a survival curve similar to the first, but differing in its slope, may be obtained. If a virus unrelated to either of the two is employed, no significant reduction in virus titer should occur. For example, bacteriophages T2, T4, and T6 are all inactivated to different extents by an antiserum to any of them, but T5 is not affected at all by these sera. Similarly, ECHO viruses 1 and 13 are serologically related, but other ECHO viruses do not fall into this unique small group.

c. Dissociation of the Virus–Antibody Complex. Clinical material may often contain virus bound to specific antibody, and thus manifests little if any infectious virus. In order to dissociate the virus and demonstrate its infectivity, treatment of the mixture at low pH is frequently employed. It is obvious that in order to succeed with this method it is essential that the viral infectivity not be destroyed at low pH. The suggested procedure is to dilute the virus fluid into citrate buffer at pH 2.5–3.0. Incubation below 2.5 may be precarious, even for viruses that can survive high acidity; above pH 3.0 the dissociation becomes increasingly less efficient. Incubation at room temperature for about 15 minutes and diluting out of the low pH buffer into pH 7 buffer, followed by assay for infectivity, complete the test. High pH has also been used to dissociate some myxovirus–antibody complexes.

Dissociation of the antigen–antibody complex can also be achieved by treatment with Genetron (trifluorotrichloroethane) in a homogenizer. Typically, 2 ml of virus fluid containing the inhibitor are mixed with an equal volume of Genetron, agitated for 30 seconds in a chilled homogenizer cup at full speed, after which the mixture is centrifuged and the aqueous layer examined for infectivity.

In order to establish more firmly that the inhibitory substance is specific antibody, such characteristics as its globulin nature and sedimentation and immune electrophoretic patterns should be determined. Further, if booster injections of the virus are given to the animals that already have antibody, the anamnestic response elicited in the immune animals should yield neutralization kinetics distinguishable from the primary response in the control animals. This problem is fairly easily resolved if only sera from a few animals are involved and if the history of the animals can be determined. It is infinitely more difficult when the sera in question come from an unknown number of animals whose history is completely unknown.

In conclusion, the reader is referred to the article by Klein (1958), in which the criteria that identify a viral inhibitor as antibody are laid down in detail.

B. Antibody to the Host Cell

1. *Effect of Cellular Antibody*

a. *Bacteriophage System.* Naturally occurring antibody to tissue culture cells in animal sera is probably a rare event. Under laboratory conditions, however, distinct possibilities for their appearance exist. Sera prepared against any virus are likely to contain anticellular components unless the antigen has been stringently purified prior to immunization. Thus, if a suspension of infected cells, for example, *Escherichia coli* B infected with T2, is treated with antiserum against any phage prepared on strain B and if this serum is not absorbed with B cells, many of the infected bacteria may be agglutinated, and a count of infective centers would be a distinct underestimate of the true number. It has also repeatedly been shown that antiserum to the host cells will protect them from attack by lytic phages.

b. *Animal Cell Cultures.* The effect of cellular antibody on animal virus infection has been described by many workers. Thus, Quersin-Thiry (1958) impregnated small discs of filter paper with antiserum to monkey kidney cells prepared in a rabbit and placed them on the agar overlay of a plate previously infected with virus. The decrease in plaque formation around the disc was used as an index of viral inhibition. In a different method, anti-HeLa cell serum was added to tube cultures infected a few hours earlier. It was shown that where the concentration of the antiserum was not so excessive as to cause cellular agglutination or toxic degeneration, the cells were protected against viral cytopathic effect. This protection was not absolute and was dependent on the virus dose as well as on a minimal antibody titer. Also, some viruses, such as Newcastle disease virus (NDV) were not at all inhibited, while others, such as poliovirus, were very sensitive. No consistency in response was detected; e.g., some coxsackieviruses were inhibited and others were not. The mechanisms that function here are still largely unknown.

Interference with the expression of cytopathic effects and cytotoxic destruction of the cells in tissue cultures by certain viruses has been described by Habel and his associates (1958).

Another interesting report dealing with anticellular antibody is that by Rubin (1956). When Rous sarcoma virus (RSV) was mixed with serum prepared against normal chick embryo tissue, the number of tumors induced by the virus in the developing chick embryo was markedly reduced. The reaction, unlike many viral neutralizations by specific antibody, required complement and was reversible when the virus–serum mixture was diluted. The antiserum was effective even when it was added after the virus had adsorbed to the chorioallantoic membrane of the egg. At this stage antiviral serum would act only on unadsorbed or eluted virus. At the time of this report, the observed effects were considered to be the result of anticellular components only. In the light of more recent knowledge, it is clear that the sera may have contained an antiviral component as well. Rubin (1962) demonstrated that many flocks of chickens are infected with avian leukosis viruses. These viruses are serologically closely related to, if not identical with, RSV. The infections manifest themselves by extensive viremia without circulating antibody in the animals in the case of congenital infection, or by antiviral serum in high titer without infectious virus in acute infections. The viruses do not cause obvious cytopathic effects in chick embryo tissue cultures, and they are assayed by the interference they exert on the cytopathogenicity of RSV. Since, therefore, "normal" chick embryo tissue may contain high concentration of virus, serologically identical to RSV, it follows that antiserum produced against such chick embryo tissue may have a high titer against both tissue and RSV. This phenomenon, although thus far clearly demonstrated only for the chick embryo, is inherent in all cell cultures and many different virus systems.

2. Removal of Cellular Antibody

The removal of cellular antibody presents little difficulty. In most instances absorption of the serum with a large number of homologous cells or cell debris removes the interfering specific antibody. For instance, to remove the antibacterial activity from antiphage sera, 1 ml of serum is mixed with 10^9 cells that have been killed by UV irradiation or disrupted by sonic vibration and left overnight at 4°C. The serum is then centrifuged to remove the cells. If need be, this procedure may be repeated. Mammalian cells can be similarly used to absorb sera prepared with crude tissue culture fluids.

If the simple method of absorption fails to distinguish clearly between antiviral and anticellular serum components, some other differential aids are available. Since complement is required for expression of some of the anticellular activity, inactivation of the serum at 56°C for 30 minutes is recommended. Another technique makes use of the neutralization procedure outlined earlier. Addition of virus to an anticellular serum should not result in loss of viral infectivity.

III. Nonspecific Inhibition of Virus Infections

A. INTRODUCTION

1. Outline of the Problem

The following section will be concerned with many different conditions which share the common characteristic that in each case there is interference with the normal and unencumbered functioning of a viral infection or viral action. There is, however, no common mechanism of interference. In some instances inhibition is caused by reasonably well-defined chemical compounds such as the inhibitors of myxoviruses containing neuraminic acid. In others the causal agent defies definition except in broad terms. Conditions exist where the previous host cells so modified a virus that the progeny of this passage are profoundly affected with respect to a following passage in other cells (see Section III,K). In other circumstances, the virus may have lost its infectivity because it was in some way damaged by adsorption to and elution from cells in a previous cycle of growth (see Section III,O). It is clear, therefore, that a vast set of variables must be considered and sorted out to account for nonspecific inhibitors.

2. Classification of Inhibitors

All of the examples of inhibition to be covered here are involved with viral infectivity, viral hemagglutination, or both. Because these are probably the most significant biological considerations, it would seem proper to discuss the inhibiting condition with respect to these criteria. Unfortunately, many diverse substances manifest identical behavior or produce similar effects, so that it is impractical to organize this section on the basis of biological activity. Rather, it appears most useful and least confusing to arrange the order of discussion according to the properties of the inhibitors, their target viruses, and, finally, according to the specific conditions that enable inhibition to occur.

Our purpose here is to outline some of the techniques used to determine the nature of the inhibitions. It should be pointed out at the beginning that there is no one procedure in any of the steps to be described; rather, each investigator modifies a technique to suit his purpose, and the modifications are often predicated on the stability of the virus, the sensitivity of the assay system, the ease with which a certain test can be performed, and sometimes even on the availability of a particular compound.

B. α-(Neuraminic Acid) Inhibitors of Myxoviruses

1. Characterization

Almost as soon as the first quantitative measurements of viruses were made during the early 1940's, inhibitors were described that were present in sera from normal animals, in urine, allantoic fluid, egg white, and other material, and that were capable of interfering with the hemagglutinating activity and only rarely with the infectious capacity of several viruses. These inhibitors are often referred to as "Francis inhibitors," after the investigator who was one of the first to describe them. The initial work was performed almost exclusively with members of the myxovirus group, although inhibitors of encephalomyelitis viruses had also been reported. Research on virus–host cell interactions had established that the infectious agent adsorbs to the host cell or to the erythrocyte at sites that are rich in mucoprotein or mucopolysaccharide. It was further shown that the virus possessed the enzymatic capacity to destroy the receptor sites and elute from the cells. Such eluted virus was unchanged in its adsorbing and hemagglutinating properties, but the red blood cells were no longer able to serve as viral receptors. Virus that was heated to destroy its enzymatic capability could adsorb normally to erythrocytes, but could no longer elute. It is not within the scope of this chapter to review the papers that bear on this subject and on the work that established the chemical nature of the receptor substances. For this, the reader is urged to consult Burnet's (1951) excellent and concise review of the earlier work and to refer to the publication of Buzzell and Hanig (1958) for detail on later developments. We shall discuss here the conditions that influence the activity of the neuraminic acid inhibitor.

a. Effect of Periodate. It is characteristic of this class of inhibitors which contain mucopolysaccharides that they are universally sensitive to oxidation by several periodates. Both lithium and potassium periodate are commonly used, the first in 0.1 M and the second usually in 0.01 M concentration. In principle, inhibitor, either purified or in its crude form, is mixed with periodate and permitted to interact at room temperature or somewhat lower temperature for a given period of time. Depending on the virus, the inhibitor, and the cations present, the volumes used and the conditions of incubation are variables to be adjusted at the investigator's option. For example, 3 volumes of allantoic fluid may be mixed with 1 volume of $LiIO_4$. However, with KIO_4, 1 volume of inhibitor is usually mixed with 3 volumes of oxidizing agent. Regardless of the periodate used, the excess still remaining must be inactivated before assay. This may be accomplished by the addition of 2 volumes of 7.5% glucose in the procedure with $LiIO_4$, or 1% glycerol–saline when KIO_4 is used.

It has been frequently observed that the inhibitors present a spectrum of responses to inactivation by periodate. Some will show an increase of activity against certain viruses at the start of oxidation treatment and then diminish. This has been explained as a reduction in susceptibility to the enzyme as the first step in periodate action. With other inhibitors, prolonged treatment is necessary before their effect becomes manifested. It must be firmly understood that the absolute levels of inhibitor can be determined only with heated virus, since the unheated virus contains enzyme that destroys the inhibitory action. Many of these apparently contradictory observations were made using viruses with unimpaired enzymatic capacity.

b. *Effect of Trypsin.* The protein moiety of the inhibitors is sensitive to cleavage by proteolytic enzymes; the inhibiting effect, however, is usually not completely destroyed. Crystalline trypsin is weighed out and is conveniently dissolved in 0.1 M phosphate buffer at pH 8.2 at a final concentration of 4 μg/ml. Equal volumes of trypsin solution and inhibitor are mixed and incubated at 37°C up to 2 hours. At this point it may be necessary to add a stoichiometric amount of soybean trypsin inhibitor in order to stop the enzymatic action. It is important to point out that many biological inhibitors, such as serum and allantoic fluid, contain natural trypsin antagonists. Because of this, it is advisable to ascertain that high enough levels of trypsin are used so that premature inactivation of the proteolytic enzyme is ruled out as a source of error. Many workers prefer, for this reason, to dialyze crude fluids against buffered saline at pH 7.2 to remove trypsin inhibitors. In addition, because of their low solubility in salt solution, some inhibitors may be lost in this step.

It is often economical to combine the trypsin and periodate treatments. A suggested method is to inactivate with trypsin at elevated temperature (56°C) for 30 minutes, allow to cool, and then to follow with $M/90$ KIO_4 for 15–30 minutes. The remainder of the procedure is unchanged.

Here, as in most of the other procedures, one must bear in mind that the schemes include inherent dilution of the inhibitor. In order to provide a valid control, untreated inhibitor should be diluted in parallel.

c. *Effect of Receptor-Destroying Enzyme (RDE).* It is a common property of the inhibitors containing neuraminic acid that they are inactivated by RDE of animal, bacterial, and viral origin. Incubation of equal volumes of inhibitor and enzyme at 37°C for different periods of time up to 20 hours has been resorted to. It is imperative that excess enzyme be removed by repeated absorption of the mixture with fowl erythrocytes in order to avoid further enzyme action in the assay system.

d. *Effect of Low pH.* The class of mucoid inhibitors is generally precipitable at low pH. Crude inhibitor in serum or allantoic fluid is unstable when acidified to approximately pH 3. The observations recorded in the literature differ, and this may be explained by the fact that only a few experiments were performed with purified material. Typically, the material, if pure, is dissolved in distilled water and then adjusted by dropwise addition of acid to the desired pH. Crude material can be used without the dilution step. It should be remembered that when the source material is opalescent and the inhibitor is present in small amounts, any acid-insoluble precipitate formed may be difficult to detect. If the pH is brought back to neutrality, the inactivation is reversed and the inhibitor is again solubilized.

e. *Effect of Hyaluronidase.* Pneumococcal hyaluronidase (0.001 μg/ml) has been effectively used to inactivate inhibitors of myxoviruses. The mixtures are incubated at 37°C for 30 minutes and assayed without need for further treatment.

f. *Solubility of the Inhibitor.* The α-inhibitors are water soluble and highly insoluble in sodium chloride. As is shown in detail below, precipitation in 0.58 M NaCl is a method of purification of these inhibitors. It is, however, possible to render them soluble in salt solution by treating them with 5 M urea. If the concentration of urea becomes high enough, the inhibiting capacity is attacked. Treatment with 5 M urea will also eliminate the pseudohemagglutination (the spontaneous clumping of red blood cells by inhibitor in the absence of virus). This phenomenon frequently interferes with the reproducibility of inhibitor assays.

2. *Purification*

A classic procedure for purifying a mucoid inhibitor, the details of which follow below, is that described by Tamm and Horsfall (1950). The source of the material in this case was urine from normal human males. Only 6% of the potential inhibitor activity was demonstrable in untreated urine, but dialysis against distilled water or heating at 70°C for 30 minutes at pH 6.5 greatly enhanced the yield. It was consistently observed that the inhibiting titer increased with time as the

TABLE I
ALCOHOL PRECIPITATION OF INHIBITOR FROM URINE

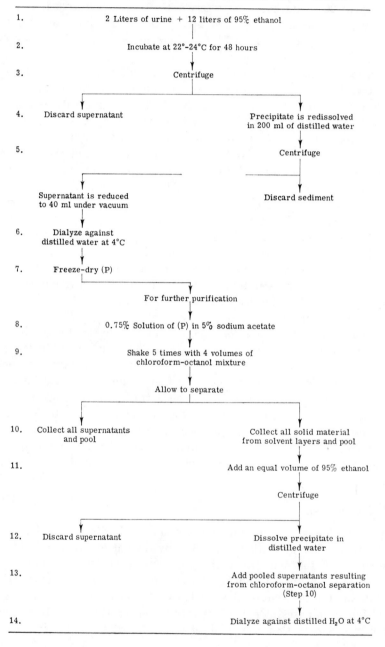

1.   2 Liters of urine + 12 liters of 95% ethanol

2.   Incubate at 22°-24°C for 48 hours

3.   Centrifuge

4.   Discard supernatant   Precipitate is redissolved in 200 ml of distilled water

5.   Centrifuge

    Supernatant is reduced to 40 ml under vacuum   Discard sediment

6.   Dialyze against distilled water at 4°C

7.   Freeze-dry (P)

    For further purification

8.   0.75% Solution of (P) in 5% sodium acetate

9.   Shake 5 times with 4 volumes of chloroform-octanol mixture

    Allow to separate

10.   Collect all supernatants and pool   Collect all solid material from solvent layers and pool

11.   Add an equal volume of 95% ethanol

    Centrifuge

12.   Discard supernatant   Dissolve precipitate in distilled water

13.   Add pooled supernatants resulting from chloroform-octanol separation (Step 10)

14.   Dialyze against distilled H_2O at 4°C

urine–virus mixture stood at room temperature. A rapid rise occurred during the first 2 hours, followed by a lesser, but constant, rise to 12 hours. Analogous but less dramatic rises in inhibiting titers have been reported for the inhibitor in egg white and cow's milk treated in like fashion. Such rises do not occur when the urine is incubated by itself without virus. It is important to point out that in order to reproduce these findings it is essential that all of the components be sufficiently stable to survive the incubation period. As an additional precaution, heating the source material of the inhibitor at 70°C will remove non-specific pseudohemagglutinins.

a. Precipitation by Ethanol. Six volumes of 95% ethanol are mixed with 1 volume of urine at 22°–24°C (see Table I). Maximum yields are obtained with fresh undialyzed urine in about 48 hours. The resulting precipitate is centrifuged and dissolved in a small amount of distilled water. Any insoluble material appearing after this step is discarded by centrifugation. The volume of the supernatant is reduced under vacuum and then dialyzed against distilled water at 4°C. The residue may be lyophilized and its composition analyzed by standard chemical procedures.

b. Precipitation by Salt. When urine is adjusted to 0.58 M salinity with NaCl and filtered, all of the inhibiting activity can be retained on the filter (see Table II). Porcelain filter candles or fritted glass or membrane filters serve the purpose. The filter is washed repeatedly with 0.14 M NaCl until no further pigment appears to be released into the filtrate. In the case of the original purification, the best results were obtained when the urine was diluted 1 : 1 in distilled water, then adjusted to 0.58 M NaCl at pH 5.5 and incubated for 24 hours at 4°C. The highly viscous water-soluble material is then centrifuged and may be reprecipitated with 0.58 M NaCl and freeze-dried.

c. Isoelectric Precipitation. The precipitate obtained with 95% ethanol (see above) is made into a 2.5% aqueous solution (see Table

TABLE II

SODIUM CHLORIDE PRECIPITATION OF INHIBITOR FROM URINE

1. Add 1 volume of urine to 1 volume of distilled water.
2. Add NaCl to a final concentration of 0.58 M.
3. Adjust pH to 5.5.
4. Hold at 4°C for 24 hours.
5. Centrifuge the highly viscous insoluble substance at 7000 g for 30 minutes.
6. Wash the sediment with 0.58 M NaCl and centrifuge again.
7. Freeze-dry the sediment.

III). The pH is lowered to 3.0 by the dropwise addition of 1 M HCl. The resulting precipitate is redissolved in distilled water, the pH brought to neutrality with 1 M NaOH, and freeze-dried. The acid-insoluble product has about twice the inhibitor content of the alcohol precipitate.

The procedures of purification outlined here are only examples of the many effective techniques that exist to study the various aspects of this type of inhibitor. The reader is again referred to the review of Buzzell and Hanig (1958) and to that of Gottschalk (1958) for the chemical basis of the observations.

TABLE III

ISOELECTRIC PRECIPITATION OF INHIBITOR FROM URINE

1. Concentrate 2 liters of urine 40 times by reduction of volume under vacuum.
2. Adjust to pH 3.0 with 1 N HCl.
3. Dissolve the precipitate in distilled water and repeat the treatment at pH 3.0.
4. Dissolve the precipitate in distilled water, adjust to pH 7.0 with 1 N NaOH, and freeze-dry.

C. γ-INHIBITORS OF MYXOVIRUSES

A second group of neuraminic acid-containing inhibitors, differing from the α-inhibitors in that they both neutralized virus infectivity and inhibited hemagglutination of influenza virus, have been described by Cohen and Belyavin (1959). Of particular significance was the unusually high titer these inhibitors (which were found in horse sera) demonstrated against certain epidemic strains of influenza A_2 virus. Further work by Cohen and his group (1963) established that other types of influenza virus were also affected, but to a lesser extent. At first all the equine inhibitors tested appeared homogeneous, but, as more sera were screened, atypical inhibitors were encountered that were non-neutralizing, failed to show the high hemagglutination inhibition activity against A_2 strains, and that were more active against heated B strains of influenza virus than the usual γ-inhibitors.

1. Effect of Neuraminidase

The atypical inhibitors are very sensitive to neuraminidase. When serum is diluted 1 : 10 or 1 : 20 and mixed in equal volume with purified neuraminidase diluted in calcium acetate buffer at pH 6.2, incubated at 37°C for 5 hours, and subsequently heated at 56°C for 30 minutes to destroy residual enzyme, all inhibitory activity against A_2 strains is removed. This test also serves to distinguish the inhibitor from antibody. Heating the sera at 70°C for 1 hour results in marked enhancement of anti-A_2, but not anti-B hemagglutination-inhibition activity. This heat treatment also raises the neutralizing titer of the normal inhibitors but fails to affect the atypical ones. Enzymatic treatment of the sera releases all of the neuraminic acid possessed by the normal ones, but liberates only about 50% of that contained by the atypical inhibitors. In this complete loss of neuraminic acid, and concomitantly the inhibitor function, the normal γ-inhibitors resemble the α-inhibitors.

The observed differences between normal and abnormal γ-inhibitors are no doubt controlled genetically and reflect, in all probability, differences in the composition of the serum mucoproteins. These differences may form the basis for some of the nonspecific variation in host susceptibility to infection *in vivo*.

2. Purification

There have been conflicting reports regarding the actual number of active substances that make up the γ-inhibitors. Recent work (Biddle et al., 1965) has shown that the chemical treatment of the source material determines to a great extent whether the inhibitor is recovered as a single component or distributed among several separable fractions. The steps involved in the extraction and purification of the γ-inhibitor as a single homogeneous compound are outlined here. Fresh horse serum is centrifuged at 40,000 rpm for 20 hours. The pellet is then frozen and subsequently dialyzed against 0.15 M barbiturate buffer at pH 8.6. The final volume is adjusted to one fifth of the original and subjected to electrophoresis at 60 mA and 410 V for 22 hours. The inhibitor is then passed on to an inert cellulose column and eluted with barbiturate buffer. All fractions having a high inhibitor titer are pooled and again dialyzed against 0.15 M saline and 20 M Carbowax. This yields material whose sedimentation pattern in sucrose density gradients displays two major peaks. More than 80% of the biological activity of the inhibitor is contained in the faster, 18 S, component. Failure to recover the inhibitor quantitatively, encountered by many investigators, may be ascribed to maintenance of other than optimum ionic strength during dialysis. Failure to recover the inhibitor as a single component may be attributed to the breakdown of the 18 S material as a result of drastic treatment.

D. Mucopolysaccharide Inhibitor of Theiler's Virus (GD VII)

1. Properties

Mandel and Racker (1953a,b) have given a detailed description of a mucopolysaccharide inhibitor found in the intestines of normal mice and guinea pigs that inactivates both the hemagglutinating activity and the infectivity of GD VII virus. In this respect, this inhibitor resembles the γ-inhibitor of influenza virus.

2. Purification

The inhibitor is obtained from mouse intestines that have been excised, washed out, and well minced with scissors. The material is then homogenized in a blender at room temperature with 10 volumes of acetone and sedimented by low-speed centrifugation. The sediment is successively washed with 10 volumes of acetone and 10 volumes of ether and dried under vacuum. Prior to use, each sample of acetone-dried powder is extracted with 10 volumes of 0.85% saline at 37°C for 1 hour; the suspension is centrifuged and the supernatant is titrated for inhibiting activity. Much higher purification was achieved by the treatment outlined in Table IV. Many tissues of several small animal species contain this mucopolysaccharide inhibitor, but the small intestines of mice yield by far the most.

3. Mode of Action

The formation of the virus-inhibitor complex requires the presence of electrolytes; decreasing the electrolyte concentration results in prompt dissociation of the virus–inhibitor complex with regeneration of free virus. Formation can be achieved by adding $CaCl_2$, NaCl, or Na_3PO_4 ranging from 0.1 to 0.001 M in strength. Dissociation is most conveniently measured by placing the samples in an ice bath for 30 minutes and then adding red blood cells to test for hemagglutination.

The kinetics of formation of the virus–inhibitor complex in 0.1 M NaCl follow a first-order reaction over most of the time intervals tested, but a slight initial shoulder is noticeable in the curves, indicating a more complex situation. After formation, inhibitor can be recovered quantitatively if the complex is heated at 100°C for 10 minutes. Studies of the quantitative relationship between the inhibitor and the viral hemagglutinin reveal a linear dependence on the inhibitor concentration over a wide range of dilutions, while that between inhibitor and the viral infectivity shows a distinct curvilinear response when surviving infective virus is measured. This may be explained by the fact that red blood cells do not support virus multiplication and therefore represent a static state with respect to virus, cells, and inhibitor, though host cells subject to viral attack undergo changes in the course of the experiment.

The inhibitor is specific for the GD VII strain and has no effect on the closely related FA and TD strains of Theiler's encephalomyelitis virus of mice or on a mouse-adapted strain of poliovirus.

Although the virus lacks demonstrable activity against the inhibitor, enzymatic destruction of the mucopolysaccharide was demonstrable in fecal extracts from uninfected mice. It is likely that the enzyme, which is devoid of RDE activity, is of microbial origin (Mandel, 1958). The significant point is that the enzyme can reactivate GD VII virus that had previously been inactivated by the intestinal inhibitor. This has obvious ramifications for the possible detection of "latent" virus infections. A potentially infective virus, bound to an inhibitor, may remain undetected until exposed to an appropriate enzyme in the intestinal tract or in the bloodstream of a host.

E. MUCOID INHIBITORS OF MUMPS VIRUS AND PNEUMONIA VIRUS OF MICE (PVM)

Certain polysaccharides, either of bacterial or nonbacterial origin, have been shown to modify the activities of mumps virus and PVM. One of these substances, which can be extracted from ground up lung and also other tissues of hamsters and mice, inhibits the hemagglutination of PVM. The other substance, the capsular polysaccharide of *Klebsiella pneumoniae* B, exerts its effect on the infectivity of the mumps virus and PVM. It can manifest its activity both in the mouse lung against PVM and in the chick embryo against mumps virus. The inhibition is still effective if the polysaccharide is introduced into the chick embryo 4 days after infection with mumps virus (Ginsberg *et al.*, 1948). The inhibition apparently is associated with the multiplication of the virus rather than with its adsorption. Several other myxoviruses were not affected at all. Hemagglutination inhibition is not clearly correlated with inhibition of viral multiplication. Ginsberg and Horsfall (1949a) reported the selection of a strain of mumps virus resistant to the effect of the polysaccharide. As long as it was grown in the presence of the inhibitor, it remained resistant, but in the absence of this substance, it quickly reverted to sensitive type. Ordinarily an inhibitor of this nature is, as mentioned in the introductory remarks, outside

TABLE IV
PURIFICATION OF INHIBITOR OF THEILER'S VIRUS

1. Excise tissue from mice.

2. Slit open stomach and intestines and wash out the contents.

3. Mince all tissues well with scissors.

4. Homogenize mince in a blender at room temperature with 10 volumes of acetone.

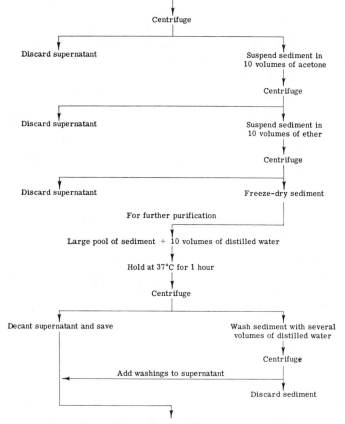

1 Liter of supernatant + 250 ml of 25% trichloracetic acid (TCA)

Table IV continued on facing page.

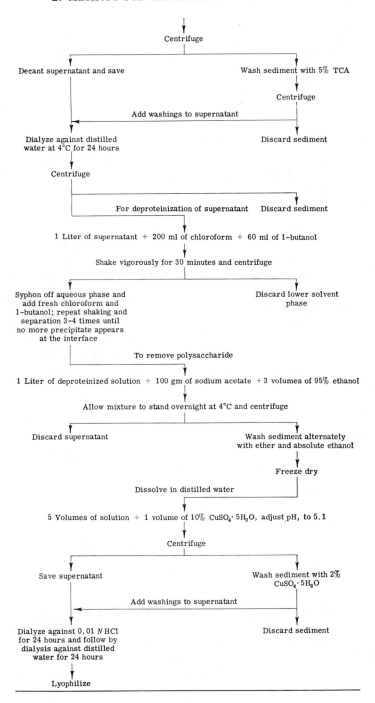

the scope of this discussion. It is included here for two reasons. First, it is possible that a similar gummy polysaccharide can find its way into a pool of normal sera used to supplement tissue cultures and in this way inhibit viral multiplication. Second, as is shown below, such polysaccharides produce natural inhibition of bacteriophage infection under normal laboratory conditions.

F. MUCOID INHIBITORS OF BACTERIOPHAGES

It has been known for a long time that receptor substances and somatic antigens isolated from bacterial cells can inactivate those bacteriophages to which the cells are susceptible. It must be pointed out that the chemical treatment used in the isolation and purification of these lipomucoproteins may remove the inhibitor activity of a preparation against a particular bacteriophage without impairing the activity against other phages. Goebel and Jesaitis (1952) studied the relationship between the bacteriophages of the T series and the somatic antigens of several strains of *Shigella sonnei* of phase II. Using the techniques commonly employed to isolate bacterial mutants resistant to bacteriophages, they found that the somatic antigens of such single-step mutants failed to inactivate those bacteriophages to which they were resistant and to which the wild type was sensitive.

Adams and Park (1956), among others, studied a virus–host system with *K. pneumoniae*. Unless an enzyme that hydrolyzes the capsular polysaccharide of the host cells was produced during phage infection, little phage was liberated and the efficiency of phage infection was markedly lowered.

The methods used in the bacteriophage studies have been detailed in the book by Adams (1959). Because of the excellence of that presentation, it is inappropriate to review the techniques here.

G. LIPID INHIBITORS IN NORMAL SERA

Normal animal sera are known to contain lipids that inactivate several different viruses. According to Casals and Olitsky (1947), the viruses of St. Louis, Russian, Far East, and Japanese B encephalitis were reduced in titer when they were incubated in normal clear sera of mice, hamsters, rabbits, and horses. The inactivating substances were stable to heating to 99°C for 1 hour and were not dialyzable. Whole lipids from egg yolks were not effective. The viral inhibition is unusual in that in whole serum it appears as if only arboviruses were affected, whereas after successive extraction with petroleum ether, acetone, and ethyl ether, the lipid fractions were reactive with arboviruses and psittacosis virus (Utz, 1948). Since the psittacosis virus stocks were prepared in eggs and the arboviruses were grown in mouse brain, host-related factors might have been responsible for the selective effect of the serum. The active substances were shown to be cephalin- and lecithinlike. Utz (1949) further showed that the infectivity but not the hemagglutination of influenza virus and NDV could be inhibited with the lecithinlike fraction. The inactivation of these viruses was temperature dependent; i.e., it was demonstrable at 37°C, but not at 24°C.

The lecithinlike material was extracted in the following manner (Utz, 1949) (Table V): One volume of serum or other source of inhibi-

TABLE V

PURIFICATION OF LECITHINLIKE INHIBITOR OF ARBOVIRUSES

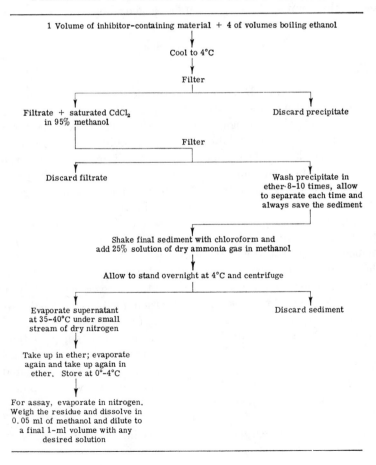

tor was added to 4 volumes of boiling ethanol and cooled to 4°C. The precipitate was discarded and the alcoholic extract precipitated with saturated cadmium chloride in 95% methanol. After thorough and repeated washing with ether, the residue was shaken with chloroform until a slightly opalescent suspension was achieved. To this was added a 25% solution of dry ammonia gas in methanol, and the mixture allowed to stand at 4°C for several hours. After centrifugation the clear supernatant fluid was evaporated at 35°–40°C in dry nitrogen gas under negative pressure. The waxy, purified lecithin could be taken up once more in ether, reevaporated, and stored at 4°C in ether. At time of use, an aliquot portion was evaporated in nitrogen, weighed, dissolved in methanol, and further diluted in water or buffer.

There is some question as to the identity of the inhibitor with lecithin. Egg yolk, which is rich in lecithin, is a poor inhibitor, while liver, whose lecithin content is low, is usually a good inhibitor.

H. Nonlipid Inhibitors in Normal Sera

1. Heat-Labile Inhibitors

a. β-Inhibitors of Myxoviruses. Besides the neuraminic acid-containing inhibitors already discussed, nonspecific inhibitors occur in normal sera and other biological material that are characterized mainly on the basis of their thermolability and their ability to inactivate both infectivity and hemagglutination. These inhibitors are frequently referred to as β- or Chu inhibitors, after one of their early investigators (Chu, 1951). Ginsberg and Horsfall (1949b) made a detailed study of an inhibitor of myxoviruses that occurs in the sera of man, rabbit, guinea pig, and mouse. Markedly more active material was required to inhibit infectivity than hemagglutination. This is a commonly observed phenomenon with this group of inhibitors.

The nature of the active heat-labile substances is not definitely determined. Although most workers agree that trypsin completely inactivates the inhibitor, the results with periodate are equivocal. An inhibitor from allantoic fluid was sensitive to oxidation; another from serum was not (Ginsberg and Horsfall, 1949b). This suggests that the substance from allantoic fluid was a mucoprotein, but the presence of a mixture of inhibitors may be offered as a more likely explanation. More recent work tends to rule out a periodate-sensitive component as an integral part of the β-inhibitors. Complement is ruled out by the finding that absorption of the serum with stepwise addition of large amounts of virus and sedimenting the virus–inhibitor complex result in almost complete removal of inhibitor from the supernatant without a significant reduction in complement. Since the complex fails to dissociate spontaneously into either free virus or active inhibitor, it appears that the bond between virus and this inhibitor does not involve the RDE of the virus.

A specific study was made by Henry and Youngner (1957) to determine to what extent inhibitors present in normal sera from several mammalian species could interfere with the cytopathogenic effect of influenza virus on monkey kidney cells. The plaque technique served as the assay system. The sera were treated with trypsin or heated at 65°C for 30 minutes. Controls were left untreated. Virus of known titer was mixed with a measured amount of serum and incubated at 4°C for 1 hour. The mixtures were then diluted and inoculated into cells. The essential findings were that those inhibitors which were able to neutralize the cytopathogenicity of influenza A_1 strains were heat labile and that no inhibitor was encountered that affected B_1 strains or mouse pathogenic A strains. The inhibitors combined rapidly with the virus and formed a stable, nondissociable complex.

The possibility exists that if the inhibitors are present in sufficiently high titer, they may not only neutralize the input virus but also exert an inhibitory effect on progeny virus released from successfully infected cells.

b. *Variola Virus.* Two thermolabile inhibitors of variola virus have been found in normal human sera (McCarthy and Germer, 1952), which could neutralize the virus or actually potentiate the specific effect of heated immune serum. These reactions were easily separable by simple dilution of the sera, indicating the independence of the inhibitors present.

c. *Arbovirus.* Morgan (1945) and Whitman (1947) described heat-labile substances in sera that possessed both neutralizing and hemagglutinating inhibitory effects with Western equine encephalomyelitis virus. The material was probably complement.

In conclusion, the experiments of Karzon (1956) should be noted. He found that many mammalian tissues contained substances that could counteract naturally occurring viral inhibitors. This finding has practical importance. Absorption of normal sera with ground guinea pig kidney, kaolin, or one of several resins could free the sera of nonspecific inhibitors. An interesting finding that hinted at the mechanism of this interaction was that streptokinase would stop all antiviral activity of human sera, but not of rabbit sera so treated. Since rabbit serum is poor in plasmin, it was thought that the latter acts as a serum protease on the inhibitor. This explanation was supported by the finding that the addition of streptokinase did cause inactivation of the inhibitor in rabbit sera, provided that fresh human serum had also been introduced.

2. Properdin

Properdin has been described as a heat-labile substance, apparently a component of normal serum, which possesses nonspecific antimicrobial activity. There is considerable controversy over the real nature of this substance, and the current view is that properdin may be a naturally occurring antibody or group of antibodies requiring complement for its activity. The work of Pillemer's group (Wedgewood et al., 1956) clearly showed that the four components of complement, properdin itself, and magnesium ions were essential to demonstrate neutralization of NDV. Heating at 56°C for 30 minutes removed the inhibiting effect. Comparable results were obtained with herpesvirus (Finkelstein et al., 1959). Dilution of the virus–properdin mixtures into 2.5% sodium citrate or incubation with an ion-exchange resin that removes divalent cations resulted in reactivation of the virus.

Although Ginsberg and Wedgewood (1959) reported that properdin neutralized a broad spectrum of viruses, including herpes, vaccinia, some arboviruses, bacteriophage, and probably RSV, they pointed out that viral inactivation by properdin is not a universal phenomenon. Southam and Greene (1959) failed to find an antiviral effect in the normal sera they examined with respect to certain arboviruses. These workers showed that rabbit antiserum to human properdin has a distinct depressing effect on the inhibiting activity of human sera against NDV. They could, however, not exclude other inhibiting substances, because even after absorption of the sera with zymosan, which effectively removes all properdin, significant hemagglutination inhibition of NDV still remained.

3. Heat-Stable Inhibitors

The sera and milk of apparently normal animals have on occasion been found to inhibit infectivity of poliovirus. In some instances, this was indistinguishable from antibody, while in others there was no doubt of the nonimmune origin of the viral inhibition.

a. Inhibitors in Bovine Serum. Takemori and co-workers (1958) selected sera containing inhibitors to poliovirus in the following manner: Monolayer cell cultures were infected and then overlaid with nutrient medium in agar supplemented with 10–20% of the sera. A known noninhibiting medium served as control. On plates containing inhibiting sera, the diameter of the plaques was smaller than that of the controls. Using commonly accepted techniques for the selection of viral mutants, they found that it was possible to isolate strains resistant to the inhibitors from the bovine sera that breed true and remain resistant when grown for several passages in the absence of inhibitor. They are identical to wild poliovirus in all respects except for the resistance to the bovine inhibitor. Although the inhibitor is associated with the γ-globulin fraction of the serum and is heat stable, several observations suggest that the inhibitor is not antibody. First, the mutants respond to a different degree to specific antipoliovirus serum and inhibitor. Second, mutants differ among themselves in their response to inhibitors from different sera, but are identical in their response to antiserum. Third, all attempts to isolate mutants resistant to specific antibody have failed.

b. *Inhibitors in Equine Serum.* Takemoto and Habel (1959) studied inhibitors from equine sera, which differ from those in bovine sera in that they do not neutralize poliovirus. Their effect is measured largely by the difference in the size of the plaques produced by the wild-sensitive and the mutant-resistant strains in a population of polioviruses. Experiments carried out to determine the mechanism of the inhibition showed that the resistant virus is released more efficiently from the infected cell in the presence of inhibitor than is the wild virus. This was shown by adding known amounts of wild and mutant pfu to monolayer cultures in both the presence and absence of inhibitor. The appearance of intracellular and extracellular virus was measured as a function of time. The increase in intracellular virus, measured by plating the disrupted infected cells, was the same for both strains. Extracellular wild virus, however, lagged 4 hours behind mutant virus when inhibitor was present. An indication that adsorption, too, is interfered with was obtained when washed monolayers that had been grown with and without inhibitor were infected with wild poliovirus. At various times a serum-free overlay was added and the plates incubated. The efficiency of plating was lower on the plates that had been treated with inhibitor.

It seems probable that this inhibitor is unrelated to specific antiviral antibody, since it shows no viral neutralizing effect. The distinct possibility that it is antibody to the cells was ruled out when it was found that specific anticellular antibody affects the wild and mutant strains identically.

Further evidence for the nonidentity of the inhibitors from bovine and equine sera was provided by the observations of Takemoto and Habel (1959) that a double mutant resistant to both inhibitors can originate from a single-step mutant and that such single-step mutants can recombine (Hirst, 1962).

I. Inhibitors in the Overlay Plating Agar

It is a common occurrence to encounter situations that cause both bacteriophage and animal viruses to form almost invisible pinpoint plaques under one set of conditions and to be fully developed under another. It has been found, also, that too high an agar concentration, dehydration of the agar as a result of prolonged storage, and aging host bacteria all may account for reduced plaques produced by bacteriophage. Animal virus plaques are subject to similar effects, including adverse pH, cystine content of the agar, and, of course, variation in the susceptibility of the host cells. In addition, differences in plaque size, which are not under genetic control, may be caused by viral inhibitors in the medium and the agar itself. Here we shall discuss the latter.

1. *Inhibitor of Encephalomyocarditis Virus*

Takemori and Nomura (1960) described an inhibitor extractable from agar that had a profound influence on the size of poliovirus plaques, but that did not neutralize the virus itself. Takemoto and Liebhaber (1961) investigated similar material with respect to encephalomyocarditis (EMC) virus. The inhibitor substance is present in agar and is released in its active form during autoclaving of the agar. There is reason to believe that both of these substances from agar are identical. The procedure used to purify the inhibitor was described by Takemoto and Liebhaber as follows (Table VI): Five grams of agar were suspended in 500 ml of distilled water and autoclaved for 20 minutes at 121°C. After the agar had cooled and gelled, it was frozen at −20°C and subsequently thawed. Any liquid was decanted, the sediment placed on cheesecloth, and the excess liquid squeezed out. After resuspension in 500 ml of distilled water, the procedure was repeated twice. The extracts thus obtained were pooled and cleared by centrifugation. The solution was reduced to dryness in a rotary flash evaporator at 40°C. The powder was dissolved in $\frac{1}{100}$ of the original volume in distilled water and then dialyzed for 24 hours against distilled water. Any precipitate formed was discarded. To 1 volume of the viscous solution, 9 volumes of absolute ethanol were added at −10°C. The white flocculent precipitate was centrifuged, repeatedly washed with cold alcohol, and air dried. Chemical analysis showed it to be a sulfated polysaccharide. When EMC virus was exposed to it, both viral multiplication and hemagglutination were inhibited. Growth curves performed in the absence of the polysaccharide showed continued viral synthesis over at least two cycles, whereas in the presence of the inhibitor there was no increase in yield after the first cycle. This seemed to suggest that the effect was not on the virus but rather that adsorption of the virus to the cells was in some way interfered with. This was further

TABLE VI

PURIFICATION OF THE INHIBITOR OF ENCEPHALOMYOCARDITIS VIRUS FROM AGAR

1. Suspend 5 gm of agar in 500 ml of distilled water.
2. Autoclave for 20 minutes at 121°C and 10 lb pressure.
3. Allow agar to cool; then freeze at −20°C and thaw.
4. Decant any liquid separated from the agar.
5. Place agar between several layers of cheesecloth and express any excess liquid.
6. Resuspend agar in 500 ml of distilled water.
7. Repeat steps 2 through 6 twice.
8. Pool all liquid extracts.
9. Centrifuge liquid to eliminate all sediment.
10. Evaporate to dryness in a rotary flash evaporator at 40°C.
11. Dissolve viscous remainder in 15 ml of distilled water.
12. Dialyze against 100 volumes of distilled water at 4°C for 24 hours.
13. Reduce dialyzate to a 15-ml volume in the flash evaporator at 40°C.
14. 1 volume of dialyzed solution is mixed with 9 volumes of absolute ethanol at −10°C. Hold at 4°C for 24 hours.
15. The precipitate is removed by centrifugation, washed 3 times with cold ethanol, and air-dried.
16. Dissolve in a small volume of distilled water and freeze-dry.

tested by Liebhaber and Takemoto (1963). Monolayers of Earle's L cells were infected with the wild strain of EMC virus mixed with varying concentrations of sulfated polysaccharide. At 15-minute intervals, culture plates were washed and overlaid with agar. The results showed that increasing concentrations of the inhibitor slowed adsorption of the virus to the monolayer. When a mutant that formed large plaques in the presence of inhibitor was tested, more than 100-fold the polysaccharide concentration was needed to obtain the same degree of inhibition of adsorption of this virus to the cells. Experiments with radioactive ^{35}S-labeled polyglucose sulfate showed that none of this substance was bound to the cells.

If the mechanism of the inhibition were by ionic binding of the virus to the sulfated polysaccharide, pH and ionic strength would be expected to influence the interaction. This was tested by preparing dilutions of both wild and mutant strains of EMC virus at 500 pfu/ml in bicarbonate-buffered saline in the pH range 6.0–8.0. Inhibitor was added to each in concentration of 1 μg/100 pfu of the wild strain and 1000 μg/100 pfu of the resistant mutant. At each pH value a number of plates were infected. After 30 minutes of adsorption the inoculum was washed off and overlay agar was added. The results showed that pH below 7.0 favors adsorption in the presence of inhibitor of the mutant, but that pH above and below neutrality was deleterious to the adsorption of the wild strain. At pH 7.0 the inhibiting effect was least pronounced.

In parallel procedure, virus dilutions were prepared in Earle's salt solution adjusted to varying ionic strength with NaCl. Any increase of salinity above 0.018 M resulted in a fall of the inhibitor activity. This finding tended to confirm the notion that two oppositely charged groups are involved in the inhibiting mechanism. As further evidence, the sulfated polysaccharide could be removed from agar by binding with polycationic compounds such as protamine or diethylaminoethyl-(DEAE) dextran. The latter was more efficient in removing the inhibitor from the agar. It can be added directly to the melted agar medium with 50 μg/ml as the optimum concentration.

2. Inhibitors of Poliovirus

Agol and Chumakova (1962) found that the use of a simple washing procedure to remove the sulfated polysaccharide from plating agar rendered this agar henceforth unsuitable for the differentiation between the acid-tolerance ("d") markers of poliovirus.

Although inhibitors of this kind may be the reason that many viruses which cause cytopathic effects in fluid tissue culture fail to do so under agar, removal of the sulfated polysaccharide from agar has not substantially shortened the list of nonplaque-forming viruses.

3. Inhibitors of Group A Arbovirus

Using the extraction procedure of Takemoto and Liebhaber (1961), Colón and his associates (1965) isolated a polysaccharide from agar that inhibited both growth and hemagglutination of group A arboviruses. In contrast to the findings of the earlier workers, they showed a distinct interaction with the inhibitor of such viruses as Eastern and Western equine encephalomyelitis viruses (EEE and WEE). Both infectivity and hemagglutination dropped following mixing of virus and inhibitor *in vitro*. This loss increased proportionally with incubation time and was irreversible by dilution of the virus–inhibitor complex. Not all viruses were equally affected. Strains of Venezuelan equine encephalomyelitis virus (VEE), for instance, were variable, in that one strain was inhibited and another was not at all. A gradient effect of the agar polysaccharide was discernible, with EEE generally most susceptible, WEE next, and VEE least susceptible to inhibition. The authors caution, however, that the virus–inhibitor interaction *in vitro* and the apparent lack of dissociability may be artifacts of the particular system used here. Indications are that slight modifications, such as 0.02 M phosphate ion or additional protein, cancel some of the observed effects.

Besides the direct interaction with the virus, this inhibitor exerted the previously observed interference with adsorption of the virus. Experiments in which chick fibroblast monolayers were infected after inhibitor had been added for 1 hour prior to infection showed that the number of infective centers was reduced, but that the yield per cell was normal. This suggests that the efficiency of release of virus from the cell was not influenced.

In these experiments, too, the antagonistic effect of DEAE-dextran on the polysaccharide was noted.

4. *Inhibitors of Group B Arbovirus*

Inhibition of both infectivity and hemagglutination of dengue virus, a group B arbovirus, was reported by Schulze and Schlesinger (1963). The method of extraction of the inhibitory substance was to autoclave a 0.9% suspension of agar in distilled water at 121°C for 20 minutes and to allow the agar to solidify. The gel was broken into small pieces and incubated in a small volume of water at 37°C for 48 hours. Following centrifugation, the supernatant was stored at 4°C and subsequently further purified by adjusting it to pH 3.0 with 0.1 N HCl. Bovine serum albumin was added to a final concentration of 0.4%. The heavy precipitate formed was collected and redissolved in distilled water at pH 7.5. The precipitation procedure was repeated twice and the final precipitate dissolved in one tenth of the original volume at pH 7.5. Three consecutive extractions with 80% phenol at 4°C removed all the bovine serum albumin. The phenol was removed in turn by a single extraction with ethyl ether. Finally, the solution was dialyzed for 12 hours against tap water. The inhibitor contained reducible polysaccharides and sulfate. Mice given mixtures of virus and inhibitor were not fully protected from the lethal effects of dengue virus, although both the 50% lethal dose and the plaque titer of the original preparation were reduced. A comparable drop in hemagglutinating titer was observed. The effect of the inhibitor is thus probably on the virus and not on the cells. An experiment to establish this more firmly was to treat goose erythrocytes with the inhibitor. In a subsequent hemagglutination titration there was no difference between treated and control cells.

Since the data suggested an effect of the sulfated polysaccharide on the virus itself, experiments to elucidate the mechanism of the inhibitor were performed (Schulze, 1964). A suspension of cells was divided into two parts; one portion was treated with inhibitor and one was left untreated. Both were then grown in monolayer, and cell counts were made periodically from trypsinized preparations. As expected, no differences were observed in either growth rate or number of cells. Virus–inhibitor mixtures were then centrifuged at 41,000 rpm for 3 hours. The sedimented virus and the supernatant fluid were examined for infectivity and hemagglutination. The inhibition was always found associated with the virus. It had been observed that when virus–inhibitor complexes were diluted before plating, inhibition was inversely proportional to the dilution factor. To test the possibility that the inhibition was reversible, virus was treated with concentrated inhibitor in two ways. In the first, virus and inhibitor were diluted separately, then mixed and plated. In the second method, virus–inhibitor mixtures at very much higher concentration than those usually plated were incubated for 10 minutes at room temperature. They were then so diluted that the individual concentrations of virus and inhibitor corresponded to those in the first set. The series gave almost identical results, indicating that treatment of the virus with concentrated polysaccharide did not lead to inhibition in excess of that accounted for by the amount of inhibitor in the sample actually plated. Thus, in the second set, the inhibition was reversed when the concentration of free inhibitor was reduced by dilution of the virus–inhibitor complex.

From these experiments Schulze (1964) developed a procedure for studying the conditions necessary for the formation of the virus–inhibitor complex. It was based on the assumption that since prolonged incubation of the complex prior to plating did not increase the inhibitory effect, equilibrium probably was established even at low inhibitor concentration at the time of plating or during the adsorption of the virus to the monolayer. Tenfold dilutions of virus and inhibitor were mixed in equal volumes and plated. The results of these infectivity titrations showed clearly that the proportion of residual infectivity was independent of the virus concentration and that changes in the inhibitor concentration did not result in proportional changes in the degree of inhibition. These findings are compatible with a reversible binding of virus by the inhibitor.

In order to determine the ratios of bound to free virus at various inhibitor concentrations, two-dimensional hemagglutination inhibition titrations were performed in such a way that by checkerboard pattern 2-fold dilutions of inhibitor and virus were exposed to each other. The free virus was then determined by hemagglutination in the presence of varying amounts of inhibitor. Since the initial total virus input in the absence of inhibitor was known, bound virus, that is total virus minus free virus, could easily be determined. From these calculations it appeared that the ratio of virus to inhibitor was approximately 2.

Finally, with dengue virus, as with other viruses, the addition of inhibitor to the growth medium decreased and delayed cytopathic effect and virus yield. Schulze (1964) showed that this was caused by binding of the virus after its release from the host cell. The experiments performed here have the advantage over the similar ones performed by Takemoto and Liebhaber (1961) in that only a single growth cycle is considered. This rules out additional effects of the agar extract. Monolayers were infected at high multiplicity. After penetration was virtually complete, one set of plates received overlay containing inhibitor; the other set received no inhibitor. At different times during the viral latent period the medium was removed and replaced, after thorough washing of the monolayer, with inhibitor-free growth medium. In one set the steps were duplicated, but inhibitor remained throughout. Samples were now removed periodically from all plates, frozen at $-76°C$, and then assayed all together for infectivity. It was shown that extracellular virus increased exponentially and that there was no difference either in virus or rate of synthesis between cultures maintained free of inhibitor, part of the time in inhibitor, or all of the time in inhibitor, provided that no inhibitor was present in the final assay of the system. It was thus clearly established that as long as inhibitor was not present at the time of adsorption or penetration, it had no effect on viral infectivity. Although more sophisticated in design, this experiment rendered complete support to the findings of Takemoto and Liebhaber (1961).

The inhibitor was not equally effective against all group B arboviruses. Thus Murray Valley and St. Louis encephalitis viruses were fully resistant. Such differences are reminiscent of the findings with arboviruses of group A (Colón *et al.*, 1965).

5. *Inhibitors of Herpesvirus*

Experiments performed by Takemoto and Fabisch (1964) demonstrated that strains of herpesvirus are also sensitive to acid polysaccharides. Substances recovered from agar as well as commercially available material were found to inhibit adsorption of virus to the cells, plaque formation, and the yield from infected cells grown in fluid tissue culture medium. Differences were observed, however, in the inhibitor patterns of the various polysaccharides tested. Thus, dextran sulfate inhibited both adsorption and subsequent plaque formation, while the crude polysaccharide extracted from agar in the laboratory inhibited only the adsorption step. The mechanisms involved here are not clear; it is difficult to understand how adsorption of the virus to the cells can be interfered with without also inhibiting subsequent plaque formation. In the case of herpesvirus, no resistant strains were found.

Takemoto and Spicer (1965) demonstrated by histochemical methods that HeLa cells could take up acid polysaccharides into their cytoplasm. These substances also cause agglutination and interfere with the ability of the cells to attach to glass. Cells pretreated with inhibitor and then infected with herpesvirus yielded significantly less virus than untreated cells. This occurred regardless of the multiplicity of infection, and was interpreted to mean that the inhibition took place independently of adsorption of virus to the cells. Moreover, the effect was not a generally observed one: poliovirus yields were not depressed.

6. *Inhibitor of Influenza Virus*

Takemoto and Fabisch (1963) also investigated the effect of sulfated polysaccharides on plaque formation by influenza virus. They found that in this instance, too, the addition of DEAE-dextran to the agar resulted in higher efficiency of plating and in improved appearance of the plaques. The experimental evidence ruled out inactivation of the virus by the inhibitor in the agar. It suggested instead that the critical step had to do with the adsorption of the virus to the cells. The question, however, whether the observed inhibition was caused by interaction of the polysaccharide with the virus or the host cell receptors remains unresolved.

J. Nonspecific Inhibitor of Bacteriophage T2 (Sagik)

A unique inhibitor of bacteriophage T2 was described by Sagik (1954). He found that fresh lysates of *Escherichia coli* infected with T2 contain an inhibitor, apparently of host cell origin, that combines with the phage in a reversible manner. Because of this, lysates containing this inhibitor are characterized by a spontaneous increase in infectious titer during storage or upon dilution in distilled water. Although the inhibition is produced by many bacterial host strains, only T2 and its mutants are affected and not the closely related phages T4 and T6. These characteristics of the inhibitor were discovered by the following methods: When a known number of T2 pfu were added to fresh lysates of bacteria infected with lysis-inhibited T6 and the mixture was then tested for its T2 and T6 titer before and after dilution in distilled water, the T2 titer was found to be only 25% of the expected level before dilution, while the titer of T6 remained at the expected level before and after dilution. If T2 was added to a T6 lysate that was a few hours old, no trace of inhibition was found. Of interest was the fact that T6 lysates prepared from mutant host cells unable to support the growth of T2 did not contain the inhibitor for wild type T2, but did inhibit host-range mutants of T2 able to grow in the particular host cell. If an inhibited lysate was heated at 65°C, there was at first a rise in titer, accounted for by removal of inhibitor, and then a drop in titer, reflecting the thermal inactivation of T2 phage.

K. Host-Induced Modification (HIM)

A remarkable example of viral inhibition that occurs in several bacteriophage systems is HIM. It was originally described by Luria and Human (1952), who showed that phages T2 and T6 when grown for one cycle in a particular mutant of their normal host, *Escherichia coli* B, were so modified that their subsequent growth in wild strain B was almost completely suppressed. They could, however, grow normally in a different host, *Shigella dysenteriae* Sh, and, moreover, the progeny from this host was again normal with respect to growth in B. Recent work has established that the cause of this behavior lies in an abnormality in the metabolism of uridine diphosphoglucose in the mutant, so that the DNA of the progeny phage is improperly glucosylated (Hattman and Fukasawa, 1963; Shedlovsky and Brenner, 1963).

This type of inhibition has also been shown with other bacterial viruses, although the basic mechanism may not be the same for all modifications. It has so far not been implicated in the inhibition of the growth of animal viruses, but it is conceivable that some of the examples of failure to recover virus in primary isolation in tissue culture and the long process of adaptation of a virus to a particular cell line may be caused by HIM.

The methods used to establish whether HIM plays a role in a virus–host system involve comparing the efficiency of plating the progeny of virus from one host on another. This is done for all possible combinations. It is, of course, necessary to have one common host on which all of the progenies, modified or not, plate with equally high efficiency. It is also advisable to check on the adsorption of the viruses to the several host cell lines in order to eliminate poor adsorption as a possible cause of the inhibition.

L. MYCOPLASMA (PPLO) CONTAMINATION OF TISSUE CULTURE CELLS

Rouse and her associates (1963) studied a remarkable inhibition of the growth of adenovirus in mammalian cell culture. By the use of most elegant techniques, they demonstrated not only an absolute requirement for the amino acid arginine in adenovirus synthesis but also that failure of adenovirus to grow in certain tissue culture systems was caused by the depletion of arginine from the medium by PPLO that were contaminating the host cells. Supplementing such cultures with arginine overcame the inhibition. In order to determine the levels of available amino acid in the medium at any time during the experiment, an arginine-requiring auxotroph of *Escherichia coli* was employed. In liquid media the optical density attained by the bacterial inoculum served as the index of the arginine present, but in plating medium it was the appearance of visible colonies of the auxotroph. In the system studied, such colonies were formed in as little as 1.0 μg/ml of arginine.

This is really an example of specific viral inhibition in the sense that adenovirus seems to be affected and some other viruses are not, and also in that the requirement is absolute for arginine and cannot be replaced by ornithine or citrulline. It is nonspecific insofar as the mechanism of the arginine requirement by the infected cells is unknown. This requirement differs from that of poliovirus for glutamine, where the presence of only this amino acid in addition to glucose and salts enables the infected cells to produce a normal yield of virus (Eagle and

Habel, 1956). It also differs from the findings that psittacosis virus synthesis requires the presence of certain amino acids, but not others in the medium (Bader and Morgan, 1958).

M. INAPPARENT AND LATENT INFECTIONS

The examples of nutritional requirements just mentioned have a direct bearing on the phenomenon of inapparent infection. Cells, although infected with virus, may not manifest any sign of viral presence if they are deprived of an essential metabolite. Upon addition of the compound, however, the virus may start to proliferate and the host cells eventually exhibit the overt consequences of normal virus infection. Bader and Morgan (1958) showed that cells maintained in a medium of glucose and salts, and devoid of certain essential amino acids, do not support the growth of psittacosis virus. After the necessary supplements were added to the medium, however, the infected cells liberated newly synthesized virus. Of particular significance was the finding that phenylalanine or tryptophan was absolutely essential to viral multiplication. Without either of them, infection remained inapparent, even in otherwise complete medium. In the light of Rouse's findings (1963), it might be of interest to reexamine the present system for depletion of these aromatic amino acids within the host cells. If such a depletion were found, an attempt could be made to correlate it with the ease with which inapparent infection can be established in some cell lines and not in others.

It is important to distinguish here between inapparent and latent infection. In inapparent infection the virus is present in the cell as a result of true infection and is merely prevented from further development within the cell under the particular inhibiting circumstances. In latent infection the virus is present in the cell, frequently only in its genomic form, as a result of congenital infection, and may never show overt signs of its presence unless specifically induced or tested for. Also, in inapparent infection the cells usually are inhibited, whereas in latent infections they usually are quite normal. Latent infection also must be considered with respect to inhibition of virus infection. If cells harbor an undetected latent virus that causes them to produce interferon, their inadvertent use for growth of another virus may result in complete inhibition of this second agent. A recent example of such a case was described by Henle and Henle (1965) in a line of cells derived from Burkitt's lymphoma that was found to be resistant to several myxoviruses.

N. Miscellaneous Factors in the Tissue Culture System

1. Metaphase Arrest

A general type of interference with the growth of viruses in an otherwise susceptible population of cells can be encountered if the cells are synchronized and maintained in a specific mitotic state. Marcus and Robbins (1963) used vinblastine at approximately 0.1 μg/ml of medium to keep HeLa cell monolayers in metaphase arrest. The arrested cells could easily be shaken off the glass if the medium was devoid of calcium ion. Such cells can be maintained in metaphase arrest for about 30 hours provided vinblastine is present in the medium. Cells in metaphase arrest were unable to serve as infective centers for both RNA and DNA viruses. The reason for this failure was thought to be that the ribosomes of such metaphase-arrested cells were coated with a trypsin-sensitive material (Salb and Marcus, 1965) and could not form functional polyribosomal complexes with viral mRNA.

2. Phosphatase Content

It was found by Amos (1953) that herpesvirus, when exposed to either acid or alkaline phosphatases, suffered a loss of infectivity. The conclusion drawn was that in many instances the phosphatase activity of the tissues used to propagate the virus might have an inhibiting effect on the inoculum and subsequent viral progeny. Neither the complete spectrum of sensitive viruses nor the mode of action of the inhibition are known.

3. Tissue Cultures from Immune Animals

The question whether tissue cultures from immunized animals are less susceptible to virus infection than those from normal animals has been investigated for a long time. No conclusions have been reached, but the consensus is that poorer virus yields are obtained from the immune cultures. Steinberger and Rights (1963) studied this problem using the plaque technique, which is probably the most sensitive method for detecting both antibody in the cells comprising the primary tissue culture and quantitative changes in the viral infectivity. They found that vaccinia virus reached much higher titer in spleen cells from nonimmunized rabbits, but there was no difference in the growth of the virus in kidney cells cultured from immune or nonimmune animals. With increasing age of the cultures, any differences associable with the previous immune status vanish.

The results with the spleen cells were attributed to the presence of macrophages in the preparation early after immunization and their overgrowth later by fibroblastic cells. The macrophages, it is implied, confer some resistance to the spleen cells. Specific antibody could be ruled out as the cause of the diminished growth of virus in the cells from the immune animals because no trace of virus neutralization was demonstrable. The possible role of interferon, however, was not tested.

O. Virus Inactivation following Virus–Cell Interaction

Joklik and Darnell (1961) showed that a large proportion of poliovirus that had attached to cells eluted rapidly when the cells were held at 37°C. Furthermore, this virus subsequently no longer adsorbed to fresh cells. Infectious RNA extracted from the eluted virus was identical to RNA from normal poliovirus both in amount and biological activity. Fenwick and Cooper (1962) made similar observations. The data have an obvious, albeit academic, bearing on a discussion of inhibition of viral infection. It is possible to visualize a situation in which virus has had contact with certain cells *in vivo* and, following elution from these cells, became incapable of adsorbing to tissue culture cells *in vitro* without a prior passage in these cells. This block could perhaps be overcome by the use of infectious nucleic acid extracted from the virus.

P. Inhibition of Plant Viruses

1. *Inhibitor and Augmenter from the Same Source*

A large number of substances of natural origin exist that inhibit plant virus infection. Many of these inhibitors apparently act on the host plant rather than on the virus particle. One of them, a substance occurring in the juice of New Zealand spinach (*Tetragonia expansa*), has been studied by Benda (1956) with respect to its effect on the growth of tobacco ringspot virus on cowpeas. The inhibitor was prepared from young leaves of plants raised from seed in the greenhouse. Leaves were ground with mortar and pestle, and the juice expressed through cheesecloth. It was found that the active component was labile to heating at 80°C for 10 minutes, was not dialyzable against distilled water at 4°C, and did not sediment with 105,000 *g* in 2 hours. Further, partial purification to remove smaller and larger impurities, achieved by dialysis against distilled water at 4°C, low-speed centrifugation, and heating at 60°C for 10 minutes resulted in a product that was effective at approximately 1 mg/ml of aqueous solution provided the material was kept lyophilized prior to use.

It is believed that the augmenter is a soluble oxalate. The experiments presented here lead to the conclusion that the suppressor acts on the host cells and not on the virus itself. A delay was observed when trypsin was substituted for the inhibitor or when the material from spinach juice was used in a different plant with the same virus inoculum.

A unique finding was that the crude juice contained not only an inhibitor for tobacco ringspot virus but an augmenter as well. Boiling the juice resulted in augmenting action manifested by an increase in the number of lesions; use of dialyzed juice suppressed viral lesions altogether, while the untreated material delayed their appearance. It is not clear whether the augmenter added after infection with a virus–inhibitor mixture can reverse the inhibiting effect.

2. Purification of an Inhibitor of Plant Viruses

Ragetli and Weintraub (1962a,b) purified and studied the mode of action of another inhibitor of plant viruses that could be isolated from carnation (*Dianthus caryophyllus* L). In this case, leaves and stems were frozen and thawed, ground, and the juices expressed through cheesecloth. The fluid was centrifuged first at low speed and then at 66,000 g for 2–3 hours. The last supernatant was immediately filtered to remove any lipid and subsequently dialyzed against 100 volumes of triethylamine buffer at pH 7.8 for 36–48 hours at 0°C. Addition of 5 gm of dry DEAE/100 ml, previously equilibrated against buffer, aided in the clarification of the liquid. The mixture was filtered and the procedure repeated with 2 gm of DEAE/100 ml. The almost water-clear and colorless material was further purified by repeated column chromatography. Purified fractions displayed many of the characteristics of a protein, but the inhibitory effect was not destroyed by papain, trypsin, aminopeptidase, or carboxypeptidase. Furthermore, when applied to leaves prior to infection, it could interfere with infectious RNA as well as with intact virus. Since the inhibitor is devoid of RNase activity and cannot block the inactivation of infectious RNA by pancreatic RNase, it appears that the effect of the inhibition is on the host cell. The mechanism is thought by the authors to be a competitive blocking of certain sites in the cell that are essential to the establishment of viral infection. It remains to be ascertained what these sites are and how they influence infection, since RNA and intact virus would probably not share the same adsorption sites.

REFERENCES

Adams, M. H. (1959). "Bacteriophages." Wiley (Interscience), New York.
Adams, M. H., and Park, B. H. (1956). *Virology* 2, 719.
Agol, V. I., and Chumakova, M. Y. (1962). *Virology* 17, 221.
Amos, H. (1953). *J. Exptl. Med.* 98, 365.
Bader, J. P., and Morgan, H. R. (1958). *J. Exptl. Med.* 108, 617.
Benda, G. T. A. (1956). *Virology* 2, 439.
Biddle, F., Pepper, D. S., and Belyavin, G. (1965). *Nature* 207, 381.
Burnet, F. M. (1951). *Physiol. Rev.* 31, 131.
Buzzell, A., and Hanig, M. (1958). *Advan. Virus Res.* 5, 289.
Casals, J., and Olitzky, P. K. (1947). *Science* 106, 267.
Chu, C. M. (1951). *J. Gen. Microbiol.* 5, 739.
Cohen, A., and Belyavin, G. (1959). *Virology* 7, 59.
Cohen, A., Newland, S. E., and Biddle, F. (1963). *Virology* 20, 518.
Colón, J. I., Idoine, J. B., Brand, O. M., and Costlow, R. D. (1965). *J. Bacteriol.* 90, 172.
Eagle, H., and Habel, K. (1956). *J. Exptl. Med.* 104, 271.
Fenwick, M. L., and Cooper, P. D. (1962). *Virology* 18, 212.
Finkelstein, R. A., Allen, R., and Sulkin, S. E. (1959). *J. Infect. Diseases* 104, 184.
Ginsberg, H. S., and Horsfall, F. L., Jr. (1949a). *J. Exptl. Med.* 90, 393.
Ginsberg, H. S., and Horsfall, F. L., Jr. (1949b). *J. Exptl. Med.* 90, 475.
Ginsberg, H. S., and Wedgewood, R. J. (1959). *Ann. N.Y. Acad. Sci.* 83, 528.
Ginsberg, H. S., Goebel, W. F., and Horsfall, F. L., Jr. (1948). *J. Exptl. Med.* 87, 385.
Goebel, W. F., and Jesaitis, M. A. (1952). *J. Exptl. Med.* 96, 425.
Gottschalk, A. (1958). *Advan. Enzymol.* 20, 135.
Habel, K., Hornibrook, J. W., Gregg, N. C., Silverberg, R. J., and Takemoto, K. K. (1958). *Virology* 5, 7.
Hattman, S., and Fukasawa, T. (1963). *Proc. Natl. Acad. Sci. U.S.* 50, 297.
Henle, G., and Henle, W. (1965). *J. Bacteriol.* 89, 252.
Henry, C., and Youngner, J. S. (1957). *J. Immunol.* 78, 273.
Hirst, G. K. (1962). *Cold Spring Harbor Symp. Quant. Biol.* 27, 303.
Joklik, W. K., and Darnell, J. E., Jr. (1961). *Virology* 13, 439.
Karzon, D. T. (1956). *J. Immunol.* 76, 454.
Klein, M. (1958). *Ann. N.Y. Acad. Sci.* 70, 362.
Lennette, E. H., and Schmidt, N. J., eds. (1964). "Diagnostic Procedures for Viral and Rickettsial Diseases," 3rd ed. Am. Public Health Assoc., New York.
Liebhaber, H., and Takemoto, K. K. (1963). *Virology* 20, 569.
Luria, S. E., and Human, M. L. (1952). *J. Bacteriol.* 64, 557.
McCarthy, K., and Germer, W. D. (1952). *Brit. J. Exptl. Pathol.* 33, 529.
Mandel, B. (1958). *Virology* 6, 295.
Mandel, B., and Racker, E. (1953a). *J. Exptl. Med.* 98, 399.
Mandel, B., and Racker, E. (1953b). *J. Exptl. Med.* 98, 417.
Marcus, P. I., and Robbins, E. (1963). *Proc. Natl. Acad. Sci. U.S.* 50, 1156.
Morgan, I. M. (1945). *J. Immunol.* 50, 359.
Quersin-Thiry, L. (1958). *J. Immunol.* 81, 253.
Ragetli, H. W. J., and Weintraub, M. (1962a). *Virology* 18, 232.
Ragetli, H. W. J., and Weintraub, M. (1962b). *Virology* 18, 241.

Rouse, H. C., Bonifas, V. H., and Schlesinger, R. W. (1963). *Virology* **20,** 357.

Rubin, H. (1956). *Virology* **2,** 545.

Rubin, H. (1962). *Bacteriol. Rev.* **26,** 1.

Sagik, B. P. (1954). *J. Bacteriol.* **68,** 430.

Salb, J. M., and Marcus, P. I. (1965). *Proc. Natl. Acad. Sci. U.S.* **54,** 1353.

Schulze, I. T. (1964). *Virology* **22,** 79.

Schulze, I. T., and Schlesinger, R. W. (1963). *Virology* **19,** 49.

Shedlovsky, A., and Brenner, S. (1963). *Proc. Natl. Acad. Sci. U.S.* **50,** 300.

Southam, C. M., and Greene, E. L. (1959). *Ann. N.Y. Acad. Sci.* **83,** 533.

Steinberger, A., and Rights, F. L. (1963). *Virology* **21,** 402.

Takemori, N., and Nomura, S. (1960). *Virology* **12,** 171.

Takemori, N., Nomura, S., Nakano, M., Morioka, Y., Henmi, M., and Kitaoka, M. (1958). *Virology* **5,** 30.

Takemoto, K. K., and Fabisch, P. (1963). *Proc. Soc. Exptl. Biol. Med.* **114,** 811.

Takemoto, K. K., and Fabisch, P. (1964). *Proc. Soc. Exptl. Biol. Med.* **116,** 140.

Takemoto, K. K., and Habel, K. (1959). *Virology* **9,** 228.

Takemoto, K. K., and Liebhaber, H. (1961). *Virology* **14,** 456.

Takemoto, K. K., and Spicer, S. S. (1965). *Ann. N.Y. Acad. Sci.* **130,** 365.

Tamm, I., and Horsfall, F. L., Jr. (1950). *Proc. Soc. Exptl. Biol. Med.* **74,** 108.

Utz, J. P. (1948). *Proc. Soc. Exptl. Biol. Med.* **69,** 186.

Utz, J. P. (1949). *J. Immunol.* **63,** 273.

Wedgewood, R. J., Ginsberg, H. S., and Pillemer, L. (1956). *J. Exptl. Med.* **104,** 707.

Whitman, L. (1947). *J. Immunol.* **56,** 97.

3 Methods of Inactivation by Ultraviolet Radiation

A. Kleczkowski

I. Sources of Radiation 94
   A. Different Kinds of Lamps and Filters 94
   B. Low-Pressure Mercury Lamps 96
   C. Monochromators 97
II. Methods of Exposure 98
III. Absorption of Radiation Energy 99
   A. Methods of Measurement 100
   B. Terminology and Methods of Computation 102
IV. Measurement of Radiation Intensity 118
   A. Units of Energy and Power 118
   B. Methods of Measurement 120
V. Progress of Inactivation 129
   A. Rate of Inactivation 129
   B. Absorbed Energy and Inactivation 132
   C. Action Spectra 137
   References 138

Photochemistry and photobiology of proteins, nucleic acids, and viruses have recently been dealt with comprehensively by McLaren and Shugar (1964). There are also earlier reviews of work on inactivation of viruses by UV (A. Kleczkowski, 1957, 1960b), and here we shall deal only with methods of such work.

The choice of methods for work on inactivation of viruses obviously depends on the purpose of the work, which may range from such purely practical problems as the production of a vaccine, to exact quantitative features of inactivation such as kinetics, quantum yields, or action spectra. The methods described below are mainly those used in exact quantitative work on inactivation, and all of them will not be needed for all problems.

Inactivation can refer to the loss of any activity, such as infectivity, antigenicity, or ability to agglutinate red blood cells. However, we shall be concerned only with loss of infectivity.

Monochromatic and polychromatic radiations (i.e., those composed of radiations of a single narrow band of wavelengths and those that consist of radiations with widely different wavelengths) will often be considered separately, because some rules of behavior that apply to monochromatic radiation do not apply to polychromatic radiation.

I. Sources of Radiation

Amounts of radiation energy that must be absorbed by a unit mass of virus to inactivate most of its infectivity are much smaller than those that must be absorbed by the unit mass of almost any UV-absorbing material to cause structural changes detectable by physico-chemical methods or by microscopy. Consequently, sources of radiation that are too weak for photochemical work may suffice for such photo-biological work as the inactivation of viruses, and there is usually no need for any special arrangements to insure the use of nearly total outputs of lamps. However, radiation sources of relatively high intensity may be needed when large quantities of virus preparations are to be inactivated, when preparations are highly concentrated, and/or when a virus-containing medium also contains other materials that absorb much UV radiation.

A. DIFFERENT KINDS OF LAMPS AND FILTERS

There is a great range of commercial lamps that can be used as sources of UV radiation. Descriptions of various kinds and types of lamps, and such details as intensity and spectral distribution of radiation energy, are given by their makers, and only a few general remarks are needed here. The currently most-used lamps are mercury arcs, but also widely used are carbon and high-pressure xenon arcs. There are also several "spectral lamps" (for example, made by Philips of Holland) that produce discrete spectral lines, some of which can be isolated by means of optical filters or monochromators.

All these lamps are discharge lamps, and, except for carbon arcs, the quality of their radiation depends greatly on gas pressure. For example, low-pressure mercury lamps (not exceeding 10^{-4} atmospheres) give radiation mainly at a wavelength of 2537 Å, corresponding to the lowest level of excitation of 4.9 electron volts (eV), a small amount of radiation at 1849 Å corresponding to the second level of excitation of 6.7 eV, and very little at other wavelengths. Medium-pressure mercury lamps (up to a few atmospheres) produce a number of discrete intense spectral lines corresponding to electronic transitions from various higher excitation levels to any of possible lower levels. As the pressure and temperature are increased, spectral distribution becomes more diffuse, and high-pressure mercury lamps (from a few up to almost 300 atmospheres) produce an almost continuous spectrum, because spectral lines are broadened by the "damping effect" of atomic collisions and by the "Stark effect" of electrostatic fields of ions. High-pressure mercury lamps can be extremely powerful sources of light, most of which is in the visible part of the spectrum, but the use of very powerful lamps may be complicated by the need of air or water cooling. With some lamps not themselves hot enough to need any special cooling arrangements, irradiated samples may need to be cooled by water or ice. However, most types of work on the inactivation of viruses do not require radiation intensities that call for any cooling of the specimens.

Mercury lamps have the form of sealed quartz tubes of varying widths and lengths and are usually provided with transformers. Much more compact sources of radiation are carbon arcs ·and high-pressure xenon arcs producing powerful radiation with continuous spectra. Their compactness may be convenient, especially when using monochromators. Tungsten electrodes in some xenon lamps are only a few millimeters apart, so that such lamps can almost be considered as point sources of light. In addition to such lamps, rather expensive control gear (including a starter and current control) must also be obtained.

All the above-mentioned lamps, except low-pressure mercury lamps, are polychromatic, with most energy delivered in the visible part of the spectrum. Filters made of special glass (e.g., Chance OX 7 or Corning 9863) can eliminate most of the visible radiation while passing a considerable proportion of UV radiation of a wide range of wavelengths (down to about 2400 Å) with a broad peak between 3000 and 3500 Å. When monochromatic radiation is required, it can be isolated by means of a monochromator (see below). Without a monochromator, or when the intensity obtainable from one is insufficient, filters can be used to obtain selected bands of UV radiation. It is possible, for example, by combination of commercial solid filters with filters that are solutions of various inorganic salts and organic compounds to isolate one of several bands of radiation in the UV range of the spectrum (Kasha, 1948). However, the band widths are quite considerable (about 200 Å), and the choice of wavelengths corresponding to the peaks of the bands is at the moment limited to five.

There are now also interference filters available for UV (made, for example, by Barr & Stroud Ltd., Great Britain). Any filter based on interference transmits two or three bands of wavelengths centered around well-defined peaks, one of which may be in the UV and others in the visible range, but unwanted peaks can be eliminated by auxiliary absorption filters. There remains, however, some background transmission (the ratio of peak to background transmissions is about 30), the band width around the peak is quite considerable, and there may be some uncertainty about the position of the peak of a band. Thus the precision of isolation obtained with existing filters is much less than that with monochromators, but for many kinds of experiments the degree of precision obtainable with monochromators is unnecessary. Details concerning the performance of various filters are obtainable from makers and agents. An extensive review of optical filters of various kinds has been published by Mohler and Loofbourow (1952).

B. Low-Pressure Mercury Lamps

Low-pressure mercury lamps, which are often called "germicidal" lamps, have been used in photobiological and photochemical work more than all other kinds of lamps, because usually over 90% of their total radiation energy is at a wavelength of 2537 Å, and so the radiation is almost monochromatic. The remaining proportion of energy is distributed throughout the spectrum, from about 2500 Å upward, being very small in any one part of it, but there is some radiation corresponding to the resonance line at 1849Å. This radiation, the presence of which is easily detectable by the smell of ozone, is strongly absorbed by the quartz envelope of the lamp, and so only a small proportion, which depends on the thickness of the envelope, passes through. However, the quantum energy of this radiation is high, and it can produce effects different from those produced by radiation at 2537 Å, so its presence may be undesirable. It can be easily eliminated by passage through a quartz container filled with about 5% acetic acid. Some low-pressure mercury lamps are provided with a filter, incorporated in the envelope, that eliminates the 1849 Å radiation, so that the resulting radiation is almost exclusively of 2537 Å.

Low-pressure mercury lamps have usually the shape of long tubes that may be straight or curved in various ways. The advantage of a long straight tube is that the intensity of radiation along a segment of a straight line parallel to the axis of the tube is nearly constant, and so several samples or objects can be placed in a line and irradiated simultaneously with about the same intensity.

C. Monochromators

When UV inactivation is to be done by precisely isolated radiations of specified wavelengths, a monochromator must be used. There is a great range of commercial monochromators, but they all belong to one of the two basic types: one is based on a prism (for the UV range of the spectrum, the prism can be either of solid quartz or of water in a quartz container) and the other on a diffraction grating. Monochromators can be constructed by prospective users themselves, who may be guided by descriptions of monochromators based on a water prism or on a diffraction grating by Harrison (1934) and French *et al.* (1947), respectively.

Figures 1 and 2 give schematic presentations of monochromators based on a prism and on a diffraction grating. Radiation coming from a source is focused on the entrance slit by means of a quartz lens. Then it proceeds as a divergent beam to a concave mirror, from which it is reflected as a parallel beam toward a prism or a plane grating. After passing through the prism, or after reflection from the grating, the beam falls on another or on the same concave mirror, respectively, from which it is reflected as a convergent beam toward the exit slit on which

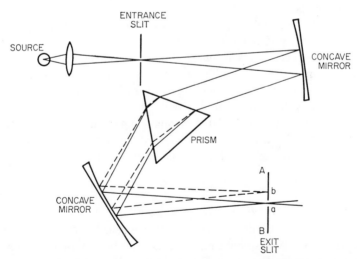

Fig. 1. A schematic presentation of a prism monochromator. The slits are perpendicular to the plane of the paper and the spectrum is spread in the direction AB. If radiation of a wavelength, λ_a, is focused on the exit slit (point a) and that of a wavelength λ_b at a point b (not on the slit), the latter can be brought to the slit, and the former moved away from the slit by rotating the prism anticlockwise.

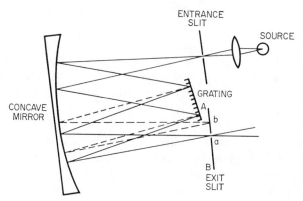

FIG. 2. A schematic presentation of a grating monochromator. The technique is the same as that for the prism monochromator (see caption to Fig. 1).

it is focused. It emerges from the slit as a divergent beam. When necessary, it can be made parallel by means of a quartz lens. The choice of wavelength is made by rotating the prism or the grating, as shown in Figs. 1 and 2.

Various commercial monochromators differ from the schemes shown in Figs. 1 and 2 mainly by having plane mirrors whose function is to deflect radiations so that the instruments can be compact and convenient in shape.

Many commercial monochromators are primarily designed to be used as spectrometers, and some may not be suitable for work on inactivation of viruses because sufficiently intense radiation of selected wavelengths cannot be obtained. Therefore, the instrument must be large, with a large aperture, and the source of radiation must be powerful. For example, a large-aperture quartz prism monochromator in conjunction with an air-cooled 250-W xenon lamp is just sufficient for work on inactivation of dilute solutions of viruses or virus nucleic acids in the wavelength range of 230–290 mμ with a band width of about 5 mμ.

II. Methods of Exposure

When a lamp with or without a filter is used directly as a source of UV radiation, virus-containing fluids can be exposed in open, flat dishes placed under the lamp. When dilute virus preparations are irradiated, times of exposure are usually so brief that no evaporation can be assumed to occur. When concentrated preparations, or preparations containing much UV-absorbing material, are irradiated, time of exposure may be long enough for evaporation to occur. Should it be important to avoid this, exposures must be done in a closed quartz container or in a container covered with a quartz plate.

The distance from the lamp can be chosen either after several trial exposures at different distances when the rate of inactivation is measured by infectivity tests or by measuring radiation intensity at different distances, for example, by actinometry (see Section IV,B,2), provided it is known in advance what intensity is most convenient for a given purpose.

When a monochromator is used, samples can be irradiated in suitably shaped quartz cells (cuvettes of spectrophotometers can be used), and these can be placed in such a way that all or most of the radiation emerging from the exit slit is used.

When irradiated virus preparations are so dilute that nearly 100% of incident radiation passes through the irradiated fluid (which can be ascertained by spectrophotometry; see Section III,A,1), it can be assumed that no virus particle is shaded. Also, provided that radiation intensity is about the same over the whole irradiated surface, it can be assumed that all virus particles "see" the source of radiation equally well, and there is, in principle, no need to agitate the fluid during irradiation. However, when the optical density of an irradiated fluid is such that all, or a considerable proportion of, incident radiation is absorbed, the fluid must be continuously stirred during irradiation to insure that all virus particles are equally exposed to the radiation. When fluids are irradiated in Petri dishes or watch glasses, these can be rocked by a circular movement. With other kinds of containers some kind of a stirrer may have to be used, such as a suitably shaped glass or quartz rod rotated by hand or by a mechanical stirrer.

A simple and convenient arrangement for measuring rates of inactivation of viruses or enzymes by UV at 2537 Å is described by Oster and McLaren (1950). This incorporates a low-pressure mercury lamp and two circular quartz cells with two parallel flat walls, one to be filled with 5% acetic acid to filter off the radiation at 1849 Å and the other with the fluid to be irradiated. The second cell is provided with a mechanical stirrer. For measuring intensity of incident radiation, the second cell can be filled with an actinometric solution.

III. Absorption of Radiation Energy

Radiation affects the chemical structure of materials only if it is absorbed. Mere passage of radiation has no catalytic effect. Thus the problem of absorption must be considered before considering inactivation of viruses. It must also be considered before describing methods of measuring intensities of radiations, because measurement of proportions of absorbed radiation energy is an integral part of some methods of measuring intensities.

This section considers only the effect of absorbing materials on the radiation. Effects of radiation on absorbing materials will be partly considered in Section IV,B,2 (actinometry) and mainly discussed in Section V. Whenever absorption by solutions is considered, solvents will be assumed transparent to the radiation (nonabsorbing) unless stated otherwise.

A. METHODS OF MEASUREMENT

1. Spectrophotometers

Spectrophotometers are used to determine the proportion of incident monochromatic radiation of any selected wavelength (UV, visible, or near-infrared) that passes through a material under examination. Details of construction and manipulation of different makes of spectrophotometers are described in manuals supplied by the makers. Those mentioned below apply particularly to the S.P. 500 Unicam spectrophotometer, but those of other makes are similar in principle.

For the purpose of description the instrument can be conveniently divided into three main parts: a source of radiation with continuous spectrum, a monochromator to select radiation of a desired wavelength, and a measuring device to compare two different intensities of radiation. A material to be examined is placed between the exit slit of the monochromator and the measuring device. Intensity of radiation that passes through the material is compared with that that passes through a "blank," i.e., through air or through another material that is used as blank. For example, when a solution is examined, the solvent alone can be used as blank. Fluids are examined in suitable cells (cuvettes) supplied by the makers of the instruments. They are rectangular in cross section, and the distance radiation travels through the fluid will be referred to as "optical depth" of the cell or "light path." The instrument is usually provided with two alternative sources of radiation, one (such as a tungsten filament lamp) for the visible part of the spectrum and the other (such as a hydrogen discharge lamp) for the UV part. Radiation from any one of these lamps is focused on the entrance slit of a small monochromator, based on a quartz prism (see Section I,C).

A device to compare intensities of radiation consists of a photoelectric cell connected to an amplifier with a meter, and to a potentiometer. The meter of the amplifier functions as a "null" instrument to show that no cell current is flowing when it is compensated by the potentiometer. When the spectrophotometer is switched on and a shutter in front of the photocell is still closed, a potentiometric adjustment is made to compensate "dark current" of the cell to give a "zero" reading when no radiation reaches the cell. The shutter is then opened, and with the blank in the light path, the width of the exit slit of the monochromator is adjusted so that a reading corresponding to 100% transmission is obtained. The blank is then replaced by the material under examination, and a second potentiometric adjustment is made to compensate the cell current. The knob of this adjustment is combined with a scale that is calibrated in terms of $(I/I_0) \times 100$ and also in terms of $\log_{10} I_0/I$, where I/I_0 is the ratio of the intensity of radiation that passes through the material under test to the intensity of radiation that passes through the blank. When passage of radiation through the blank can be assumed to correspond to 100% transmission, then I/I_0 is the ratio of intensity of incident radiation to the intensity of radiation transmitted by the material under test. The ratio I/I_0 is then called "transmittance"; $(I/I_0) \times 100$ is percent transmittance, i.e., the percentage of incident radiation that is transmitted, and $\log_{10} I_0/I$ is called "optical density" or "absorbance."

Radiation intensities to which tested solutions are exposed in spectrophotometers are of the order of 0.01 μW/cm^2 or less; i.e., they are so small that no photochemical reaction can be assumed to occur during a spectrophotometric measurement (which lasts only a few seconds). A solution affects the radiation, and the extent of this is measured. Radiation can be assumed not to affect the solution.

2. *Colorimeters*

These cheap and simple instruments are designed to estimate concentrations of solutions of colored materials by comparing the amount of light absorbed by a solution of unknown concentration with that absorbed by a standard of comparison. There is a great range of such instruments, but they can be divided into two kinds, depending on whether they are based on visual comparison or on measurement with a photoelectric cell.

A Duboscq colorimeter is an example of the first kind. It is based on an optical arrangement, whereby it is possible to look simultaneously through two plungers into two cups containing solutions of a colored material at different concentrations; white light is supplied from underneath (by a reflecting surface or otherwise). The depths of the solutions under the plungers are changed by turning control knobs, until colored light of equal intensity is seen on both sides. Assuming the contribution of the solvent to the absorption to be negligible, the ratio of the concentrations of the colored material can be taken to be inversely proportional to the depths of the solutions. The main disadvantage of instruments of this kind is that such a visual comparison is subjective.

As an example of instruments of the second kind, an EEL photoelectric colorimeter will be considered. In this instrument white light from a small electric bulb passes through a solution under examination to reach a selenium photocell, thus generating a current that passes through a meter and that is proportional to the intensity of light reaching the photocell. A filter is inserted between the source of light and the solution to be examined, the color of the filter being "complementary" to that of the solution, so that only light that is absorbed by the solution passes through the filter. A calibration curve should be prepared by plotting readings of the meter against concentrations of the colored material. Detailed instructions in the use of the colorimeter are provided by the makers.

B. TERMINOLOGY AND METHODS OF COMPUTATION

1. Absorption by Single Solutes

a. Absorption. Some terms that apply to absorption of light are used differently by different authors. To avoid confusion the terms to be used will be defined.

"Intensity of radiation," I, usually means the rate of supply of radiation energy, E, to a unit area of flat surface, say a square centimeter, perpendicular to the direction of radiation, so that $I = (dE/dt)/cm^2$, where t is time. When dealing with the total power of a beam of radiation, or with total radiation from a lamp, we may simply have $I = dE/dt$.

All the considerations that follow are based on the assumption that, when a monochromatic radiation passes through an absorbing solution, the decrease in intensity of the radiation caused by a passage through a layer of the solution of thickness dl (which is infinitesimally small) is proportional to the concentration of the absorbing material, c, to the intensity of radiation that reaches the layer I and to the length of light path, dl, so that

$$-dI = kcIdl \tag{1}$$

where k is a constant that will be called "absorption coefficient." (The value of dI is negative because it is a decrease in intensity. The negative sign on the left-hand side of Eq. (1) makes the left-hand side positive, as is the right-hand side.)

Integrating Eq. (1), we get

$$-\ln I/I_0 = kcl \tag{2}$$

or

$$I = I_0 e^{-kcl} \tag{2a}$$

where I_0 is intensity of incident radiation, I is that of radiation that is transmitted by the solution, and l is the length of the path of radiation through the solution (light path).

Equation (2a) shows that intensity of transmitted light falls off exponentially with the concentration and with the length of light path through the solution; this is known as the Beer–Lambert law.

The ratio $T = I/I_0$ is called "transmittance," and $T\% = 100 \times I/I_0$ is called "percent transmittance." Using T, and also using decimal instead of natural logarithms, one can rewrite Eq. (2) as follows:

$$-\log T = Kcl \tag{3}$$

where K is another constant that equals $0.4343k$.

One of the most important terms relating to absorption of radiation energy by solutions is "absorbance," or optical density, D, which is defined as

$$D = \log 1/T = \log I_0/I$$

Using this term, one can rewrite Eq. (3) as follows:

$$D = \log I_0/I = Kcl \tag{4}$$

Optical density is, therefore, directly proportional to the concentration of absorbing material and to the length of light path.

When c is given in terms of grams/liter, and light path, l, in centimeters, the constant, K, becomes what is called the "extinction coefficient," or "specific absorbance," of a given material, and will be designated by the symbol α. When c is given in terms of molarity (i.e., in moles/liter) and l in centimeters, the constant, K, becomes "molecular extinction coefficient," or "molar extinction coefficient," and will be designated by the symbol ϵ. Obviously $\epsilon = M\alpha$, where M is the molecular weight.

The values of α or ϵ for a given material are easy to obtain by measuring optical densities, D, of solutions of known concentrations with a spectrophotometer, using a cell with a known length of light path (e.g., 1 cm), and substituting all the values into Eq. (4). The value of K becomes α or ϵ when c is in terms of grams/liter or moles/liter, respectively. Concentrations should be adjusted so that spectrophotometric readings of D are within the range where reasonable accuracy can be expected. Measurements should be made with solutions at several concentrations to check proportionality between D and c. As the values of α and ϵ vary with the wavelength, the wavelength to which they apply must be specified.

When the value of α or of ϵ for a given solute and for a given wavelength is already known, the concentration of the solute can be determined by measuring the optical density, D, of the solution. In terms of grams/liter the concentration will be

$$c_g = D/\alpha l \tag{5}$$

and in terms of molarity,

$$c_m = D/\epsilon l \tag{6}$$

A term that is sometimes used is the "absorption cross section" of a molecule. Derivation of this term usually starts from the area of actual cross section through a molecule. However, such an area cannot be easily and conveniently defined and computed, so we shall define the absorption cross section as a fictitious area on a molecule that absorbs a photon whenever it hits the area. The area will be considered in units of square centimeters/molecule, and we shall designate it by the symbol σ, which may be smaller than the area of actual cross section through a molecule, which we may designate by the symbol a. Thus $\sigma = pa$, where p is a fraction representing the probability of a photon that hits the area a being absorbed. However, we can find the value of σ without knowing the values of a and p.

Let us consider a layer of irradiated solution of thickness dl (in centimeters) that is infinitesimally small, and let the irradiated area be A (in square centimeters). Thus the volume of the layer is Adl (in cubic centimeters), and, when the concentration of irradiated material in terms of molarity is c, the number of molecules of the material in this volume is $10^{-3}NcAdl$, where N is Avogadro's number, 6.02×10^{23}. Thus the sum of absorption cross sections through all the molecules in this volume (in square centimeters) is

$$10^{-3}\sigma NcAdl = 6.02 \times 10^{20}\sigma cAdl$$

This is the area that will absorb all photons that will hit it. The ratio of this area to the total irradiated area, A, is $6.02 \times 10^{20}\sigma c \, dl$, so this is the proportion of incident radiation energy that will be absorbed. When the intensity of radiation that reaches the layer is I, and the decrease in intensity caused by the passage of the radiation through the irradiated layer is $-dI$ (dI being a negative quantity), the proportion of incident radiation that is absorbed is $-dI/I$, so that we can write

$$-dI/I = 6.02 \times 10^{20}\sigma c \, dl$$

Integrating this, we obtain

$$D = \log I_0/I = 0.4343 \times 6.02 \times 10^{20}\sigma cl$$
$$= 2.614 \times 10^{20}\sigma cl$$

where, as before, I_0 and I are intensities of incident and of transmitted radiation, respectively, and l is the length of light path through the solution in centimeters.

When c is in terms of molarity, the value of D is also given by Eq. (6) as a function of the molecular extinction coefficient, ϵ; namely, $D = \epsilon cl$, so that we can write

$$\epsilon cl = 2.614 \times 10^{20}\sigma cl$$

so that the value of σ in square centimeters/molecule is

$$\sigma = 3.83 \times 10^{-21}\epsilon \qquad (7)$$

As the values of α and ϵ for a given material vary with the wavelength, we can plot their values, or logarithms of their values, against the wavelengths and thus obtain a curve called the "absorption spectrum" of the material. Absorption spectra are useful for identifying materials and for testing their purity. For example, Fig. 3 shows absorption spectra of potato virus X and of isolated RNA and protein components of the virus. Characteristic features of absorption spectra of nucleic acids are a maximum at about 260 mμ and a minimum at about 230 mμ, and of proteins a maximum at about 280 mμ and a minimum at about 250 mμ. Absorption spectra of different viruses differ, but most have a maximum at about 260 mμ and a minimum between 240 and 250 mμ.

Absorption spectra can also be given as optical densities, D, at different wavelengths plotted against the wavelengths, provided the concentration of the material at which measurements were made, and also the length of light path, are specified.

   b. *Computations of Amounts of Absorbed Energy.* We shall now con-

sider amounts of energy absorbed by an irradiated material, still assuming that no change occurs in the material as a result of irradiation
to affect its absorbing capacity. We shall first consider absorption by
a solute when the solvent is transparent to the radiation.

When the intensity of incident radiation is given as $I_0 = (dE/dt)/$
cm^2 (see above) and is constant, the amount of radiation energy (the
dose) supplied to a surface perpendicular to the direction of the radiation is I_0At, where A is the area of the surface in square centimeters and t is time of irradiation. When transmittance, T, is almost
zero, i.e., when all the incident radiation energy is absorbed, and the
solution is stirred during irradiation to insure that all molecules are

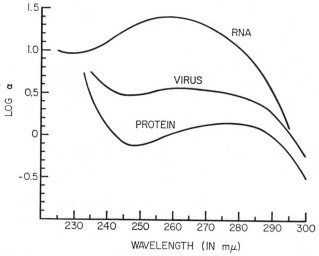

FIG. 3. Absorption spectra of potato virus X, RNA and protein isolated from
the virus.

equally exposed, the energy absorbed per unit mass of the solute is
simply computed as the total amount of supplied energy divided by the
total mass, m, of the solute; i.e., I_0At/m. Similarly, when the value of
transmittance, T, is between 0 and 1.0, i.e., when the proportion of
incident radiation energy that is absorbed is $1 - T$, the amount of energy absorbed per unit mass of the solute is $I_0At(1 - T)/m$.

When transmittance, T, is almost 1.0, i.e., when the solution is so dilute that it is almost transparent to the radiation and/or when the irradiated layer is extremely thin, so that optical density is nearly zero,
the amount of energy absorbed per unit mass of the solute is also easily computed using a formula we now have to derive. Since the solu-

tion is transparent, there is no mutual shading between molecules of the solute, so that all molecules are equally exposed and there is in principle no need to stir the solution during irradiation.

According to Eq. (2a) the intensity of transmitted radiation is $I = I_0 e^{-kcl}$, where I_0 is the intensity of incident radiation, c the concentration of irradiated material, and l the length of light path in centimeters. Thus e^{-kcl} is the proportion of incident radiation that is transmitted. The rate of absorption of energy per square centimeter of irradiated surface, therefore, is

$$I_{ab} = I_0(1 - e^{-kcl})$$

and so the total amount of absorbed energy is

$$E_{ab} = I_{ab}At = I_0At(1 - e^{-kcl}) = E_0(1 - e^{-kcl})$$

where $E_0 = I_0At$, the amount of supplied energy. Since we have assumed that $D = 0.4343kcl$ tends to zero, this means that $kcl \to 0$, and so $(1 - e^{-kcl}) \to kcl$; therefore, we have

$$E_{ab} = E_0kcl = 2.3E_0Kcl$$

If c is in grams or moles/liter, and since Al is the volume of irradiated solution in cubic centimeters, the mass of irradiated material in grams or in moles is $m = cAl \times 10^{-3}$. Thus, the amount of energy absorbed per unit mass is

$$E_{ab}/m = 2.3(E_0/A)K \times 10^3$$

As the value of K becomes specific absorbance, α, or molecular extinction coefficient, ϵ, when the concentration, c, of irradiated material is given in grams or moles/liter, respectively, the amount of energy absorbed per gram is

$$E_{ab}/gm = 2.3(E_0/A)\alpha \times 10^3 \tag{8}$$

per milligram

$$E_{ab}/mg = 2.3(E_0/A)\alpha \tag{9}$$

and per mole

$$E_{ab}/mole = 2.3(E_0/A)\epsilon \times 10^3 \tag{10}$$

where E_0/A is the amount of energy supplied per square centimeter of irradiated surface. Thus, when the concentration of an irradiated material is so low that the optical density is almost zero, we need not know the concentration to compute the amount of energy absorbed per unit mass.

c. Absorption of Polychromatic Radiations. The method of measuring proportions of radiation energy absorbed by materials exposed to monochromatic radiations and equations relating absorption to the concentration of an absorbing material do not apply when radiations are polychromatic, because radiations of different wavelengths are absorbed differently. The proportion of total supplied radiation energy that is absorbed cannot be obtained from a spectrophotometric reading in the simple way applicable to a monochromatic radiation. To obtain the proportion, the simplest way would probably be by measuring with a thermopile (see Section IV,B,1,*a*) the total radiation intensity transmitted through a solution and through a blank (pure solvent) and by comparing the results of the two measurements.

Having obtained the proportion, it can be used to compute the amount of energy absorbed per unit mass of a solute, provided the concentration and length of light path are the same as when the measurements were made. This proviso is necessary because there is no simple way of relating the concentration and/or the length of light path to the proportion of incident polychromatic radiation that is absorbed. Optical density and the concentration or the length of light path are directly proportional [Eq. (4)] with monochromatic radiations, but not with polychromatic radiations, for the following reason.

Let us for convenience consider a radiation composed of radiations of only two different wavelengths, and let their intensities be $^1I_0$ and $^2I_0$, so that the total intensity is $I_0 = {}^1I_0 + {}^2I_0$. According to Eq. (2a), intensities of transmitted radiations are $^1I = {}^1I_0e^{-k_1cl}$ and $^2I = {}^2I_0e^{-k_2cl}$ ($k_1 \neq k_2$), so that the total intensity of transmitted radiation is

$$I = {}^1I + {}^2I = {}^1I_0 \exp(-k_1cl) + {}^2I_0 \exp(-k_2cl)$$

Optical density, D, will, therefore, be

$$D = \log I_0/I = \log({}^1I_0 + {}^2I_0)/({}^1I_0e^{-k_1cl} + {}^2I_0e^{-k_2cl})$$

As the values of k_1 and k_2 differ, D is not a linear but a curvilinear function of c and of l, and the Beer-Lambert law is not applicable. Should one of the values of k, say k_2, be 0 (which means that the radiation of the corresponding wavelength is not absorbed at all), the optical density will never rise above $\log ({}^1I_0 + {}^2I_0)/{}^2I_0$, however concentrated the solute is.

Since Eq. (4) is not applicable when a radiation is polychromatic, there is nothing to correspond to a constant, K, and, therefore, there is nothing to correspond to a specific absorbance, α, or to a molecular extinction coefficient, ϵ, which apply only to particular wavelengths and vary with the wavelength. Consequently, Eqs. (8)–(10) are not relevant when a radiation is polychromatic, and, therefore, there is no simple way of finding the amount of energy absorbed per unit weight of a solvent when an extremely dilute solution is exposed to a polychromatic radiation. It could be computed rather laboriously when the spectral distribution of energy of the radiation is known (or found by means of spectrometry), by measuring absorption at different parts of the spectrum and integrating for the whole of the spectrum. Details of the procedure would depend on spectral distribution of energy of a particular radiation. The final result may be only a very rough approximation.

2. Absorption by Mixtures of Solutes

This section will consider absorption of energy of a monochromatic radiation by a mixture of solutes, assuming that the solutes do not interact chemically or physically. When the radiation passes through an infinitesimally thin layer of the solution, each solute will be assumed to contribute independently to the decrease in radiation intensity as the radiation passes through the layer. Let $-d(^1I)$ be the decrease in intensity owing to absorption of radiation energy by one solute, $-d(^2I)$ by the other, and so on. According to Eq. (1), we have

$$-d(^1I) = k_1 c_1 I \, dl$$
$$-d(^2I) = k_2 c_2 I \, dl \qquad (11)$$
$$-d(^3I) = k_3 c_3 I \, dl$$

where k_1, k_2, k_3 . . . are absorption coefficients of the solutes, c_1, c_2, c_3 . . . are their respective concentrations, I is the intensity of radiation that reaches the layer, and dl is the length of light path (the thickness of the layer). Therefore

$$d(^1I)/d(^2I) = k_1 c_1 / k_2 c_2$$

which means that, in each infinitesimally thin layer, and therefore in all layers, i.e., in the whole volume of irradiated solution, the ratio of the amount of energy absorbed by one solute, E_1, to that absorbed by the other solute, E_2, is

$$E_1/E_2 = k_1 c_1 / k_2 c_2 \qquad (12)$$

This ratio will remain unaltered when the absorption coefficients are substituted by specific absorbances, α, or by molecular extinction coefficients, ϵ, when concentrations are in appropriate units. And so we have

$$E_1/E_2 = \alpha_1 c_1/\alpha_2 c_2 \qquad (13)$$

when c_1 and c_2 are in grams/liter, or

$$E_1/E_2 = \epsilon_1 c_1/\epsilon_2 c_2 \qquad (14)$$

when c_1 and c_2 are in moles/liter, or

$$E_1/E_2 = \alpha_1 c_1/\epsilon_2 c_2 \qquad (15)$$

when c_1 is in grams/liter and c_2 is in moles/liter.

Generally, the ratios of amounts of energy absorbed by different solutes are

$$E_1/E_2/E_3/E_4 \cdots = k_1 c_1/k_2 c_2/k_3 c_3/k_4 c_4 \cdots \qquad (16)$$

As above, all the absorption coefficients, k_n, can be substituted by specific absorbancies, α_n, or by molecular extinction coefficients, ϵ_n, depending on whether concentrations are in grams or in moles/liter, but we cannot substitute some absorption coefficients and leave the others.

Equations (11) show that the total decrease in intensity of a monochromatic radiation when it passes through a thin layer of a solution containing several solutes is

$$-dI = -d(^1I) - d(^2I) - d(^3I) \cdots$$

$$= (k_1 c_1 + k_2 c_2 + k_3 c_3 \cdots) dl$$

Integrating this, we get

$$I = I_0 e^{-(k_1 c_1 + k_2 c_2 + k_3 c_3 \cdots) l} \qquad (17)$$

or

$$D = \log I_0/I = (K_1 c_1 + K_2 c_2 + K_3 c_3 \cdots) l \qquad (18)$$

where I_0 and I are intensities of incident and transmitted radiation, respectively, D is optical density of the solution, $K_1 = 0.4343 k_1$, $K_2 = 0.4343 k_2$, and so on, and l is the length of light path.

Were the solutes alone, their optical densities, according to Eq. (4), would be

$$D_1 = K_1 c_1 l, \quad D_2 = K_2 c_2 l, \quad \text{and so on.}$$

Thus the optical density of the mixture is

$$D = D_1 + D_2 + D_3 + \cdots \qquad (19)$$

so that optical density is an additive quantity.

As the values of D_n are proportional to those of $k_n c_n$, we can use them to determine ratios of amounts of radiation energy absorbed by different solutes. Thus, if E_1, E_2, $E_3 \cdots$ are the amounts of energy, we have, from Eq. (12),

$$E_1/E_2 = D_1/D_2 \tag{20}$$

and from Eq. (16),

$$E_1/E_2/E_3/E_4 \cdots = D_1/D_2/D_3/D_4 \cdots \tag{21}$$

We shall now consider the amount of energy absorbed by one of solutes of a mixture. According to Eq. (17), if E_0 is the amount of supplied energy, the amount of transmitted energy is

$$E = E_0 \exp -(k_1c_1 + k_2c_2 + k_3c_3 \cdots)l$$

so that the amount of energy absorbed by all solutes is

$$E_{ab} = E_0[1 - \exp -(k_1c_1 + k_2c_2 + k_3c_3 \cdots)l] \tag{22}$$

This energy is divided between the solutes according to Eq. (16), so that the amount of energy absorbed by solute 1 is

$$E_1 = E_0[1 - \exp-(k_1c_1 + k_2c_2 + k_3c_3 \cdots)l]k_1c_1/ \\ (k_1c_1 + k_2c_2 + k_3c_3 \cdots) \tag{23}$$

If solute 1 were alone, the amount of energy absorbed by it would be

$$E'_1 = E_0(1 - \exp -k_1c_1l) \tag{23a}$$

The fact that $E_1 < E'_1$ means that the presence of other solutes decreases the amount of energy absorbed by solute 1. The effect of one solute in decreasing the amount of energy absorbed by another will be referred to as the "inner filter effect."

That $E_1 < E'_1$ may not be obvious at first glance. However, the ratio

$$R = \frac{E_1}{E'_1} = \frac{1 - \exp -(k_1c_1 + k_2c_2 \cdots)l}{(k_1c_1 + k_2c_2 \cdots)l} \frac{k_1c_1l}{1 - \exp -k_1c_1l}$$

is obviously smaller than 1 because $y = (1 - e^{-x})/x$ decreases with increasing x (tending to zero as $x \to \infty$). It is also obvious that if the values of $k_2c_2 + k_3c_3 + k_4c_4 \cdots$ tend to zero, R tends to 1; i.e., the amount of energy absorbed by solute 1 is then not affected by the presence of other solutes.

3. Absorption by a Solute When the Solvent Is Not Transparent

So far we have considered absorption of radiation energy by solutes in a solvent that itself is transparent, i.e., does not absorb radiation energy. If a solvent does absorb radiation energy, it behaves in all respects like an additional absorbing solute in a nonabsorbing solvent. It functions, therefore, like an inner filter and decreases the amount of energy absorbed by a solute.

According to Lambert's law, the intensity of radiation transmitted by the pure solvent is

$$I' = I_0 e^{-sl}$$

where I_0 is the intensity of incident radiation, s is a constant called absorption coefficient of the solvent, which depends on the wavelength, and l is the length of light path. The presence of a solute will further lessen the intensity of transmitted radiation by the factor e^{-kcl}, where k is absorption coefficient of the solute and c its concentration. The intensity of transmitted radiation will, therefore, be

$$I = I' e^{-kcl} = I_0 \exp -(kc + s)l$$

Therefore, the amount of energy asborbed by both solute and solvent is

$$E_{ab} = E_0[1 - \exp - (kc + s)l] \qquad (24)$$

where E_0 is the amount of supplied energy.

A comparison of this equation with Eq. (22) shows that the solvent with absorption coefficient s behaves like an additional solute with absorption coefficient k' and concentration c' such that $s = k'c'$. Therefore, the energy absorbed by solute and solvent given by Eq. (24) is divided between them according to Eq. (12), and so the amount of energy absorbed by the solute is

$$E_s = E_0[1 - \exp -(kc + s)l]kc/(kc + s) \qquad (25)$$

If the solvent were transparent $(s = 0)$, the amount of energy absorbed by the solute would be

$$E'_s = E_0(1 - \exp -kcl) \qquad (25a)$$

which is greater than E_s.

4. Scatter of Radiation Energy

So far we have assumed that radiation energy not absorbed by an irradiated solution is transmitted. This can be assumed when the longest dimension of a molecule or a particle of the absorbing solute is very small compared to the wavelength of the radiation, or when the refractive index of the solute is the same as that of the solvent. When these conditions are not fulfilled, the molecules or particles function as secondary sources of radiation in all directions, mostly with unaltered wavelength, and the phenomenon is called "scatter" of radiation. A spectrophotometric measurement of the proportion of incident radiation that is transmitted does not distinguish between absorption and scatter. Thus, when the value of the optical density read in a spectrophotometer is D, a component of it, say D_{ab}, may owe to absorption, and another, say S, to scatter, so that

$$D = D_{ab} + S \qquad (26)$$

D_{ab} will be referred to as "optical density owing to absorption" and S as "optical density owing to scatter." As sizes of virus particles are well within the range of those that scatter radiations from the visible and UV range of the spectrum, a few points relating to the problem of scatter must be considered here. For an extensive treatment the reader is referred to reviews and monographs (for example, Oster, 1948; Stacey, 1956).

When the concentration of an irradiated virus is such that the total optical density is appreciably greater than zero, the distinction between D_{ab} and S is absolutely necessary to compute radiation energy that is absorbed. When, however, the concentration is so small that D is almost zero, we may be able to compute the amount of energy absorbed per unit mass of a virus, or of a component of the virus, without concerning ourselves at all with the problem of scatter. The cases $D > 0$ and $D \to 0$ will, therefore, be considered separately.

a. $D > 0$. At a wavelength at which a given solution does not absorb radiation energy, the optical density owes entirely to scatter. Assuming that the proportion of incident radiation energy scattered by each infinitesimally thin layer of the solution is proportional to the length of light path, dl, so that $-dI/I = \tau dl$, where τ, which is called "turbidity," is a constant characteristic for a given set of conditions, the intensity of radiation transmitted by the whole volume of irradiated solution is

$$I = I_0 e^{-\tau l} \qquad (27)$$

where I_0 is the intensity of incident radiation and l is the length of light path (in centimeters) through the solution. The value of turbidity (τ) is proportional to the concentration (c) of scattering material within wide limits. It must be borne in mind, however, that proportionality may break down when the concentration (c) exceeds a certain limit. For example, Oster (1950) found considerable deviation from proportionality when the scattering material was tobacco mosaic virus and when its concentration was greater than 1%. The extent of deviation depended not only on the concentration of the virus, but also on that of salt in the medium. For these reasons, no value of turbidity equivalent to specific absorbance (α) or to molar extinction coefficient (ϵ) will be used below.

When the wavelength is such that the solution both absorbs and scatters radiation energy, some of the radiation that has been scattered can subsequently be absorbed. This must be borne in mind, but since there is no easy way of dealing with it, we shall disregard it. We shall assume that the decrease in intensity of radiation by absorption, $-dI_{ab}$, and by scatter, $-dI_{sc}$, occur independently when the radiation passes through any thin layer of the solution, and so we shall have

$$-dI_{ab} = Ikc\ dl$$

$$-dI_{sc} = I\tau\ dl \tag{28}$$

where I is the intensity of radiation that reaches the layer, dl is the thickness of the layer, and k is the absorption coefficient (see Eq. 1). Therefore, the ratio of absorbed amount of energy, E_{ab}, to scattered amount of energy, E_{sc}, in the whole volume of irradiated solution is

$$E_{ab}/E_{sc} = kc/\tau \tag{29}$$

If the concentration, c, is in grams/liter, Eq. (29) becomes

$$E_{ab}/E_{sc} = \alpha c/\beta \tag{29a}$$

where $\beta = 0.4343\tau$ and α is specific absorbance (see Section III,B,1,a).

According to Eqs. (28), the total decrease in intensity of radiation passing through a thin layer, dl, of the solution is

$$-dI = -dI_{ab} - dI_{sc} = I(kc + \tau)dl$$

so that the intensity of radiation transmitted through the solution is

$$I = I_0 e^{-(kc+\tau)l} \tag{30}$$

where I_0 is the intensity of radiation falling on the solution. Therefore, if c is in grams/liter, the total optical density is

$$D = \log I_0/I = \alpha cl + \beta l = D_{ab} + S \tag{31}$$

so that we have derived Eq. (26). Obviously $D_{ab} = \alpha cl$ and $S = \beta l$.

According to Eq. (30), the amount of energy transmitted by the solution is

$$E = E_0 \exp -(kc + \tau)l$$

when E_0 is the amount of supplied energy, so that the total energy absorbed and scattered, is

$$E_t = E_0[1 - \exp-(kc + \tau)l] \tag{32}$$

This energy is distributed between absorption and scatter according to Eq. (29), so that the amount of absorbed energy is

$$E_{ab} = E_0[1 - \exp-(kc + \tau)l]kc/(kc + \tau) \tag{33}$$

If there were no scatter, the amount of absorbed energy would be

$$E'_{ab} = E_0(1 - \exp-kcl)$$

Since $E'_{ab} > E_{ab}$, the amount of energy absorbed in the presence of scatter is less than the amount that would be absorbed if there were no scatter. Therefore, scatter produces an inner filter effect similar to that produced by another absorbing solute [compare Eqs. (23) and (23a)] or by a solvent that is not transparent to the radiation [compare Eqs. (25) and (25a)].

The value of turbidity, τ, depends on various conditions, which include the concentration of the scattering material and the wavelength. To obtain the value of τ we can make use of what is usually referred to as Rayleigh's law, according to which, when all the conditions other than the wavelength are kept constant,

$$\tau = C/\lambda^4 \tag{34}$$

where C is a constant called "scattering constant" and λ is the wavelength. Thus, if the values of τ at wavelengths λ_1 and λ_2 are τ_1 and τ_2, respectively,

$$\tau_1/\tau_2 = (\lambda_2/\lambda_1)^4 \tag{35}$$

Obviously, this also means that

$$S_1/S_2 = (\lambda_2/\lambda_1)^4 \tag{35a}$$

where S_1 and S_2 are the corresponding optical densities owing to scatter (because $S_i = \beta_i l = 0.4343\tau_i l$, where l is the length of light path). Therefore, when a value of S has been measured at a wavelength at which the solution can be assumed not to absorb radiation energy, so that the optical density read with a spectrophotometer is the value of S, $(D = S)$, a value of S at another wavelength, at which absorption may also occur, can be computed using Eq. (35a).

With viruses, optical densities owing to scatter, S, are usually measured at a wavelength of $\lambda = 3200$ Å or longer, since it can be assumed that viruses do not absorb within a range of wavelengths starting from 3200 Å and extending into the visible part of the spectrum.

Equations (35) and (35a) can be assumed to apply approximately to scattering by small particles. If they are spherical or nearly spherical, their diameter or the longest dimension should not exceed about one-tenth the wavelength. If they are strongly anisodimensional, the necessary conditions cannot be defined with any precision.

When virus particles are too large for Eqs. (34) and (35) to apply, the more general equation

$$\tau = C/\lambda^n \tag{36}$$

may apply. To find the values of n and C, optical density owing to scatter must be measured at several wavelengths at which there is no absorption. If we transform Eq. (36) into $\log \tau = \log C - n \log \lambda$, the values of C and of n can easily be found by plotting the values of $\log \tau$ against the values of $\log \lambda$, which should give a straight line. The slope of the line will be $-n$, and the intercept of the perpendicular axis by the line will give the value of $\log C$.

Values of n for large particles are usually smaller than 4. Having obtained the value of n, we have

$$S_1/S_2 = \tau_1/\tau_2 = (\lambda_2/\lambda_1)^n \tag{37}$$

which is analogous to Eqs. (35) and (35a) and can be used similarly. Apparently $n = 4$ for tobacco mosaic virus (Reddi, 1957), but $n = 3.7$ for T2 bacteriophage (Dulbecco, 1950).

Having computed the value of S for a wavelength at which absorption also takes place, the value of optical density owing to absorption, D_{ab}, can be obtained according to Eq. (26) by measuring the total optical density, D, at this wavelength and subtracting from it the computed value of S.

The value of D_{ab} can also be measured directly if the refractive index of the medium is made equal to that of virus particles, so that scatter is eliminated. This can be done by adding different amounts of glycerol to the water or buffer medium containing the virus and measuring optical density, D. The minimum in a plot of D/cl against concentration of glycerol can be taken as the value of α (the value of D_{ab} is $D_{ab} = \alpha cl$). Having obtained the values of D_{ab} and S, and, therefore, the values of α and τ, the amount of radiation energy absorbed by a virus can be computed using Eq. (33) (remembering that $k = 2.3\alpha$ and $\tau = 2.3\beta = 2.3S/l$).

Another way of obtaining the value of D_{ab} is by isolating components of the virus as solutions that do not scatter radiation to any appreciable extent and measuring their optical densities (provided that methods of isolation do not alter structure and affect absorption of radiation energy). Alternatively, values of specific absorbancies of the components may be assumed or computed from the knowledge of their chemical composition. Let protein and nucleic acid be the only components of a virus, and let their specific absorbancies be α_p and α_n, respectively. Optical densities owing to absorption by protein and by nucleic acid then are $D_p = \alpha_p c_p l$ and $D_n = \alpha_n c_n l$, respectively, where c_p and c_n are concentrations of protein and of nucleic acid in grams/liter. With respect to absorption of radiation energy, a virus can be considered to be equivalent to a mixture of its isolated components provided the ratio of concentrations is maintained. Therefore, the optical density owing to absorption by the virus is

$$D_{ab} = D_p + D_n = \alpha_p c_p l + \alpha_n c_n l$$

If the proportions in which protein and nucleic acid occur in the virus are P_p and P_n, and if c is the concentration of the virus in grams/liter, $c_p = P_p c$ and $c_n = P_n c$, so that

$$D_{ab} = (\alpha_p P_p + \alpha_n P_n)cl$$

which also means that specific absorbance of the virus is

$$\alpha = \alpha_p P_p + \alpha_n P_n$$

Energy absorbed by the virus is divided between its protein and nucleic acid according to Eqs. (12) and (13). Thus, the amounts of energy absorbed by protein and nucleic acid are

$$E_p = E_{ab}\alpha_p P_p/(\alpha_p P_p + \alpha_n P_n)$$

and

$$E_n = E_{ab}\alpha_n P_n/(\alpha_p P_p + \alpha_n P_n) \tag{38}$$

respectively, where E_{ab} is the total amount of energy absorbed by the virus, which is given by Eq. (33). Therefore, the amount of energy absorbed by any of the components of the virus is affected by the presence of scatter according to Eq. (33) and by the presence of the other component according to Eq. (38).

b. $D \to 0$. When an irradiated virus preparation is so dilute that the optical density, D, is almost zero (i.e., the irradiated fluid is almost transparent to the radiation), the amount of energy absorbed per unit mass of the virus or of a component of the virus is given by Eqs. (8)–(10), irrespective of any scatter and irrespective of absorption by any other material that may be present. The fact that $D \to 0$ means that the amount of scatter and the amounts of any absorbing materials are so small that each material, or each component of a material, absorbs radiation energy as if it were alone and as if there were no scatter. Thus, to compute the amount of energy absorbed per unit mass of a virus, or per unit mass of a component of a virus, all we need to know is the relevant specific absorbance, α, or the molecular extinction coefficient, ϵ, and the amount of energy supplied per square centimeter of irradiated surface. The virus preparation need not be purified. Since this fact is not always fully appreciated, a formal proof will now be given.

When there is no scatter, Eq. (23) gives the amount of radiation energy absorbed by a material in the presence of other absorbing materials. The presence of scatter with turbidity τ affects the amount of absorbed energy according to Eq. (33). Therefore, the amount of energy absorbed by a material in the presence of other absorbing materials and in the presence of scatter with turbidity τ is

$$E_1 = E_0[1 - \exp-(k_1c_1 + k_2c_2 + k_3c_3 + \cdots + \tau)l]$$
$$\times \frac{k_1c_1}{k_1c_1 + k_2c_2 + k_3c_3 \cdots + \tau} \quad (39)$$

If no other absorbing materials were present and if there were no scatter, the amount of energy absorbed by the material would be

$$E'_1 = E_0(1 - \exp-k_1c_1l)$$

Consider the ratio

$$R = \frac{E_1}{E'_1} = \frac{1 - \exp-(k_1c_1 + k_2c_2 + k_3c_3 \cdots + \tau)l}{(k_1c_1 + k_2c_2 + k_3c_3 \cdots + \tau)l} \frac{(k_1c_1l)}{1 - \exp-(k_1c_1l)}$$

The fact that $D \to 0$ means that all the quantities in the brackets tend to zero, since

$$D = \log I_0/I = 0.4343(k_1c_1 + k_2c_2 + k_3c_3 \cdots + \tau)l$$

Since $(1 - e^{-x}) \to x$ when $x \to 0$, this means that $R \to 1$.

IV. Measurement of Radiation Intensity

A. UNITS OF ENERGY AND POWER

Radiation intensity is given in terms of power (i.e., the rate of supply of energy or quanta) per unit area of the surface that is normal to the direction of the radiation. We may also deal with the total power of a beam of radiation, such as, for example, a beam emerging from the exit slit of a monochromator, without any reference to the surface area. Let M, L, and T be units of mass, length, and time, respectively. Remembering that the dimensions of force and energy are MLT^{-2} and ML^2T^{-2}, respectively, one finds that the dimensions of the total power of a beam are ML^2T^{-3}, and those of intensity, i.e., of power per unit area, are MT^{-3}.

Before dealing with methods of measuring radiation intensity, we shall first consider the units of energy and power most commonly used in photochemistry and photobiology, and which are shown in Table I.

TABLE I
UNITS OF ENERGY AND POWER

Qualification and dimensions	Name of unit	Symbol	Equivalent to
Energy ML^2T^{-2}	Erg		1 dyne $\times$ 1 cm
	Joule	J	10^7 ergs
	Quantum		$1.986 \times 10^{-8}/\lambda$ ergs
	Einstein		6.02×10^{23} quanta
	Electron volt	eV	1.6×10^{-12} ergs
Power ML^2T^{-3}	Watt	W	1 joule/second
	Milliwatt	mW	10^{-3} W
	Microwatt	μW	10^{-6} W

λ is the wavelength in angstroms.

A dyne is the force that, when acting on a mass of 1 gm, gives it an acceleration of 1 cm/sec². An erg is the amount of energy (work) equivalent to exerting the force of 1 dyne over a distance of 1 cm, and a watt is the amount of power equivalent to supplying energy at a rate of 1 joule (10^7 ergs)/second.

The amount of energy in one quantum is $h\nu$ ergs, where h is the Planck's constant whose value is 6.625×10^{-27} and ν is the frequency of a radiation in terms of the number of oscillations/second. The frequency at a given wavelength is the velocity of light in some units of length per second, divided by the wavelength in the same units of length. Velocity of light is 2.998×10^{10} cm/second. Thus, the frequency of radiation of a wavelength λ (in angstroms) is $2.998 \times 10^{10}/(\lambda \times 10^{-8}) = 2.998 \times 10^{18}/\lambda$ oscillations per second (as 1 Å $= 0.1$ m$\mu = 10^{-8}$ cm).

Therefore, the quantum energy is $2.998 \times 10^{18} \times 6.625 \times 10^{-27}/\lambda =$ $1.986 \times 10^{-8}/\lambda$ ergs. For example, when $\lambda = 2537$ Å, the quantum energy is $1.986 \times 10^{-8}/2537 = 7.83 \times 10^{-12}$ ergs.

When the concentration of irradiated material is given in molarity, it may be convenient to express the amount of irradiation in einsteins, 1 einstein corresponding to the number of quanta equal to the number of molecules in a mole. As Avogadro's number (6.02×10^{23}) is the number of molecules in a mole, 1 einstein corresponds to 6.02×10^{23} quanta. As the energy of 1 quantum of radiation of a wavelength λ (in angstroms) is $1.986 \times 10^{-8}/\lambda$ ergs, 1 einstein corresponds to $6.02 \times 10^{23} \times 1.986 \times 10^{-8}/\lambda$ ergs $= 1.196 \times 10^{16}/\lambda$ ergs of radiation energy. Note that the amount of energy corresponding to 1 einstein is not constant, but depends on the wavelength. When $\lambda = 2537$Å, 1 einstein corresponds to $1.196 \times 10^{16}/2537 = 4.71 \times 10^{12}$ ergs. The convenience of using einsteins is apparent from the fact that if n einsteins are absorbed by m moles of a material, n quanta are absorbed by m molecules.

Amounts of energy needed to break various molecular bonds, or to cause ionizations, are usually given in electron volts (eV). It is, therefore, necessary to express quantum energy in this unit to know whether quanta of radiation of a given wave-length carry enough energy to cause specific molecular processes. An electron volt (eV) is equivalent to the work needed to transfer an electron across a potential difference of 1 V. The charge of an electron is 1.6×10^{-19} coulombs (C). The energy needed to transfer the charge of 1 C across a potential difference of 1 V is 1 joule. Therefore, 1 eV corresponds to the energy of 1.6×10^{-19} joules $= 1.6 \times 10^{-12}$ ergs. As the quantum energy of radiation of a wavelength λ (in angstroms) is $1.986 \times 10^{-8}/\lambda$ ergs, it equals $1.986 \times 10^{-8}/(1.6 \times 10^{-12})\lambda = 12400/\lambda$ eV. Thus, when $\lambda = 2537$ Å, energy of a quantum is $12400/2537 = 4.9$ eV.

B. METHODS OF MEASUREMENT

1. Physical Methods

a. Thermopiles. A thermocouple depends on the thermoelectric effect of heating a junction between two different metals, and a thermopile consists of several thermocouples connected in series as shown in Fig. 4. Black surfaces (A) at upper junctions between metals a and b are heated by incident radiation, which is absorbed. The lower surfaces at points B are protected from radiation and kept at room temperature. The current resulting from connecting the extreme left and right points at B is measured by a sensitive galvanometer, G, or by a galvanometer and an amplifier.

Temperature at points A is a result of an equilibrium between absorption and dissipation of energy (which usually takes only a few seconds to become established), and so is a function of intensity of incident radiation. The galvanometric reading is, within reasonable limits, proportional to the intensity of radiation in terms of energy per unit time per unit area irrespective of wavelength (and, therefore, not necessarily proportional to the number of quanta per unit time per unit area).

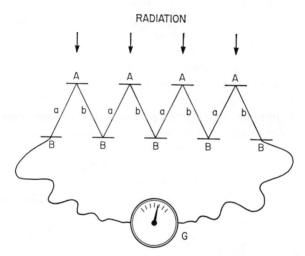

FIG. 4. A schematic presentation of a thermopile.

Thermopiles have to be calibrated. Any calibration must ultimately refer to absolute measurements made with an instrument, such as a bolometer or a pyrheliometer, provided with a "perfectly black" receiving surface, but in practice a calibration can be done using certified standard lamps or by comparison with other methods of measurement, such as actinometry (see below).

For measuring intensity of radiation isolated by a monochromator, a thermopile, such as a Schwarz thermopile, specially designed so that it can be mounted facing the exit slit, can usually be bought together with a monochromator, a galvanometer, and an amplifier. If the monochromator is primarily designed as a spectrometer, the galvanometer may be too sensitive when the monochromator is used for photobiological work such as inactivation of a virus, i.e., when the source of radiation must be powerful. The galvanometer must then be made less sensitive by including a resistor.

The thermopile can be calibrated against an actinometric measurement (using, for example, the ferrioxalate actinometer) at any particular wavelength that is convenient, and the thermopile can then be used to measure radiation intensity at this and at any other wavelength. The calibration should be checked from time to time.

b. Photoelectric Cells. These are based on radiations ejecting free electrons from some metallic surfaces, such as, for example, that of selenium. When another metal is suitably placed to function as an anode, and when the circuit is closed, an electric current is set up. The current is measured with a sensitive galvanometer or potentiometrically, and shows the intensity of radiation. There is a great range of commercial photocells, which include so called barrier cells and phototubes. They all have to be calibrated, which can be done by comparison with thermopiles. Photocells are convenient to use and can be very sensitive. Their main disadvantage is that, unlike thermopiles, they respond differently to radiations of different wavelengths, so that measurements can be meaningful only with monochromatic radiations, and calibration must be made separately for each wavelength.

Relatively simple arrangements for measuring intensity of UV radiations, based on selenium photocells that can be constructed by prospective users, have been described by Latarjet *et al.* (1953) and by Jagger (1961).

2. Chemical Methods (Actinometry)

These methods are based on a dissolved substance (actinometric solution) changing as a result of absorbing monochromatic radiation. The amount that changes is estimated by titration or by spectrophotometry. When the amount of energy needed to change a given amount of the substance is known, and the proportion of incident radiation that is absorbed is also known, the amount of supplied radiation energy during the time of irradiation can be computed. Actinometric solutions can be exposed to radiations either in flat dishes (such as Petri dishes) placed under lamps, in quartz cells placed in a beam of radiation from a monochromator, or from an opening in the housing of a lamp. Intensity of radiation in terms of energy per unit time per unit of irradiated area can then be computed.

Since these methods integrate the amounts of energy supplied over a period of time, they have the advantage of measuring the energy irrespective of any possible fluctuations of intensity in the meantime. They do not detect fluctuations, which is a serious disadvantage when one needs to know how long it takes for the intensity to become constant after a lamp has been started and what the initial fluctuations are. This can be found easily with a thermopile or a photoelectric cell. Actinometrically this can be found only when radiation intensity and susceptibility of an actinometric solution are so great that only a few seconds of exposure are needed.

There are several different actinometers in use. Three convenient ones are described below.

a. *Uranyl Oxalate Actinometer.* This method (details described by Bowen, 1946) is based on irradiating a mixture of oxalic acid and uranyl oxalate, when oxalic acid, photosensitized by uranyl ion, is decomposed as follows:

$$(COOH)_2 \rightarrow H_2O + CO_2 + CO$$

Uranyl oxalate is prepared by mixing hot solutions of oxalic acid and uranyl nitrate and then drying *in vacuo* and then for 3 hours in air at 110°C.

Actinometric stock solution is made by dissolving 3.75 gm of uranyl oxalate and 6.3 gm (0.05 mole) of oxalic acid $[(COOC)_2 \cdot 2H_2O]$ in water and adjusting the volume of the mixture to 1 liter. The stock solution is diluted 1 : 10 for wavelengths 2500–3300 Å (it is used undiluted for the region 3300–4350 Å). A sample of the solution is mixed with one fourth of its volume of 10 N H_2SO_4, heated to about 80°C, and titrated (using a microburet) with 0.01 N potassium permanganate (or 0.1 N when the actinometric stock solution is used undiluted). Another sample of the same volume is titrated in the same way after exposure to radiation, using the acid to wash out the cell. (Heating to about 80°C is needed to expel CO from the irradiated sample.) Let the difference between two titrations be x ml; this means that the amount of oxalic acid decomposed by irradiation corresponds to x ml of 0.01 N KMnO$_4$.

Oxygen is provided by KMnO$_4$ for oxidation in acid solution according to the equation:

$$2KMnO_4 + 4H_2SO_4 = 2KHSO_4 + 2MnSO_4 + 3H_2O + 5O$$

By definition, 1 liter of 0.01 N KMnO$_4$ provides 0.01 gram equivalent of oxygen (0.08 gm), and so, as the molecular weight of KMnO$_4$ is 158, it is prepared by dissolving

$$158 \frac{2}{2 \times 5 \times 100} = 0.316 \text{ gm of KMnO}_4$$

in water and adjusting the volume to 1 liter. Actually it is better to prepare a 0.1 N solution and then dilute it 1 : 10. The solution should be checked by titration against a solution of oxalic acid in the presence of H_2SO_4.

Oxidation of oxalic acid proceeds according to the equation

$$(COOH)_2 + O = 2CO_2 + H_2O$$

so that two gram equivalents of O (16 gm) are needed to oxidize one mole of $(COOH)_2$. Therefore, x ml of 0.01 N $KMnO_4$ corresponds to $x/(2 \times 10^5)$ moles of oxalic acid.

Therefore, the number of einsteins, y, that fell on the surface of the actinometric solution is

$$y = x/(2 \times 10^5\ \phi f)$$

where ϕ is the quantum yield (quantum efficiency), which means that, on average, $1/\phi$ quanta must be absorbed to decompose 1 molecule of oxalic acid, and f is the proportion of incident radiation that is absorbed by the actinometric solution. Table II gives the values of ϕ and f for different wavelengths.

To obtain accurate results, the actinometric solution should be stirred during irradiation, and not more than half the oxalic acid should be decomposed. The main advantage of this method is that the actinometric solution is not affected appreciably by dull daylight, so no special precautions are needed when measuring the intensity of UV radiation.

The method is suitable for measuring intense monochromatic radiations of the order of 1 mW/cm². Radiations with intensities of this order are obtained from lamps, directly or with the use of filters, at some

TABLE II

VALUES OF ϕ AND f FOR URANYL OXALATE ACTINOMETER

Actinometer	Wavelength (Å)	ϕ	f (for a 1-cm light path)
Undiluted	4350	0.57	0.242
stock	4050	0.56	0.284
solution	3650	0.48	0.343
Stock	3135	0.55	0.658
solution	3030	0.56	0.82
diluted	2650	0.57	1.0
1 : 10	2540	0.60	1.0

distance from the burner. In principle, the radiation should be mono-chromatic, but when it is not, the method may give a good approxi-mation to the intensity of UV radiation. It is quite unsuitable for measuring intensities of radiations that may be isolated with mono-chromators, when the total power of the beam may be as small as a few microwatts, since it would need prohibitively long times of exposure.

b. Malachite Green Leukocyanide (MGL) Actinometer. The method is based on UV radiation transforming malachite green leukocyanide, $[(CH_3)_2NC_6H_4]_2(C_6H_5){\equiv}C{-}CN$, which is colorless, into an intensely colored photoproduct, presumably $[(CH_3)_2NC_6H_4]_2(C_6H_5){\equiv}C^+$, with absorption maximum at 6200 Å, at which wavelength absorbancy is pro-portional to the number of previously absorbed quanta of UV radiation.

This actinometer is now mostly used to measure UV radiations iso-lated by monochromators, but is unsuitable for measuring more intense filtered or unfiltered radiations directly from lamps. Details concern-ing the actinometer and its use are given by Harris *et al.* (1935), Harris and Kaminsky (1935), and Calvert and Rechen (1952). Its inconvenient features are that (1) it must be kept in darkness when not in use, and during use it can be exposed only to red safelight (except, of course, when exposed to the radiation to be measured) and (2) that if unobtainable commercially, MGL must be prepared from malachite green oxalate and potassium cyanide by a rather lengthy procedure, described by Calvert and Rechen (1952).

It is recommended that a sample of a 10^{-3} M solution of MGL be irradiated in absolute ethanol (0.355 gm of MGL dissolved in ethanol and the volume brought up to 1 liter) in a quartz cell which is also used for a photobiological or photochemical experiment, for example, in a cuvette of a spectrophotometer, with 0.02 ml of 0.3 M HCl added to each 3.8 ml of the solution (to prevent the color of the photo-product from fading). The solution should be stirred during irradiation either with a mechanical stirrer or by bubbling nitrogen through a cap-illary tube. Absorbance of the solution at 6200 Å can then be meas-ured in the same cuvette with the spectrophotometer to which it belongs, using the nonirradiated solution as a blank for comparison.

The molecular extinction coefficient of MGL in UV is so great (about 10^4 or more at wavelengths shorter than 3000 Å) that all the incident radiation can be assumed absorbed by the 10^{-3} M solution if the length of light path is 1 cm. The quantum yield for transforming MGL into the colored photoproduct by UV radiation is 1.0. Thus, the number of moles of the photoproduct equals the number of einsteins delivered to the solution. As the molecular extinction coefficient, ϵ, of the photoproduct at 6200 Å is 9.49×10^4, and Beer's law is obeyed, the number of einsteins, y, delivered to the solution is

$$y = \frac{D \times v}{1000 \times 9.49 \times 10^4 l} = \frac{D \times v}{9.49 \times 10^7 l}$$

where D is optical density at 6200 Å, v is the volume of irradiated solution in milliliters, and l is the length of light path in centimeters when D was measured. The method is very sensitive and suitable for measuring UV radiations isolated with monochromators. It is not suitable for measuring much more intense radiations because any appreciable accumulation of the photoproduct, which absorbs UV radiations about as intensively as MGL, interferes with absorption by MGL (inner filter effect). Neither is it suitable for measuring UV radiations that are accompanied by radiations from the visible range, since the actinometer is sensitive to radiations from the near-UV range of the spectrum with a quantum yield of about 1.0.

c. *Potassium Ferrioxalate Actinometer.* These methods, developed by Parker (1953) and Hatchard and Parker (1956), are based on decomposition by radiation of ferrioxalate ion according to the equation

$$2Fe(C_2O_4)_3{}^{3-} \rightarrow 2Fe(C_2O_4) + 3(C_2O_4)^{2-} + 2CO_2$$

Oxidation and decomposition of 1 mole of oxalic acid ion, $(C_2O_4)^{2-}$, into 2 moles of CO_2 can be considered as a primary photochemical reaction, which is conditioned by the simultaneous reduction of 2 moles of ferric into ferrous iron, resulting in the formation of 2 moles of ferrous ions (Fe^{2+}). Thus, the quantum yield for the formation of ferrous ions is twice the quantum yield for the primary photochemical reaction, and can, therefore, exceed 1.0.

The amount of ferrous ion, which is proportional to the amount of radiation energy absorbed by the irradiated solution of potassium ferrioxalate, is determined by spectrophotometric or colorimetric estimation of the colored compound formed between ferrous ions and phenanthroline at pH 3.5. Absorption by the compound is at a maximum at 5100 Å.

(i) *Preparation of Potassium Ferrioxalate*

Three volumes of 1.5 M potassium oxalate are mixed with 1 volume of 1.5 M ferric chloride with vigorous stirring. Crystals of K_3Fe $(C_2O_4)_3 \cdot 3H_2O$ form in a few hours. The compound should be recrystallized three times from warm water or filtered off and washed on the filter with water, when some of the compound dissolves and is lost (which saves time at a small cost). Finally the crystals are dried. This and all subsequent manipulations of potassium ferrioxalate should be done in a dark room illuminated, for example, with Kodak OB safelights.

(a) *0.006 M Actinometric Solution.* Dissolve 2.947 gm of ferrioxalate crystals in 800 ml of water, add 100 ml of 1.0 N H_2SO_4, and adjust the volume to 1 liter with water. The solution keeps for long periods when stored in an amber bottle in a dark room.

(b) *Buffer.* Sodium acetate, 600 ml, 1.0 N, + 360 ml of 1.0 N H_2SO_4 + water to adjust the volume to 1 liter.

(c) *Phenanthroline Solution in Water.* A 0.1% (w/v) solution of 1 : 10 phenanthroline monohydrate in water.

(d) *Phenanthroline Solution in Buffer.* A 0.1% (w/v) solution of 1 : 10 phenanthroline monohydrate in a solution containing 1.8 N sodium acetate and 1.08 N H_2SO_4.

(ii) *Actinometric Procedures*

When intensity of radiation is large (direct radiations from lamps with filters), the following method can be used. A convenient volume (10 ml or less) of the actinometric solution (a) is exposed in a flat dish or in a quartz cell. The depth of the solution should not be less than 2 mm, for then it can be assumed that all incident radiation energy is absorbed. The solution should be stirred or rocked during irradiation. To determine the amount of Fe^{2+} ions formed as a result of irradiation, some (or all) of the irradiated solution is transferred to a 20-ml flask. Add 0.1 N H_2SO_4 to make up the volume to 10 ml, then in succession 2 ml of the phenanthroline solution (c), 5 ml of buffer (b), and water to make up the total volume to 20 ml. The red color develops almost immediately, and this is measured spectrophotometrically at 5100 Å in a cell with 1 cm light path, using a nonirradiated but otherwise similarly treated actinometric solution as a blank for comparison. Since absorption by ferrous phenanthroline corresponds to the molecular extinction coefficient of 11,050 with respect to the Fe^{2+} ion, and since Beer's law is obeyed, the number of einsteins, y, delivered to the irradiated solution is

$$y = \frac{D \times V \times 20}{1000 \times v \times 11050 \times \phi} = \frac{D \times V \times 1.81}{v \times \phi \times 10^6}$$

where D is the optical density at 5100 Å, V is the volume of irradiated actinometric solution, v is the volume of the sample taken to estimate Fe^{2+}, and ϕ is the quantum efficiency for the formation of Fe^{2+}, which depends on the wavelength, as shown in Table III.

When radiation intensities are small (e.g., from the exit slit of a monochromator), the following method can be used. Three ml of the actinometric solution (a) is irradiated in a cuvette of a spectrophotometer (light path 1 cm). Then 0.5 ml of the phenanthroline solution in buffer [solution (d)] is added, and the mixture is stirred. Color develops almost immediately and the optical density at 5100 Å is measured in the same cuvette with the spectrophotometer to which it belongs, using a nonirradiated but otherwise similarly treated sample of

TABLE III

VALUES OF ϕ FOR FERRIOXALATE ACTINOMETER

Wavelength (Å)	ϕ	Wavelength (Å)	ϕ
5790	0.015	3610	1.21
5460	0.15	3660	1.21
5090	0.86	3340	1.23
4800	0.93	3130	1.24
4360	1.11	2970	1.24
4050	1.14	2540	1.25

the actinometric solution as a blank for comparison. If the value of optical density is D, the number of einsteins, y, that fell on the solution is

$$y = \frac{D \times 3.5}{1000 \times 11050 \times \phi} = \frac{D \times 3.17}{\phi \times 10^7}$$

where ϕ is the quantum efficiency for the formation of Fe^{2+} at a given wavelength. This method is quite suitable for measuring intensities of radiations isolated with monochromators, but it is somewhat less sensitive than the method based on malachite green leucocyanide actinometer.

Absorbance by the photoproducts is 5% at 2530 Å, and less at longer wavelengths, of the absorbance by ferrioxalate. It increases to 38% at 2000 Å. Thus, at wavelengths longer than about 2300 Å there is no appreciable inner filter effect of photoproducts on photolysis of ferrioxalate. One must take care, however, when measuring very intense radiations not to exhaust ferrioxalate below half of its original amount. At wavelengths shorter than 2300 Å a special investigation is necessary to find how far the photolysis can progress before the inner filter effect of photoproducts starts interfering appreciably.

A colorimeter can be used instead of a spectrophotometer to determine Fe^{2+}. A calibration curve must then be prepared to correlate concentrations of Fe^{2+} with readings in the colorimeter. This can be done using 0.4×10^{-3} M $FeSO_4$ in 0.1 N H_2SO_4, which should be freshly prepared from standardized 0.1 N $FeSO_4$ in 0.1 N H_2SO_4 by diluting it $1 : 250$ in 0.1 N H_2SO_4. Different amounts of the 0.4×10^{-3} M $FeSO_4$ are taken, made up to a known volume (for example, 10 ml) with 0.1 N H_2SO_4, and treated in the same way as described above for estimating Fe^{2+} in irradiated actinometric solutions. Intensities of color are measured in the colorimeter using a green filter. Colorimetric readings obtained with irradiated actinometric solutions can then be translated into concentrations of Fe^{2+}, and the amounts of Fe^{2+} in the irradiated solutions can be computed. The number of einsteins, y, that fell on the irradiated solution is $y = m/\phi$, where m is the number of moles of Fe^{2+} in the whole irradiated solution and ϕ is the quantum efficiency for the formation of Fe^{2+} at a given wavelength.

With a spectrophotometer it can be assumed that the molecular extinction coefficient of Fe^{2+} (in the form of ferrous phenanthroline) is 11,050 at 5100 Å. For exact measurements, however, allowance should be made for "instrumental variation" by checking this value with the particular spectrophotometer used, and a correction factor can then be introduced if necessary. This can be done using solutions of $FeSO_4$ as described for calibrating a colorimeter.

V. Progress of Inactivation

Virus preparations lose most of their infectivity when exposed to UV before their optical properties, or those of any of their components, are appreciably affected. We shall assume, therefore, that unless doses of irradiation are unduly large, inactivated and still infective virus particles absorb and scatter radiation energy to the same extent. The term "total virus" will be used to mean noninfective plus infective virus. Similarly, when the nucleic acid from a virus is irradiated, the term "total nucleic acid" will mean noninfective plus infective nucleic acid.

A. RATE OF INACTIVATION

Inactivation of viruses usually follows the first-order kinetics at least approximately, which means that when an infinitesimally small amount of radiation energy, dE, is supplied, the decrease in concentration of infective virus, $-dC$, is proportional to the concentration of virus that is still infective, C, and to the amount of supplied energy, so that

$$-dC = FC\,dE \tag{40}$$

where F is a constant whose value depends on conditions under which the preparation is irradiated. If the preparation is so dilute that it is almost transparent to UV, the value of F is characteristic for a given virus. If the preparation is not transparent to UV (optical density, D, significantly greater than zero), the value of F may depend on such factors as the concentration of total virus, the presence and concentration of other materials, the size and shape of the container, etc., all factors that must be kept constant. It is also assumed that all virus particles are equally exposed to the radiation, which means that if the preparation is not dilute enough to be almost transparent to UV, it must be stirred when irradiated.

Integrating Eq. (40), we get

$$C = C_0 e^{-FE} \tag{41}$$

where C is the concentration of virus that is still infective, C_0 is its initial concentration (or the concentration of total virus), and E is the total amount of supplied energy. If radiation is at a steady intensity, I, so that $E = aIt$, where a is irradiated area and t is time of irradiation, Eqs. (40) and (41) become

$$-dC = F'CI\,dt \tag{42}$$
and

$$C = C_0 \exp{-F'It} \tag{43}$$

where $F' = aF$ and t is time of irradiation.

All these equations are applicable irrespective of whether radiation is monochromatic or polychromatic. As this statement is of basic importance, a formal proof will now be given, even though this may seem obvious.

Let a polychromatic radiation with total intensity, I, be composed of monochromatic radiations with intensities $I_1 = P_1I$, $I_2 = P_2I$, $I_3 = P_3I \cdots (P_1 + P_2 + P_3 \cdots = 1)$. During an infinitesimally small time increment, dt, any of the monochromatic radiations will decrease the concentration of still infective virus, C, according to Eq. (42), so that

$$-dC_1 = F_1CI_1dt$$
$$-dC_2 = F_2CI_2dt$$
$$-dC_3 = F_3CI_3dt$$

where F's are different constants. Thus the total decrease in the concentration of infective virus is

$$-dC = -dC_1 - dC_2 - dC_3 \cdots = (F_1 I_1 + F_2 I_2 + F_3 I_3 \cdots)C \, dt$$
$$= (F_1 P_1 + F_2 P_2 + F_3 P_3 \cdots)IC \, dt = F''IC \, dt \quad (44)$$

where

$$F'' = F_1 P_1 + F_2 P_2 + F_3 P_3 \cdots$$

Integrating this, we have

$$C = C_0 \exp{-F''It} \quad (45)$$

Equations (43) and (45) show that if p is the proportion of the original infectivity remaining after irradiation for time t $(p = C/C_0)$, we have

$$\log (1/p) = \log (C_0/C) = fIt \quad (46)$$

where f is a constant. Thus $\log (1/p)$ is directly proportional to the time of irradiation, provided everything else remains constant. Therefore, if after irradiation for time t_1, p was found (by an infectivity test) to have a given value, say p_1, and if we wish to obtain another value of p, say p_2, we shall have to irradiate the same preparation and in the same conditions for time t_2, such that

$$t_2/t_1 = \log (1/p_2)/\log (1/p_1) \quad (47)$$

This procedure is applicable irrespective of whether radiation is mono- or polychromatic, and irrespective of the state of purity of virus preparation, provided all the conditions are kept constant.

The result obtained by applying Eq. (47) may not be exact, first because the conditions may not have been exactly the same, and second because the course of inactivation may not follow exactly the first-order kinetics. Thus, if after the second irradiation the value of p is not what was intended, another adjustment of the time of irradiation may be required.

Equations (43) and (45) show that mathematically there is no such thing as "complete" inactivation. The concentration, C, of virus that still remains infective after irradiation for time t tends to zero asymptotically as t increases and never quite reaches zero.

In practice, however, infectivity will not be detected when C is less than some value. What this value should be for inactivation to be considered "complete," depends on circumstances, in some of which a decision can be made *a priori* and in others only by experience.

The value of the constant, F', of Eq. (43) can be considered a measure of the efficiency of a radiation in inactivating a given material under a given set of conditions, or a measure of the susceptibility of the material to the inactivating effect of the radiation. If there is a mechanism that can reverse some kind of damage caused by the radiation, the value of F' will obviously depend on whether or not the mechanism is operating. For example, when residual infectivity of an irradiated material, such as a bacteriophage or a plant virus, is assayed, the result may depend on whether or not the bacteria or the plants on which the assay is made are exposed for a few hours to daylight immediately after inoculation with the UV-irradiated material. Exposure to daylight can repair one kind of damage caused in the infective material by exposure to UV, so that only irreversible kind of damage will remain; consequently the residual infectivity will be greater. This phenomenon is called "photoreactivation." The rate of inactivation by UV approximately follows the first-order kinetics irrespective of whether or not photoreactivation operates, but is faster when without than with photoreactivation; consequently, the value of the constant, F', is greater without photoreactivation.

B. ABSORBED ENERGY AND INACTIVATION

Equation (41) gives the extent of inactivation of a virus as a function of supplied radiation energy, E, and applies only to a particular set of conditions. In any given set of conditions, the amount of energy absorbed by the total virus is a given proportion of the amount of supplied energy, so that E of Eq. (41) can also mean the amount of absorbed energy, when the constant F will take another value. It will take still another value if E means the amount of energy absorbed by a component of the total virus, for example, its nucleic acid.

We shall now limit ourselves to monochromatic UV radiations and to solutions of infective materials (viruses or nucleic acids isolated from viruses) that can be assumed free from any contaminants that absorb and/or scatter radiation energy. The term "total material" will mean infective plus noninfective material. We shall assume that at any particular wavelength the extent of inactivation of a material is a function of the amount of energy absorbed per unit mass of the total material. Equation (41) will thus become

$$C = C_0 \exp(-gE_{ab}/m) \qquad (48)$$

where E_{ab} is the amount of absorbed energy, m is the mass of the total material, and g is a constant that is characteristic for a given material (or its component) and depends only on the choice of units of energy and mass. The amount of absorbed energy can be computed from the amount of supplied energy, as described in Section III.

It is convenient to use joules or einsteins as units of energy and milligrams or moles as units of mass. If joules and milligrams are used, E_{ab}/m usually does not differ from 1 by many orders of magnitude when infectivity is halved. For example, the following numbers of joules are absorbed per milligram of material when its infectivity is halved and photoreactivation is not in operation: 0.18 for nucleic acid isolated from tobacco mosaic virus (A. Kleczkowski, 1963), 0.27 for nucleic acid of tobacco necrosis virus, whether or not isolated from the virus (Kassanis and Kleczkowski, 1965) (both for $\lambda = 2300$–2900 Å), and 0.083 for nucleic acid of a *Rhizobium* bacteriophage not isolated from the bacteriophage (for $\lambda = 2400$–2900 Å) (J. Kleczkowski and Kleczkowski, 1965). Another advantage of expressing amounts of absorbed energy in joules/milligram is that molecular weights of materials are not needed, and these may be unknown or uncertain.

Giving absorbed energy in numbers of einsteins/mole has the advantage of corresponding to numbers of quanta/molecule (or particle). This is convenient because the value of the constant, g, of Eq. (48) then becomes what is called "quantum efficiency" or "quantum yield," which will be designated by the symbol ϕ. If absorbed energy is given in joules/milligram, the value of the constant, g, of Eq. (48) will be designated by the symbol G. Thus, for future reference, we have

$$C = C_0 \exp[-G \times \text{(joules absorbed/milligram)}] \qquad (49)$$

and

$$C = C_0 \exp[-\phi \times \text{(einsteins absorbed/mole)}] \qquad (50)$$

In both equations units of mass are those of total material.

The quantum efficiency, ϕ, is the reciprocal of the average number of quanta that are absorbed by a molecule (or particle) when it becomes inactivated. In other words, ϕ is the probability that a quantum absorbed by a molecule (or particle) will inactivate it. That a molecule is usually inactivated when it is in a state of excitation caused by absorption of only one quantum is suggested by the fact that excitation is so brief that a molecule is extremely unlikely to absorb a quantum while it is still in a state of excitation caused by absorption of another quantum.

Since quantum efficiency is one of the most important concepts in photochemistry, it will now be proved that ϕ of Eq. (50) is indeed quantum efficiency.

We shall use the term "effective quantum" to mean the quantum that happens to inactivate and the term "molecule" to mean a virus particle or a molecule of nucleic acid isolated from a virus.

When an effective quantum is absorbed by a solution, the probability of a given molecule absorbing this quantum is infinitesimally small. However, when a sufficiently large number of such quanta have been absorbed, the mean number of absorbed quanta/molecule becomes finite. Therefore, the frequency distribution of molecules that have absorbed different numbers of effective quanta will be Poissonian, as shown in Chapter 17. This means that the proportions of molecules that have absorbed 0, 1, 2, 3, and so on, effective quanta equal successive terms of the Poisson series, which are

$$ e^{-m}, \qquad me^{-m}, \qquad m^2e^{-m}/2!, \qquad m^3e^{-m}/3! \qquad \cdots $$

where m is the mean number of effective quanta absorbed per molecule. Therefore, if absorption of one effective quantum is sufficient to inactivate a molecule, the proportion of molecules that are still infective, $p = C/C_0$, is the proportion of those that have not absorbed an effective quantum, and this is e^{-m}, so that

$$ p = C/C_0 = e^{-m} \tag{51} $$

By definition, ϕ is the probability that an absorbed quantum is effective. Therefore, on average one out of $1/\phi$ quanta is effective. Thus, when the mean number of effective quanta absorbed per molecule is m, the mean number of all absorbed quanta is $M = m/\phi$, which is also the number of einsteins absorbed per mole of total material. Therefore, Eq. (51) becomes

$$ p = C/C_0 = e^{-\phi M} $$

which is identical with Eq. (50).

The values of ϕ for inactivation of viruses or their nucleic acids are usually very small. For example, its value is about 0.4×10^{-4} for tobacco mosaic virus at a wavelength of 2537 Å (Oster and McLaren, 1950), about 10^{-3} for the free nucleic acid from tobacco mosaic virus (A. Kleczkowski, 1963), and about 0.7×10^{-3} for the nucleic acid of tobacco necrosis virus (Kassanis and Kleczkowski, 1965).

There has been controversy about inactivation of viruses by single quanta. It should be made clear, however, that the objection against the view of inactivation by single quanta was not against the general concept as presented above but against the "target" theory (see A. Kleczkowski, 1957, 1960a). According to the target theory, there is a "susceptible region" within a virus particle. Inactivation occurs necessarily when this region is "hit" by a quantum, but not when any other region is "hit."

Equations (48)–(50) show the extent of inactivation as functions of absorbed energy. To convert any one of them into a function of supplied energy, absorbed energy must be substituted by a suitable function of supplied energy, as shown in Section III. Let us assume that a virus solution is irradiated by a monochromatic radiation and that we are interested in the amount of energy absorbed by nucleic acid of the virus on the assumption that this determines the extent of inactivation of the virus. Let us assume that the virus is composed of nucleic acid and protein only, which occur in proportions P_n and P_p, respectively. Equation (33) of Section III gives the amount of energy absorbed by the virus, E_{ab}, as a function of the total supplied energy, E_0, and the proportion of this that is absorbed by the nucleic acid of the virus is given by Eq. (38) of Section III. Thus the amount of energy absorbed by the nucleic acid of the virus is

$$E_n = E_0[1 - \exp{-(kc + \tau)l]} \frac{kc}{kc + \tau} \frac{\alpha_n P_n}{\alpha_n P_n + \alpha_p P_p}$$

which can be transformed into

$$E_n = E_0\{1 - \exp[-2.3(\alpha c + \beta)l]\}\alpha_n P_n c/(\alpha c + \beta)$$

where E_n is energy absorbed by the nucleic acid, E_0 is the total supplied energy, both in joules, c is the concentration of total virus in grams/liter, α, α_n, and α_p are specific absorbancies of the whole virus, of nucleic acid, and of protein of the virus, respectively $(\alpha = P_n\alpha_n + P_p\alpha_p)$, τ is turbidity of the virus solution, and $\beta = 0.4343\tau$. Thus, Eq. (49) can be transformed into

$$\log C_0/C = 0.4343GE_0\{1 - \exp[-2.3(\alpha C_0 + \beta)l]\}\alpha_n/(\alpha C_0 + \beta)Al \quad (52)$$

where E_0 is the amount of supplied energy in joules, C is the concentration of remaining infective virus, and C_0 is its original concentration (both in grams/liter), A is the area of irradiated surface (in square centimeters), and l is the length of light path (in centimeters), so that the volume of irradiated solution is Al (in cubic centimeters), and therefore AlC_0P_n is the amount of total nucleic acid in milligrams.

If the amount of supplied energy, E'_0, is in einsteins and the concentration of the virus, C', in moles/liter, the amount of energy absorbed by nucleic acid of the virus is

$$E'_n = E'_0\{1 - \exp[-2.3(\epsilon C' + \beta)l]\}\epsilon_n P_n C'/(\epsilon C' + \beta)$$

where ϵ_n and ϵ are molecular extinction coefficients of virus nucleic acid and of the whole virus, respectively. It should be remembered that $\epsilon = P_n\epsilon_n + P_p\epsilon_p$, where ϵ_p would be the molecular extinction coefficient of virus protein if the "molecular weight" of the protein were assumed to correspond to the amount of the protein in one virus particle.

Thus, Eq. (50) can be transformed into

$$\log C'_0/C' = 0.4343\phi E'_0\{1 - \exp[-2.3(\epsilon C'_0 + \beta)l]\}$$
$$10^3\epsilon_n/(\epsilon C'_0 + \beta)Al \quad (53)$$

where E'_0 is the amount of supplied energy in einsteins, C' is the concentration of remaining infective virus, and C'_0 is its original concentration (both in moles/liter), A is the area of irradiated surface (in square centimeters), and l is the length of light path (in centimeters). Therefore, the volume of irradiated solution is Al (in cubic centimeters), and the amount of nucleic acid is $AlC'_0P_n \times 10^{-3}$ in moles.

When virus is so concentrated that transmittance, T, of the irradiated solution is almost zero (so that the value of $\exp[-2.3(\alpha C_0 + \beta)l]$ is almost zero), Eq. (52) becomes

$$\log C_0/C = 0.4343GE_0\alpha_n/(\alpha C_0 + \beta)Al \quad (54)$$

Similarly, Eq. (53) becomes

$$\log C'_0/C' = 0.4343\phi E'_0 10^3\epsilon_n/(\epsilon C'_0 + \beta)Al \quad (55)$$

When the virus is so dilute that transmittance, T, is almost 1, so that optical density, D, is almost zero (which means that the value of $(\alpha C_0 + \beta)l$ can be assumed to tend to zero), Eq. (52) becomes

$$\log C_0/C = G(E_0/A)\alpha_n \quad (56)$$

Similarly, Eq. (53) becomes

$$\log C_0/C = \phi(E'_0/A)\epsilon_n 10^3 \quad (57)$$

Thus, once we know the value of G or ϕ and of α_n or ϵ_n, we can compute the extent of inactivation of a virus, $\log C_0/C$, from the amount of radiation energy supplied per square centimeter of irradiated surface, E_0/A or E'_0/A, or, conversely, the value of the constant G or ϕ can be determined when the value of $\log C_0/C$ is found by infectivity test. We need not even know the concentration of irradiated material. Equations (56) and (57) are applicable even to virus preparations containing other materials that absorb and/or scatter radiation, provided the preparations are so dilute that optical density, D, is nearly zero (see Section III,B,4,b).

It would, therefore, be of great advantage if virus preparations could be irradiated at such dilutions that D is almost zero. Fortunately this can be easily done with many viruses, because their infectivity is most accurately assayed at dilutions much greater than those needed to bring the value of D almost to zero.

C. ACTION SPECTRA

The values of G or ϕ of Eqs. (49) and (50) may or may not vary with the wavelength, and various conclusions can be drawn from this fact. If G or ϕ does not depend on the wavelength, it means that the extent of inactivation is a function of radiation energy or of the number of quanta, respectively, absorbed per unit mass of a given material or component, whatever the wavelength. It is obvious that G and ϕ cannot both be independent of the wavelength, because quantum energy varies with the wavelength.

Whether or not G or ϕ is independent of the wavelength can be tested by irradiating a preparation of infective material, by monochromatic radiations at different wavelengths, with known amounts of energy, estimating the proportions of surviving infectivity and finding the values of G and ϕ using any of Eqs. (52)–(57) that is applicable under the circumstances. Another way of doing it is by obtaining so-called action spectrum for inactivation, since if G or ϕ is independent of wavelength, the action spectrum will coincide with the absorption spectrum of the material or component.

The action spectrum is obtained by plotting the values of log C_0/C (which may be called action) against the wavelength, keeping constant either the amount of supplied energy (if G is expected to be constant) or the number of supplied einsteins (if ϕ is expected to be constant). Assuming G or ϕ, and also E_0 or E'_0, to be constant, and remembering that $\alpha = \alpha_n P_n + \alpha_p P_p$ and $\epsilon = \epsilon_n P_n + \epsilon_p P_p$ (see Section V,B), log C_0/C is not a linear function of α_n or ϵ_n in Eqs. (52)–(55), which apply to conditions when optical density, D, is significantly greater than zero. By contrast, log C_0/C is a linear function of α_n or ϵ_n in Eqs. (56) and (57), which apply when irradiated material is so dilute that the optical density is almost zero. Therefore, to obtain a useful action spectrum, irradiated material should be so diluted.

Thus, if G or ϕ is independent of the wavelength, and if the irradiated material is dilute enough, the action spectrum, i.e., the plot of log C_0/C against the wavelength, will be parallel to the plot of α_n or ϵ_n against the wavelength, which is the absorption spectrum of irradiated material or component. If the scales are "normalized" to make the action spectrum coincide with the absorption spectrum at one point, they will coincide at all points. If G or ϕ is constant only within a certain range of wavelengths, absorption and action spectra will coincide only within this range.

In practice we do not have to irradiate a preparation with the same amount of energy or with the same number of einsteins at all tested wavelengths. It may be more convenient to vary the amount of energy to obtain similar values of log C_0/C. Since at any particular wavelength the value of log C_0/C is directly proportional to the amount of supplied energy or to the number of supplied einsteins, it can then be adjusted to correspond to a chosen amount of energy or number of einsteins before it is plotted.

REFERENCES

Bowen, E. J. (1946). "The Chemical Aspects of Light," 2nd ed., p. 283. Oxford Univ. Press (Clarendon), London and New York.
Calvert, J. G., and Rechen, H. J. L. (1952). *J. Am. Chem. Soc.* 74, 2101.
Dulbecco, R. (1950). *J. Bacteriol.* 59, 329.
French, C. S., Rabidean, G. S., and Holt, A. S. (1947). *Rev. Sci. Instr.* 18, 11.
Harris, L., and Kaminsky, J. (1935). *J. Am. Chem. Soc.* 57, 1154.
Harris, L., Kaminsky, J. and Simard, R. G. (1935). *J. Am. Chem. Soc.* 57, 1151.
Harrison, G. R. (1934). *Rev. Sci. Instr.* 5, 149.
Hatchard, C. G., and Parker, C. A. (1956). *Proc. Roy. Soc.* A235, 518.
Jagger, J. (1961). *Radiation Res.* 14, 394.
Kasha, M. (1948). *J. Opt. Soc. Am.* 38, 929.
Kassanis, B., and Kleczkowski, A. (1965). *Photochem. Photobiol.* 4, 209.
Kleczkowski, A. (1957). *Advan. Virus Res.* 4, 191.
Kleczkowski, A. (1960a). *Ann. N.Y. Acad. Sci.* 83, 661.
Kleczkowski, A. (1960b). *Rept. Rothamsted Expt. Sta.* pp. 234–245.
Kleczkowski, A. (1963). *Photochem. Photobiol.* 2, 497.
Kleczkowski, J., and Kleczkowski, A. (1965). *Photochem. Photobiol.* 4, 201.
Latarjet, R., Morenne, P., and Berger, R. (1953). *Ann. Inst. Pasteur* 85, 174.
McLaren, A. D., and Shugar, D. (1964). "Photochemistry of Proteins and Nucleic Acids." Pergamon Press, Oxford.
Mohler, N. M., and Loofbourow, J. R. (1952). *Am. J. Phys.* 20, 499 and 579.
Oster, G. (1948). *Chem. Rev.* 43, 319.
Oster, G. (1950). *J. Gen. Physiol.* 33, 445.
Oster, G., and McLaren, A. D. (1950). *J. Gen. Physiol.* 33, 215.
Parker, C. A. (1953). *Proc. Roy. Soc.* A220, 104.
Reddi, K. K. (1957). *Biochim. Biophys. Acta* 24, 238.
Stacey, K. A. (1956). "Light Scattering in Physical Chemistry," Butterworth, London and Washington, D.C.

4 Inactivation of Viruses by Ionizing Radiation and by Heat

William Ginoza

I. Introduction 139
II. Ionizing Radiation 140
   A. Introduction 140
   B. Ionizing Radiations: Their Nature, Production, and
      Action on Biological Macromolecules 143
   C. Dosimetry 146
   D. Target Theory 148
   E. Selective Inactivation of Viral Functions by Ionizing
      Radiations 174
   F. Summary of the Use of Ionizing Radiation for Virus
      Inactivation 179
III. Thermal Inactivation of Viruses 180
   A. Reaction Rate Theory 181
   B. Structure of Viruses 184
   C. Kinetic Analysis of Virus Inactivation 196
   D. Summary of the General Characteristics of Virus
      Inactivation 199
   Acknowledgments 205
   References 205

I. Introduction

Ionizing radiation and heat are destructive to virus. A controlled use of these agents followed by a careful analysis of the way the virus responds to their action helps to provide insight into the structural attributes that control its function and survival. One of the principal objectives of the use of ionizing radiation and heat, then, is analytical. Procedures to be described in this chapter are basically simple; but the data, although easily obtained, do not always yield to simple interpretation. The emphasis in this chapter, then, is more on discussion of the data and their interpretation than on the methods. The physics of

140   WILLIAM GINOZA

ionizing radiation is a specialized subject deserving much greater emphasis than is given here. Since excellent texts are available, they will
be referred to at appropriate places in the text.

II. Ionizing Radiation

A. INTRODUCTION

A striking aspect of the action of ionizing radiation on a living system is the large amount of energy released within a small volume of
the system. The direct consequence of such a localized action initiated
by ionization, and possibly to a minor extent by excitation energy, may
be as simple an alteration as a rupture of a single covalent bond. If
that bond is in a critical macromolecule, such as the nucleic acid of a
virus, it could result in failure of the virus to replicate; yet the physical or chemical damage done to the population of virus so inactivated
may be virtually undetectable. With respect to the effectiveness of the
localized damage, the action of radiation is like that of chemical mutagens.

The assessment of the detailed mechanisms of radiation action on
living systems is especially difficult because the span between the cause
and effect is long and the reactions occurring in it are complex, as
shown by the following illustration, using the simplest biological system, the virus:

Radiation $\xrightarrow{1}$ ionization $\xrightarrow{2}$ redistribution of the positive charge
$\xrightarrow{3}$ stable radical $\xrightarrow{4}$ permanent chemical alteration $\xrightarrow{5}$ attachment $\xrightarrow{6}$ injection $\xrightarrow{7}$ replication and maturation $\xrightarrow{8}$ plaque
formation

We make the assumption here that the nucleic acid is the sensitive target.

The principal aim of quantitative radiation biology is to establish a
direct correspondence between the initial action of ionizing radiation
and biological effect. Yet a consideration of the steps from the primary
effect, ionization, to the final plaque formation shows a series of complex and little-understood reactions. Moreover, each of these reactions
may be modified by the immediate environment. First of all, the initial
displacement of an electron leaves an unpaired electron at the site of
the ejection, thus creating a positive charge. The positive charge may
have a chance to migrate about the molecule until it finds a suitable
chemical grouping that can support the charge for a greater duration
than can the site of its formation (e.g., the heteroaromatic rings of the

purine and pyrimidine bases of the nucleic acid). If an electron or a hydrogen donor is present close to the ionized molecule, the radical will, with some probability, be neutralized by them, and the "hit" molecule is restored to its original state. Otherwise, the unstable radical in time will react to form a more permanent chemical lesion. Keeping in mind that one such lesion, essentially a point damage within a large macromolecule, can inactivate a biological function, that types of radiation lesions are varied, and that biological experiments make use of very small doses, one can only infer the presence and nature of lesions. Assuming that the hit virus has not lost its function of attachment and injection, an assumption not admissible in all experiments, its nucleic acid after injection finds itself in a complex cell milieu. The question arises whether or not the host cell possesses some capability of repairing the lesion in the nucleic acid. In the final step of the reaction chain, the virus is tested for its ability to replicate within the cell. Given an irradiated population of uniform biological units, a dose–response curve, a basic radiobiological result, is obtained and its interpretation attempted. If the plot is linear on a semilogarithmic graph, as is generally the case for the kinetics of virus inactivation, a one-to-one correlation between the initial radiation event and the final biological response is usually assumed.

From the foregoing discussion it should be clear that an understanding of each of many events intervening between the initial radiation action and the final biological effects must precede any attempt at formulating hypotheses based on dose–effect curves. Indeed, the progress of quantitative radiation biology has been greatly hampered by the slow development of knowledge concerning these events. It is partly for this reason that the expectations expressed in the treatise of Lea, "Action of Radiations on Living Cells" (1962), have not been completely realized. A recent thoughtful essay by Zimmer elaborates on these points and is recommended for study (1961). It should be emphasized that the description of the physical characteristics of the action of ionization radiations on matter is on reasonably firm ground (Pollard, 1953a); it is the chemical and biological alterations brought about in the wake of the radiation that are in dire need of a better description. As we shall see, there are reasons to question whether all viruses should respond to a given radiation in the same way.

In the preceding discussion we assumed that the nucleic acid is the radiation-sensitive target of the virus. Indeed, the assumption is generally acceptable, in view of the wide variety of evidence accumulated from radiation and other experiments that the integrity of the nucleic acid must be held inviolate for the survival of the virus. More recently we have come to recognize that lesions induced in double-stranded virus DNA by a range of agents, e.g., heat, radioactive ^{32}P atoms, UV light, and ionizing radiations, do not necessarily lead to the inactivation of the virus. What this means is that a surviving virus can have sublethal damage. Moreover, it is also known that an inactivated virus can have partial function. A further burden is thus added to the interpretation of the dose–effect curve, which itself is only a basis for making hypotheses and not a source of explicit information.

The action of ionizing radiation cannot be discussed without a mention of the biological effect of the diffusible free radicals produced by the radiation in the medium in which the studied material is suspended. This effect is called indirect action and is due primarily to reactive radiolysis products of water, which are produced outside the test material and which then act on it upon collision. One is tempted to dismiss the subject, since it is peripheral to the objective of quantitative analysis in radiation biology; yet the fact that biological materials, in general, contain a great deal of water or are surrounded by it makes essential an understanding of the relative importance of indirect action on their inactivation. As was shown early by Luria and Exner (1941), bacteriophages are more rapidly inactivated when irradiated in aqueous or saline suspension than when irradiated dry or in broth. A more recent series of studies, chiefly by Scholes et al. (1960), shows that the purine and pyrimidine moieties of the nucleic acids are the major foci of chemical change when nucleic acids are irradiated in dilute solution, while the pentose phosphate group is damaged less frequently. Other components of viruses are known to be damaged by diffusible radicals in varying degrees, as demonstrated by a long series of work by radiation chemists on a variety of bioorganic compounds. Organic peroxides (Latarjet et al., 1963) and irradiated phosphate ions (Ginoza, 1963), both possessing a longer lifetime than reactive radiolysis products of water, are also produced by radiation and are found to have radiomimetic action on biological materials at low concentrations. The relative contribution to the total biological damage by indirect effects, if allowed to take place, can be considerable.

Important as these facts are toward an understanding of the total radiation action on living cellular systems, the essential argument remains that the action of diffusible agents cannot be quantitated. As Zimmer (1961) points out, their mean life, their diffusion constants, and their reaction probabilities in collision with the target material are difficult to measure.

B. Ionizing Radiations: Their Nature, Production, and Action on Biological Macromolecules

Ionizing radiations that are widely used in radiation biology are grouped as x-, γ-, and β-rays, and heavy charged particles such as protons, deuterons, and α-particles. Only a brief discussion of their characteristics can be given here, and the reader is referred to Lea's monograph (1962) and review articles by Pollard et al. (1955) and by Hutchinson and Pollard (1961) for a more comprehensive treatment of the subject.

1. X- and γ-Rays

These are short wavelength electromagnetic radiations possessing high penetrating ability. They are more energetic than visible and UV light and, unlike the latter, their action depends not on the way in which atoms are combined into molecules but only on their atomic number. When these radiations interact with matter, their energy is dispersed not homogeneously but in a quantized fashion as packets of energy ranging from 10 to 110 eV and higher. Such a localized energy absorption results mainly in ionization; that is, in ejection of an electron from an atom, the entire molecule of which the atom is a part becomes highly reactive and will undergo a chemical change with a high probability. The ejected electrons are capable of further ionization of atoms along their paths; indeed most of the ionizations causing biological damage owe to these ejected electrons rather than to the incident photons. With each ionization event, the electrons lose more of their energy, while the distance between successive ionizations becomes shorter. This behavior is described as the "tailing" effect, during which the energy absorption per unit path length increases greatly.

The mere passage of a photon or a fast electron does not necessarily produce an ionization. A photon may pass by many atoms before a chance absorption takes place. The degree of penetration into matter depends on the energy of the incident photons. Thus, x-rays having an energy of 50–250 keV have lower penetrability than γ-rays, say, of ^{60}Co (1.1 and 1.3 MeV). The degree of penetration is also dependent on the absorption coefficient of the material exposed to these radiations. The coefficient is expressed by the familiar exponential absorption law, $I/I_0 = e^{-\mu x}$, where μ contains the term Z^2, where Z is atomic number and x is the thickness of the material. We shall return to this in greater detail. Water, tissue, and viruses have approximately the same "stopping power" per gram. Calcified tissues, such as bone, have high stopping power because of their high concentration of calcium and phosphorus atoms.

Hard x-rays, useful in radiation studies, are generally produced in therapy machines. They emit a range of wavelengths or radiation energies whose peaks vary with the voltage applied. The shortest wavelength emitted equals 12.4/keV applied, while the wavelength emitted at greatest intensity is about twice that of the short wave limit. The longest wavelength depends on the filter used.

The commonly used ^{60}Co source emits γ-rays of high energies, 1.1–1.3 MeV, and the wavelengths are $\sim$0.01Å. The distinction between γ-rays and x-rays is arbitrary, for x-rays can now be generated in powerful machines, such as Van de Graaff generators, at energy levels matching or exceeding those of some γ-rays.

2. Electrons and β-Rays

β-Rays are high-speed electrons emitted from a number of radioactive isotopes, notably ^{32}P, ^{14}C, ^{3}H, ^{35}S, and ^{45}Ca, all of which are used as tracers in biological experiments. Their energies range from kiloelectron volts to megaelectron volts, depending on the isotopes from which they are emitted. As high-speed electrons, β-rays ionize biological materials in the same way that the photoelectrons produced by x- and γ-rays do; but since they are charged particles, they have a limited penetration, even at energies as high as 2 MeV. For example, the limit of penetration of a 2-MeV electron into water and tissue is about 1 cm. Photoelectrons, on the other hand, can be produced within the biological materials, since photons of x- and γ-rays themselves are highly penetrating. The limited penetrability of electrons, however, is overcome for experimental purposes through incorporation of β-emitting radioisotopes into the very biomolecules being studied.

At least four reactions, which may lead to biological effects, are involved in the nuclear decay of incorporated radioisotopes, ^{32}P, ^{35}S, ^{14}C, ^{45}Ca, and ^{3}H: (1) transmutation to a different atom, (2) production of recoil energy, (3) excitation energy, and (4) emission of β-rays. Hershey et al. (1951) and Stent (1955) concluded from their work that phage particles containing ^{32}P atoms in their DNA were not inactivated primarily by ionization produced by the emitted β-rays. Their data naturally suggest that recoil energy (67 eV) or transmutation (P → S), or both, may be the cause of lethality. More recently, Apelgot and Latarjet (1967) compared the efficiency of inactivation by decay of ^{32}P and ^{33}P atoms incorporated into bacterial nucleic acids and found that the lethal efficiencies of both radioactive transmutations were the same, even though the maximum recoil energies are 77.3 and 5.1, respectively. Thus, they conclude that the biological effect results mainly from the chemical reaction of the ionized and highly excited S atoms left *in situ* after the ^{32}P or ^{33}P decay and whose valence state differs from the parental atom. Funk *et al.* (1967), on the other hand, find that for the decay of ^3H atoms incorporated into the phage protein or for ^3H atoms incorporated into the thymine (or cytosine) of the nucleic acid moiety of phage the lethal efficiency is proportional to the path length of a β-particle through the phage DNA. This suggests, assuming the rates of energy losses to be equivalent in the two cases, that the β-radiation is solely responsible for phage inactivation. The energy of the recoil nucleus has a maximum value of 3 eV.

High-speed electrons can also be produced by electron generators. They are useful in the study of virus structure and function in that their penetrability can be varied according to need by the control of energy input into the generator. For example, Pollard and his associates used the technique effectively for determining the thickness of virus capsids in relation to the radiosensitive nucleic acid cores (1953a).

3. *Positive Ions*

Among the positive ions that have been used in virus research are protons, deuterons, α-particles, and, to a lesser extent, the very heavy ions (e.g., oxygen and argon). These are classed as heavy charged particles, and for irradiation work they are accelerated in a nearly parallel beam in particle accelerators against virus particles under vacuum. The linear energy transfer (LET) of these ion particles of a given energy per nucleon varies as the square of their charge and for a given charge is inversely proportional to the square of their velocity. Their range of penetration into virus, although nearly proportional to the mass, is inversely proportional to the square of the charge. Thus, protons and deuterons moving at the same velocity will produce the same number of ions per unit path length, whereas α-particles with double the charge will produce four times as many. The number of ionizations per unit length of solids is difficult to estimate, although in gases it is obtained by dividing LET by 34 eV.

Compared to γ- and x-rays, these charged particles have feeble penetrating ability. They pass through matter in essentially a straight line only for a few microns; then, as the particles slow down, they release their energy with increasing density, accompanied by increasing fluctuation in their path. The tracks of ionizing particles themselves, in passage through virus, have a core of closely packed ionization that may be a few angstroms to several tens of angstroms in diameter, but spurs of ionizing δ-rays radiate out from the core to produce more secondary ionizations. The distal effects of these spurs undoubtedly contribute significantly to the total biological damage (Schambra and Hutchinson, 1964; Dolphin and Hutchinson, 1960).

Fast charged particles are useful in virus research in that the energy of the beams can be controlled to produce different spacings between ionizations and can be directed in nearly parallel streams. These particles are used in the determination of the sensitive cross-sectional area and the thickness of sensitive targets and of the insensitive protein coat of viruses (Pollard, 1953a).

C. DOSIMETRY

A brief consideration of the nature of ionizing radiations and their interaction with matter leads us to expect that quantitative measurement of the amount of energy absorbed by irradiated materials can be quite complex. Indeed, this is the case. Even a brief survey of the radiobiological literature will soon reveal the disconcerting disagreement on dose required to inactivate a given virus, thus indicating the inherent difficulty of dosimetry measurements or the lack of sufficient care given to them. We shall make no attempt here to cover even the basic principles and techniques involved in dosimetry, but rather refer the reader to the texts on this subject by Johns (1964), Hine and Brownell (1956), and Allen (1961). Basic review articles on radiations by Pollard et al. (1955) and the monograph by Lea (1962) are highly recommended for background reading.

Fortunately there are two simple procedures that can be performed in a normally equipped virus laboratory which yield results that agree well with dose measurements made by "absolute" procedures. The first is the chemical method called Fricke dosimetry, which depends on spectrophotometric measurement of ferric ions produced by irradiating a solution of ferrous sulfate. The second is the biological procedure using well-characterized viruses, especially T1 phage and the single-stranded nucleic acid viruses, such as $\phi X174$ and tobacco mosaic virus (TMV), whose radiation sensitivity or inactivation rate is known for a given radiation.

1. Fricke Dosimetry

There are numerous chemical dosimetries in use, but the ferrous–ferric sulfate system, first described by Fricke and developed by Weiss *et al.* (1956), is accepted by numerous workers as the best chemical method for measuring x-rays and γ-rays. It is independent of dose rate up to 10^{10} rads/second (Keene, 1957) and is useful over a total dosage range of 4×10^4 rads. It is dependent on LET, which limits its use to hard x-rays, γ-rays, and high-energy β-rays.

Procedure. Dissolve 2 gm of $FeSO_4 \cdot 7H_2O$ or $Fe(NH_4)_2(SO_4)_2 \cdot 6H_2O$, 0.3 gm NaCl, and 110 ml of concentrated (95–98%) H_2SO_4 (analytical reagent grade) in sufficient distilled water to make 5 liters of solution.

A volume of this solution is placed in a glass or polyethylene container that has been carefully washed with the same solution. Since the geometry of the beam is such that the radiation intensity varies with the position of the sample, one must do the dosimetry in the same position within the beam using the same type of container that would be used for the experimental samples. The duration of irradiation time should be carefully noted. A Beckman spectrophotometer model DU is suitable for measuring the amount of ferric ion produced by the radiation. The absorption maximum of the ferric ion is at approximately 304 mμ. The absorbancy (optical density) of the irradiated sample is compared with the nonirradiated sample. The dose is calculated by the following formula:

$$\text{Dose in rads} = \frac{10^9}{\epsilon b Y} (A_i - A_{un}) \tag{1}$$

where A_i and A_{un} = absorbancy of irradiated and unirradiated solutions, respectively, ϵ = molar extinction coefficient, Y = ferrous sulfate yield, μM of ferric ions/liter/1000 rads = 15.3 ± 0.3 μM, and b = path length of absorption cell in centimeters. The dose divided by time of irradiation gives the dose rate. The molar extinction coefficient, ϵ, of Fe^{3+} is 2174 at 23.7°C with a temperature coefficient of 0.7% per degree Centigrade. The dose rate is expressed in rads/hour, where a rad specifies the energy absorbed by the target material, or 100 ergs/gm. One rad is approximately equal to 1.1 roentgen (r).

Another chemical procedure has been recently introduced by Levinson and Garber (1965), which is based on the measurement of a blue color produced by the action of γ-rays on sodium cacodylate. The color is the same as that obtained in the Fiske-SubbaRow procedure for measuring phosphate ion concentration. The advantage of the method is that relatively high doses (10^6 rads) can be measured, and it is claimed to be particularly suitable for sterilization which requires high doses.

2. Biological Dosimetry

There are reports in the literature of a number of viruses whose radiation sensitivity has been measured using radiation sources that have been carefully calibrated by standard dosimetric methods. The values provided serve well as a secondary standard for estimating doses delivered by other radiation sources. For example, the D_{37} doses for T1 (Fluke, 1966), TMV (Ginoza, 1963), and ϕX174 (Ginoza, 1963) are 5.7×10^5 r, 3×10^5 r, and 3.8×10^5 r, respectively. Any one of these viruses may be irradiated, under conditions specified in the literature, and a plot of the log of surviving fraction versus time of irradiation is prepared. The reported D_{37} dose divided by the time required by the radiation source in question to reduce the survival to 37% gives the dose rate of the source. Experimental details for TMV and ϕX174 are given in Section II,D,3,a. For simple biological systems such as viruses, D_{37} dose is independent of the dose rate.

Alternatively, a reference virus whose D_{37} is known and a test virus may be cosuspended in a suitable medium (see Section II,D,3,a) and irradiated for various lengths of time. The mixed irradiated samples are assayed on differential hosts and the respective survival curves obtained. The ratio of the slopes will provide a direct quantitative relationship between the inactivation dose of the reference virus and that of the test virus (see Fig. 3).

D. TARGET THEORY

1. Introduction

Dessauer in 1922 first considered the important and then new concept of physics that radiation is absorbed by matter in a quantized rather than continuous process, and then related the concept to the dose–effect curves observed when a biological system is exposed to radiation. He proposed a "hit" theory that, based on the Poisson law of statistical distribution, solidifies the notion that an observed property of a living system is effectively destroyed when a chance absorption event occurs at a point within that system. The energy involved in the event as we know it today is around 60 eV (Rauth and Simpson, 1964). Crowther in 1938 considered the possibility of calculating the target volume from a dose–effect curve, assuming that the measured dose can be directly related to the probability that a given volume will incur a hit and that each hit has an efficiency of unity in bringing about a biological effect under observation. A steady development of their ideas followed (Holweck, 1938; Zimmer, 1941); Lea and his co-workers successfully implemented the target theory into a concrete workable tool, as may be found summarized in Lea's monograph, "The Actions of Radiations on Living Cells" (1962). Pollard and his associates (1955) gained further ground by demonstrating the validity of the theory on a wide range of biological materials, notably viruses and enzymes, using combinations of radiation sources.

Although steady progress is being made, there are still some assumptions in the theory that are not fully substantiated, and criticisms are apt to become more intense as one presses for higher precision from the method. Deviations from the expected results frequently arise, pointing either to our imperfect knowledge of the detailed processes of radiation or to the complexity of the biological system studied. In the following presentation of the target theory methods, the determination of size and shape of the radiosensitive components of viruses will be discussed. It will include discussions of the newer, although essentially minor, problems that have arisen subsequent to Lea's classical summary of the theory.

2. Methods and Application

In applying the simple target theory to determine target dimensions of a molecule, one makes the following assumption: the probability that a molecule exposed to radiation gets inactivated is equal to the probability that an ionization event or a hit will occur within its mass. Thus, if one or more hits occur in the sensitive target within the virus particle, some biological function of the virus is expected to be inactivated. Indeed, virtually all viruses that have been subjected to radiation target analysis are inactivated by a first-order or a single-hit process, which is described by the relationship $N/N_0 = e^{-kD}$, where k is the target sensitivity, D is the dose, and N/N_0 is the fraction of the virus population surviving a given dose. A plot of log N/N_0 versus D will give a straight line whose slope is k. For an estimate of k in terms of mass, D is expressed in roentgens, r, and the radiation used is a kind that distributes its ionization sparsely and randomly in volume. (For an estimate of the radiosensitive cross-sectional area of a target, D is expressed in the number of ionizing particles per square centimeter, and the radiation used for this type of analysis, which will be discussed in Section II,D,3, is of the densely ionizing type.)

Experimentally what is sought is the dose of radiation in roentgens that will, on the average, place one hit per target in question. Since ionizations occur at random, the process of inactivation of a large number of identical biological units follows a Poisson distribution law. Thus, the probability of hitting the target with one or more hits is $1 - e^{-1}$, or 0.63, and the probability of the target escaping a hit is e^{-1}, or 0.37. This dose is called the D_{37} dose. In the equation $N/N_0 = e^{-kD}$, k has the dimensions of grams per target and D, of roentgens, the number of hits per gram. It follows that $kD = 1$ and $N/N_0 = e^{-1}$ at a dose for which there is, on the average, one hit per target.

As already discussed, primary ionizations or ionization events following a passage of x- or γ-rays are spatially distributed along tracks that themselves are randomly distributed. Assuming that the spacing between ionization events is large compared to the target volume, the distribution of primary ionizations is also random in volume. To calculate the number of ionization events/gram of target material, we rely on two experimentally derived values: (1) the energy absorbed by a gram of tissue, 87 ergs/gm/r, and (2) the energy absorbed per ionization event in tissue (or solid simulating the atomic composition of soft tissue), which is estimated to be 60 ± 10 eV (Rauth and Simpson, 1964). Since the energy required to ionize an atom is 10–35 eV, this finding would indicate that each ionization event contains on the average two to six ionizations in a cluster.

These two values provide the number of ionization events per gram of nucleic acid absorbing 1 r of radiation. Thus,

$$\frac{\text{energy absorbed/gm/r}}{\text{energy in ergs/pi}} = \frac{87 \text{ ergs/gm/r}}{60 \text{ eV/pi} \times (1.6 \times 10^{-12} \text{ ergs/eV})}$$
$$= 9.1 \times 10^{11} \text{ pi/gm/r} \qquad (2)$$

The single-hit kinetics obtained with nucleic acids indicates that one primary ionization (pi) in a nucleic acid molecule inactivates it. Since a D_{37} dose will cause an average of 1 pi/molecule, the number of pi's at that dose will be equal to the total number of nucleic acid molecules. Using D_{37} in roentgens, we get $D_{37} \times 9.1 \times 10^{11}$ molecules/gm. Thus, the radio-sensitive molecular weight (MW) is calculated as follows:

$$\text{MW} = \frac{\text{Avogadro's no.(molecules/mole)}}{\text{no. of molecules/gm}}$$
$$= \frac{6.03 \times 10^{23}}{D_{37}(9.1 \times 10^{11})} \text{ gm/mole} \qquad (3)$$

a. Action Probability of a Hit. The foregoing calculation of target molecular weight started with an assumption that a single hit (defined as a primary ionization event) in the target leads to an observable biological effect. There is no *a priori* reason to assume, however, that the efficiency should be unity for converting the initial radiation lesion to a stable chemical lesion that ultimately scores as inactivation of an observed function. In recent years it has become clear that there are many compounds, particularly the sulfhydryls, that, when present in the medium during irradiation, protect against radiation damage even under conditions of direct action (Alexander and Charlesby, 1954; Ginoza and Norman, 1957; Eldjarn and Pihl, 1958; Hotz, 1966). The reaction involves the transfer of electrons and/or hydrogen atoms to the ionized target molecules, which then are restituted before stable chemical lesions form. Cysteine, cysteamine, and reduced glutathione are examples of these protective agents. The protective process is known as intermolecular energy transfer. The inactivation curve will remain exponential when such a reaction takes place, but its slope can decrease several-fold over a curve obtained in the absence of the reaction. Thus, the probability of producing a biological result from an initial ionization may be less than one.

b. Indirect Effects. The indirect effect of radiation is the damage done to the target by diffusible free radicals produced in the irradiated medium. These radicals are of two classes. The first of these are the radiolysis products of water, namely, H, OH, hydrated electrons, HO_2, and H_2O_2. Their effects on target sensitivity are noticeable when irradiation is done in dilute solution at temperatures above freezing, particularly in the absence of organic materials. The target calculation results in estimates far out of proportion to the actual dimensions. These radicals are capable of producing a variety of chemical lesions in nucleic acids and proteins. Aside from cleavage of phosphodiester bonds (Scholes *et al.*, 1960), the following nucleic acid conversions have been detected in solutions as a result of indirect action of x- and γ-rays: cytosine → uracil, cytosine → 5-hydroxycytosine, uracil → isobarbituric acid, thymine → 5-hydroxymethyluracil, and adenine → 8-hydroxyadenine. Undoubtedly, other unidentified products are formed. Examples of protein lesions are deamination, decarboxylation, and other covalent bond cleavage [see review by Weiss (1964)].

The second class of indirect effects that have come to our attention in recent years are those caused under conditions generally considered to give only direct effect (frozen or dry). For example, it has been shown that when viruses are irradiated frozen in the presence of phosphate ions, the calculated target size is found to be as much as 10 times the known dimension of the molecule. This potentiation of radiation action is due to some long-lived radiomimetic products of phosphate ions that are as yet unidentified (Ginoza, 1963). Their action is linearly dependent on the log of the concentration of phosphate ions, persists after irradiation, and is depressed by added nutrient broth. Commonplace inorganic ingredients, such as NaCl and sodium acetate, also have been found to potentiate radiosensitivity when present as the predominant molecular species. Chloroform, used occasionally for lysing infected cells, also has this effect (Cotton and Lockingen, 1963). Like the phosphate effect, its effect is neutralized, to some degree, by nutrient broth.

Until more work is done, it seems safer to assume that there is no clear boundary between direct and indirect action, nor between the classes of compounds that, by intermolecular energy transfer, do or do not protect against direct effects of radiation. At the present, two criteria are generally used to satisfy the conditions for direct action: (1) there is no further decrease in radiation sensitivity upon increasing addition of broth, and (2) samples are adequately dry during irradiation. Tryptone broth, nutrient broth, gelatin, concentrated bacterial lysates, and the like have been shown to be good protective agents against diffusible radicals; moreover, the target sensitivity for a given virus suspended in these media and irradiated frozen has been found to be the same, suggesting that they protect maximally and in the same way (Ginoza, 1963). Where virus samples are available in generous quantity, e.g., TMV, the virus itself provides self-protection against radicals, even if irradiated wet. Lea *et al.* (1944) found that the concentration of TMV at which this applies is 0.02 mg/ml or more. Scholes *et al.* (1960) showed that the damage to DNA irradiated in solution could be reduced by as much as 90% if it were in a complex with nucleoprotein. The work of Buzzell and Lauffer (1952) would indicate, however, that where the virus possesses a complex structure for injecting its nucleic acid into its host, freezing in addition to the broth at the usual concentration (1%) may be necessary. They observed that the irradiated survivors were more heat sensitive than the unirradiated control, whereas survivors from the 4% broth had the same heat sensitivity as the unirradiated control. This strongly suggests that residual indirect effect still prevails at the lower concentration of broth. Takebe (1964) in his radiation studies on P22 phage did, indeed, show that indirect effects of x-rays greatly affected the phage's ability to adsorb and, to a lesser extent, to inject DNA into its host. These functions were unaffected when 4% (w/v) nutrient broth was present in the medium during irradiation. Nor was any aftereffect observed when the irradiated virus was stored in the same medium at 4°C for several days.

c. *Anoxic Effect.* Targets irradiated in the presence of an atmosphere of air generally show greater sensitivity than in the absence of air. A current notion of the effect of oxygen in promoting radiation damage is as follows: radiation ejects an electron from a target molecule and gives rise to a site of an unpaired electron; e.g., the site may be a carbonium radical, $\equiv$C$\cdot$, which is highly reactive (Howard-Flanders and Alper, 1957). In the presence of air, an oxygen molecule can react with the ionized atom to yield a stable chemical lesion. In the absence of air, there is a chance that some restitution (energy transfer) may operate to restore the lost electron or a hydrogen atom. It might well be argued that oxygen is essential in target analysis insofar as it confirms a hit that otherwise may escape detection because of restitution.

However, it should be noted that "oxygen lesion" is not the only type of damage biomacromolecules suffer by direct action; anoxic conditions do not confer full protection, rather they show only that inactivation is less efficient than under aerobic conditions. Other kinds of chemical lesions must, therefore, be induced. The work of Gordy et al. (1965) using electron-spin resonance technique on γ-irradiated dry thymidine crystals shows that H atoms add to the 6-carbon of this heterocyclic base. This creates an unpaired electron on the 5-carbon. If this reaction took place in a nucleic acid molecule, it could lead to a point mutation or lethality. Undoubtedly more work like this in the dry state combined with radiation chemistry will help to clarify problems in radiobiology. For the present, one can only infer, from numerous radiation studies of protein and nucleic acid conducted at very high radiation doses and under conditions of indirect action, that chemical lesions formed are heterogeneous.

d. *Host-Cell Reactivation.* The question of the possible repair of radiation lesions occurring in viral nucleic acid by a repair mechanism of the host bacteria has arisen in recent years. It has been shown in a series of studies that UV-induced chemical lesions in the DNA, identified as thymine dimers, are excised by the cell nucleases, and the deposed chain is replaced by a new polynucleotide chain segment. Moreover, T4 phage is known to possess v-gene that specifies a repair mechanism for UV damage. While convincing evidence for the detailed mechanisms of excision resynthesis has accumulated for UV-irradiated bacteria, similar restitution mechanisms for viruses subjected to ionizing irradation have yet to be uncovered* (Latarjet, 1964; Winkler, 1964; Sauerbier, 1962). In view of this question, it seems advisable to check the slopes of the x-ray dose–effect curves using the widest permissible range of host cells, for it is possible that host-cell repair enzymes may yet be discovered that will act on the x-ray–irradiated viruses.

We have discussed several factors that can influence the value of k, the target sensitivity. It can be seen that radiation target size, M, can be $M/10$, M, or 10 M, depending on the conditions of the experiment. With a reasonable consideration of the factors discussed, perhaps the uncertainties can be reduced to a much narrower range. It is the purpose of the following section to examine these factors experimentally using three simple viruses and their free nucleic acids whose molecular dimensions are well established.

3. Application of Target Theory for Determining Radiosensitive Molecular Weight of Viruses

a. *Single-Stranded Nucleic Acid Viruses and Their Free Nucleic Acids.* Comparative radiation target analyses on three viruses, TMV and coliphages R17 and ϕX174, and their free nucleic acids were performed in the author's laboratory to test the general validity of the simple target theory and to examine factors that can lead to results contradicting its validity. These factors, largely unknown at the time Lea's monograph (1962) appeared, are (1) the modifying effects of chemical substances present in the virus suspension ·during irradiation, (2) the effect of temperature (Setlow, 1952), (3) the effect of the protein capsid on the radiation sensitivity of the nucleic acid, (4) the reliability of the estimate of the radiation energy absorbed in biological materials (87 ergs/gm/r) and the average energy associated with the absorption event, called a primary ionization, and (5) the efficiency of biological inactivation per primary ionization. The method described here is not a standard technique, but one that the author has found useful in his laboratory. In the detailed procedures to be given below, it will be obvious that any number of useful modifications can be made.

(i) *Physicochemical properties of the viruses examined.* TMV is an RNA virus whose rod-shaped structure measures 150 × 3000 Å and with a particle weight of 40 × 10^6 daltons. Its single-stranded RNA helix extends the length of the rod in a tight structural conformity with its

---

* Fluke and Beinecke (1967) reported evidence of appreciable repair of γ-irradiated T1 phage.

protein capsid, which, in turn, is made up of 2200 identical subunits helically arranged along its longitudinal axis. The RNA portion is 5% of the total mass, or 2×10^6 daltons. This virus has been the subject of numerous radiation studies, particularly target analyses (Gowen, 1940; Lea et al., 1944; Pollard and Dimond, 1956; Buzzell et al., 1956; Ginoza and Norman, 1957; Ginoza, 1963). Most of these studies have involved the use of sparsely ionizing radiation for radiosensitive molecular weight determination, while Pollard and Dimond (1956) and Whitmore and Pollard (1955) used a combination of radiation sources, including densely ionizing radiations, for determining the shape and position of the sensitive target in the virus.

The second virus, R17, is a spherically shaped coliphage (Paranchych and Graham, 1962) whose diameter is about 200 Å and whose particle weight is 3.6×10^6, 31% of which is RNA. Centrifugal analyses indicate that the molecular weight of the RNA is 0.8–1.1×10^6 (Mitra et al., 1963; Gesteland and Boedtker, 1964).

The third virus, ϕX174, is also a spherical coliphage discovered by Sertic and Bulgakov (1935). It bears a single-stranded DNA that has a molecular weight of 1.7×10^6 daltons (Sinsheimer, 1959). The diameter of the virus particle is 300 Å, and its particle weight is 6×10^6 daltons. This virus has also been the subject of target studies (Ginoza, 1963).

(ii) Preparation of samples for irradiation. Bacterial lysates containing about 10^{10} plaque-forming units of ϕX174 and of R17 are diluted 100-fold or more in 1% tryptone broth. This simple step insures uniformity of one of the radiation conditions, namely, the suspending medium. In effect, it dilutes out agents possibly present in the crude extract that cause indirect action and, also, it renders purification of the virus unnecessary. Nucleic acids purified by phenol extraction procedure are suspended in the same medium for irradiation. TMV is purified by several cycles of alternate high–low speed centrifugation in pH 7.0 phosphate buffer, then dialyzed against several changes of distilled water. Samples are then irradiated frozen at a virus concentration of 1–10 mg/ml. It is reported by Lea et al. (1944) that at these concentrations indirect effect is eliminated. Samples of TMV RNA, 0.1 ml, suspended in 10^{-4} M sodium acetate buffer at pH 6 and a concentration of 1 mg/ml are irradiated either frozen or after they are vacuum-dried to a thin film, either on polyethylene or paraffin planchets.

(iii) Procedure for irradiation experiments. A 50 kV Picker x-ray machine fitted with a beryllium window was operated at maximum voltage and with a current of 7 mA. The source was calibrated by Fricke dosimetry (Section II,C,1). Samples of virus or nucleic acid (0.05 ml) suspended in 1% tryptone broth (0.05 ml or less) are placed on polyethylene planchets of 10-mm diameter and 3-mm thickness and placed on the floor of an aluminum chamber. The top of the chamber is covered with a thin mylar film. To the bottom of the chamber is attached an aluminum rod, the size of which is adequate to serve as a thermal conductor. The rod portion of the irradiation chamber is immersed in Dry Ice bath or liquid nitrogen. Control samples are also placed within the chamber but shielded from the direct beam with a 3-mm-thick lead foil, principally as a check for scattered x-rays. A series of experiments has indicated that there is no measurable dependence of radiation sensitivity on the dose rate nor on the length of time the irradiated samples are stored (frozen) before assaying the surviving virus activity.

For irradiation with γ-rays (^{60}Co source), a relatively greater volume of samples (a few milliliters) can be used because of the greater penetrability of γ-rays. Calibration of the source is performed by placing dosimetry (Fricke) samples in the same type of test tube and container as those used for virus irradiation and in the same position within the irradiation chamber of the γ-ray source. Generally the tubes are arranged in cylindrical array, since the ^{60}Co rods in the source are so arranged. While tryptone broth and nutrient broth are known to reduce indirect action of diffusible radicals, for these radiations the samples are frozen in crushed Dry Ice for irradiation as additional precaution against indirect effects and temperature effect (Section II,D,2,b) (Setlow, 1952). Dry irradiation can also be performed at ambient temperature, although that temperature should be kept below 30°C. Because of the high density of ionizations in the tail of β-ray tracks, thus of the possible overlap of ionizations within a target, the use of [60]Co γ-rays is preferred over x-rays where the target is large (see Fig. 9, Chapter III, Lea, 1962).

The results of the irradiation experiments on the three viruses mentioned above and their nucleic acids are illustrated by φX174 and φX174 DNA and are summarized in Fig. 1. The effects of added modifying agents, glutathione and phosphate buffer, on the radiation sensitivity of viruses are illustrated in Fig. 2. The results obtained by the author (Ginoza, 1963) using the procedure outlined may be summarized as follows:

1. The survival curves for TMV, φX174, and R17 and their free nucleic acids are all exponential to the limit of the dose given, indicating

that the virus preparations are homogeneous with respect to radiation sensitivity and that inactivation does not require cumulative damage.

2. The slopes show no dependence on the dose rate.

3. Frozen samples ($-180°$ and $-60°C$) show the same radiation sensitivity as the dried samples irradiated at $30°-40°C$.

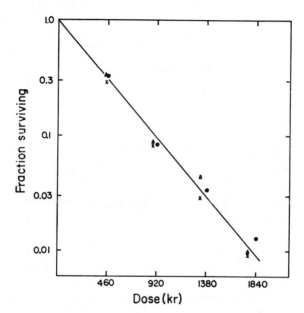

FIG. 1. X-ray inactivation curve of ϕX174 suspended in 1% tryptone broth (Difco). Bacterial lysate in broth containing 1×10^{10} plaque forming units (pfu)/ml of the virus was serially diluted in tryptone broth to 1×10^8 pfu/ml. Samples (0.5 ml) of the final dilution were either frozen or dried on plastic discs for the irradiation. X = irradiated dry at $25°-30°C$ (average of seven experiments); $\blacktriangle$ = irradiated frozen at $-60°C$ (average of three experiments); $\bullet$ = irradiated frozen at $-180°C$ (average of three experiments). A 50 kV Picker beryllium window x-ray machine was operated at maximum voltage with a current of 7 mA; dose rate, 23–24 kr/minute. (Ginoza, 1963; reproduced by permission from *Nature*.)

4. D_{37} doses for TMV, ϕX174, and R17 are 3.0×10^5 r, 3.8×10^5 r, and $7.5 \pm 1.0 \times 10^5$ r, respectively. The target molecular weights calculated from these figures are the same as the physical molecular weights of the nucleic acids of the corresponding viruses.

5. The free nucleic acids show the same radiation sensitivity as the parent viruses.

6. ^{60}Co γ-ray and 50 keV x-rays inactivate with the same efficiency per unit dose (r).

7. Radiation hits on the capsid or the presence of the capsid do not affect the sensitivity of the nucleic acids it encapsulates.

8. Sulfhydryl compounds (e.g., glutathione) and phosphate ions modify direct action of radiation (Fig. 2).

It is concluded from these observations that the radiosensitive target of the virus is its nucleic acid and that a single primary ionization event occurring anywhere on this target destroys the capacity of the nucleic acid for viral replication. The agreement between the target

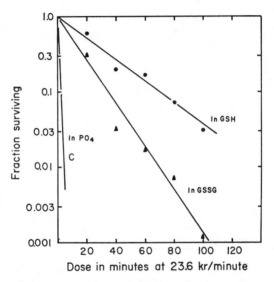

FIG. 2. The effect of 1% reduced glutathione (GSH), 1% oxidized glutathine (GSSG), and 0.1 M sodium phosphate buffer pH (curve C) on the sensitivity of ϕX174 to x-irradiation. GSH and GSSG solutions were prepared in water and the pH adjusted to 6.8 with NaOH. The virus preparations in this case were irradiated dry at 25°C–30°C. (Ginoza, 1963; reproduced by permission from *Nature*.)

molecular weight and the physical molecular weight is surprisingly good and shows that the independently derived figure of 60 eV (Rauth and Hutchinson, 1962; Rauth and Simpson, 1964) is the average energy of the primary ionization associated with lethality and that this energy kills with an efficiency of 1. The results also indicate that primary ionizations produced by both γ-rays and x-rays are distributed at random in volume and far enough apart to deposit no more than one ionization per virus or nucleic acid molecule. Finally, it seems clear that the validity of the target theory calculation can be upheld, at least for the three single-stranded nucleic acid viruses described above, and also for several other viruses of this class analyzed by Lea and Smith (1942).

In Table I are shown target molecular weights of single-stranded nucleic acid viruses studied in other laboratories, together with those obtained by the author (Ginoza, 1963). The D_{37} values given by others were used to calculate the radiosensitive molecular weight according to the procedure given in Section II,D,2. The ratio of the radiosensitive molecular weight to the physical molecular weight is not 1 in all cases; the disagreement may owe either to the radiation technique employed or to the uncertain values of the nucleic acid content of the viruses. For example, the reported D_{37} values for Rous sarcoma virus differ by a factor of 4, and the reported estimate of the physical molecular weight of its nucleic acid also varies by a factor of 4. In other cases, it is not certain whether or not the virus samples were irradiated under conditions known to give maximum protection against indirect effects. It is of interest to point out that radiosensitive molecular weight calculated according to the method given above from the D_{37} of viruses reported by Lea and Smith 25 years ago agrees very well with the more recently calculated physical molecular weight of these viruses.

b. Radiation Target Analysis of Double-Stranded DNA Virus. The simple target theory that is seen to apply reasonably well to small single-stranded nucleic acid viruses has not yet clearly resolved the simple questions it was originally designed to answer for all viruses, notably the viruses possessing double-stranded DNA. This question will now be discussed at length, since it is important to know the general validity of the simple target theory. It was observed by Lea that the target size did not increase in direct proportion to the increase in size of the virus. This point is made clear from noting the ratios, *b/a*, for the double-stranded DNA viruses in Table I. From the work of Watson (1950), Pollard and Forro (1951), and Fluke and Pollard (1955), it became clear that T phages are not inactivated by a single ionization occurring in the sensitive target volume. Surviving phage was shown to have partial damage, and inactivated phage was shown to have partial function. Sublethal hits appeared to be cumulative in effect but could not add up to complete inactivation. Nevertheless, the survival curves were observed to be single hit. About 40 primary ionization events, on the average, occur in the T1 phage for each lethal event. Hershey *et al.* (1951) and Stent and Fuerst (1955) also observed that each disintegration event of ^{32}P atoms incorporated into the genome of T-even phages has a probability of about 0.1 of inactivating them; here, also, their survival curves are single hit, whereas, for small single-stranded

TABLE I

Radiosensitive Molecular Weight of Single- and Double-Stranded Nucleic Acid Viruses

Type of virus	Nucleic acid content (a, daltons)	Radiosensitive molecular weight* (b)	D_{37} (kr)	b/a
Single-stranded RNA viruses				
Tobacco mosaic	2.2×10^6 (Ginoza and Norman, 1957)	2.2×10^6	300 (Ginoza and Norman, 1957)	1
Tobacco mosaic RNA	2.2×10^6 (Ginoza and Norman, 1957)	2.2×10^6	300 (Ginoza and Norman, 1957)	1
R17 coliphage	$0.7-1.1 \times 10^6$ (Mitra et al., 1963)	$0.8-1.0 \times 10^6$	750 ± 100 (Ginoza, 1963)	1
Bushy stunt	1.5×10^6 (Schachman and Williams, 1959)	1.3×10^6	450 (Lea and Smith, 1942)	1
Tobacco ringspot	1.5×10^6 (Schuster, 1960)	1.3×10^6	460 (Lea and Smith, 1942)	1
Tobacco necrosis	1.5×10^6 (Schuster, 1960)	1.0×10^6	670 (Lea and Smith, 1942)	0.7
Rous sarcoma	10×10^6 (L. V. Crawford and Crawford, 1961)	3.3×10^6	200 (Latarjet, 1964)	0.3
Rous sarcoma	33×10^6 (Schuster, 1960)	14.6×10^6	45 (Bryan et al., 1950)	1.5
Newcastle disease	7.5×10^6 (Duesberg and Robinson, 1965)	13×10^6	50	0.4
Newcastle disease		13×10^6	50	2.0
Single-stranded DNA viruses				
φX174	1.7×10^6 (Sinsheimer, 1959)	1.7×10^6 (± 0.2)	380 (Ginoza, 1963)	1
φX174 DNA	1.7×10^6 (Sinsheimer, 1959)	1.7×10^6	380 (Ginoza, 1963)	1
S13	1.7×10^6 (Tessman et al., 1957)	1.7×10^6	390 (Wollman and Lacassagne, 1940)	1
Double-stranded DNA viruses				
RF DNA of φX174	3.4×10^6	0.85×10^6	780 (Ginoza and Miller, 1965)	0.25
Polyoma	3.0×10^6 (Weil and Vinograd, 1963)	1.32×10^6	500 (Basilico and Di Mayorca, 1965)	0.44
T1	42×10^6 (Sinsheimer, 1960)	1.2×10^6	570 (Fluke, 1966)	0.03
T1		1.2×10^6	550 (Schambra and Hutchinson, 1964)	0.03
T2	130×10^6 (Hershey et al., 1962)	12×10^6	55 (Hotz and Müller, 1961)	0.09

T2	130×10^6 (Hershey et al., 1962)	6.5×10^6	100 (Ginoza and Vessey, 1966)	0.05
T4	130×10^6 (Rubinstein et al., 1961)	6.5×10^6	100 (Ginoza and Vessey, 1966)	0.05
T7	42×10^6 (Luman and Sinsheimer, 1956)	4.3×10^6	150 (Hotz and Müller, 1961)	0.1
Phage λ	31×10^6 (Burgi and Hershey, 1963)	1.7×10^6	380 (Ginoza and Vessey, 1966)	0.06
Phage 22	39×10^6 (Sinsheimer, 1960)	4.6×10^6	140 (Garen and Zinder, 1955)	0.12
Phage BM	25×10^6 (Aurisicchio et al., 1959)	2.1×10^6	210 (Castagnoli et al., 1959)	0.12
Adenovirus type V	66×10^6 (Allison and Burke, 1962)	8.5×10^6	77	0.13
Shope papilloma	14×10^6 (Watson and Littlefield, 1960)	1.4×10^6	480 (Syverton et al., 1941)	0.10
Vaccinia virus	156×10^6 (Allison and Burke, 1962)	9.5×10^6	80 (Lea and Salaman, 1942)	0.06

* Radiosensitive molecular weight calculated by the method given in Section II,D,2.

nucleic acid viruses, the efficiency per disintegration is 1 (Tessman *et al.*, 1957). The questions that are immediately evoked from these observations are, what is the basis for the resistance shown by these viruses and what is the single critical physicochemical event that inactivates?

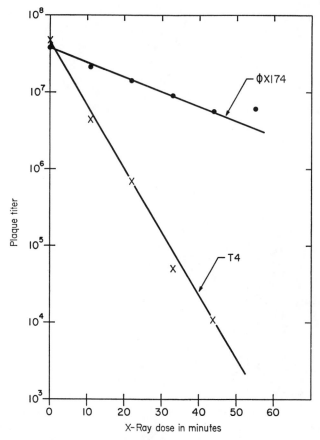

Fig. 3. Survival curves of bacteriophages T4 and øX174 mixed in 1% tryptone broth and co-irradiated at −60°C by x-rays. Assays for plaque-forming ability were conducted separately on their respective host bacteria at low multiplicities of infection.

The problem raised by these viruses may be illustrated by the following experiment summarized in Fig. 3. Two viruses, ϕX174, a single-stranded DNA virus described in Section II,D,3,a, and T4 phage, were co-irradiated with x-rays in a mixed suspension at −60°C. The assay for survival of plaque-forming ability was conducted by plating irradiated aliquots on their respective host bacteria at low multiplicity of infection. Radiation conditions are, therefore, identical, and ϕX174, for which the D_{37} and target size is known, serves as an internal calibration for the dose delivered. The survival curves show that the slope is 3.8 times that of ϕX174. From the D_{37} for T4, a target molecular weight of 6.5×10^6 daltons is obtained. This is one-twentieth the physical molecular weight of the DNA of this virus (Rubinstein et al., 1961).

Three hypotheses can be offered to explain the apparent low efficiency of inactivation: (1) only double-strand scission or simultaneous base-pair damage can kill, and the efficiency for either of these possibilities is one-twentieth; (2) a critical target within a phage genome with a molecular weight of 6.5×10^6 must be hit to inactivate, and hits elsewhere in the genome are innocuous; and (3) the host cell can repair the x-ray lesions occurring in double-stranded DNA but not those occurring in single-stranded DNA, which is found to be the case for UV-damaged DNA (Jansz et al., 1963).

The first explanation has already received long and serious deliberation by Stent and his colleagues (Stent and Fuerst, 1955). The argument to follow is not altered in principle, even though their experiments were based on decay of incorporated ^{32}P atoms. To explain the low efficiency of killing per ^{32}P decay, Stent originally suggested that single-strand scission of the polynucleotide chain, which is virtually certain to occur after each decay, is of no consequence to virus survival, for the integrity of the Watson-Crick double helices can be maintained as long as the breaks are not coincident or nearly coincident. Once in 10 decay events, a double scission is thought to occur to sever the helices, and inactivation results. However, more recently Harriman and Stent (1964) reported their new finding that double-strand breaks in T4 phage do not account for the entire efficiency of inactivation. They now propose that there are two types of ^{32}P decays that are lethal: long-range hits, presumed to be double-strand scissions, which cause functional inactivation of the entire T4 genome, and those short-range hits, which are thought to cause localized damage in the messenger readout strand destroying cistronic functions only. The short-range hits in the opposite, nonreadout strand are believed to be innocuous as their lesions would be repaired in the course of DNA replication.

Freifelder (1965) attempted to determine the cause of x-ray lethality to T7 phage by centrifugal analysis of DNA extracted from the phage irradiated in phosphate buffer solution (see Section II,D,2,b). He concluded that only double-strand scissions are lethal while the more frequent single-strand breaks are of no biological consequence, presumably because they are repaired by host-cell reactivation. It is difficult to interpret his data by formal target theory analysis because of the large contribution of indirect effects prevailing under his conditions of irradiation. Moreover, it is difficult to assess the extent of loss of infectivity due to injection-damage alone, which is very likely when phage is irradiated wet in unprotected medium. Still another uncertainty is the effect of postirradiation manipulation on shear-sensitive DNA, which is made even more sensitive to shear degradation after accruing single-strand scissions (Studier, 1964; Hagen, 1967). In a separate experiment Freifelder shows that phage irradiated wet in moderately protective medium are inactivated more frequently by lesions which are less drastic than double-strand scissions. He did not make clear the relevance of this observation to his main conclusion.

As another test of the double-strand scission hypothesis, RF DNA of ϕX174 has been used as a working model (Taylor and Ginoza, 1967). This small (3.4×10^6 daltons), shear-insensitive, infectious DNA (see Section III,B,2) sustains, on the average, three nonlethal x-ray hits for each lethal hit. The killing efficiency per primary ionization event is 0.25 compared to 0.05 for the T4 phage (Ginoza and Miller, 1965). This fivefold disparity in values is difficult to rationalize, as we would expect that ionizing radiations should cause double-strand scissions without distinction in all DNA with the same efficiency. On this argument, a series of experiments was carried out in which RF DNA was irradiated with ^{60}Co γ-rays under conditions of direct action effects and the rates of single- and double-strand breaks, measured by analytical and sucrose gradient centrifugation, were compared with the rate of loss of infectivity. Results showed that the frequency of single-strand breaks was over fifty times greater than that of double-strand breaks. With the observed killing efficiency per hit event of 0.25, it was concluded that double-strand scission must be a very minor cause of the destruction of infectivity of this DNA.

This conclusion leads us to consider the second hypothesis stated above, namely, that lethality is caused by a hit in some critical segment of the phage genome, hits elsewhere being innocuous. With regard to this hypothesis two immediate questions arise: What is the nature of the critical target? How do irradiated survivors overcome sublethal hits? A series of UV-inactivation experiments performed by Benzer (1952), Symonds and McCloy (1958), Barricelli (1956), Epstein (1958), and Krieg (1959) on T-even phages suggests that the hypothetical target could be a single-stranded segment of the phage genome specifying the expression of the "early" phenotypic functions required in the initiation of vegetative development of the phage in the host cell. For example, the T4 phage has genetic information specifying about 13 early enzymes for the replication of its own DNA (Kornberg et al., 1959). One strand of the dual helix is transcribed for these functions. Conceivably, a single radiation hit scored within this critical DNA segment could cripple the entire machinery for the single function, DNA synthesis. Hits outside of this target area are, we shall assume for the moment, somehow erased in the course of DNA replication. This notion has direct relevance to the ideas that arise from the classical Luria–Latarjet experiment performed by Benzer (1952). In this experiment, one observes a steadily increasing radiation resistance of the ability of the intracellular phage to complete its infectious cycle, as tested by irradiating virus-host complexes at various times after infection. From this observation, Benzer postulated that T2 phage after invading the cell undergoes a series of successive steps, $A \rightarrow B \rightarrow C \rightarrow D \rightarrow E \rightarrow$ etc, in the course of its replication. Each of these steps, presumed to be some enzyme function, was viewed as having a certain target size. A radiochemical lesion induced in the DNA segment specifying any one of these functions prior to its expression stops the infectious cycle. Thus, the phage-killing target size of T2 just after infection, which is observed to be the same as that for the free phage, is the sum of the sizes of these individual targets. As shown in Table I, the target size for lethality of T2, like its genetically related T4, is 6.5×10^6 daltons or a sequence of about 2×10^4 nucleotides. The target sensitivity of the infectious center remains a single target throughout the early latent period, as indicated by the exponential inactivation kinetics. It continues to decrease steadily until about 9 minutes after infection, at which time the infectious center attains its maximum radiation resistance. This is to be expected of a critical target "shrinking" in size as the individual early functions are expressed successively until, finally, the critical target becomes as insensitive to radiation as are other noncritical targets of the phage genome.

The second question that necessarily follows under the critical target hypothesis, again using T4 phage as a model system, is the manner in which sublethally damaged phage reproduce normal viable progeny particles in a singly infected cell. As implied in Fig. 3, sublethal hits do not affect the all-or-none character of the inactivation kinetics. Nevertheless, their cumulative effects have been demonstrated in T1 phage (Fluke and Pollard, 1955), in T4 (Benzer, 1952), and in RF DNA of ϕX174 (Ginoza and Miller, 1965). Examples of these effects are, as shown in Fig. 4, dose-dependent decrease in the burst size (average number of viable progeny produced per infected cell) and

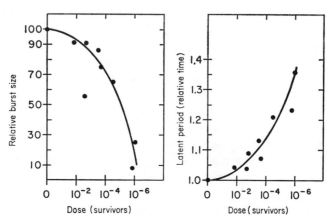

FIG. 4. The dependence of burst size and latent period of T4 phage on x-ray dose.

increase in the latent period of the infectious cycle, a reasonable expectation of a virus population destined to survive but bearing different degrees of injury which they must overcome during replication. This question of restitution, though a difficult one, is no more formidable than that posed by the well known phenomenon of multiplicity reactivation, whereby two or more differently inactivated phage particles invading the same cell can produce viable progeny through complementation of cistronic functions or through material exchange of undamaged DNA parts through recombination. From this, one might propose that sublethally damaged phages in a single infection situation can restitute at least one complete lesion-free phage genome, through rounds of incestuous recombination among the replica DNA's it can synthesize, to perpetuate the infectious cycle. A crude model presented in Fig. 5 illustrates a possible mechanism of screening out sublethal lesions. This picture of incestuous recombination is not in conflict with the known facts of T4 replication, namely, that parental DNA is normally found dispersed among progeny particles in single-stranded segments measuring 5–10×10^6 daltons (Kozinski, 1961; Roller, 1961). The process visualized is similar to exchange of homologous genetic segments between donor and recipient DNA in bacterial transformation by a breakage–reunion process (Fox, 1965).

Finally, we come to the third hypothesis to explain the resistance of T4 to ionizing radiation, namely, that the host cell can repair radiation lesions occurring in double-stranded DNA. This idea suggests itself from the recent work of Setlow and Carrier (1964) and of Boyce and Howard-Flanders (1964). These workers demonstrated that UV light-

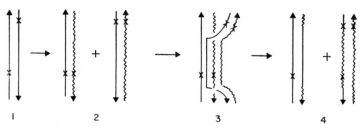

Fig. 5. A hypothetical model of a mechanism employed by T4 phage in restoring lesion-free replicas from sublethally damaged DNA: X = radiation lesion; ~~~~~~ = new polynucleotide chain. Breakage and reunion of replicated DNA strands result in the insertion of lesion-free segments into some of the newly synthesized DNA strands in the vegetative pool. The cycle is repeated in the course of DNA replication, during which those strands containing restituted DNA segments are expected to have some selective survival advantage over those possessing radiochemical lesions.

induced thymine dimers in bacterial DNA are excised by the cell's enzymes, and the deposed chain is resynthesized using the intact complementary chain as its template. The repair process is called "host-cell reactivation" and is a genetic trait possessed by some strains of bacteria and absent in others. According to Sauerbier (1962) and Latarjet (1964), a similar repair has yet to be demonstrated for x-irradiated phages infecting cells that are known to have the repair capability for its own UV-treated DNA. Ginoza and Vessey (1966) showed that the x-ray survival curves of T4 assayed on *E. coli* strains B, K-12, B/r, B_{s-1}, and a thymine-minus strain in enriched or in minimal media are indistinguishable. This supports the suggestion that the killing efficiency is a measure of the intrinsic sensitivity of the T4 phage to ionizing radiations. The strain B/r is known to have a relatively greater resistance to both x-rays and UV than other B strains of *E. coli*, and B_{s-1} has no capacity for dark repair of UV-induced lesions. The fact that T4 DNA contains odd bases, hydroxymethylcytosine, which in turn are glucosylated, may in part explain the apparent nonrepair of this DNA by hosts capable of repair. Weiss and Richardson (1967) reported finding a T4-specified enzyme, polynucleotide ligase, that catalyzes the covalent joining of two segments of interrupted strand present naturally in the DNA duplex of T7 phage. Although not tested on free T4 phage DNA, this enzyme conceivably could be employed by the system for covalently joining interrupted strands following their fragmentary semiconservative replication. Gellert (1967) has also reported finding an *E. coli* enzyme that converts hydrogen-bonded circles of λ phage DNA to covalent circles. However, Hradečná (1967) has found that x-irradiated, unlike UV-irradiated, λ phage is not measurably host-cell reactivated. On the other hand, Fluke and Beineke (1967) reported that x-irradiated T1 phage has a survival slope that is 30% greater when assayed on *E. coli* strain B_{s-1} than when assayed on strain B. This latter demonstration of possible repair does not necessarily invalidate the critical target hypothesis discussed above, but a rigorous test of the hypothesis would require using a virus-host system in which host-cell reactivation can be proven to be absent. It is important to point out that (1) radiation-induced single-strand scissions, which are demonstrable by centrifugal analysis, arise very frequently as a direct consequence of damaged sugar and nucleic acid bases (Weiss, 1964) and (2) base destruction alone can inactivate viruses. Thus, any conjecture about repair must take into consideration both the need to replace the bases and sugar moiety and to seal covalently the phosphodiester bonds. For example, how can hydroxymethylcytosine be replaced in the T4 early enzyme target unless first the target has been transcribed for hydroxymethylase enzyme?

Besides direct damage to the DNA, radiochemical alterations in the protein structures required for host attachment and for injecting DNA into the host cell may be responsible for part of the inactivation by ionizing radiations of some viruses, e.g., the T-phages (Watson, 1952; Stahl, 1959; and Takebe, 1964), particularly when viruses are irradiated wet in medium containing insufficient broth for protection against diffusible free radicals (see Section D,2,b). However, under irradiation conditions where only or mainly direct effects prevail, the target sensitivities for attachment and injection are observed to be small relative to virus survival (plaque-forming ability or infectivity), as indicated in Fig. 10; also it has generally been observed that the target sensitivity of free T-phages is the same as that for the survival of the infectious centers soon after infection, showing that the processes for transferring DNA from the virus to the host have small or virtually no target size (Luria–Latarjet experiment). Another test indicative of injection failure would be the measure of efficiency of marker transfer in the conventional cross-reactivation and functional rescue experiments.

In summary, we have in this section analyzed selected experimental data mainly in an attempt to deduce what might be the minimum damage that is necessary to inactivate the reproductive capacity of double-stranded DNA viruses by the direct action of ionizing radiations. The evidence that the DNA is the radiosensitive target of these viruses and that a single direct hit in it can, but need not, inactivate this capacity rests on fairly safe grounds. However, there remain two conflicting views as to what the lethal single-hit event is: the first is that only the ionization event causing a double-strand scission in the genome is effective, and the other view rests on the argument that the double-stranded viral genome consists of critical and non-critical targets, the lethal event being one which causes a radiochemical lesion anywhere within a critical single-strand DNA segment that specifies early enzyme functions concerned with initiating vegetative development of virus particles. In what manner these viruses overcome sublethal radiation lesions and how much of this restitution or recovery is due to repair by the host cells are important corollary questions raised by the same experimental data we have considered above. Resolution of these questions would be helpful toward clarifying the essential features of the still unclear classical Luria–Latarjet experiments, of multiplicity reactivation, and even perhaps of the mechanism of phage replication itself.

   c. *Target Theory for Determination of Size and Shape of Viruses.* Lea and Salaman (1942), in their radiation analysis of staphylococcus phage K and vaccinia virus, speculated that these large double-stranded DNA viruses must have a radiosensitive internal structure and an insensitive outer coat to account for the marked deviation of target theory values from the known dimensions of these viruses. This speculation led to the development of a technique using radiations of different linear energy transfer (Lea, 1962); Pollard, 1953a). The technique is analytically powerful and adds a second dimension to radiation target analysis.

   We first consider a virus being hit by a heavy ion particle whose track is so densely ionizing that a single passage has a probability of causing an ionization within the virus and inactivating it. The tracks, and thus the hits, are random in area. Thus, the cross-sectional area, S, can be obtained by the following treatment. The probability of the target area being hit is

$$P_{(x)} = \frac{e^{-SD}(SD)^x}{x!} \tag{4}$$

where $S =$ cm²/ionizing particle, $D =$ ionizing particles/cm², and $x =$ the number of passages of particles. The probability of zero hits, $P_{(0)} = e^{-SD}$, i.e., the fraction surviving a dose, D, is $N/N_0 = e^{-SD}$.

   Before S can be accepted as a reasonable value, we need to know (1) the certainty that each passage of particles has a probability of 1

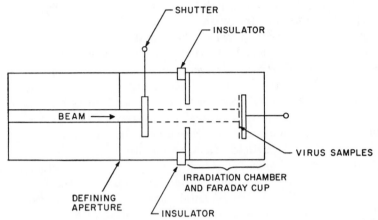

FIG. 6. Schematic diagram of a cyclotron bombardment chamber in which dry viruses are irradiated under vacuum. (Courtesy of Dr. E. C. Pollard.)

of inactivating and (2) the diameter of the swath of ionizations penetrating perpendicular to the projected target cross section. The first problem is solved in the following way: virus samples are spread in very thin layers on 0.5-inch diameter glass cover slips, dried under vacuum in a desiccator using a liquid nitrogen trap, and irradiated by a beam of charged particles of a given energy, E, in a cyclotron or other particle accelerator, under vacuum as shown diagrammatically in Fig. 6. A second, third, $\cdots$, n series of samples are also bombarded at increasing LET, where $\mathrm{LET} = f(Z,v)$. $Z =$ charge of ionizing particles and $v = f(E)$. Because of the poor penetration of charged particles, the virus must be irradiated as a thin film. Survival curves for varying E's of the beam are made, from which the cross section S (apparent) is estimated using the relationship $N/N_0 = e^{-SD}$, where S (apparent) $= 1/D_{37}$ for a given E. Dose is expressed as the number of charged particles/cm². By knowing the beam area and the total charge measured in the Faraday cup per unit time, one can calculate the number of charged particles impinging per unit area. The beam energy is determined from the range–energy curve by placing aluminum foils of different known thicknesses in the path of the beam. Details are given by Pollard (1953a). From the known energy, E, the charge of the particle, and the stopping power of the sample, the LET is calculated from the Bethe-Bloch equation:

$$-\frac{dE}{dx} = \frac{4\pi e^4 z^2 N}{mv^2} \ (B) \qquad\qquad (5)$$

where $B = Z[\ln(2mv^2/I_0) - \ln(1 - \beta^2) - \beta^2]$, $e =$ the electronic charge in esu, $z =$ the charge multiplicity of the fast particle, $N =$ the number of atoms per cubic centimeter of the materials traversed, $m =$ the mass of the electron in grams, $\beta = v/c$, where c is the velocity of light, $I_0 =$ the average ionization or excitation potential of the atom and is determined by experiment, and $Z =$ the number of electrons per atom. Next a plot of S (apparent) versus LET is made as in Fig. 7. It can be seen that as the LET is increased, the S (apparent) approaches S_0, the true cross-sectional area, indicating that the probability that each particle traversing the sensitive cross section will inactivate is approaching unity. Since, from the exponential survival curve, we can assume that one ionization event is sufficient to inactivate, further ionizations along the

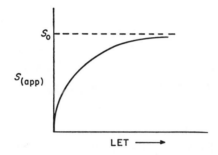

Fig 7. The relationship between cross-sectional area of a target and linear energy transfer.

track within a target volume are considered superfluous; hence, the plateau of effectiveness is reached after some LET value is reached.

The second question, the diameter of the cylindrical ionization track, is complicated by the fact that when any charged heavy particle traverses a material, δ-rays radiate out from the track, causing further molecular damage. An idea of the diameter of the ionization core, independent of δ-rays caused by deuterons, is presented in Fig. 8. Although the cylindrical track containing the main body of ionizations and excitation energy is confined to a small volume with a diameter of a few angstrom units, as shown in the diagram, δ-rays pass outside of this volume, causing further ionization along their tracks. This gives rise to an overestimate of the true cross-sectional area. Corrections for the δ-rays, therefore, must be made. Another complication to consider is that the path length of the δ-rays varies with the energy of the ionizing particles. For example, α-particles are known to produce more δ-rays than deuterons of equal energy loss (Hutchinson and Pollard,

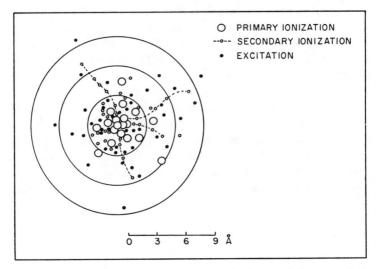

Fig. 8. The distribution of ionizations and excitations radially around the path of a deuteron. Note that the majority of energy releases are within 3 Å of the deuteron path (Pollard, 1953b).

1961). Once S_0 is obtained, corrections for the δ-ray contribution to the inactivation must be made. These may be performed by following the illustrations provided by Pollard and Barrett (1959) for deuterons and α-particles of different energies. One can estimate the radiation-sensitive volume using sparsely ionizing radiation, x- and γ-rays (see Section II,D,3). The experimental samples are irradiated in air while dry or frozen. Here the inactivation process may be described by:

$$N/N_0 = e^{-VD} \qquad (6)$$

where $V =$ the sensitive volume $= 1/D_{37}$ and D = the number of pi per unit volume. One roentgen $= 9 \times 10^{11}$ pi/cm³. The quantity V is independent of the target shape. With the estimates of S_0 and V made, the shape of the target consistent with the two values can now be deduced.

Qualitatively it can be stated that the chance of hitting long, thin targets, such as DNA and RNA, increases less rapidly as the linear energy transfer increases than the chance of hitting thicker targets. This reasoning is graphically presented in Fig. 9. Leveling of the curves at high LET would indicate that the spacing between ionization events along a track is sufficiently small that more than one lethal ionization event takes place within the target molecule. The position of the plateau is farther away from the origin or the abscissa than the plateau

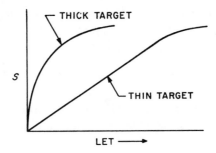

FIG. 9. The relative increase in the cross-sectional area of thick and thin targets with increase in linear energy transfer.

for thicker molecules of the same mass. The thickness, t, of the target may be determined from the following relationship:

$$S = S_0(1 - e^{-it})$$

where $S =$ the apparent cross section; $S_0 =$ the true cross section; $i =$ function (LET), the number of primary ionizations per unit path length along the track; and $t =$ the thickness of the sensitive target. This equation can be empirically fitted to experimental results such a shown in Fig. 9 in order to obtain a value of t. Pollard and associates applied the technique just described to deduce the size, shape, and component functions of viruses. Their experimental results led to some interesting conclusions, which now must be considered in the context of the information available in the early 1950's. First, Pollard and Forro (1951) demonstrated that T1 phage has a radiosensitive internal structure surrounded by an insensitive coat. Later refinement of the study showed that the sensitive portion is confined entirely to the head of the virus, a finding that paralleled the conclusions derived from the classical experiments of Hershey and Chase (1952). Second, they demonstrated (Pollard and Dimond, 1956) that TMV has an asymmetric radiosensitive core, which was measured to be 57 Å in diameter and 3070 Å long. These values are in satisfactory agreement with those derived later from the combined analyses of x-ray diffraction data of Franklin (1956) and Caspar (1956) and electron microscopy of Hart (1955). Third, the technique demonstrated that transforming DNA was a large, thin molecule having a molecular weight of the order of 10^6 (Fluke et al., 1952). A similar conclusion was reached for a type of RNA that, subsequently, became known as mRNA (Kempner and Pollard, 1961). The technique is useful in getting approximate target dimensions of viruses in their impure state as long as reliable assays of their biological activity can be performed. It should be pointed out that the experimental procedure permits examination of component functions of viruses, e.g., hemagglutinins, without dissociating them from the virus system. Additional results are summarized in Table II and in a report prepared by McCrea (1960). Two reports, one by Fluke and Forro (1960) and another by Schambra and Hutchinson on T1 and ϕX174 coliphages (1964), are current good examples of experiments that apply the techniques explained in this section.

E. SELECTIVE INACTIVATION OF VIRAL FUNCTIONS BY IONIZING RADIATIONS

Stanley, in 1936, observed that TMV inactivated by UV light retained essentially all of its initial antigenicity. Subsequent work involving the use of ionizing radiation shows that infectivity of viruses may be selectively destroyed while leaving such functions as attachment, antigenicity, and ability to inject nucleic acid comparatively intact. Of all the functions of the virus, the reproductive ability (plaque-forming ability or viability) is perhaps the most sensitive to ionizing radiations. This follows from the fact that the nucleic acid, upon which the reproductive ability depends, is, in a molecular sense, the largest single target of the virus. The protein moiety of virus may be greater in total mass, but it occurs as aggregates of smaller repeating molecular subunits. These are hit, of course, with about the same probability per unit mass as the nucleic acid. From target theory considerations, the probability of their escaping hits is greater because of their smaller size and because their multiplicity assures greater probability that a number of these units will escape hits. These ideas are illustrated in Fig. 10.

Some interesting current examples of the use of x-rays and γ-rays in selective inactivations of viral functions are seen in the work of Benjamin (1965), Basilico and Di Mayorca (1965), and Latarjet (1964) dealing with relative target sizes for the inactivation of the transforming and reproductive ability of tumor viruses. For example, when polyomavirus infects tissue culture cells, two virus–cell interactions occur. The first is a cytocidal interaction, accompanied by virus multiplication in mouse embryo cells, and the second, a noncytocidal interaction in hamster cells causing permanently altered characteristics that are akin to those of malignant cells. The latter is called transformation. It is found that the radiation sensitivity of the transforming ability of the virus is about 60% that of the reproductive ability. From this finding it is concluded that transformation requires the use of 60% as

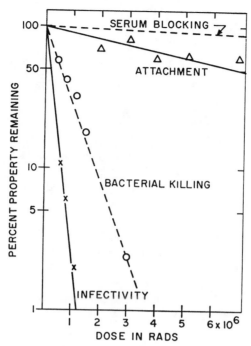

FIG. 10. Radiation inactivation of four properties of the bacterial virus T1: infectivity, bacterial killing, attachment to the host, and serum blocking power. (Data provided by Dr. E. C. Pollard.)

much of the viral DNA as does plaque formation. No estimate of the target sizes in absolute values are given in the case of the virus. Latarjet and Chamailland (1962) in a similar study with Friend virus, an RNA virus, showed that its oncogenic function has an x-ray sensitivity indicating a target molecular weight of 2.4×10^6 daltons, or one fourth the physical size of the viral genome (Crawford and Crawford, 1961).

In still other examples, Delihas (1961) and Ebisuzaki (1962) compared the radiation sensitivity and sensitivity to decay of incorporated ^{32}P atoms of the T4 phage enzyme functions, such as d-cytidine monophosphate hydroxymethylase and d-cytidylicdesaminase, to the ability of the phage to form plaques. Their findings show that the relative target sizes of the functions are a third to a half of the latter function. Pollard and colleagues (see summary McCrea, 1960) earlier compared the sensitivity of functions such as hemagglutination with infectivity of influenza A virus and the ability of T1 to crossreactivate with the ability to form plaques. These and other experimental findings are summarized in Table II.

TABLE II

SELECTIVE INACTIVATION OF VIRAL FUNCTIONS BY IONIZING RADIATIONS

Virus	Function	Radiation or other	Medium	Function (D_{37}, kr)	Viability of virus (D_{37}, kr)	Ratio of sensitivities (function/viability)
Polyoma	Oncogenicity	γ-Rays	Eagle's medium + 30% calf serum	1200 (Basilico and Di Mayorca, 1965)	500 (Basilico and Di Mayorca, 1965)	0.42
Polyoma	Oncogenicity	X-rays	Not given	280 (Benjamin, 1965)	180 (Benjamin, 1965)	0.6
Polyoma	Oncogenicity	^{32}P decay	Not given			0.6 (Benjamin, 1965)
Polyoma	Oncogenicity	UV	Not given			0.6 (Benjamin, 1965)
Polyoma	Hemagglutinin	X-rays	Not given			Very low (Benjamin, 1965)
Friend	Oncogenicity	40 keV x-rays	Tissue extract, 5°C	500 (Latarjet and Chamaillland, 1962)	130 Latarjet and Chamaillland, 1962)	0.26
Rous sarcoma	Oncogenicity	40 keV x-rays	Tissue extract, frozen	250 (Latarjet and Golde, 1962)	45 (Bryan et al., 1950)	0.18
Influenza A	Hemagglutinin	X-rays		330 (Kroeger and Kempf, 1959)	65 (Kroeger and Kempf, 1959)	0.2
Influenza A	Hemagglutinin	Deuterons 3.9 Mev	Dry in gelatin	2.3×10^{12} particles/cm²	4.5×10^{10} particles/cm²	0.02 (Jagger and Pollard, 1956)
T1 phage	Cross-reactivation of a function	250 keV x-rays	0.8% Nutrient broth			0.6 (Till and Pollard, 1958)
T1 phage	Cross-reactivation of a function	Deuterons	Dry			0.6 (Till and Pollard, 1958)
T1 phage	Bacterial killing ability	2 MeV electrons	Dried in broth	220 (Fluke and Pollard, 1955)	450 (Fluke and Forro, 1960)	0.3

T2 phage	dCMP-hydroxy-methylase	1 MeV electrons	Synthetic medium, + 0.5–1.0% glutathione, 40°C	134 (Delihas, 1961)	45 (Delihas, 1961)	0.34
T2 phage	Bacterial killing ability	X-rays	Broth	100 (Watson, 1950)	34 (Watson, 1950)	0.34
T4 phage	dCMP-hydroxy-methylase	^{32}P decay				0.38–0.5 (Ebisuzaki, 1962)
T4 phage	dHMP-kinase	^{32}P decay				0.47–0.5 (Ebisuzaki, 1962)
T4 phage	Lysozyme	UV				0.35 (Ebisuzaki, 1965)
T4 phage	rII, measured by functional rescue	UV				0.15 (Krieg, 1959)
T4 phage	rII, measured by functional rescue	^{32}P decay				0.13 (Harriman and Stent, 1964)
T4 phage	rII, measured by marker rescue	50 keV x-rays	Tryptone broth	200 (Ginoza and Vessey, 1966)	100 (Ginoza and Vessey, 1966)	0.5

In considering the data in Table II, three main points stand out. First, the target sizes of the cistronic or gene functions of the double-stranded DNA viruses appear to be anomalously high relative to the target sizes for viability or reproductive ability. For example, the DNA segment responsible for the enzyme functions of T4 phage appears to be 40–50% the size of the DNA segment required for viability. This anomaly has been discussed by several authors (Stent, 1963; Ebisuzaki, 1962; Delihas, 1961) but with no satisfying solution. Perhaps the difficulty is due to the fact that "target size for the viability" of the double-stranded DNA viruses has carried no real meaning in terms of actual physical dimensions in absolute molecular weight units. From one hypothesis discussed in Section II,D,3,a, the sensitive target for viability is not the entire genome; rather, it is thought to consist of some critical target. If this assumption is correct, the critical targets, e.g., of T4 and RF DNA of ϕX174, are 6.5×10^6 (one twentieth of the genome) and 0.85×10^6 (one quarter of the genome) daltons, respectively. In this light it becomes immediately apparent that the relative size of the gene functions is now a figure reasonably close to what one might expect for an average gene. For example, dCTP hydroxymethylase function of T4 would be specified by a DNA segment having a molecular weight of about 2×10^6, or enough to specify a protein molecule of about 200,000 molecular weight; similarly, the rII function of this virus would have a target molecular weight of 1×10^6 ($0.15 \times 6.5 \times 10^6$).

Second, the table suggests several useful ideas for experiments. The greater inactivation rate of infectivity over that of other viral functions obviously permits one to observe the effects of the latter alone while at the same time to estimate the fraction of genome concerned with function or the target dimension of functional protein. A few provocative experimentations in cancer research making use of this radiation approach are indicated in the report of Latarjet (1964). The work of Flaks et al. (1959) and Dirksen et al. (1960) shows that the ability of T4 phage to direct the synthesis of its DNA is selectively destroyed, while some of the enzymes concerned with that synthesis are produced in the cell at an undiminished, if not uncontrolled, rate. These observations suggest an important implication of the role of the T4 DNA system as a molecular model of regulation of gene action. Another example of the applications of the techniques of selective inactivation is the preparation of vaccines (Traub et al., 1951). It is clear that functions that depend on protein, e.g., hemagglutinins and attachment to host, are much less sensitive to radiation than infectivity.

A third point to be noted in Table II is the striking difference in the radiation sensitivity observed for the same polyomavirus by two groups of workers whose reports appear back to back in the same journal, although the conclusions derived from their experiments are identical. Indeed, this is but an example of the countless disagreements found in the radiation literature which point to an urgent need for standardization of radiation procedures, particularly dosimetry and elimination of indirect effects of radiation.

F. Summary of the Use of Ionizing Radiations for Virus Inactivation

The principal objective of the use of ionizing radiations as an experimental tool for studying viruses has been to determine the size and shape of their radiosensitive components. The tool has proven useful, particularly where virus specimens are impure and not obtainable in amounts amenable to conventional physical and chemical analyses. Generally, radiation experiments are easily performed and can provide useful preliminary estimates of the target dimensions within a relatively short time. For the case of single-stranded nucleic acid viruses, the estimates of the size of the infectious component are found to be in close agreement with those obtained on pure preparation by independent methods. Ionizing radiations have also been useful for selective inactivation of functions, especially reproductive capacity, thus permitting study of a variety of viral functions without dissociating the functional components from the virus particles. Another important use is for studying the course of vegetative development of viruses in the cell. In addition to these, the methodology can generate valuable ideas for critical and more definitive experiments.

The principal weakness of the radiation methods is that in many cases the experimental data are difficult to interpret. The major factors contributing to the difficulty are (1) the heterogeneity of the radiochemical lesions induced by the radiant energy; (2) the lack of precise information as to the way the absorbed energy is distributed within the target molecules; (3) the medium effects, which can either potentiate or protect against direct radiation action; and (4) the still unknown extent of repair of potentially lethal radiochemical lesions in double-stranded nucleic acid targets by the host cells or independently by the viruses themselves. Therefore, the information gained from radiation inactivation experiments is essentially inferential and provisional.

III. Thermal Inactivation of Viruses

A study of thermal inactivation of viruses serves two principal purposes. First, it provides a means of analyzing the physicochemical basis of virus inactivation, and, second, it gives a rationale for sterilization and, possibly, for selective inactivation of functions of the virus. In order to understand the molecular basis of the thermal inactivation processes, a quantitative approach, based on certain unifying concepts and methodology, is taken.

The formulation of Arrhenius has provided, in the past, a satisfactory method for expressing the influence of temperature on the reaction velocity. The classical Arrhenius equation is

$$k = Ae^{-E/RT} \qquad (7)$$

where k is the rate constant of the chemical process, T is the absolute temperature, R is the gas constant, E is the energy of activation, and A is a constant. Inherent in the formulation is the concept that a molecule must acquire, through random collision with other molecules, a certain amount of energy, E, before it is capable of undergoing reaction. From Eq. (7) we get

$$\log k = \log A - E/2.303RT \qquad (8)$$

This equation shows that E may be determined if the rate constants at several temperatures are known, since a plot of $\log k$ against $1/T$ results in a straight line of slope $-E/2.303R$, assuming that E does not vary with temperature. Examples of values of E for several viruses are listed in Table III.

The measurement of k involves another concept that concerns the order and the molecularity of a chemical or virus inactivation process.

TABLE III

ACTIVATION ENERGIES FOR HEAT INACTIVATION OF PHAGES IN BROTH

Phage	Activation energy (cal/mole)	Temperature range(°C)	Reference
Staph K	101,000	51–62	Krueger (1932)
Coli T5	170,000	65	Foster et al. (1949)
Coli T1	106,000	65–70	Adams (1949)
Coli T1	95,000	60–75	Pollard and Reaume (1951)
Coli T7	77,000	55–60	Adams (1949)
Coli T3	105,000	47–60	Pollard and Reaume (1951)
Coli T2	71,000	60–74	Pollard and Reaume (1951)
Coli T4	131,000	65–70	Adams (1949)

Many viruses are heat inactivated by the first-order process; i.e., the rate of virus inactivation at any time, t, is directly proportional to the concentration of the active virus remaining at that time. This may be expressed by the general relationship

$$-dc/dt = k'c \qquad (9)$$

where k' is the proportionality or rate constant and dc/dt is the rate of change of concentration, c, with time, t. Integrating Eq. (9), we get

$$\ln c/c_0 = -k't \qquad (10)$$

where c_0 is the initial concentration at $t = 0$ and c is the concentration after time, t, has elapsed. Alternatively, Eq. (10) is expressed in terms of the common logarithm, so that

$$\log c/c_0 = -k't/2.303 \qquad (11)$$

and the plot of $\log c/c_0$ against t should yield a straight line of slope $-k'/2.303$ if the reaction obeys a first-order process. The constant k is the "specific reaction rate." That virus and viral nucleic acids are inactivated by the first-order process indicates that (1) a single random event occurring in the virus particle is sufficient to inactivate, and (2) the reaction is presumably not concerned with any other external reagent besides heat (i.e., the reaction appears to be monomolecular). As we shall see below, the kinds of single events range from a discrete single-bond scission of single-stranded RNA to a complex and catastrophic collapse of large macromolecular viral components such as DNA and proteins. A description of the molecular process involved in the inactivation event is one of the principal aims of the study of the reaction kinetics. The first experimental step in this direction is to establish the order of the inactivation process and the second the speed of the reaction at various temperatures.

A. Reaction Rate Theory

The main assumptions of this theory, developed by Eyring and his associates (Glasstone *et al.*, 1941), are that a reaction proceeds via a transition or activated state that is in thermodynamic equilibrium with the reactants, and that, regardless of the chemical properties of the activated complex, its rate of decomposition into products depends only on temperature. This is illustrated as follows:

$$R \rightleftharpoons A^* \rightarrow \text{Products}$$

where R denotes reactants in the ground state and A^* denotes reactants in the activated state. Assuming that A^* molecules are in true equilibrium with the R molecules, then $K^* = A^*/R$, where K^* is the equilibrium constant for the formation of the activated molecule and A^* and R are the concentrations of the activated and of the reactant molecules. The rate, m, of the overall reaction is proportional to A^*, thus

$$dR/dt = mA^* \tag{12}$$

and by definition of the first-order rate constant

$$dR/dt = k'R \tag{13}$$

By equating Eq. (12) and Eq. (13), $k' = mA^*/R$, and since $K^* = A^*/R$,

$$k' = mK^* \tag{14}$$

Eyring has shown that the rate of decomposition of A^* into the reaction products is equal to kT/h, where k is the Boltzmann constant $(1.380 \times 10^{-16}$ ergs/degree), T is the absolute temperature, and h is the Planck's constant $(6.625 \times 10^{-27}$ erg/second). Thus, m in Eq. (12) is equal to kT/h, and by substitution we get

$$\kappa = \frac{kT}{h} K^* \tag{15}$$

K^* cannot be measured experimentally, but it is related to useful thermodynamic parameters as follows:

$$\Delta F^* = -RT \ln K^* = \Delta H^* - T\Delta S^* \tag{16}$$

assuming that the activated molecules are in true thermodynamic equilibrium with molecules in the ground state. Then ΔF^* is the standard free energy of formation of the activated state, ΔH^* is the standard enthalpy of formation of the transition state, and ΔS^* is the standard entropy of formation of the activated state.

Equation (15) by substitution now becomes the formal expression for the absolute rate theory rate constant:

$$k' = \frac{kT}{h} e^{-\Delta F^*/RT} = \frac{kT}{h} e^{\Delta S^*/R} e^{-\Delta H^*/RT} \tag{17}$$

Then ΔF^* is the work that must be done in distorting the molecules so that they can react. Eyring stresses this free energy of activation rather than the energy of activation stressed in the Arrhenius collision or rate theory. The entropy of activation, ΔS^*, is the increase of randomness of the molecules in the activated state, and the enthalpy of activation, ΔH^*, is related, in general, to the strength of the bonds that are broken or formed in the activated state. Its similarity to the energy of activation, E, from the Arrhenius formulation is seen in the following relationship: $E = \Delta H^* + RT$. This shows that the difference between the two is small when the value of ΔH^* is high and when the temperature is in the range $300°-400°K$.

Equation (17) shows that the primary experimental data, the rate constants, obtained from inactivation curves at different temperatures can be used to derive the three thermodynamic constants, ΔS^*, ΔF^*, and ΔH^*, of the inactivation process. Rearranging Eq. (17) to a useful form, we have

$$\log k' = \log \frac{kT}{h} + \frac{\Delta S^*}{2.303R} - \frac{\Delta H^*}{2.303R}\left(\frac{1}{T}\right) \tag{18}$$

Now ΔH^* may be obtained by plotting $\log k'$ against $1/T$. A straight line may be obtained whose slope will be $-\Delta H^*/2.303R$ ($\log T$ increases very slowly when T is between $300°$ and $400°K$). If the slope changes over a given temperature range, so that two or more slopes are obtained, it indicates that the reaction process for inactivation differs at different temperatures.

We obtain ΔF^* from the rearranged form of Eq. (17):

$$\Delta F^* = -2.303RT \log \frac{k'h}{kT} \tag{19}$$

using a k' value obtained at a given temperature. Having obtained a set of ΔF^* values for different temperatures, these are plotted against T. From the relationship $\Delta F^* = \Delta H^* - T\Delta S^*$, it can be seen that a slope is obtained that gives the value of ΔS^*. As in the case of ΔH^*, ΔS^* may or may not be constant over the experimental temperature range; a change would indicate that the mechanism of the inactivation process is not the same at all experimental temperatures.

The more modern treatment by Eyring and associates retains the Arrhenius concept of equilibrium between the reactants and the activated molecules, and the enthalpy of activation differs only slightly from the Arrhenius activation energy. However, the newer approach shows that activation energy alone does not determine the magnitude of the rate constant but that the entropy of activation is also a determining factor. Thus, the Eyring formulation helps to explain why denaturation of many proteins proceeds at an appreciable rate at moderate temperature despite the high positive energies of activation. As we shall see, the denaturation process usually shows a high entropy, indicative of a great disorder of molecular structure in the activated state, which results in lowering the free energy of activation. This allows the reaction to proceed at a measurable rate.

Thermodynamic constants of the inactivation reactions for a wide variety of biologically active macromolecules are simply obtained from the foregoing procedure, but, as Stearns (1949) warns, "the ease of application of the formal theory is not an unalloyed advantage, for in many cases care must be taken in interpreting its findings." Indeed, the care must include a thorough understanding of the physicochemical properties of the materials under study, and supplementary experiments, the designs of which are inspired by the interpretation of the kinetics data, must be performed.

B. STRUCTURE OF VIRUSES

The morphological variations of viruses are many (Caspar and Klug, 1962; Horne and Wildy, 1963). It was pointed out by Crick and Watson (1956) that the nucleic acid of small viruses could code for only a small number of protein molecules of limited size. They predicted, therefore, that the virus shell would be made up of a large number of identical protein subunits arranged in some symmetrical way. Their expectation has been borne out for the simple viruses. For example, the much-studied TMV (Klug and Caspar, 1960) has a structure consisting of about 2200 equivalent protein subunits helically arranged around its hollow cylindrical core. The molecular weight of the subunits is 17,-000. They are known to assemble spontaneously to form a viruslike rod, with or without the nucleic acid. The second example of structural pattern of simple viruses is the icosahedral symmetry (Caspar and Klug, 1962). Adenovirus, polyomavirus, ϕX174 phage, and poliovirus are but a few examples possessing this form. An icosahedron is characteristic of these near-spherical, regular, or semiregular viruses possessing axial symmetry, which are themselves symmetrically disposed to one another. Their subunit proteins cannot be packed in an equivalent environment as in the case of helically symmetrical capsids, but are arranged as a group called capsomeres. The latter are, in turn, substructures of the capsid, and their morphological features are resolvable by electron microscopy. Capsomeres of polyomavirus and herpes simplex virus appear to be short hollow tubes, suggesting that they are made up of a number of helically arranged subunits. The number of capsomeres range from 12 for ϕX147 to 254 for canine hepatitis virus and adenovirus type 5. Caspar and Klug (1962) suggested that subunit proteins of these viruses may be self-assembling, also. Self-assembly, on the one hand, and the ease of dissociation, on the other, imply that only weak bonds hold virus subunits together.

The next order of complexity in structure can be seen in the T-even phages. Brenner *et al.* (1959) showed with electron microscopy details of some of the several morphological components, e.g., the sheath consisting of 200 helically arranged repeating units of 50,000 molecular weight each, and the head protein consisting of a large number of equivalent protein subunits of 80,000 molecular weight each. Tail fibers about 1500 Å long and 20 Å in diameter and the tail plates to which they are apparently attached are additional features of these phages. The complexity of their structure reflects the complexity of their functions, e.g., tail fibers for recognition of their host membrane and contractile sheath for injection of their DNA. Finally, there is a group of viruses whose components have no apparent symmetry of structure, such as Rous sarcoma virus, or that possess a structure with helical symmetry, such as TMV, but the structure is coiled and contained within a loosely fitting membrane. An example of the latter is Newcastle disease virus.

This very brief sketch of virus morphology serves as a reminder of the variety of external protein components of the virus that are subject to thermal dissociations and denaturation. In some cases viruses may be thermally inactivated by denaturation of the external protein coat, perhaps a morphological structure concerned with attachment and injection, even though the infective potential of their nucleic acid remains unscathed. In other cases, the nucleic acid core may be selectively inactivated, leaving the protein coat relatively intact, as may be discerned by comparing the rate of loss of infectivity with that of loss of antigenicity. This is observed when the virus is inactivated below the temperature that denatures protein. In still other cases, the nucleic acid alone can gain entry into a cell and complete the infectious cycle, albeit with much lower efficiency than the intact virus. Clearly, a simple generalization of thermal inactivation of virus cannot be made, since, as we shall see, protein, DNA, and RNA each has its own characteristic rate process of degradation and loss of function. In the following sections a brief review of the current thinking on the structural stability of these three classes of biomolecular components of viruses will be presented as a prelude to consideration of specific cases of thermal inactivation of viruses.

1. *Protein*

The native structure of protein is maintained by a complex interplay of various forces that act to fold and hold its primary structure, the polypeptide chain, in a specific conformation. When the conformation is destroyed by some environmental stress, the protein molecule generally loses its function and is said to be denatured. The alteration is irreversible or, at least, difficult to reverse. The types of intramolecular noncovalent bonds contributing to the stabilization of the native structure are interpeptide H bonds, side chain hydrogen bonds, ionic bonds, and hydrophobic bonds. Intramolecular covalent bonding between two sulfur atoms occurs in some proteins. The relative contribution of these forces to the stabilization has been the subject of a long series of studies. In recent years, the question of the role of structured water around the protein molecule in the stabilization has been debated. Reviews by Kauzman (1959) and Schachman (1963) suggest, however, that despite the great strides made in recent years in these investigations, our knowledge concerning the basis for the stabilization is still inadequate and that, for the present, it would be prudent to consider the possibility that all types of forces, regardless of the weight of their individual contributions, act in some cooperative manner for the stabilization. The long-standing belief that H bonds are the principal forces is, however, no longer favored.

Numerous existing data gathered over a long period indicate that denaturation of proteins in physiological medium is characterized by very high ΔH^* and ΔS^*. Stearns (1949) studied a number of enzymes and proteins and concluded that these high values cannot be accounted for by breakage of strong covalent bonds; therefore, the activation process must involve cooperative rupture of several weak bonds, notably H bonds, with concomitant increase in configurational entropy. It would appear that the newer hypothesis of stabilization by structured water is, also, consistent with the high ΔH^* and ΔS^* observed.

2. *Thermostability of DNA*

Studies of the thermal effects in the biological behavior of DNA have lagged behind similar studies on enzymes and proteins chiefly because of the slow recognition of the importance of DNA in living systems. The first systematic study of this kind was undertaken by Zamenhof and his collaborators (1953), who showed that DNA preparations of *Hemophilus influenzae* with transforming activity possessed extraordinary heat stability in physiological medium. They found that the biological activity decreases in exactly the same high temperature range over which a large change in the secondary structure occurs. Rice and Doty (1957) used heat as one of the principal agents to analyze the basic physicochemical parameters of the DNA molecule. They found that thermal denaturation of calf thymus DNA in physiological medium is characterized by high enthalpy and entropy of activation, and they concluded that the collapse process is initiated by a cooperative rupture of a large number of hydrogen bonds followed by irreversible derangement of the Watson-Crick double helices. The helix-coil transition was found to occur sharply within a narrow temperature range (85°–90°C), with the midpoint of transition, T_m, varying according to the guanine–cytosine content of the DNA (Doty et al., 1959). The basis for the stability of the DNA structure to thermal denaturation is a subject of current debate (Gibbs and DiMarzio, 1959; Crothers and Zimm, 1964; Sinanoglu and Abdulmur, 1965).

In extending the early work of Zamenhof and co-workers, Ginoza and Zimm (1961), Roger and Hotchkiss (1961), and Lerman and Tolmach (1959) found that the transforming function decayed dramatically with the same kinetics as those of denaturation. This finding is illustrated in Figs. 11 and 12. Several features are revealed by the set of inactivation curves, as exemplified by the loss of the streptomycin resistance genetic marker. First, the inactivation of the biological function occurs by two processes: (1) depurination, as indicated by the exponential survival curves at temperatures below 87°C, and (2) a collapse or denaturation, as shown by a rapid initial decrease in transforming activity beginning at temperatures above 87°C. The rapid reaction is followed by a slower exponential curve that measures the rate of depurination of the fraction of the DNA population resistant to denaturation at the temperature given. The extent of denaturation at any temperature is measured by extrapolating the trailing linear portion of the curve and noting the intercept. The plot of the extent of denaturation at different temperatures against temperature provides a biological melting transition shown in Fig. 12. The sharpness of the transition (Ginoza and Zimm, 1961) is even more striking than that shown by measurement of hyperchromicity (OD at 260 mμ). The latter measures the transition of an entire population of DNA molecules, while the former measures the transition of only one molecular species within the population bearing the streptomycin resistance marker, hence the comparative sharpness of the streptomycin curve.

A second feature of the set of inactivation curves (Fig. 11) is the fact that the collapse process never leads to complete loss of activity; a

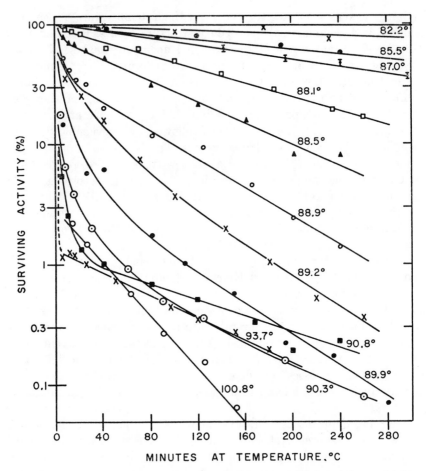

Fig. 11. Activity for transformation to streptomycin resistance of phenol purified, pneumoccal DNA after heating for various times at various temperatures. Sodium phosphate buffer, 0.1 M, pH 7.25 at room temperature, DNA concentration 0.05–20 μg/ml (Ginoza and Zimm, 1961).

small percentage of the initial activity remains even when the temperature is raised well above that required to initiate the denaturation. This has been observed by others (Roger and Hotchkiss, 1961; Lerman and Tolmach, 1959; Marmur and Lane, 1960) for the same DNA. Ginoza and Zimm (1961) reasoned from their collateral kinetic data that the residual activity was due to completely denatured single-stranded DNA, which can gain entry into the receptor cell with an efficiency of a few percent of the native unheated control DNA, and

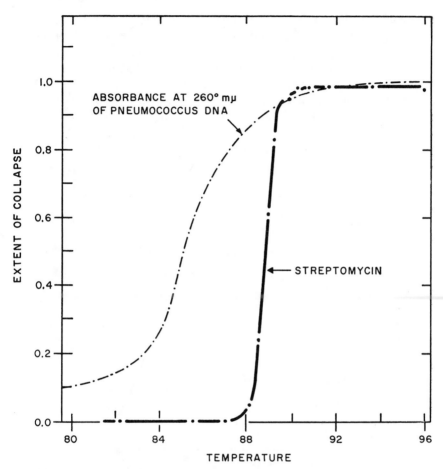

FIG. 12. Extent of collapse plotted against temperature. The straight lines of Fig. 11 were extrapolated to the ordinate; the loss of activity at these extrapolated points is taken as the extent of collapse (denauration). Also included is the optical density curve of Marmur and Doty (1961). From Ginoza and Zimm (1961).

once in the cell can transform the cell with high efficiency. Guild and Robson (1963) separated the thermally denatured unpaired strands by density-gradient centrifugation and found that, indeed, both strands are separately active. This information is relevant to thermal inactivation of double-stranded viral DNA, as may be shown in studies on RF DNA of ϕX174 (Ginoza and Miller, 1965) and polyoma DNA (Weil and Vinograd, 1963).

The exponential inactivation process shown in part or all of the survival curves is due to single-hit depurination events occurring at sites of occasional loops opened in the double helix in the region of the genetic marker by thermal energy. The rate of the depurination measures the degree to which the native helical structure is opened up and is, as to be expected, very temperature dependent. An Arrhenius plot (Fig. 13) gives some indication of the complex reaction. While no figures for the thermodynamic parameters are given, it is easily seen that the rate of

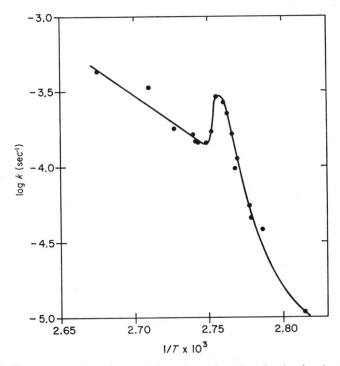

FIG. 13. Temperature dependence of the rates of heat inactivation by depurination of pneumococcal transforming DNA (streptomycin resistance marker) in 0.1 M sodium phosphate buffer at pH 7.15. Data from Ginoza and Zimm (1961).

change of the first-order rate constant with temperature, or ΔH^*, is very great from 85° to 89°C. Roger and Hotchkiss showed that depurination rate of this transforming DNA increases with decreasing pH (1961). Once the melting transition is completed, the rates for the single-hit process are those of separated single-stranded DNA; it should be pointed out that the rates are one-half those for DNA inactivated as double strands, which is to be expected because the target is half the size of the native DNA. The plot of the rates against temperature is linear in the Arrhenius plot, showing an activation energy of about 34 kcal/mole. This value is the same as that determined for ϕX174 DNA (Ginoza et al., 1964), also single stranded, and indicates that the inactivation process is that of normal chemical reaction. The high ΔH^* surmised for depurination reaction of the double-stranded DNA can be explained by the high energy requirement for the local denaturation necessary before depurination can occur.

One final remark on the nature of the denatured, unmatched single-stranded DNA may bear on the thermal properties of the double-stranded DNA's that have no ends, i.e., that are circular. It has been clearly demonstrated by Marmur and Doty (1961) that denatured DNA can be annealed with considerable restoration of the native double helices and of biological activity by incubation of the mixture for 1 hour at 65°C. The process is concentration dependent, as is to be expected for bimolecular interactions, and can occur only between two polynucleotide chains having a specific complementarity of base pairing and sequence.

Circular DNA. In more recent years circular DNA molecules having no ends have become almost commonplace experimental material in biological laboratories, although thermal inactivation studies, such as those described above, have yet to be extended. Sinsheimer and co-workers (Fiers and Sinsheimer, 1962a,b) discovered that ϕX174 DNA is not only single stranded but also circular. Moreover, the replicating factor, RF DNA, made by the host cell soon after the infectious single-stranded DNA enters it, is also circular in structure (Sinsheimer, et al., 1962). Almost simultaneously, the circularity of the polyoma DNA was established. More recently, a group of adenovirus DNA were put in this class (Smith, 1965). Genetic evidence for the circularly permuted genetic information in bacteria and in bacteriophages encourages the belief that circularity may be a common structural feature of the self-replicating mechanism, at least in these simple systems. While, for the most part, they have no structural dissimilarity to the Watson-Crick DNA, they possess one strikingly different characteristic: the linker joining the two ends is more thermostable than the intermolecular bondings. Complete separation of the circular complementary chains cannot be affected by heat under conditions where a linear molecule will separate. Evidence for this property in polyoma DNA is shown by the fact that the annealing reaction is efficient and independent of the DNA concentration (Weil, 1963; Dulbecco and Vogt, 1963). Further, the denatured RF DNA of ϕX174 shows two-hit inactivation kinetics (Ginoza and Miller, 1965). The chemical nature of the linker creating the circular form is unknown; the linker in ϕX174 DNA is insensitive to exonucleases (Fiers and Sinsheimer, 1962b).

Heat-inactivation kinetics of polyoma DNA reveals certain characteristics that are in striking contrast to that of the transforming DNA described above. Weil and Vinograd (1963) showed that the biological activity of the DNA heated at 100°C for 16 minutes in buffered saline and quick-cooled to prevent reannealing increased 3-fold over the initial activity of the unheated control sample. RF DNA shows a similar, although much greater, increase (Pouwels and Jansz, 1964; Ginoza and Miller, 1965). Weil (1963) attributed the rise to increased efficiency of adsorption or uptake of the denatured DNA by the host cells. The kinetics of thermal inactivation of RF DNA, which resembles polyoma DNA in size and structure, are shown in Fig. 14.

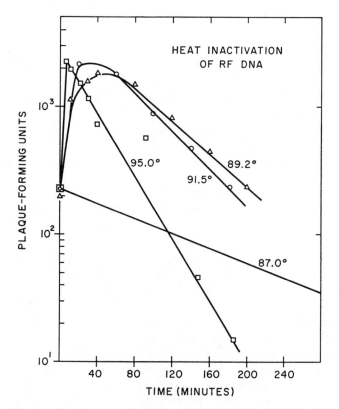

FIG. 14. Heat inactivation survival curves of RF DNA OD ϕX174 in 0.1 M potassium phosphate buffer pH 7.0 at various temperatures. DNA concentration was about 0.1 μg/ml during heating (Ginoza and Miller, 1965).

Several features of the rate process can be listed. (1) The attainment of maximum potential infectivity (and denaturation) is time dependent; the higher the temperature, the faster the rate of attaining the maximum level. (2) Following the plateau of maximum activity, there is an exponential decrease in the infectivity, the rate of decrease being similar to that measured for the single-stranded ϕX174 DNA at a comparable temperature (Ginoza et al., 1964). (3) The biological melting transition begins sharply at some temperature between 87° and 88°C. The T_m by hyperchromicity measurements is 86.5°C (Hayashi et al., 1963). (4) Inactivation at temperatures below the melting transition (< 87°C) proceeds by simple exponential kinetics and is due, most likely, to depurination, as shown for the case of the transforming DNA. It is concluded here, as from the x-irradiation experiments, that this DNA in the double-stranded state sustains, on the average, three nonlethal heat-depurination hits per lethal hit.

3. Thermostability of RNA

One of the basic characteristics that distinguishes RNA from DNA is the chemistry of the pentose ring. The presence of the 2'-OH function in the pentose of RNA has a decided influence on the thermostability of RNA and on the reaction mechanisms by which the molecule degrades under thermal treatment. The low stability is reflected in the rapid loss of biological activity and molecular integrity under conditions where single-stranded DNA is stable. For example TMV RNA and ϕX174 DNA are similar in size, yet in the same physiological medium at 37°C TMV RNA is inactivated approximately 30 times faster than the DNA. This feature of TMV RNA has contributed to the confusion in the early efforts to determine its molecular weight. The target theory analysis, described in Section II, is admirably suited for such labile RNA, since, by the very principle of the technique, only the molecularly intact, infectious molecules respond to the analysis. The physicochemical basis for the instability of TMV RNA has been investigated by Ginoza (1958) and by Gordon and Huff (1962). It was shown that the kinetics of inactivation is, in marked contrast to the case of the double-stranded DNA, very simple (Fig. 15); the biological activity is lost by a simple first-order process whose rate increases exponentially with temperature. The kinetic data show no indication that denaturation process is in any way associated with the inactivation reaction. Rather, they suggest that some simple bond scission is sufficient to destroy its infectivity. The following thermodynamic constants characterize the inactivation: $\Delta H^* = 19$ kcal/mole/degree and $\Delta S^* = -19$ cal/mole/degree in experiments conducted at pH 7.0 in 0.1 M phosphate buffer. These thermal constants were then considered in the light of the reaction scheme proposed earlier by Brown and Todd (1953) to explain the presence of mixed isomers, E and F, in their products following alkaline treatment of RNA (Fig. 16). Brown and Todd postulated that the formation of the cyclic triester intermediate, B, is necessary in order to explain the reaction products, 3'-monophosphate (E) and 2'-monophosphate (F). The formation of B is possible because of the 2'-OH group of the pentose, and product C results because of the inherent instability of the intermediate triester structure. The thermal constants for the inactivation process for TMV RNA are consistent with this reaction scheme. They describe the activated state of the RNA

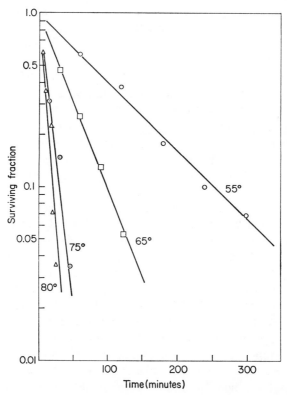

Fig. 15. Survival curves of TMV RNA heated at pH 7.15 in 0.1 M sodium phosphate buffer. The temperature range covered was 37°–95°C. (Not all curves are shown.) ΔH^* and ΔS^* of $+23$ kcal/mol and -11 entropy units, respectively, were obtained from the data obtained under these conditions (Ginoza et al., 1964). (Reproduced by permission from Nature.)

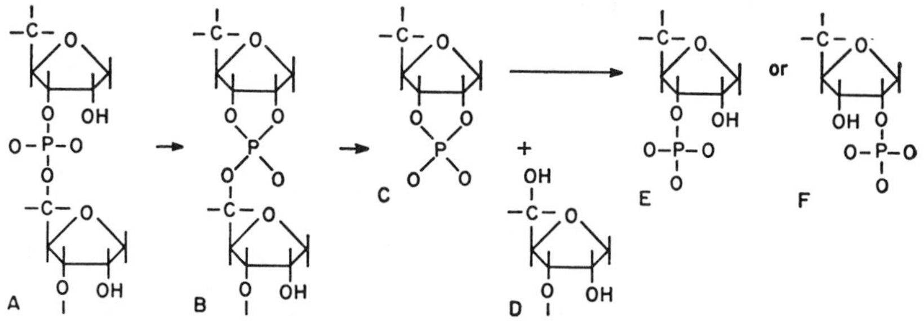

FIG. 16. Brown and Todd reaction scheme for the hydrolysis of RNA. The cyclic triester intermediate, B, is formed by phosphoryl migration; the unstable triester then hydrolyzes to cause chain scission.

molecule. The negative entropy of activation, ΔS^*, is consistent with the loss of degrees of freedom of the molecule in forming the cyclic triester, B, the activated molecule, and the moderate value of ΔH^* is believed to account for the energy required to form or break one co-covalent bond in the activation process. Since the kinetics of the loss of infectivity is first order, it is concluded that a single hydrolytic scission of the phosphodiester bond is sufficient to inactivate the RNA molecule. The direct consequence of this scission in a single-stranded structure is a complete severance of the genetic molecule into two pieces. Sedimentation-velocity analyses of the heat-inactivated RNA indicate that the breaks occur randomly along the chain (Ginoza et al., 1964).

Analysis of the hydrolytic product of TMV RNA heated for a prolonged period in the same buffer used for biological inactivation experiments shows that nucleotides and nucleosides, but no free bases, are found, indicating that inactivation is due mainly to phosphodiester backbone cleavage. DNA undergoing a similar treatment yields preponderantly free purines (Ginoza et al., 1964); the phosphodiester bonds are comparatively resistant to hydrolysis. Doty et al. (1960) estimated that the rate of backbone scission is one-twentieth that of depurination.

The difference in thermal behavior of RNA and DNA is further revealed by comparing the sensitivity of TMV RNA and ϕX174 DNA to heat inactivation as a function of pH. Figure 17 shows that the first-order inactivation rate constants of ϕX174 DNA increase as the first power of the hydrogen ion concentration, an observation clearly consistent with the chemistry of the depurination reaction (Tamm et al., 1953). The RNA, on the other hand, shows a maximum stability at pH 6 and has greater rates of inactivation on either side of this pH.

The rates of inactivation of single-stranded RNA's, viz. TMV RNA,

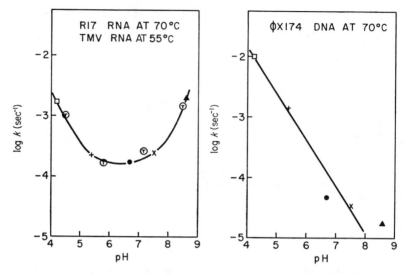

FIG. 17. pH dependence of the rates of inactivation of R17 RNA at 70°C, TMV RNA (T) at 55°C, and øX174 DNA at 70°C in Michaelis buffer.

poliovirus RNA, and soluble RNA, are in direct proportion to their chain lengths (Ginoza et al., 1964).

C. KINETIC ANALYSIS OF VIRUS INACTIVATION

Inactivation of viruses generally follows a course of first-order kinetics for one or two logarithmic units. This level of inactivation is sufficient for conventional kinetic analyses which provide useful thermodynamic values characterizing the physicochemical properties of 90–99% of the virus population under study. If the exponential slope remains constant over a more prolonged inactivation, that extension, of course, merely provides a more inclusive sampling of the population. Still, for studies related to sterilization procedures, greater inactivation than two logs would be necessary. However, more frequently than not virus survival curves at a lower survival do reveal a second component, whose inactivation proceeds at a slower first-order rate. If the second slope is extrapolated to the ordinate, the intercept is the fraction of the resistant population initially present in the virus sample. A survival curve of this type is the sum of two linear components and may be expressed as:

$$N/N_0 = (1 - m)e^{-k_1 t} + me^{-k_2 t} \tag{20}$$

where $1 - m$ is the fraction inactivated at rate constant k_1 and m is the fraction inactivated at rate constant k_2. However, the presence of a second thermally resistant fraction is not made self-evident by the kinetic analysis alone; its proof must be obtained by collateral experiments—for example, by isolating and biologically characterizing the thermally resistant fraction or determining whether or not the extrapolated intercept of the second component in the survival curves remains constant at other temperatures.

In his survey of studies on thermal inactivation of viruses, Woese noted the high frequency at which survival curves of animal viruses, in particular, deviate from the simple exponential law. Two-component curves, each following first-order kinetics, appear to be general. Moreover, the extrapolated intercept of the second components shifts downward with increasing temperature, indicating that heterogeneity is not the explanation for the kinetics. Moreover, on decreasing the inactivation temperature, the extrapolated intercept approaches 100%. Examples of this kinetic behavior are revealed in studies of vaccinia virus (Kaplan, 1958), foot-and-mouth disease virus (FMDV), (Bachrach et al., 1957), poliovirus (Younger, 1957; Koch, 1960), and Newcastle disease virus (NDV) (Woese, 1956).

The work of Kaplan (1958) illustrates these points (Fig. 18). To

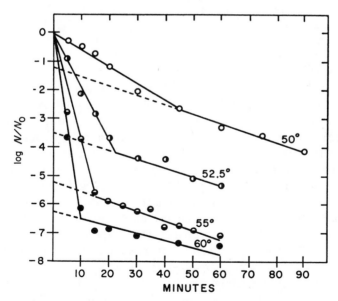

Fig. 18. Thermal inactivation of vaccinia virus (Kaplan, 1958). (Reproduced by permission from the *Journal of General Microbiology*.)

account for the kinetic behavior of this and other animal virus inactivations Woese proposed the following interesting scheme. It is assumed that these viruses are heat inactivated primarily through damage to the nucleic acid. The nucleic acid is in two interconvertible viable forms, A and B. A, which is less heat stable than B, is inactivated by two mechanisms, denaturation (high ΔH^*) and chain scission (low to moderate ΔH^*), and B, by chain scission alone. In this scheme,

$$X \xleftarrow{a \text{ or } b} A \underset{d}{\overset{c}{\rightleftharpoons}} B \xrightarrow{b} X$$

A and B are the two interconvertible forms, c and d are interconversion rate constants, X is the inactive virus, and a and b are rate constants for the collapse mechanism and the chain scission, respectively. One of the general features of viral inactivations is that at low temperatures only a single component curve, characterized by low to moderate ΔH^*, is obtained. This means b is much greater than a, and X is produced only by chain scission. The survival curve then can be described simply by

$$N/N_0 = e^{-bt} \tag{21}$$

At higher temperatures, rate a is greater than b, and assuming that d is negligible, one obtains

$$N/N_0 = e^{-(a+b+c)t}\, \frac{aA_0}{a+c} + e^{-bt}\left(B_0 + \frac{cA_0}{a+c}\right) \tag{22}$$

This equation satisfies the two-component inactivation curves that are observed. Moreover, the extrapolated intercept of the slow inactivation component at the ordinate is a function of the temperature of inactivation, and also the inactivation rate of the slow component is still governed by the same rate constant that controls the inactivations at low temperatures. Woese makes clear that this mathematical model is general and that the physical interpretation he uses may be more specific than justified. Taking due cognizance of this latter restriction, it may be added here that DNA, the core of the vaccinia virus, whose kinetics are illustrated in Fig. 17, is double stranded and as such it is unlikely that it would either be denatured or depurinated at temperatures of 50°–60°C. Also, as discussed in Section III,B,2, denaturation and depurination of double-stranded DNA are characterized by high ΔH^* and ΔS^*. Another strange phenomenon is the constancy of the slope of the slow component over a temperature range of 10°C. It does suggest that a large entropy term may be involved here to account for $\Delta H^* = 0$ and, therefore, that protein denaturation may be involved in some complex way.

Hiatt (1964) cogently points out that Woese's scheme is not sufficient to explain Kaplan's data, since the ratio $c/a + c$ would have to change a millionfold over a 10°C range to fit the data.

The possibility that heterogeneity is actually heat induced in an initially homogeneous population has been considered by Hiatt (1964). The idea is suggested by the hypothesis of Gard (1960) that poliovirus under treatment with formaldehyde becomes progressively more resistant to further action of this reagent owing to hardening of the protein coat with time of treatment. Hiatt's explanation of Koch's (1960) heat-inactivation kinetics of poliovirus points to a satisfactory reason for at least some of the observed two-component curves. He takes into account the fact that both the virus and its free nucleic acid (RNA) are infectious, although with different efficiencies. Thus, the virus can, as in Woese's model, exist in two viable states: A, with both nucleic acid and protein intact, and B, with only intact nucleic acid. B, which is freed by denaturation of the protein capsid, has a much lower efficiency of infection. The heat-inactivation reaction for poliovirus is represented as follows:

$$X \xleftarrow{k_2} A \xrightarrow{k_1} B \xrightarrow{k_2} X$$

where X is inactive virus and k_1 and k_2 are the first-order rate constants for denaturation of the virus protein and RNA chain scission, respectively. Then using the equation

$$N/N_0 = (1 - \gamma)e^{-(k_1+k_2)t} + \gamma e^{-k_2 t} \tag{23}$$

where $\gamma =$ the efficiency of the poliovirus assay for B relative to that for A under a specific condition, Hiatt constructed a theoretical survival curve that is in good agreement with Koch's inactivation data. For the same heat-inactivated samples, but assayed under another set of conditions, the intercept of the slow component changes but the slopes of the fast and slow components remain largely unchanged. It seems hopeful that more analysis of this type would help clarify the confusion now existing in the literature on heat inactivation of viruses.

D. SUMMARY OF THE GENERAL CHARACTERISTICS OF VIRUS INACTIVATION

We shall, in the following section, attempt to make some generalizations of thermal inactivation of viruses from the collected data shown in Table IV. An understanding of the mechanisms of their inactivation requires consideration of several interrelated factors. These are (1) the heat sensitivity of the protein capsid in relation to viral survival, (2) the

TABLE IV
Thermal Constants for the Inactivation of Viruses and Infectious Nucleic Acids

Virus	Conditions	Temperature range (°C)	ΔH^* (cal/mole)	ΔS^* (cal/mole/°C)	Reference
Plant viruses					
TMV	In crude sap, pH 5.5	68–80	34,600	16	Price (1940)
TMV	Purified, wet	<85	40,000	18	Pollard and Dimond (1956)
TMV	In crude sap, pH 5.5	85–95	192,270	459	Price (1940)
TMV (denaturation)	0.1 M phosphate, pH 7.05	60–73	150,195	365	Lauffer and Price (1940)
TMV	Purified, wet		27,000	0	Pollard (1953b)
Tobacco ringspot	In crude sap, pH 5.6–6.0	45–55	76,135	161	Price (1940)
Tobacco ringspot	In crude sap, pH 5.4–5.9	60–65	26,955	11	Price (1940)
Tobacco necrosis	In crude sap, pH 5.6–6.4	70–95	36,070	32	Price (1940)
Alfalfa mosaic	In crude sap, pH 5.5–5.9	50–63	72,970	151	Price (1940)
Animal viruses					
FMDV		4–43	26,000	7	Bachrach et al. (1957)
FMDV		43–61	113,000	280	Bachrach et al. (1957)
Polio slow component			30,000		Younger (1957)
Polio	In Formalin		30,000		Timm et al. (1956)
Polio	Dry		29,000	21	Kraft and Pollard (1954)
Polio	Vaccine		50,000		Powell and Culbertson (1955)
Measles	Tissue culture fluid	23–37	18,000		Black (1959)
Measles	Tissue culture fluid	37–56	70,000		Black (1959)
NDV		Low	29,000	30	Woese (1953)
NDV		High	125,000	300	Woese (1953)
Bacteriophage					
T1	Broth	60–75	95,000	207	Pollard and Reaume (1951)
T2	Broth	60–74	71,700	139	Pollard and Reaume (1951)
T3	Broth		105,000	246	Pollard and Reaume (1951)
T4	Broth		120,000		Adams (1949)
T5	Broth		82,000	165	Adams (1949)

					Reference
T7	Broth	52–60	60,700	114	Pollard and Reaume (1951)
T1	Dry	90–145	27,000	0	Pollard and Reaume (1951)
T2	Dry		18,000	−12	Pollard and Reaume (1951)
T7	Dry	25–60	12,700	−29	Pollard and Reaume (1951)
M1	Broth		76,000	165	Friedman and Cowles (1953)
M3	Broth		87,000	195	Friedman and Cowles (1953)
M5	Broth		112,000	254	Friedman and Cowles (1953)
S. lactis phage	Wet	55–65	76,000	165	Cherry and Watson (1949)
S. lactis phage	Wet	30–45	11,000	−32	Cherry and Watson (1949)
DNA					
φX174	pH 7.15, phosphate buffer	55–98	27,000	0	Ginoza et al. (1964)
RF DNA of φX174	pH 7.0, phosphate buffer	85–87	High	High	Ginoza and Miller (1965)
RF DNA of φX174	pH 7.0, phosphate buffer	>90, after denaturation	Moderate	Low	Ginoza and Miller (1965)
RNA					
TMV RNA	pH 7.15, 0.1 M phosphate	37–95	23,000	−11	Ginoza et al. (1964)
R17 RNA	pH 7.15, 0.1 M phosphate	60–92	22,000	−11	Ginoza et al. (1964)
Protein					
Serum albumin	pH 7.7		134,300	317	Stearns (1949)
	pH 3.4		96,800	224	Stearns (1949)
	pH 1.35		35,200	36.3	Stearns (1949)
Hemoglobin			76,000	153	Stearns (1949)
Pepsin			56,000	113	Stearns (1949)
RNase			33,000	19	Gajewska and Shugar (1956)

heat sensitivity of the nucleic acid, (3) the temperature range in which
the virus is heated, (4) the nature of the medium in which the virus is
heated, and (5) wet or dry heat.

1. Heat Sensitivity of the Protein

Table IV gives many examples of thermal inactivation that are characterized by high ΔH^* and ΔS^* values. These values usually indicate
that the reaction mechanism involved is protein denaturation. For example, denaturation of TMV, measured chemically, and its loss of infectivity at high temperatures (Lauffer and Price, 1940) as well as the loss
of infectivity and serological properties of SBMV and T1 phage (Pollard, 1953b), show these high values. High ΔH^* and ΔS^* values are
observed at higher temperatures, and lower values are observed at lower
temperatures, indicating a change in the inactivation process. If the
protein capsid of the virus is an absolute requirement in the transfer
of its nucleic acid into its host, a single-component exponential inactivation curve extending the limit of the sensitivity of the assay might
be obtained. If the nucleic acid released by denaturation is also infectious, a two-component survival curve may be expected, depending on
the infectiousness of the nucleic acid relative to that of the virus. The
slope (heat sensitivity) and the intercept on the y axis (fractional
contribution to the survival) of the slow component, if any, would
vary with the virus, the infectiousness of its nucleic acid, the temperature, and the nature of the medium in which the virus is heated. A
two-component survival curve is observed in the case of poliovirus
(Koch, 1960), discussed above, but not with TMV heated at 90°C,
tobacco necrosis at 86°C, or alfalfa mosaic virus at 62.5°C, all heated
in the plant sap (Price, 1940).

2. Heat Sensitivity of the Nucleic Acid

This subject was discussed in Section III,B. A few additional comments are (1) the thermal sensitivity and infectiousness of the nucleic
acids may be different when free and when heated as virus complex and
amid denatured protein, (2) the kinetics of inactivation of the nucleic
acid are influenced by the medium, and (3) in the case of double-
stranded DNA, the reaction mechanisms change with temperature as
they do for proteins. Viruses containing interlocked circular DNA (polyoma, adenovirus, etc.) are likely to add more complexity to the survival
curves, with or without their capsids; e.g., see Fig. 14, which exemplifies
kinetics of inactivation of this type of DNA.

3. Temperature Range

It has already been mentioned that at high temperatures, protein denaturation predominates. The denaturation process is a cooperative phenomenon, occurring within a narrow transition temperature region whose midpoint varies with the protein (and the virus), and as high ΔH^* values imply, the rate of change of rate constants with temperature is very high compared to that of an ordinary chemical reaction. For example, bushy stunt virus loses all its serological property between 80° and 85°C, whereas its infectivity diminishes gradually over the temperature range of 50°–80°C. At the lower temperatures, a series of single-component survival curves are obtained, e.g., FMDV (Bachrach *et al.*, 1957), TMV (Price, 1940), and NDV (Woese, 1953), from which are derived a moderate ΔH^* and a low ΔS^*. Here, the lethality is surmised to owe to some simple covalent bond scission occurring in the nucleic acid. Kinetic data alone do not prove this conclusion, but it is safe to assume that denaturation is not the cause of inactivation. A test of the antigenic activity of the inactivated virus most likely will bear out this assumption. At intermediate temperatures, as at higher temperatures, two-component curves may be obtained.

4. Medium Effect: pH, Ionic Strength, Salts, Etc.

Thermal inactivation studies reported in the literature show a confusing variety of effects. For example, enteroviruses heated at 50°C are stabilized by $MgCl_2$ but not by $MgSO_4$ (Wallis and Melnick, 1962), while myxoviruses are stabilized by $MgSO_4$ but not by $MgCl_2$ (Rapp *et al.*, 1965). T5 phage is inactivated rapidly, even at 37° C, in a medium containing 0.1 M NaCl and less than 10^{-5} M $CaCl_2$; increasing the concentration of $CaCl_2$ to 10^{-3} M reduces the rate of heat inactivation by a factor of 10^6 (Adams, 1949). In many cases, viruses are heated in broth, in others in plant sap, and still others under conditions so ill defined that the raw data are not amenable to analysis. Few, if any, generalizations can be made.

To avoid this dilemma, some recommendations may be made:

1. Conduct heat experiments in a defined or reproducible medium and carefully obtain survival curves at several different temperatures. Thermodynamic constants obtained from the rate constants should provide useful clues to the type of reactions involved.

2. Change one of the conditions of the medium, e.g., pH, and pursue experiments as in (1). Note the analysis of egg albumin summarized in Table IV. Thermodynamic parameters, ΔH^* and ΔS^*, for denaturation

of egg albumin at pH 7.7 are 134,000 cal/mole and 317 entropy units, respectively; at pH 3.4 they fall to lower values and at pH 1.35, still lower. Decreasing the pH apparently breaks intrapeptide bonds by ionizing chemical groups involved in these bondings, so that this protein requires less energy of activation for denaturation than that required at the more stable conditions.

A change in the medium might change the mechanism of reaction; in other cases, it might change the rate constants, the mechanism remaining the same. In any case, a systematic experimental approach may serve a useful purpose by elucidating the mechanism of a reaction in the case of a particular virus under particular conditions.

5. *Wet or Dry Heat*

In general, dry viruses, if they can survive the drying process itself, are more stable to heat than wet. Examples of viruses heat inactivated in the dry state (Table IV) are TMV, T1, T2, and T7 phages. All have in common low to moderate values of ΔH^* and ΔS^*, in marked contrast to high values obtained in the wet state at high temperatures. In order to get appreciable rates of inactivation, temperatures generally must

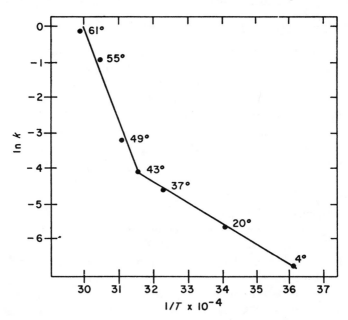

FIG. 19. Temperature dependence of the thermal inactivation rate constant for foot and mouth disease virus (Bachrach *et al.*, 1957). (Reproduced by permission from *Proceedings of the Society for Experimental Biology and Medicine*.)

be raised well beyond the temperatures of denaturation in the wet state. Infectivity is selectively destroyed, while the serological property is largely preserved in dry heat inactivation of virus (Pollard, 1953b).

Acknowledgments

The author gratefully acknowledges the helpful advice and discussions of Drs. William D. Taylor, Ernest C. Pollard, Reginald A. Deering, and Stanley Person and the excellent assistance of Miss Muriel Trask in the preparation of this manuscript. This work was supported in part by U.S. Atomic Energy Commission Contract No. AT(30-1)-3116.

References

Adams, M. H. (1949). *J. Gen. Phyisol.* **32,** 579.

Alexander, P., and Charlesby, A. (1954). *Nature* **173,** 578.

Allen, A. O. (1961). "The Radiation Chemistry of Water and Aqueous Solutions." Van Nostrand, Princeton, New Jersey.

Allison, A. C., and Burke, D. C. (1962). *J. Gen. Microbiol.* **27,** 181.

Apelgot, S., and Latarjet, R. (1967). *Intern. J. Radiation Biol.* **10,** 165.

Aurisicchio, S., Cortini, G., Emma, V., and Graziosi, F. (1959). *Intern. J. Radiation Biol.* **1,** 86.

Bachrach, H. L., Breese, S. S. Jr., Callis, J. J., Hess, W. R., and Patty, R. E. (1957). *Proc. Soc. Exptl. Biol. Med.* **95,** 147.

Barricelli, N. A. (1956). *Acta Biotheoret.* **11,** 107.

Basilico, C., and Di Mayorca, G. (1965). *Proc. Natl. Acad. Sci. U.S.* **54,** 125.

Benjamin, T. L. (1965). *Proc. Natl. Acad. Sci. U.S.* **54,** 121.

Benzer, S. (1952). *J. Bacteriol.* **63,** 59.

Burgi, E., and Hershey, A. D. (1963). *Biophys. J.* **3,** 309.

Black, F. L. (1959). *Virology* **7,** 184.

Boyce, R. P., and Howard-Flanders, P. (1964). *Proc. Natl. Acad. Sci. U.S.* **51,** 293.

Brenner, S., Streisinger, G., Horne, R. W., Champe, S. P., Barnett, L., Benzer, S., and Rees, M. W. (1959). *J. Mol. Biol.* **1,** 281.

Brown, D. M., and Todd, A. R. (1953). *J. Chem. Soc.* p. 2040.

Bryan, W. G., Lorenz, E., and Moloney, J. B. (1950). *J. Natl. Cancer Inst.* **10,** 1215.

Buzzell, A., and Lauffer, M. A. (1952). *Arch. Biochem. Biophys.* **39,** 195.

Buzzell, A., Trkula, A., and Lauffer, M. A. (1956). *Arch. Biochem. Biophys.* **63,** 470.

Caspar, D. L. D. (1956). *Nature* **177,** 928.

Caspar, D. L. D., and Klug, A. (1962). *Cold Spring Harbor Symp. Quant. Biol.* **27,** 1.

Castagnoli, C., Donini, P., and Graziosi, F. (1959). *Giorn. Microbiol.* **1,** 86.

Cherry, W. B., and Watson, D. W. (1949). *J. Bacteriol.* **58,** 1146.

Cotton, I. M., and Lockingen, L. S. (1963). *Proc. Natl. Acad. Sci. U.S.* **50,** 363.

Crawford, L. V., and Crawford, E. M. (1961). *Virology* **13,** 227.

Crick, F. H. C., and Watson, J. D. (1956). *Nature* **177,** 473.

Crothers, D. M., and Zimm, B. H. (1964). *J. Mol. Biol.* **9,** 1.

Crowther, J. A. (1938). *Brit. J. Radiol.* **11**, 132.

Delihas, N. (1961). *Virology* **13**, 242.

Dessauer, F. (1922). *Z. Physik* **12**, 38.

Dirksen, M. L., Wiberg, J. S., Koerner, J. F., and Buchanan, J. M. (1960). *Proc. Natl. Acad. Sci. U.S.* **46**, 1425.

Dolphin, G. W., and Hutchinson, F. (1960). *Radiation Res.* **13**, 403.

Doty, P., Marmur, J., and Sueoka, N. (1959). *Brookhaven Symp. Biol.* **12**, 1.

Doty, P., Marmur, J., Eignes, J., and Schildkraut, C. (1960). *Proc. Natl. Acad. Sci. U.S.* **46**, 461.

Duesberg, P. H., and Robinson, W. S. (1965). *Proc. Natl. Acad. Sci. U.S.* **54**, 794.

Dulbecco, R., and Vogt, M. (1963). *Proc. Natl. Acad. Sci. U.S.* **50**, 236.

Ebisuzaki, K. (1962). *J. Mol. Biol.* **5**, 506.

Ebisuzaki, K. (1965). *Virology* **26**, 39.

Eldjarn, L., and Pihl, A. (1958). *Radiation Res.* **9**, 110.

Epstein, R. H. (1958). *Virology* **6**, 382.

Fiers, W., and Sinsheimer, R. L. (1962a). *J. Mol. Biol.* **5**, 424.

Fiers, W., and Sinsheimer, R. L. (1962b). *J. Mol. Biol.* **5**, 408.

Flaks, J. G., Lichtenstein, J., and Cohen, S. S. (1959). *J. Biol. Chem.* **234**, 1507.

Fluke, D. J. (1966). *Radiation Res.* **28**, 336.

Fluke, D. J., and Beineke, B. (1967). *Abstr. Radiation Res. Soc.*, May 7–11, 1967.

Fluke, D. J., and Forro, F. Jr. (1960). *Radiation Res.* **13**, 305.

Fluke, D. J., and Pollard, E. C. (1955). *Ann. N.Y. Acad. Sci.* **59**, 484.

Fluke, D. J., Drew, R., and Pollard, E. C. (1952). *Proc. Natl. Acad. Sci. U.S.* **38**, 180.

Foster, R. A. C., Johnson, F. H., and Miller, V. K. (1949). *J. Gen. Physiol.* **33**, 1.

Fox, M. (1965). *J. Gen. Physiol.* **49**, 183.

Franklin, R. E. (1956). *Nature* **177**, 929.

Freifelder, D. (1965). *Proc. Natl. Acad. Sci. U.S.* **54**, 128.

Friedman, M., and Cowles, P. (1953). *J. Bacteriol.* **66**, 379.

Funk, F., Bockrath, R. C., and Person, S. (1968). *Radiation Res.*, in press.

Gajewska, E., and Shugar, D. (1956). *Bull. Acad. Polon. Sci., Classe (II)* **4**, 157.

Gard, S. (1960). *Ann. N.Y. Acad. Sci.* **83**, 638.

Garen, A., and Zinder, N. D. (1955). *Virology* **1**, 347.

Gellert, M. (1967). *Proc. Natl. Acad. Sci. U.S.* **57**, 148.

Gesteland, R. F., and Boedtker, H. (1964). *J. Mol. Biol.* **8**, 496.

Gibbs, J. H., and DiMarzio, E. A. (1959). *J. Chem. Phys.* **30**, 271.

Ginoza, W. (1958). *Nature* **181**, 1958.

Ginoza, W. (1963). *Nature* **199**, 453.

Ginoza, W., and Miller, R. C. (1965). *Proc. Natl. Acad. Sci. U.S.* **54**, 551.

Ginoza, W., and Norman, A. (1957). *Nature* **179**, 520.

Ginoza, W., and Vessey, K. B. (1966). *2nd Intern. Biophys. Congr. of IOPAB, Vienna, Austria. Sept. 1966,* p. 585.

Ginoza, W., and Zimm, B. H. (1961). *Proc. Natl. Acad. Sci. U.S.* **47**, 639.

Ginoza, W., Hoelle, C. J., Vessey, K. B., and Carmack, C. (1964). *Nature* **203**, 606.

Glasstone, S., Laidler, K. J., and Eyring, H. (1941). "The Theory of Rate Processes" (L. P. Hammett, ed.). McGraw-Hill, New York.

Gordon, M. P., and Huff, J. W. (1962). *Biochemistry* **1**, 481.

Gordy, W., Pruden, B., and Snipes, W. (1965). *Proc. Natl. Acad. Sci. U.S.* **53**, 751.

Gowen, J. W. (1940). *Proc. Natl. Acad. Sci. U.S.* **26**, 8.

Guild, W. R., and Robson, M. (1963). *Proc. Natl. Acad. Sci. U.S.* **50**, 106.

Hagen, U. (1967). *Biochim. Biophys. Acta* **134**, 45.
Harriman, P. D., and Stent, G. S. (1964). *J. Mol. Biol.* **10**, 488.
Hart, R. G. (1955). *Proc. Natl. Acad. Sci. U.S.* **41**, 261.
Hayashi, M., Hayashi, M. N., and Spiegelman, S. (1963). *Science* **140**, 1313.
Hershey, A. D., and Chase, M. (1952). *J. Gen. Physiol.* **36**, 39.
Hershey, A. D., Kamen, M. D., Kennedy, J. W., and Gest, H. (1951). *J. Gen. Physiol.* **34**, 305.
Hershey, A. D., Burgi, E., and Ingraham, L. (1962). *Biophys. J.* **2**, 423.
Hiatt, C. W. (1964). *Bacteriol. Rev.* **28**, 150.
Hine, G. J., and Brownell, G. L. (1956). "Radiation Dosimetry." Academic Press, New York.
Holweck, F. (1938). *Compt. Rend.* **207**, 380.
Horne, R. W., and Wildy, P. (1963). *Advan. Virus Res.* **10**, 101.
Hotz, G. (1966). *Z. Naturforsch.* **21b**, 148.
Hotz, G., and Müller, A. (1961). *Z. Naturforsch.* **16b**, 282.
Howard-Flanders, P., and Alper, T. (1957). *Radiation* **7**, 518.
Hradečná, Z. (1967). *Intern. J. Radiation Biol.* **12**, 169.
Hutchinson, F., and Pollard, E. C. (1961). *In* "Mechanisms in Radiobiology" (M. Errera and A. Forssberg, eds.), Vol. I, p. 1. Academic Press, New York.
Jagger, J., and Pollard, E. C. (1956). *Radiation Res.* **4**, 1.
Jansz, H. S., Pouwels, P. H., and van Rotterdam, C. (1963). *Biochim. Biophys. Acta* **76**, 655.
Johns, H. E. (1964). "The Physics of Radiology." Thomas, Springfield, Illinois.
Kaplan, C. (1958). *J. Gen. Microbiol.* **18**, 58.
Kauzman, W. (1959). *Advan. Protein Chem.* **14**, 1.
Keene, J. P. (1957). *Radiation Res.* **6**, 424.
Kempner, E. S., and Pollard, E. C. (1961). *Biophys. J.* **1**, 265.
Klug, A., and Caspar, D. L. D. (1960). *Advan. Virus Res.* **7**, 225.
Koch, G. (1960). *Virology* **12**, 601.
Konrad, M. W., and Stent, G. S. (1965). *Z. Vererbungslehre* **96**, 66.
Kornberg, A., Zimmerman, S. B., Kornberg, S. R., and Josse, J. (1959). *Proc. Natl. Acad. Sci. U.S.* **45**, 772.
Kozinski, A. W. (1961). *Virology* **13**, 124.
Kraft, L., and Pollard, E. C. (1954). *Proc. Soc. Exptl. Biol. Med.* **86**, 306.
Krieg, D. R. (1959). *Virology* **8**, 80.
Kroeger, A., and Kempf, J. (1959). *J. Bacteriol.* **77**, 237.
Krueger, A. P. (1932). *J. Gen. Physiol.* **15**, 363.
Latarjet, R. (1964). *In* "Cellular Control Mechanisms and Cancer" (P. Emmelot and O. Mühlbock, eds.), p. 326. Elsevier, Amsterdam.
Latarjet, R., and Chamailland, L. (1962). *Bull. Cancer* **49**, 382.
Laterjet, R., and Goldé, A. (1962). *Compt. Rend.* **255**, 2846.
Latarjet, R., Ekert, B., and Demerseman, P. (1963.) *Radiation Res.* Suppl. 3, 247.
Lauffer, M. A., and Price, W. C. (1940). *J. Biol. Chem.* **133**, 1.
Lea, D. E. (1962). "Actions of Radiation on Living Cells." Cambridge Univ. Press, London and New York.
Lea, D. E., and Salaman, M. H. (1942). *Brit. J. Exptl. Pathol.* **23**, 27.
Lea, D. E., and Smith, K. M. (1942). *Parasitology* **34**, 227.
Lea, D. E., Smith, K. M., Holmes, B., and Markham, R. (1944). *Parasitology* **36**, 110.
Lerman, L. S., and Tolmach, L. J. (1959). *Biochim. Biophys. Acta* **33**, 371.

Levinson, H. S., and Garber, E. B. (1965). *Nature* **207**, 751.
Lunan, K. D., and Sinsheimer, R. L. (1956). *Virology* **2**, 455.
Luria, S. E., and Exner, F. M. (1941). *Proc. Natl. Acad. Sci. U.S.* **27**, 370.
McCrea, J. F. (1960). *Ann. N.Y. Acad. Sci.* **83**, 654.
Marmur, J., and Doty, P. (1961). *J. Mol. Biol.* **3**, 585.
Marmur, J., and Lane, D. (1960). *Proc. Natl. Acad. Sci. U.S.* **46**, 453.
Mitra, S., Enger, M. D., and Kaesburg, P. (1963). *Proc. Natl. Acad. Sci. U.S.* **50**, 68.
Paranchych, W., and Graham, A. F. (1962). *J. Cellular Comp. Physiol.* **60**, 199.
Pollard, E. C. (1953a). *Advan. Biol. Med. Phys.* **3**, 153.
Pollard, E. C. (1953b). "The Physics Of Viruses." Academic Press, New York.
Pollard, E. C., and Barrett, N. (1959). *Radiation Res.* **11**, 781.
Pollard, E. C., and Dimond, A. E. (1956). *Phytopathology* **46**, 214.
Pollard, E. C., and Forro, F., Jr. (1951). *Arch. Biochem. Biophys.* **32**, 256.
Pollard, E. C., and Reaume, M. (1951). *Arch. Biochem. Biophys.* **32**, 278.
Pollard, E. C., Guild, W. P., Hutchinson, F., and Setlow, R. B. (1955). *Progr. Biophys. Biophys. Chem.* **5**, 72.
Pouwels, P. H., and Jansz, H. S. (1964). *Biochim. Biophys. Acta* **91**, 177.
Powell, H. M., and Culbertson, C. G. (1955). *Proc. Soc. Exptl. Biol. Med.* **89**, 490.
Price, W. C. (1940). *Arch. Ges. Virusforsch.* **1**, 373.
Rapp, F., Butel, J. S., and Wallis, C. (1965). *J. Bacteriol.* **90**, 132.
Rauth, A. M., and Hutchinson, F. (1962). *In* "Biochemical Effects of Ionizing Radiation at the Molecular Level." IAEA, Vienna.
Rauth, A. M., and Simpson, J. A. (1964). *Radiation Res.* **22**, 643.
Rice, S. A., and Doty, P. (1957). *J. Am. Chem. Soc.* **79**, 3937.
Roger, M., and Hotchkiss, R. D. (1961). *Proc. Natl. Acad. Sci. U.S.* **47**, 653.
Roller, A. (1961). Ph.D. Thesis, California Institute of Technology.
Rubinstein, I., Thomas, C. A., and Hershey, A. D. (1961). *Proc. Natl. Acad. Sci. U.S.* **47**, 1113.
Sauerbier, W. (1962). *Virology* **16**, 398.
Schachman, H. K. (1963). *Cold Spring Harbor Symp. Quant. Biol.* **28**, 409.
Schachman, H. K., and Williams, R. C. (1959). *In* "The Viruses" (F. M. Burnet and W. M. Stanley, eds.), Vol. 1, p. 223. Academic Press, New York.
Schambra, F. E., and Hutchinson, F. (1964). *Radiation Res.* **23**, 514.
Scholes, G., Ward, J. F., and Weiss, J. J. (1960). *J. Mol. Biol.* **2**, 379.
Schuster, H. (1960). *In* "The Nucleic Acids" (E. Chargaff and J. N. Davidson, eds.), Vol. 3, p. 245. Academic Press, New York.
Sertic, V., and Bulgakov, N. (1935). *Compt. Rend. Sol. Biol.* **119**, 1270.
Setlow, R. B. (1952). *Proc. Natl. Acad. Sci. U.S.* **38**, 166.
Setlow, R. B., and Carrier, W. L. (1964). *Proc. Natl. Acad. Sci. U.S.* **51**, 226.
Sinanoglu, O., and Abdulmur, S. (1965). *Federation Proc.* **24**, Suppl. 15. S12.
Sinsheimer, R. L. (1959). *J. Mol. Biol.* **1**, 43.
Sinsheimer, R. L. (1960). *In* "The Nucleic Acids" (E. Chargaff and J. N. Davidson, eds.), Vol. 3, p. 187.
Sinsheimer, R. L., Starman, B., Nagler, C., and Guthrie, G. S. (1962). *J. Mol. Biol.* **4**, 142.
Smith, K. O. (1965). *Science* **148**, 100.
Stahl, F. W. (1959). *In* "The Viruses" (F. W. Burnet and W. M. Stanley, eds.), Vol. 2, p. 380.
Stanley, W. M. (1936). *Science* **83**, 626.

Stearns, A. E. (1949). *Advan. Enzymol.* **9,** 25.

Stent, G. S. (1955). *J. Gen. Physiol.* **38,** 853.

Stent, G. S. (1958). *Advan. Virus Res.* **5,** 95.

Stent, G. S. (1963). "Molecular Biology of Bacterial Viruses." Freeman, San Francisco, California.

Stent, G. S., and Fuerst, C. R. (1955). *J. Gen. Physiol.* **38,** 441.

Stent, G. S., and Jerne, H. K. (1955). *Proc. Natl. Acad. Sci. U.S.* **41,** 704.

Studier, F. W. (1965). *J. Mol. Biol.* **11,** 373.

Symonds, N., and McCloy, E. W. (1958). *Virology* **6,** 649.

Syverton, J. T., Berry, G. P., and Warren, S. L. (1941). *J. Exptl. Med.* **74,** 223.

Takebe, H. (1964). *Virology* **24,** 323.

Tamm, C., Shapiro, H. S., Lipschitz, R., and Chargaff, E. (1953). *J. Biol. Chem.* **203,** 673.

Taylor, D. W., and Ginoza, W. (1967). *Proc. Natl. Acad. Sci. U.S.* **58,** 1753.

Tessman, I., Tessman, E. S., and Stent, G. S. (1957). *Virology* **4,** 209.

Till, J. E., and Pollard, E. C. (1958). *Radiation Res.* **8,** 344.

Timm, E. A., McLean, I. W., Jr., Kupsky, C., and Hook, A. E. (1956). *J. Immunol.* **77,** 444.

Traub, F. D., Friedemann, A. B., Brasch, A., and Huber, W. (1951). *J. Immunol.* **67,** 379.

Wallis, L. C., and Melnick, J. L. (1962). *Virology* **16,** 504.

Watson, J. D. (1950). *J. Bacteriol.* **60,** 667.

Watson, J. D. (1952). *J. Bacteriol.* **63,** 473.

Watson, J. D., and Littlefield, J. W. (1960). *J. Mol. Biol.* **2,** 161.

Weil, R. (1963). *Proc. Natl. Acad. Sci. U.S.* **49,** 480.

Weil, R., and Vinograd, J. (1963). *Proc. Natl. Acad. Sci. U.S.* **50,** 730.

Weiss, B., and Richardson, C. C. (1967). *Proc. Natl. Acad. Sci. U.S.* **57,** 1021.

Weiss, J. J. (1964). *Progr. Nucleic Acid Res. Mol. Biol.* **3,** 103.

Weiss, J. J., Allen, A. O., and Schwarz, H. A. (1956). *Proc. 1st Intern. Conf. Peaceful Uses Ato. Energy, Geneva, 1955* Vol. 14, p. 179. Columbia Univ. Press (I.D.S.), New York.

Weissbach, A., and Korn, D. (1963). *J. Biol. Chem.* **238,** 3383.

Whitmore, G. F., and Pollard, E. C. (1955). *Science* **122,** 335.

Winkler, U. (1964). *Virology* **24,** 518.

Woese, C. R. (1953). Ph.D. Thesis, Yale University, New Haven, Connecticut.

Woese, C. R. (1956). *Arch. Biochem. Biophys.* **63,** 212.

Wollman, E., and Lacassagne, A. (1940). *Ann. Inst. Pasteur* **64,** 5.

Younger, J. S. (1957). *J. Immunol.* **78,** 282.

Zamenhof, S., Alexander, H. E., and Leidy, G. (1953). *J. Exptl. Med.* **98,** 373.

Zimmer, K. G. (1941). *Biol. Zentr.* **61,** 208.

Zimmer, K. G. (1961). "Studies on Quantitative Radiation Biology." Hafner, New York.

5 Methods for Testing Antiviral Agents

František Link

I. Introduction: Principles of Prophylactic and Therapeutic
   Assays in Virology 211
II. Experiments in Animals 215
    A. The Biological Material 216
    B. The Design of the Experiment 224
III. Experiments in Eggs 255
    A. Embryonated Eggs 257
    B. Deembryonated Eggs 262
IV. Experiments in Tissue Cultures 263
    A. The Use of Chorioallantoic Membrane Fragments 265
    B. The Use of Monolayers 267
V. Conclusion: Comments on Statistical Evaluation of the
   Experiment 274
   Acknowledgment 277
   References 277

I. Introduction: Principles of Prophylactic and Therapeutic Assays in Virology

When speaking about antiviral agents, one would like to have a substance at his disposal that would share the therapeutic properties of a pharmacon. There is, however, an essential difference in the mode of action of antiviral agents and pharmacons. Pharmacons are usually prescribed in order to heal or at least to influence the course of developed illness, the existence of which has been proved by clinical symptoms or by biochemical tests. This means that pharmacons are used therapeutically. What is the situation in the case of a viral disease? There are two possibilities: viral diseases being infectious, the majority of them can be diagnosed when they occur in epidemic proportions, whereas many diseases that cannot be diagnosed are sup-

211

posed to be of viral origin owing to the fact that no proper diagnostic tests are available until the first clinical symptoms appear. The treatment of the latter kind of diseases may be—logically—only symptomatic, and the proper diagnosis—by means of serological tests—can be done very often even as late as the stage when the etiologic agent in its infectious form is not detectable in the organism. The treatment of a viral disease thus consists of two phases: (1) the inhibiting of the infectivity of the etiologic agent and (2) the healing of the clinical symptoms and/or of functio laesa that are usually characterized by the trophism of the pathogen. The majority of viral diseases are acute, since virus multiplication is very often blocked or diminished by several unspecific and specific inhibitors, probably also by interferon, earlier than clinical symptoms indicate the need for therapeutic procedures. The main effort in finding active antiviral agents has been focused, therefore, on substances that could be used in viral diseases occurring in epidemics, where the prophylactic use of an antiviral agent would be indicated. Since this kind of virus belongs mainly to the influenza group, it is not surprising that the majority of assays on antiviral agents has been carried out in laboratories with model infections of influenza viruses.

Prophylactic treatment should strictly mean the application of antiviral agents before the infection proper has been initiated. The initiation of infection, on the other hand, is not simply contact of the biological material with the infectious agent. As mentioned above, different factors may eliminate the infection even if the infected object was attacked with considerably high doses of the virus. Otherwise, it happens very often that a prophylactically induced antiviral principle, eventually in the early prodromal phase of the illness, must block or at least suppress the virus multiplication that has already been started.

According to the situation just described, this chapter will discuss prophylactic assays in virus infections in those cases when the antiviral agent has been applied prior to or during the eclipse phase of the infection. Therapeutic assays reflect those cases in which it might have been demonstrated that the virus was multiplying in the organism. The results obtained with antiviral agents administered after trophic or toxic effects have been observed will be considered irrelevant, since these effects should be counteracted by other special pharmacons rather than by specific antiviral agents.

The reaction of the organism toward both the infection and the antiviral agent may be quite different according to the biological material, since each experimental model may show a different pattern with respect to the effectiveness of an antiviral agent. The general rule in pharmacology that no results should be related automatically from one species to the other is also valid in virology. For this reason nobody is authorized to make a prognosis that an antiviral agent which has been found effective in one model experiment will be effective in another situation—at least not in human therapy. But the hope that this problem might some day be eliminated is as fascinating as it is worthwhile to deal at the present time with assaying antiviral agents, even in an inadequate model infection.

Antiviral agents may be assayed theoretically in all test systems according to the possible combinations of virus and susceptible host system. It is, however, a peculiarity that the same potential antivirals may differ in their effectiveness against the same virus infection, when assayed in different test systems, depending on the route of application of the virus and/or of the antiviral. This may be demonstrated in the next example, where the prophylactic antiviral effect of γ-inhibitor (GI) was studied in white mice during the first three days after infection (Link *et al.*, 1965a).

Mice were treated intranasally with 30,000 hemagglutination-inhibiting units (HIU) of GI isolated from horse serum. Two hours later the animals were inoculated with 10^7 estimated 50% infective dose (EID_{50}) of either a mouse lung adapted or unadapted line of inhibitor-sensitive A 2 influenza virus. Lungs were removed from the mice 22, 46, and 70 hours after inoculation, and the virus titers in the 10% lung homogenates were assayed in suspended chorioallantoic membrane tissue cultures. No virus multiplication could be detected for 3 days with the unadapted virus line. After administration of the adapted virus line, the infection was blocked for the first 22 hours and only significantly lowered on the 2 subsequent days (Fig. 1).

The difference in sensitivity toward GI of the model infections discussed above may be further illustrated by a therapeutic assay. Virus multiplication was studied in lungs of mice to which 30,000 HI units of GI were administered 2 hours before or 2, 6, 10, 14, or 18 hours after infection with 10^7/ml EID_{50} of the adapted (a) or unadapted (b) virus line. The virus levels in the GI-treated mice were determined 22 hours after inoculation.

The results show that after GI treatment (Fig. 2) no virus multiplication occurred in the lungs of mice inoculated with the unadapted virus line. After infection of animals with the mouse-adapted virus line, GI significantly lowered the virus titers in the lungs when

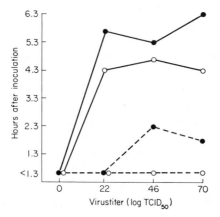

FIG. 1. Prophylactic effect of GI on A2 influenza virus multiplication in mouse lungs. Mouse lung-adapted (●) or unadapted (○) virus. Mice untreated (—) and treated (– –) with GI. Abscissa: hours after inoculation. Ordinate: virus titers in lungs (log TCID$_{50}$) (Link et al., 1965b).

administered 2–6 hours after infection. When GI was administered 10 hours after infection, there was no difference in the virus titers in the lungs, whereas compared with the controls significantly higher virus titers could be demonstrated in the lungs of mice treated with GI as late as 14 and 18 hours after infection.

In this way GI was found to be not only more effective in infection with unadapted virus but it also displayed a therapeutic effect when adminis-

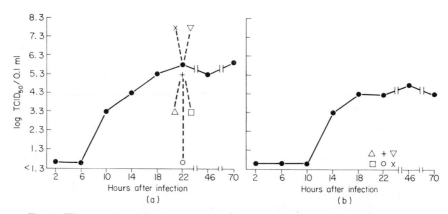

FIG 2. Therapeutic effect of GI on A2 influenza virus multiplication in mouse lungs. Treatment 2 hours before (○) and 2 (△), 6 (□), 10 (+), 14 (×), and 18 (▽) hours after infection with 10^7 ml EID$_{50}$. Adapted virus line (a), unadapted virus line (b). Controls did not receive GI (●) (Link et al., 1965b).

tered to mice as late as when at least two cycles of multiplication of the unadapted virus line had occurred in the lungs (Link *et al.*, 1965b).

This chapter cannot, indeed, discuss all methods that have been described. The author's main effort was focused on systematizing the design of antiviral testing, emphasizing that, even if the methods dealt with were prepared to be complete, they should serve only as prototypes, and the logic of the approach to any special project should be a prerequisite when testing different kinds of antiviral agents in different biological systems.

II. Experiments in Animals

Testing of antiviral agents in experimental animals will be discussed in this chapter first, even if it seems as though the building is being started with the top floor instead of the basement, and the subject of testing substances in biological systems will not be discussed in the usual hierarchical way starting with unorganized tissue cultures. The reason for this is that the author wanted to emphasize the importance of the general approach of the experimenter to this topic, which can be done better if the test substance is understood as a highly organized entity. The reaction of this kind of biological material to a stimulus is complex enough to resemble natural conditions of infection more than tissue cultures or embryonated eggs may do, but it is necessary to realize that it is not simply quantitatively different from that of human beings. Usually experiments in tissue cultures are regarded as means of screening antiviral agents in order to find the most convenient compound for testing further in laboratory animals. The concept that substances selected in such screening tests and found active in laboratory animals should be submitted to clinical trial is one of the approaches in this field of research, but not always the best one. It is a very well-known fact that all antiviral substances do not work in all model infections, and even if it is assumed that only a proportion of the antiviral agents that prove to be active in tissue cultures will work in laboratory animals, the opposite of this view may be also true. Some antiviral agents that are active in laboratory animals do not reflect this property when tested in tissue cultures or in eggs.

Since the difference in activity of an antiviral agent in laboratory animals and in human beings is not only quantitative, the testing of antiviral agents in human beings is not the next step after testing it in animals as is the case in the testing of antiviral agents in tissue cultures, when the next step is testing in laboratory animals. My intention is also, therefore, to view the testing of antiviral agents in laboratory animals as a screening test. Since the latter biological material is more complex than tissue cultures, the screening process should be also more complex than that employed with tissue cultures.

A. THE BIOLOGICAL MATERIAL

One reason for testing antiviral agents in biological material is that this sort of experiment is uniquely specific in comparison with physico-chemical reactions between virus and antiviral agent. Though the latter may give us information about some kind of inactivation of a virus by an antiviral agent, this inactivation may be drastic enough— e.g., the reaction between virus and some strong acid—to kill not only the virus but also the eventual host system. A second reason has to do with the nature of viruses, which, being parasites, require a living system for their multiplication.

The physicochemical instruments and laboratory accessories for the chemist's work are replaced in the virologist's laboratory by biological material. Although the chemist's work is reproducible with a very small range of error, the reproducibility of an experiment with biological material depends not only on the reliability of the method and on the skill of the experimenter, but also on the variability of the biological material. Variability in response is characteristic of the biological material and is a factor that cannot be fully eliminated, but it should be understood and taken into account whenever the results of an experiment are to be evaluated. The variability of laboratory animals, represented in this chapter mainly by white mice, is characteristic of the whole population. Since it is impossible to carry out the experiment in an indefinite number of mice, we must choose a sample at random from this population. Our main effort should be to choose a homogeneous sample, the response of which is characterized by some well-defined distribution law.

Each experiment must be carried out in homogeneous biological material. The homogeneity may be badly influenced by the ages and sex differences of the animals. The age of adult mice should be positively correlated with their weights, which are roughly between 14 and 20 gm; a difference in weight of no more than 2 gm should be tolerated when starting the experiment. Unfortunately, in virological laboratories sufficient importance is not placed on the sex of the animals in the experiment. The following example will illustrate this problem (Link *et al.*, 1963).

The experiments were carried out in mice weighing 16–18 gm. Each experimental group consisted of 10 mice. The mice were infected with 10-fold dilutions of the mouse-adapted Em_2 strain of A 1 influenza virus representing a variant of the Em_1 strain isolated in Moscow in 1940. Infective allantoic fluid was inoculated into the mice intranasally under light ether anesthesia in four drop quantities. The animals were observed for 2 weeks with the deaths recorded daily. The influence of the sex of the mice on the dynamics of infection was studied in three series of experiments: in the first in males, in the second in females, and in the third in a mixed population of males and females of unknown proportionality of sex. When evaluating the results, we created artificially a fourth group in which the sex ratio was 1 : 1. The mice in all the groups were infected with infected allantoic fluid in 10-fold steps from 10^{-2} to 10^{-5}.

The cumulative mortality percentage of the mice presented in log probability net illustrates the dynamics of infection in males (Fig. 3), females (Fig. 4), in a mixed population of known (1 : 1) sex ratio (Fig. 5), and in mixed population of unknown sex ratio (Fig. 6). Figure 3 shows that the 50% mortality in male mice occurred on days 4.2; 5.2; 6.2; and 7.2; after inoculation with virus dilutions of 10^{-2}–10^{-5}, respectively. In female mice (Fig. 4) the corresponding days were 3.2; 4.2; 5.2; and 6.2; i.e., as if the females were infected with as much as 1 log

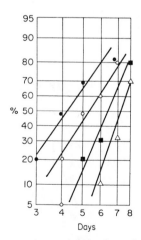

FIG. 3. Mortality rates in experimental infection of male white mice. Abscissa: days after inoculation. Ordinate: cumulative mortality percentages. Virus dilutions: (●) 10^{-2}, (○) 10^{-3}, (■) 10^{-4}, (△) 10^{-5} (Link *et al.*, 1963).

FRANTIŠEK LINK

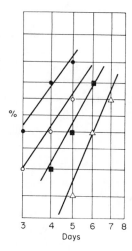

Fig. 4. Mortality rates in experimental infection of female white mice. Data points have the same meanings as those in Fig. 3 (Link *et al.*, 1963).

unit higher concentrations of virus than the males. There was no significant difference in parallelism between the corresponding regression lines in Figs. 3 and 4, nor in Fig. 5, where the mortality rate was evaluated in a mixed population of a known (1 : 1) sex ratio. Here the 50% mortality occurred on days 3.7; 4.7; 5.7; and 6.7; i.e., with just ±0.5 log differences in virus dilutions compared with Figs. 3 and 4. The paral-

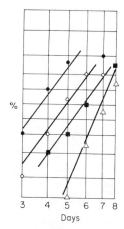

Fig. 5. Mortality rates in experimental infection of a 1 : 1 mixed population of male and female mice. Data points have the same meanings as those in Fig. 3 (Link *et al.*, 1963).

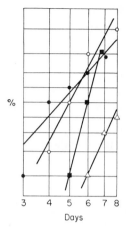

%

3   4   5   6   7   8

Days

FIG. 6. Mortality rates in experimental infection of a heterogeneous mouse population of unknown sex ratio. Data points have the same meaning as those in Fig. 3 (Link *et al.*, 1963).

lelism of the corresponding regression lines in Fig. 5 is based on the homogeneity of the biological material when the sex ratio was 1 : 1, whereas departure from parallelism tested at a 95% probability level in Fig. 6 did not allow us to gain any information on the dynamics of infection because of the heterogeneity of the biological test material.

We are often limited with respect to the number of animals in an experiment not only by financial factors but also by the time element. In general, however, experiments should not be carried out in a group consisting of less than five animals. In multiple-dose quantal-response experiments, groups consisting at least of 10 animals are recommended, whereas in single-dose experiments this number should not be less than 20 in order to obtain a sufficient amount of information for statistical evaluation of the data. Otherwise, the significance of the single-dose experiments also depends on the number of observations. This may be demonstrated easily by comparing two series of experiments characterized with the same mean responses but gathered from different numbers of subjects.

For evaluation ôf the data, the student's t test was used in this example. The techniques of the t test are as follows. First, the arithmetic means $(\bar{x})$ and their standard errors (se) must be calculated according to the equations:

$$\bar{x} = Sx/n \tag{1}$$

and

$$se = [S(x - \bar{x})^2/n(n - 1)]^{1/2} \tag{2}$$

where x denotes the individual responses, n denotes the number of responses, and S denotes the sum.

The equation for the t test is as follows:

$$t_{n-1} = \frac{\bar{x}_c - \bar{x}_e}{(se_e + se_c)^{1/2}} \tag{3}$$

where $\bar{x}_c$ denotes the arithmetic mean of the control group, $\bar{x}_e$ denotes the arithmetic mean of the experimental group, se_c denotes the standard error of $\bar{x}_c$, and se_e denotes the standard error of $\bar{x}_e$.

TABLE I[a]

THE DISTRIBUTION OF t

Degrees of freedom (f)	Probability			
	10%	5%	1%	0.1%
1	6.31	12.7	63.7	637.0
2	2.92	4.30	9.92	31.6
3	2.35	3.18	5.84	12.9
4	2.13	2.78	4.60	8.61
5	2.02	2.57	4.03	6.86
6	1.94	2.45	3.71	5.96
7	1.90	2.36	3.50	5.40
8	1.86	2.31	3.36	5.04
9	1.83	2.26	3.25	4.78
10	1.81	2.23	3.17	4.59
12	1.78	2.18	3.06	4.32
14	1.76	2.14	2.98	4.14
16	1.75	2.12	2.92	4.02
18	1.73	2.10	2.88	3.92
20	1.72	2.09	2.84	3.85
∞	1.645	1.960	2.576	3.291

[a] Abridged from Fisher and Yates (1948, Table III).

The calculated t value is then to be compared with expected t values encountered in t tables (Table I) at a number of observations less one $(n-1)$ according to different probability levels. A higher calculated than expected t value insures the significance in difference between $\bar{x}_c$ and $\bar{x}_e$ at the anticipated probability level. The following example will throw some light on how the number of responses may influence the significance of the difference between two sets of observations.

The estimated means in the control and experimental groups being

7 and 5, respectively, the significance of the difference is calculated on the basis of individual responses.

For the first set:

Control group (c)	Experimental group (e)
3	5
4	6
5	7
6	8
7	9
$x_c = 5$	$x_e = 7$
$se_c = 0.5$	$se_e = 0.5$

$$t_9 = \frac{7-5}{1} = 2$$

For the second set:

Control group (c)	Experimental group (e)
3	5
3	5
4	6
4	6
4	6
4	6
5	7
5	7
5	7
5	7
5	7
5	7
5	7
6	8
6	8
6	8
6	8
7	9
7	9
$\bar{x}_c = 5$	$\bar{x}_e = 7$
$se_c = 0.063$	$se_e = 0.063$

$$t/39/ = \frac{7-5}{0.35} = 5.7$$

The expected values according to the t table were as high as 2.26 and 2.02, respectively. The calculated t values were found to be 2.00 and 5.7. No significant difference could be tested in the first set at the 95% probability level, whereas the difference between the means in the second set was found to be highly significant at the same probability level.

In addition to the above-mentioned internal variability factor, the homogeneity of biological material is also influenced by the so-called external variability factor. The latter is characterized by error on the part of the experimenter and owes to the care of the laboratory animals prior to and during the experiment. Even if the daily regime in the animal house may be easily standardized, tolerance toward the infection may be influenced by improper handling of the animals. In the majority of experiments, when antiviral agents are to be given to infected animals daily, one cannot avoid removing the animals from their cages. If one holds them by their tails, convulsions may be evoked followed by death. The same procedure must be used, therefore, with both the experimental and the control groups in order to balance the external variability. Later on controls should be treated with the solvent of an antiviral agent at the same time intervals as the animals in the experimental group. This is very often avoided, particularly when the solvent is as inert as is distilled water or physiological solution, which exerts no side effect in the animals. The sequelae will be demonstrated in the next experiment (Link *et al.*, 1963).

Mice in control groups were infected intranasally with four drops of 10^{-2}, 10^{-3}, and 10^{-4} dilutions of influenza A 1 virus (strain Em_2) containing allantoic fluids. Mice in two experimental groups were infected with a 10^{-3} dilution of the virus. In the first group phosphate-buffered saline was given in one injection, whereas in the second group the same solution was given in two injections. Subcutaneous injections of 0.1 ml of phosphate-buffered saline were given each group daily for 10 days, starting with the day of infection. Deaths of animals were recorded daily; cumulative mortality percentages are illustrated in Fig. 7. It can be seen that phosphate-buffered saline did not alter the dynamics of infection at all; the 50% mortality of control mice occurred on days 4.5, 6, and 7.6, respectively. In the experimental group, however, after two daily injections of saline, the mice died as if they had been infected with significantly higher virus concentrations than the controls.

The experimenter's aim is to test the activity of an antiviral agent under optimal conditions. The best effect is expected from the highest

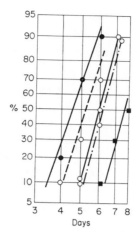

FIG. 7. Mortality rates in experimental influenza infection of white mice as affected by isotonic saline. Virus dilution: (●) 10^{-2}; (○—○) 10^{-3}; (■) 10^{-4}; (○-·-○) 10^{-3} virus dilution + 0.1 ml of isotonic saline once daily; (○- -○) 10^{-3} virus dilution + 0.1 ml of isotonic saline twice daily (Link et al., 1963).

but still nontoxic dose of a substance. Unfortunately, the toxicity of a substance in acute tests may be followed only by its lethality, since we have as yet no suitable methods to show whether or not a nonlethal dose of a drug is also nontoxic. In this case, the maximal nonlethal rather than nontoxic dose serves for dosage purposes. The hidden toxic effect of a substance will be demonstrated in the next example.

The antiviral agent under testing was urethan. Ten milligrams per mouse of subcutaneously applied urethan daily for 10 days was not found lethal for mice in preliminary experiments. In the proper experiment (Link et al., 1963) mice were infected intranasally with four drops of 10^{-4}, 10^{-5}, and 10^{-6} dilutions of A 1 influenza virus (strain Em_2) containing allantoic fluid. Mice in two experimental groups infected with a 10^{-5} virus dilution were treated subcutaneously either with 5 or 10 mg of urethan daily for 5 days, starting with the day of infection. Deaths were recorded daily; cumulative mortality percentages are illustrated in Fig. 8. This figure shows that mice treated with 5 mg of urethan died as if they had been infected by 1 log lower concentration of the virus, whereas mice treated with 10 mg of urethan were tested as in the corresponding control group. Ten milligrams of urethan per mouse was not found lethal for mice in preliminary experiments, even if given daily for 10 days, but its nonmanifested toxicity became enhanced when administered to mice together with virus infection. The potentiation of

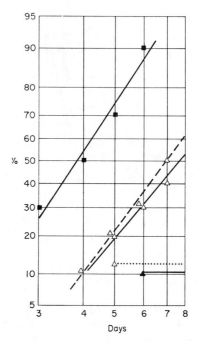

Fɪɢ. 8. The effect of urethan on experimental influenza infection in white mice. Virus dilutions (controls): (■) 10^{-4}; (△—△) 10^{-5}; (▲—) 10^{-6}; (△- -△) 10^{-5} virus dilution + 10 mg of urethan/mouse daily; (△ ···) 10^{-5} virus dilution + 5 mg of urethan/mouse daily (Link *et al.*, 1963).

its toxicity counteracted its antiviral effect, which could be demonstrated with doses as low as 5 mg of urethan/mouse in single daily injections.

B. The Design of the Experiment

By the design of an assay is meant the choice of the number and of the levels of the dose to be tested, the scheme of allocation of subjects to doses, and the arrangement of all experimental constraints that determine the character of the proper statistical analysis.

While testing antiviral agents, the experimenter would like to obtain the best possible results, with respect to precision and sensitivity, and to learn whether or not the reaction of the biological system is affected in some way after an experimental treatment. The results of the experiment are evaluated according to the responses of the biological system, which are usually influenced by the techniques of the experiment as well as by the heterogeneity of the system itself. The evaluation of the results must therefore be carried out statistically in order to be sure whether or not the difference between the responses of the experimental and the control groups is significant.

Different designs will be discussed, and it will be seen that the selection of a design for a particular purpose necessarily involves a compromise among precision of information, factors representative of the convenience, difficulty and expense of experimental procedure, and the statistical analysis.

As a rule a representative method of assay will be described in this chapter. While this method is one that has proved practicable and satisfactory, it is emphasized that its use is not in any way compulsory; individual workers are expected to use those methods that they have already regularly used and/or in which they have confidence.

1. Single-Dose Experiments

The single-dose experiment is characterized by the fact that the animals in both the control and experimental groups are infected with a single dose of the virus, and therefore no quantitation of the activity of a substance under testing can be carried out.

The simplest way of obtaining information on the antiviral activity of a substance is to have the animals in the experimental group treated similarly with the antiviral agent at only one dose level, which can be applied several times to the animals.

Testing of antiviral agents is a sort of biological assay. Biological assays, in general, are used for measuring the specific activity of a substance, which cannot be done by other methods. As an example, we can mention here the biological titration of heart glycosides. In this case the end point of the titration is a well-defined effect on the heart. This effect, however, is a relative one, and comparison of activity of different heart glycosides may be made only with respect to a proper standard preparation. In pharmacological laboratories, the experimenter chooses the dose levels and the number of subjects at each dose in relation to preexisting knowledge of the potency of the test preparation.

While testing antiviral agents, however, the experimenter must first of all screen different compounds, since he lacks the above-mentioned knowledge of the potency of the standard preparation. His interest will be focused on the possibilities of suppression by some antiviral agents, of virus multiplication in the biological system. In this sort of biological assay, the standard preparation in the control group is replaced by the virus itself, and the activity of an antiviral agent is expressed by the relationship of the end points of the virus infection between the control and the experimental group. This relationship in single-dose experiments may be only a qualitative one, even if, on behalf of the biological material, we may obtain qualitative as well as quantal or quantitative responses, according to the design of the experiment.

a. Qualitative Responses. The simplest way of obtaining some information on the antiviral activity of a substance is the qualitative-response design. The biological subject reacts to the stimulus in this sort of experiment positively or negatively, and the magnitude of impulse is measured by the number of alternatively reacting animals. A statistically significant difference between the responses of the control and the experimental group then indicates the effectiveness of the treatment, as will be seen in the following experiment.

TABLE II

QUALITATIVE RESPONSE OF MICE TO ANTIVIRAL TREATMENT

Mice treated with	Number of mice positively reacting	
	Control group	Experimental group
Substance I	45 (90%)	15 (30%)
Substance II	45 (90%)	25 (50%)

One hundred and fifty mice weighing 14–16 gm were infected intranasally in the control and experimental groups under light ether anesthesia with four drops of 10^4 EID_{50} of influenza virus (type A 1; strain Em_2). Mice in two experimental groups, each consisting of 50 mice, were treated subcutaneously for 2 hours before infection and then at daily intervals with substances I and II, respectively. The number of mice in the groups and the number of positively (by death) reacting animals on the 10th day after infection are given in Table II.

The difference in the mortality rate between the control and the experimental groups treated with substance I was as high as 60%, and between the control and the second experimental group it was 40%. The significance of the difference may be tested statistically, supposing a normal or at least a nearly normal distribution of the responses, as follows:

As the first step, the variances of the means (*se*) are to be calculated according to the equation

$$se = (PQ/N)^{1/2} \tag{4}$$

where P denotes the number of positively reacting animals, Q denotes the number of negatively reacting animals, and N denotes the total number of animals in the group. Thus

$$se_{\text{control}} = (45.5/50)^{1/2} = \pm 2.1\%$$
$$se_{\text{substance I}} = \pm 3.24\%$$
$$se_{\text{substance II}} = \pm 3.53\%$$

The fiducial limits at the 95% probability level of the mean responses are calculated by multiplying the relative standard errors with the factor 1.96. According to this, the corresponding means with their fiducial limits being as high as

Control	90% (85.89–94.11)
Substance I	30% (23.65–36.35)
Substance II	50% (43.09–46.91)

significant difference at a probability level $p < 0.05$ could be proved between the responses of the experimental groups with respect to the control. Both substances were found to have an antiviral effect in white mice, and a significant difference between the activities of the corresponding substances was also found in favor of substance I. Whether or not we should prefer substance I for further studies depends on the therapeutic index of the corresponding substances.

The statistical evaluation of qualitative responses may be carried out also by means of a χ^2 test, using 2×2 or $2 \times n$ contingency tables. In order to evaluate the significance in difference between two treatments (substance I — substance II), the numbers of alternatively reacting animals are placed in a 2×2 contingency table (Table III), as follows.

TABLE III

A 2×2 CONTINGENCY TABLE

After treatment with	Survivors	Dead	Total
Substance I	a	b	$a + b$
Substance II	c	d	$c + d$
	$a + c$	$b + d$	$N = (a + b + c + d)$

The evaluation of the χ^2 happens according to the equation

$$\chi^2 = \frac{(ad - bc)^2(a + b + c + d)}{(a + b)(a + c)(b + d)(c + d)} \tag{5}$$

The data obtained with substances I and II are now located in Table IV as follows:

TABLE IV

QUALITATIVE RESPONSE OF MICE IN 2×2 CONTINGENCY TABLE

After treatment with	Survivors	Dead	Total
Substance I	35	15	50
Substance II	25	25	50
	60	40	100

According to this

$$\chi^2 = \frac{(35 \times 25 - 15 \times 25)^2 \times 100}{50 \times 60 \times 40 \times 50} = 4.1$$

The observed value (4.1) is compared with the expected values of the χ^2 distribution in χ^2 tables (Table V) at 1 degree of freedom, which at the 95% probability level is as high as 3.8. The higher observed than expected value indicates that there is a significant difference between the two treatments. In this way we have come to the same conclusion concerning the antiviral activity of substances I and II as

TABLE V

THE DISTRIBUTION OF χ^2 VALUES[a]

Degrees of freedom (f)	Probability			
	10%	5%	1%	0.1%
1	2.7	3.8	6.6	10.8
2	4.6	6.0	9.2	13.8
3	6.3	7.8	11.3	16.3
4	7.8	9.5	13.3	18.5
5	9.2	11.1	15.1	20.5
6	10.6	12.6	16.8	22.5
7	12.0	14.1	18.5	24.3
8	13.4	15.5	20.1	26.1
9	14.7	16.9	21.7	27.9
10	16.0	18.3	23.2	29.6
12	18.5	21.0	26.2	32.9
14	21.1	23.7	29.1	36.1
16	23.5	26.3	32.0	39.3
18	26.0	28.9	34.8	42.3
20	28.4	31.4	37.6	45.3
40	1.68	2.02	2.70	3.55

[a] Abridged from Fisher and Yates (1948, Table IV).

by comparing the mean responses with the corresponding fiducial limits. This sort of evaluation of qualitative differences between more than two substances can be enlarged to a $2 \times n$ contingency table. This method will not be discussed in this chapter in more detail, since the technique requires special training in mathematical statistics.

b. *Quantal Responses.* In the foregoing section we attempted to estimate the activity of an antiviral substance by relating its activity to the difference in mortality between the experimental and the control group. Such a qualitative assay may be used if the mortality rates if both the experimental and control groups lie between 90 and 10%. It happens very often, however, that 100% of the animals in both groups die, and/or no significant difference is found between the responses of the two groups even if the experimental animals were treated with a potential antiviral agent. Such problems may be solved while using a quantal response design by assaying the dynamics of the infection.

The quantal information is to be used for the estimation of the mean of the tolerance distribution. The estimation of potency is made by use of the relationship between the percentage responses and the corresponding metameter. This may be the dose of an impulse or the time element. The potency of the impulse may be evaluated by means of the corresponding parameters (ED_{50}; ET_{50}) showing an alternative response of 50% of the biological system involved in the experiment. For this reason we must record the cumulative alternative responses of the animals in the course of the whole observation period. This will be demonstrated in the following experiment.

White laboratory mice were infected in the control and in the experimental group with 10^4 EID_{50} of a mouse-adapted A 1 influenza virus (strain Em_2). The mice in the experimental group were treated with an antiviral agent (substance C). The alternative responses of the animals are given in Table VI in cumulative percentages; the data show 85% death in the control and 80% death in the experimental group by day 10. It is not possible to evaluate the antiviral activity of this substance by comparing the corresponding mortality rates by means of a qualitative-response design. By having a look at Table VI, however, we may see a delay in the mortality rates of animals in the experimental group, in comparison with the control, which will become much clearer when we plot the cumulative percentages into a log probability net (Fig. 9).

According to the diagram, the corresponding ET_{50} values, i.e., the time when 50% of the subjects responded to the stimulus alternatively,

TABLE VI

MORTALITY OF INFECTED MICE[a]

Inoculum (EID$_{50}$)	Days after infection							
	3	4	5	6	7	8	9	10
Virus 10^4	20	40	60	75	85	85	85	85
Virus 10^4 + substance C	4	12	36	54	70	80	80	80

[a] In cumulative percentages.

can be read off, these being 5.6 and 6.8 days, respectively. In order
to evaluate the significance of these values, their standard errors must
first be calculated. Since the original probit analysis (Finney, 1952)
is too complicated, a substitute method will be presented here, in
which the standard error of the mean is estimated by a single nomogram (Link, 1959).

Before proceeding, however, the homogeneity of the biological subject
is tested by means of the χ^2 test. For a simple method of testing
homogeneity, one may use Table VII.

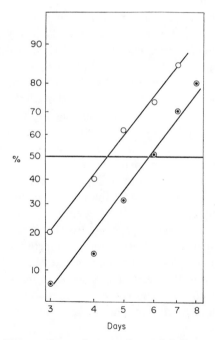

FIG. 9. Effect of substance C on the experimental influenza infection of white
mice: (O) virus 10^4 EID$_{50}$; ($\odot$) virus 10^4 EID$_{50}$ + substance C.

TABLE VII

Test of Linearity of Quantal-Response Regression Lines by Means of χ^2's

A	B	C	D	E	F	G	H	K
Metameter (abscissa) (days)	Number of positive animal reactions	Cumulative percentage of animals with positive reactions	Cumulative percentage on straight line	Absolute number of animals from line reaction	$(100 - D)/100$	$(E - B)^2$	EF	G/H (χ^2 values)
3	3	9	6	2	0.94	1	1.88	0.6
4	4	12	18	6	0.82	4	4.92	0.8
5	12	36	33	11	0.67	1	7.37	0.13
6	18	54	50	17	0.50	1	8.50	0.11
7	23	70	67	22	0.33	1	7.26	0.13
8	26	80	76	25	0.24	1	6.00	0.17
							Sum of χ^2	1.94

By adding the individual χ^2 values, we compute their sum, 1.94. This value must not exceed the expected χ^2 value encountered in the χ^2 tables (see Table V) at a degree of freedom of $n-2$ in order to insure homogeneity of the biological subject at the anticipated (usually 95%) probability level. This prerequisite is fulfilled in our case; the calculated value of χ^2 is less than the expected one ($1.9 < 9.5$).

In the case of homogeneity, the standard error of the mean ET_{50} may be easily computed. This is done by entering the values from ET_{50}, ET_{84}, and ET_{16} (which may be read off from Fig. 9) in Table VIII and by computing the coefficient of regression b according to the equation

$$b = 2/(ET_{84} - ET_{16}) \tag{6}$$

In the nomogram (Fig. 10), s, i.e., the standard error of ET_{50}, is found between b and n (the number of animals in the group). In this

TABLE VIII

CALCULATION OF STANDARD ERROR(S) OF QUANTAL RESPONSES

ET_{50}	ET_{84}	ET_{16}	$b = 2/(ET_{84} - ET_{16})$	s (nomogram)
5.8	3.8	10	0.32	0.2

way, with the ET_{50} values and their corresponding fiducial limits, being

$$ET_{50} \pm 2se_{\text{control}} = 4.4\ (4.1 - 4.7)$$

$$ET_{50} \pm 2se_{\text{experimental}} = 5.8\ (5.4 - 6.2)$$

significant difference was found between the control and the experimental group. Thus, the antiviral activity of substance C could be tested by means of a quantal-response design, which would be impossible with a qualitative-response design.

c. *Quantitative Responses.* In the discussion of the design of quantal responses, we saw that specified doses were given to several subjects, and their responses to the stimulus were of an all-or-nothing nature. Alternatively, the magnitude of some property of the subject may be measured under some circumstances: this is a quantitative response. With suitable restriction on the choice of doses, quantitative

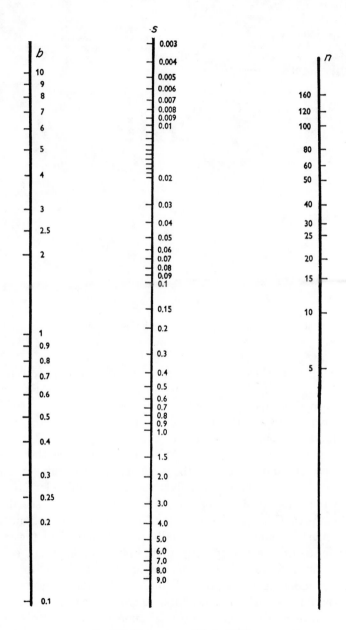

FIG. 10. Nomogram (Link, 1959).

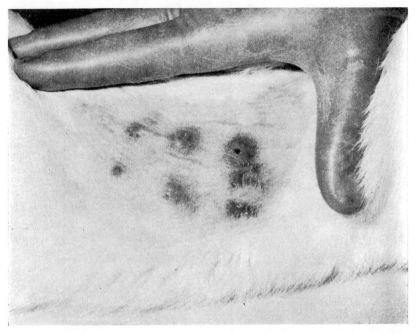

FIG. 11. Local effect of vaccinia virus inoculation in rabbit skin (Šmejkal and Šorm, 1962).

assays could be analysed by rejection of all observations except those that showed a specified response. In testing of antivirals, the relationship between dose and the magnitude of response is to be considered in the control group and the antiviral effect may be evaluated according to the difference between the control and the experimental group.

The specified response in quantitative assays may be the time that elapses between application of the stimulus to the subject and the occurrence of some reaction—usually the death of animals, an increase in the virus titer in the appropriate organ, or some specific skin (Fig. 11) or eye (Fig. 12) lesion owing to local virus infection. Special attention must be paid to the essentially positive nature of the response in order to assure the homogeneity of the observation when measuring the time, since there are some characteristics peculiar to response that may complicate the statistical analysis of time data from laboratory experiments with animals. First, there is a considerable increase in the variance as the average survival time increases (Brownlee and Hamre, 1951). This problem may be overcome if a reciprocal transformation of the mean is introduced (Gard, 1940), a technique that is use-

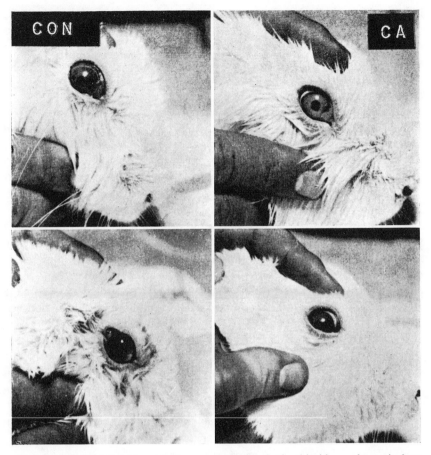

FIG. 12. Effect of 1-β-D-arabinofuranosylcytosine hydrochloride on herpetic kera-titis. Both eyes of different rabbits were infected with herpes virus on scarified cornea on April 3, 1962. Subjects were treated hourly during the day from April 4 to April 9 and every 4 hours at night from April 4 to April 7. Photos labeled CA were treated with 1% drug in ointment; controls labeled CON were treated with ointment only. Average picture of 12 treated CA eyes and 10 controls (Stuart-Harris and Dickinson, 1965).

ful in the equalization of variance of time responses. In a way, this happens if, instead of the mean survival time, the metameter Y is used:

$$Y = 1.00/\text{Number of days} \qquad (7)$$

Second, if the virus dilution is very high, there may be survivors at the end of the observation period, and thus the parameter of survival time would suffer a discontinuity, jumping from some finite value to infinity. Though an infinite time can also be transformed by Eq. (7), thus obtaining the metametric value of zero, it is always better to choose virus dilutions that will cause the subjects to die within the observation period. The testing of the activity by means of a quantitative response to an antiviral agent will be demonstrated in the next example (Bauer and Sadler, 1960).

Groups of six mice were infected intracerebrally with about 1000 50% lethal doses (LD_{50}) of neurovaccinia virus. The mice in the experimental group were treated with different doses: 0.25, 0.5, and 2.5 mg/kg of 1-propylisatin β-thiosemicarbazone. The number of surviving mice was recorded daily, and the mean reciprocal survival times were found to give a linear regression of the doses. The regression line is shown in Fig. 13.

For comparing the antiviral activity of different substances, where the control group is represented by the linear log dose–survival time relationship of the standard preparation, the conventional four-point design may be used.

Since with the statistical analysis of a four-point design it is possible to check only the significance in regression and the parallelism between the corresponding regression lines without control of their linearity, two doses of the antiviral agents, in both the control and in the experimental group, are to be used, the higher being a multiple of the lower, giving responses within the region of linearity, according to a preliminary experiment, upon infection with the virus. The results of a typical assay (Bauer and Sadler, 1960) are shown in Fig. 14, where the antiviral activity of 7-methylisatin β-thiosemicarbazone in

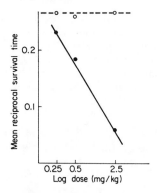

FIG. 13. Dose–response curve of antiviral activity of 1-propylisatin β-thiosemicarbazone in mice infected intracerebrally with about 1000 LD_{50} of neurotropic vaccinia virus. ($\bullet$) Treated; ($\bigcirc$) controls (Bauer and Sadler, 1960).

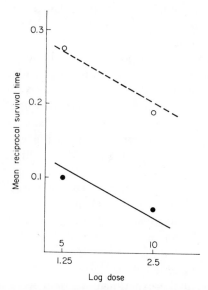

FIG. 14. Four-point assay of antiviral activity of 7-methylisatin β-thiosemicarbazone in mice infected intracerebrally with about 1000 LD$_{50}$ of neurotropic vaccinia virus. Ordinate: mean reciprocal survival time. Upper abscissa: log dose of test compound; lower abscissa: log dose of isatin β-thiosemicarbazone. (●) 7-methylisatin β-thiosemicarbazone; (○) isatin β-thiosemicarbazone (Bauer and Sadler, 1960).

mice infected intracerebrally with about 1000 LD$_{50}$ of neurotropic vaccinia virus was compared with the activity of isatin β-thiosemicarbazone. After the regression b and the parallelism of the corresponding treatments, including the homogeneity of the responses, are checked by means of a variance analysis, the relative potency R of the test preparation may be calculated as a function of the horizontal distance between the individual regression lines for the standard and the test preparation according to Eq. (8):

$$R = \log x_s - \log x_t - \frac{Y_s - Y_t}{b} \qquad (8)$$

where x_s is the mean dose of the standard preparation, x_t is the mean dose of the test preparation, Y_s is the reciprocal mean survival time with the standard preparation, Y_t is the reciprocal mean survival time with the test preparation, and b is the joint regression coefficient of the corresponding regression lines. The therapeutic index, based upon the relationship of the relative activities and the relative toxicities of the compounds, must then be taken into account for purposes of clinical recommendation of any of the substances.

As in quantal-response assays, some further special responses may result with a quantitative-response assay besides the death of the subject. In systemic model infection with an unadapted virus line, the animals do not succumb to the infection. The extent of multiplication of the virus in the appropriate organ may be quantitatively measured by means of corresponding parameters, for example, EID_{50}, $TCID_{50}$, or the plaque count. The difference between the virus titer of the control group and the experimental group then indicates the activity of the antiviral agent, as will be seen in the next example.

Mice in the control group were infected intranasally with 10^5 EID_{50} of the A_2/Sing/57 inhibitor-sensitive influenza virus strain. According to Fig. 15, the virus multiplied in the lungs to high titers for 5 days. The antiviral agent used in this study (Link et al., 1965c) was the γ-inhibitor (GI), isolated and partially purified from horse serum. Two hours prior to infection with the same virus dose as given in the control group, mice in the experimental group were intranasally inoculated with 30,000 HIU of GI. No virus could be detected in the lungs of the mice in the experimental group for 5 days, thus demonstrating the antiviral activity of γ-inhibitor, which was clear-cut without any sta-

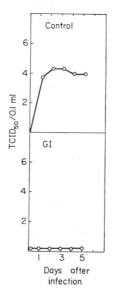

Fig. 15. Effect of 30,000 HIU of GI on the multiplication of nonadapted virus in mouse lungs. Inoculum of virus: 10^5 EID_{50} (Link et al., 1965c).

tistical evaluation of the data. Depending on the dilution of the antiviral agent, graded responses on its activity are available, as will be shown in the next experiment.

Mice in control and experimental groups were infected with 10^5 EID_{50} of the same virus strain. In two experimental groups 3000 and 300 HIU of γ-inhibitor were administered 2 hours before infection. The effect of γ-inhibitor is demonstrated in Fig. 16.

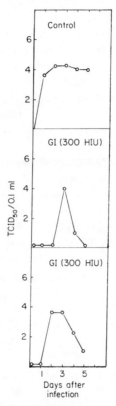

FIG. 16. Effect of 3000 and 300 HIU of GI on the multiplication of nonadapted virus in mouse lungs. Inoculum of virus: 10^5 EID_{50} (Link *et al.*, 1965c).

The antiviral activity of 3000 and 300 HIU of GI is quite clear when comparing virus multiplication in the control and experimental groups 5 days after infection. One may, however, miss this effect if the virus titers are compared only 3 days after treatment with either GI dose or on day 2 after treatment with 300 HIU, the corresponding infectivity titers being as high as $10^{4.2}$ $TCID_{50}$ in the control group and

$10^{3.8}$ $TCID_{50}$ in the experimental groups. A magnitude difference of 0.4 log units between the corresponding $TCID_{50}$ values could not be proved to be significant.

2. Multiple-Dose Experiments

In multiple-dose assays the biological material is infected at different virus dose levels in the control groups in order to make possible the quantitation of the activity of an antiviral agent. A dose–response relationship is then established, which may serve to express the activity of an antiviral agent in units of the control. The dose–response relationship is represented by one or several regression lines, according to whether the activity of the substance is assayed by means of a quantal or a quantitative design. For quantitation of the activity of an antiviral agent, however, the establishment of a dose–response relationship alone is not a sufficient criterion. For this purpose parallelism between the corresponding regression lines must also be proved.

a. *Quantal Responses.* In multiple-dose quantal-response experiments the evaluation of the activity of an antiviral agent may be based on the relationship of surviving time to response to virus infection. Several (at least three) groups of control mice are infected with different virus dilutions and the corresponding parameters are calculated using a log probability net, as discussed in Section I,B,1,*b*. A sort of calibration curve may be constructed according to the corresponding ET_{50} values. In the experimental group(s) the same parameters (ET_{50}) are to be computed. The quantitation of the activity of the antiviral agent is then carried out by interpolating the ET_{50} values of the experimental group into the calibration curve. This procedure will be demonstrated in the following experiment (Link et al., 1965c).

Tenfold dilutions of mouse lung-adapted influenza A 1 virus (strain Em_2), in a range of 10^3–10^{-1} LD_{50} were instilled intranasally into groups of 10–30 mice and the mice observed daily for a period of 10 days. The cumulative mortality percentage is shown in Table IX. When cumulative mortality percentages are plotted into a log probability net against days after infection (Fig. 17), the parallel regression lines illustrate the dynamics of the infection over a period of 10 days. A significant 2-day delay in death is seen ($p < 0.05$) at the 50% mortality level according to the different virus dilutions, thus characterizing the difference between the corresponding regression lines. The testing of parallelism requires some preliminary training in mathemati-

TABLE IX

MORTALITY OF INFECTED MICE[a]

Inoculum (LD$_{50}$)	Days after infection									
	1	2	3	4	5	6	7	8	9	10
10³	—	—	30	50	70	87	100	100	100	100
10²	—	—	—	—	20	50	70	80	80	80
10¹	—	—	—	—	—	—	20	50	60	70
10⁰	—	—	—	—	—	—	—	20	30	50
10⁻¹	—	—	—	—	—	—	—	—	5	10
10³ + urethan, 2.5 mg	—	—	—	20	40	67	76	85	85	85
10³ + urethan, 25 mg	—	—	—	7	13	36	53	70	80	80

[a] In cumulative percentages.

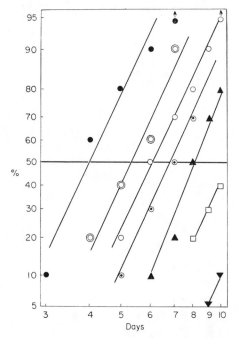

Fig. 17. Effect of urethan in mice after influenza virus infection. (●) 10^3; (○) 10^2; (▲) 10^1; (□) 10^{-1} LD$_{50}$ of virus; (◎) virus (10^3 LD$_{50}$) + 2.5 mg of urethan; (⊙) virus (10^3 LD$_{50}$) + 25 mg of urethan (Link *et al.*, 1965c).

cal statistics and therefore will not be discussed in this chapter. A calibration curve may now be constructed between the dilutions of the virus and the corresponding ET$_{50}$ values, as demonstrated in Fig. 18.

In the experimental groups, mice were given two doses of urethan, 25 mg/mouse in a single dose prior to infection with 10^3 LD$_{50}$ of the virus and 2.5 mg/mouse prior to and daily after infection with 10^3 LD$_{50}$ of the virus, for 10 days. As indicated in Table IX, the drug treatment reduced the mortality from 100 to 85 and 80%. Although this mortality could not be considered significant by means of a qualitative-response experiment, nevertheless, the antiviral effect of urethan could be observed by comparing the corresponding ET$_{50}$ values. Since there was no departure from parallelism between the corresponding regression lines, the antiviral activity could be measured quantitatively by interpolating the ET$_{50}$ values of the urethan-treated groups into the calibration curve (Fig. 19).

The data indicate that mice receiving 2.5 mg of urethan died as if they had been inoculated with $10^{2.4}$ LD_{50} of virus, while those receiving 25 mg behaved as though they had received only $10^{1.6}$ LD_{50} of virus rather than the 10^3 LD_{50} they were actually given.

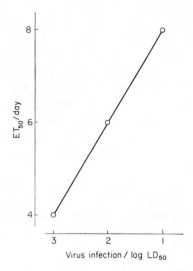

FIG. 18. Calibration curve of ET_{50} values in mice infected with influenza virus (Link *et al*, 1965c).

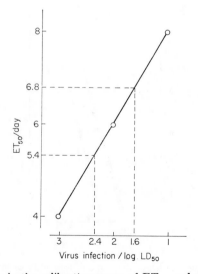

FIG. 19. Interpolation in the calibration curve of ET_{50} values after urethan treatment of mice infected with influenza virus. (Link *et al.*, 1965c).

To prove further the reliability of this method, control mice were given 10, 1, and 0.1 LD_{50} of virus. Three groups of mice treated with 5 mg of urethan daily for 10 days were given the same virus dose, as indicated in Table X. The drug lowered the mortality from 100% to 60% in mice receiving 10 LD_{50}, from 40% to 10% in those receiving 1 LD_{50}, and from 10% to no deaths in those receiving 0.1 LD_{50}. The regression lines of the treated mice again parallel those of the untreated mice. The antiviral effect of urethan could therefore be evaluated by the corresponding mean values, which were found to be up to 0.8 log units on the 10th day after infection (Fig. 20). The activity of 5 mg of urethan was found to lie between that of the 2.5 and 25 mg activities, as illustrated by the linear log dose relationship illustrated in Fig. 21. Thus it is possible to evaluate even quantitatively an antiviral effect in mice receiving more than 1 LD_{50} of virus.

  b. *Quantitative Responses.* In multiple-dose quantitative-response as well as quantal-response assays the control is represented by several groups of the biological subject infected with graded virus dilutions in order to make possible the quantitation of the antiviral agent that

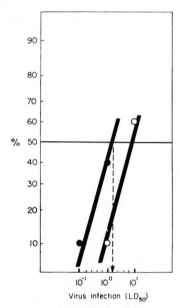

Fig. 20. Relationship between LD_{50} of virus and mortality of mice after administration of urethan. Treatment was on the 10th day after inoculation. (●) Virus alone; (○) virus + 5 mg of urethan (Link *et al.*, 1965c).

TABLE X

EFFECT OF 5% URETHAN ON MORTALITY OF INFECTED MICE[a]

	Dilution of virus inoculum (LD_{50})																	
	10^1						10^0						10^{-1}					
Inoculum	Days after inoculation																	
	5	6	7	8	9	10	5	6	7	8	9	10	5	6	7	8	9	10
Virus	—	30	50	70	90	100	—	—	—	20	30	40	—	—	—	—	10	10
Virus + urethan	10	20	30	60	60	60	—	—	10	10	10	10	—	—	—	—	—	—

[a] In cumulative percentages.

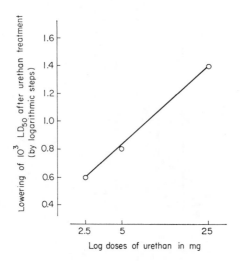

F<small>IG</small>. 21. Dose–response relationship between different concentrations of urethan and the lowering of the LD_{50} of the influenza virus by logarithmic steps (Link *et al.*, 1965c).

was found significantly active in single-dose experiments. In the next example, the quantitation of the activity of GI will be demonstrated; this has been found active in single-dose quantitative-response design (Section II,B,1,*c*).

Mice were infected with 10-fold dilutions of virus containing allantoic fluid, the inocula corresponding to $10^2–10^7$ $EID_{50}/0.05$ ml. Virus reproduced in the lungs of control mice could be detected 24 hours after infection with $10^3–10^7$ EID_{50} (Fig. 22). In the experimental group, in which mice were pretreated with GI, no virus could be detected in the lungs from mice given 30,000 HIU of GI and challenged with as much as 10^7 EID_{50} of virus, whereas virus was present in the lungs of control mice infected even with 10^3 EID_{50} of virus. In the experimental group, GI was as effective as if the control mice had been infected with a virus concentration at least 5 log units higher.

In the foregoing experiment, the quasi absolute effectiveness of γ-inhibitor could be demonstrated. This phenomenon, however, does not occur very often, and in quantitative-response experiments one rather expects a graded response of the antiviral agent upon different doses of the virus.

One of the characteristics of the biological assay is the variance in responses, which occurs even if the experiment was carried out in a homogeneous biological material. Therefore, the mean responses of the subjects are chosen for comparison of dose–response relationships, represented by corresponding regression lines of multiple-dose quantitative assays. To enable the quantitation of graded activity of an antiviral agent, the use of survival time metameter is recommended; this has a linear regression on the log dose of virus over an adequate range. Such a dose–response relationship of neurovaccinia virus is demonstrated after the transformation of the mean survival times of infected mice to their reciprocal values. The reason for this transformation was discussed in Section II,B,1,c (Bauer, 1961).

Five 10-fold dilutions of the virus were inoculated into six mice per group and the animals were observed over a period of 14 days, with the days of death recorded daily. A regression line of reciprocal mean survival times was then plotted against the log doses of the virus, as illustrated in Fig. 23. A reduction in the virus dose of 1 log unit decreased the mean reciprocal survival time by 0.0427, which was equivalent to an increase in mean survival time of 1.30174 days. The activity of an antiviral agent could then be evaluated quantitatively according to a significant difference between the parallel regression lines of the control and experimental groups treated with the antiviral agent.

The numerical measure of the antiviral activity can be obtained by dividing the difference between the mean total responses of the control and experimental groups by their common regression coefficient.

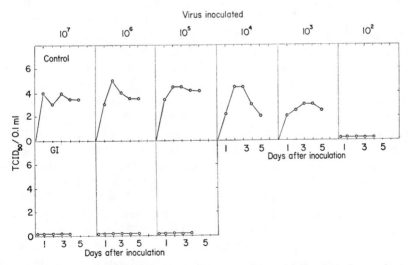

FIG. 22. Effect of 30,000 HIU of γ-inhibitor on the multiplication of nonadapted virus in mouse lungs. (Link *et al.*, 1965c).

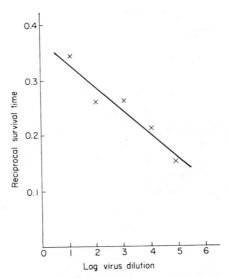

FIG. 23. Dose–response curve of neurovaccinia virus. Each point represents the reciprocal harmonic mean of the survival times of a group of six mice (Bauer, 1958).

The antiviral effect of copper sulfate in mice infected with neuro-vaccinia virus is demonstrated in the next experiment (Bauer, 1958).

Mice in control groups were infected with 10-fold dilutions of neuro-vaccinia virus in a range of 10^{-1}–10^{-5}. Mice in the experimental groups infected with corresponding virus doses were treated with repeated doses of 0.25 mg of copper sulfate. The results are shown in Fig. 24. No departure from parallelism could be provided between the two regression lines; the joint regression coefficient was 0.0415. The regression line of the experimental groups was displaced 0.9614 log units from the control line. The ratio calculated from the difference between the mean survival time of the control and that of the experimental groups by the common regression coefficient indicated that the treatment was equivalent to reducing the infecting virus dose by 89%.

The quantitation by means of a different type of calibration curve of the virostatic activity in rabbits of 6-azauracilriboside (AzUR) (Šmejkal and Šorm, 1962) will be demonstrated in the next example.

After AzUR was found effective against vaccinia virus in tissue culture, its effect was studied in albino "VBM" rabbits weighing 2–2.5 kg infected with a live dermovaccinia, as used for vaccination against smallpox. Eight rabbits were inoculated intracutaneously with 0.2 ml doses of 10^{-1}, 10^{-2}, and 10^{-3} virus dilutions, administered in

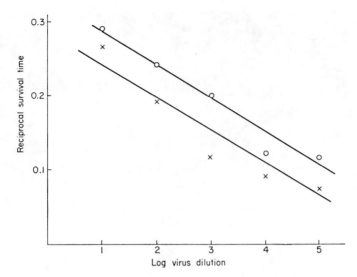

FIG. 24. Assay of activity of copper sulfate against neurovaccinia virus. ×: Reciprocal harmonic mean survival time of treated group; ○: reciprocal harmonic mean survival time of treated control group (Bauer, 1958).

two rows bilaterally. Four of the inoculated rabbits were given intravenous injections of AzUR under light anesthesia twice daily for 3 days, starting immediately after inoculation. The dose of AzUR administered daily was 300 mg/kg of body weight.

The changes occurring after infection in the place of inoculation were as follows: 24 hours, slight erythema; 48 hours, erythema larger and deep red; 72 hours, a pustule containing yellow purulent infiltrate. With the virus dilutions used the diameters of the pustules and erythema were as follows: 10^{-1}, pustule up to 10 mm, erythema 15–20 mm; pustule 6 mm, erythema 10–12 mm; and 10^{-3}, pustule 3–4 mm, erythema 4–6 mm (see Fig. 25). These skin reactions were marked 72–96 hours after inoculations; from the 120th hour they gradually declined but were still marked after 14 days.

In rabbits given AzUR, erythema was absent after 24 or 48 hours; after 72 hours faint signs of erythema appeared with a 10^{-1} dilution of virus, but not with 10^{-2} and 10^{-3} dilutions (see Fig. 25). Deep red erythema did not occur in any of the AzUR-treated rabbits up to the 14th day. The pustules in these rabbits were pink, as was the surrounding skin, and markedly smaller and lower, containing less purulent infiltrate, than those in the controls. Thus AzUR showed quantitative virostatic activity.

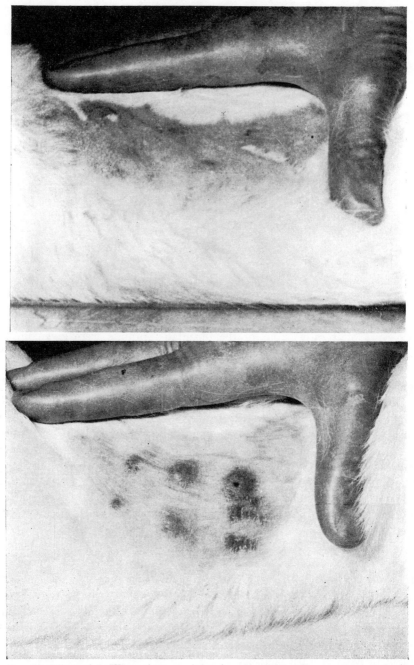

Fig. 25. Effect of AzUR against vaccinia virus in rabbits. Upper: treatment after AzUR; lower: control (Šmejkal and Šorm, 1962).

The logical approach in testing an antiviral agent is to select a substance by a screening test and to extend its testing for quantitation of the antiviral activity. After successful quantitation, the antiviral agent may be used as a standard preparation for comparing its activity with different substances against the same virus by means of multiple-dose assay; however, such a design is not yet suitable for comparing the activity of the same compound against different viruses.

Bauer (1961) recommended that this problem be solved by introducing a further parameter into the quantitation of antiviral agents when studying the activity of isatin β-thiosemicarbazone. It was found that the dose–response lines of the vaccinia–isatin β-thiosemicarbazone system possesses the following properties, which made it possible to measure activity of the given compound against members of the poxvirus group in absolute numerical terms:

1. There was found to be a relationship between linear log of the dose and reciprocal mean survival time.

2. No departure from parallelism occurred between the corresponding regression lines.

3. The activity of the antiviral agent did not depend on the concentration of the virus.

In this way the classification of certain members of the poxvirus group could be carried out with respect to their sensitivity to the same chemotherapeutic agent by means of the doses of the compound, yet exerting no activity in this system, called E_0 (zero effective dose), as shown in Figs. 26a and 26b.

3. Therapeutic Index

As mentioned earlier, the value of a substance does not depend on its explicit antiviral activity for its eventual toxicity. Therefore, the therapeutic index of a substance in a screening project must be taken into account whenever the substance is studied in detail. The therapeutic index is based on a relationship between toxic and effective but nontoxic doses. Most frequently it is expressed by the ratio of maximal nontoxic and minimal effective concentrations of a substance. The proper concentrations may be determined if the experiment is designed as a quantal-response assay, where the end points of the titration evoking alternative effects in 50% of the subject must be taken into account. This end point, designated as ED_{50} and/or LD_{50} according to the character of the response, possesses some further characteristics, which are the corresponding—presumably linear—regression curve and the standard error of the mean. Both of these parameters are to be respected while computing the therapeutic index of

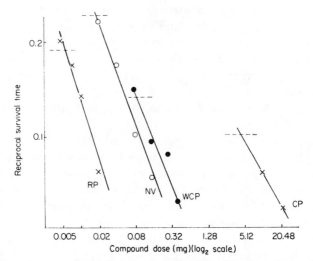

Fig. 26a. Dose–response lines of the antiviral action of isatin β-thiosemicarbazone against four poxviruses. RP, rabbit pox; NV, neurovaccinia; WCP, white cowpox; CP, cowpox. The dotted lines indicate the mean values of the ordinates in the absence of treatment (Bauer, 1961).

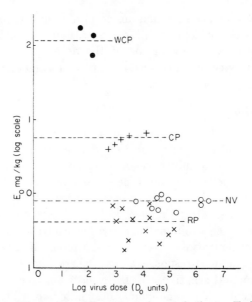

Fig. 26b. Values of E_0 for four different poxviruses. Ordinate: E_0 in mg/kg on $\log_{10}$ scale. Abscissa: $\log_{10}$ dose of virus used for infection in D_0 units. RP, rabbit pox; WCP, white cowpox; CP, cowpox; NV, neurovaccinia. The dotted lines indicate the respective mean value of E_0 (Bauer, 1961).

the antiviral agent. In the following paragraphs, a rapid, graphic method for estimating and comparing therapeutic indexes of quantal responses will be discussed.

The therapeutic index of a substance may be directly calculated by the ratio of the corresponding ED_{50} and LD_{50} values whenever there is no departure from parallelism between the corresponding regression lines (Fig. 27). It is quite clear that such an operation may not be valid in an opposite case (see Fig. 28), where the ratios of effective and lethal doses would differ according to different response levels. To overcome this problem, one of the regression lines, representing the lethal doses of the compound, is to be drawn into the log probability net with a negative regression coefficient, thus giving the pattern shown in Fig. 29.

In this case, the intercept of the regression lines indicates the therapeutic index of the substance, which can be given some relative value. We will use in this case an arbitrary arithmetic scale, originating at the 50% response abscissa. The therapeutic index, however, does not depend only on joint LD_{50}–ED_{50} intercept, since the end point of a quantal-response assay possesses a further characteristic, that is, the standard error of the mean. The calculation of this parameter was discussed in Section II,B,1,b. After having computed the respective standard errors, two additional parallel regression lines are drawn on the original diagram, at ±1 se distance from the corresponding means. The next step is to connect the newly recorded intercepts through the intercept of the original regression lines. Thus the therapeutic index of the substance is depicted with its fiducial limits at an approxi-

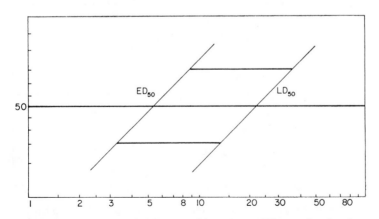

Fig. 27. Parallel regression lines; stable ratios at different dose levels.

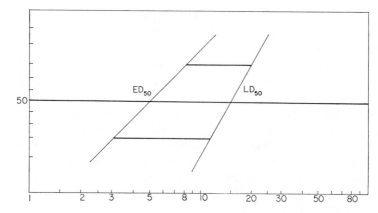

FIG. 28. Departure from parallelism between two regression lines. Different ratios at different dose levels.

mately 95% probability level. For comparing two substances with respect to their therapeutic indexes, the same procedure is carried out with the second substance. If the therapeutic index (the intercept of the main regression lines) of one substance is located within the range of the fiducial limits of the other, no significant difference between the substances is proved. The therapeutic index lying outside the fiducial limits of the standard preparation indicates a significant difference between the substances, always in favor of the substance holding a higher therapeutic index (Figs. 30 and 31).

This simple and quick graphic method is recommended for routine

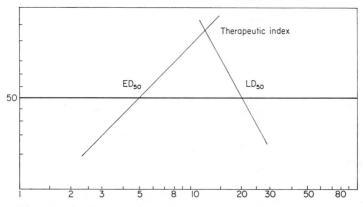

FIG. 29. Regression line from LD_{50} (from Fig. 28) drawn with a negative regression coefficient. The intercept of the regression lines indicates the therapeutic index.

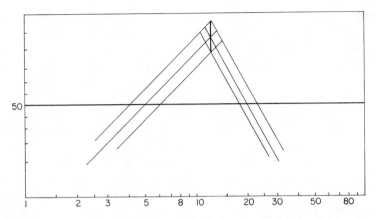

Fig. 30. Fiducial limits of the therapeutic index, established by intercepts owing to ±1 *se* of the individual regression lines.

workers, who in a screening project have to make relatively quick decisions with respect to selecting substances with the highest therapeutic indexes for further studies.

For calculating the therapeutic index in a combined design, where the effectiveness of a substance is assayed by quantitative responses and the toxicity by quantal ones, the assistance of a professional statistician is necessary.

III. Experiments in Eggs

The choice of fertile eggs as a substrate for antiviral testing is suitable for several reasons, even if their use has been rather restricted

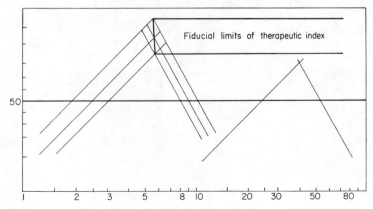

Fig. 31. Comparison of two therapeutic indexes by means of fiducial limits.

recently. Working with eggs is relatively simple and advantageous. They represent a closed system on the one hand, and, on the other, a large number may be introduced into the egg that will readily multiply there. Prophylactic and therapeutic assays may be then carried out with different antiviral agents, since a wide choice of the route and timing of application of both virus and antiviral agents are available, for example, injection into the allantoic cavity and into the yolk sac or direct application of virus to the chorioallantoic membrane. By this means one may insure that there will be no contact between the virus and the antiviral agent. A contact test may be performed easily in order to estimate whether or not the antiviral agent has any *in vitro* activity by mixing different concentrations of virus and antiviral agent and allowing them to act on each other before injecting the mixture into the egg.

The activity of an antiviral agent may be determined by means of different parameters, for example, the suppression of hemagglutinin formation or of the number of infective foci (Fig. 32), the decrease of mortality and/or the increase in embryo survival time. According to this, the design of the experiment is similar to that in experi-

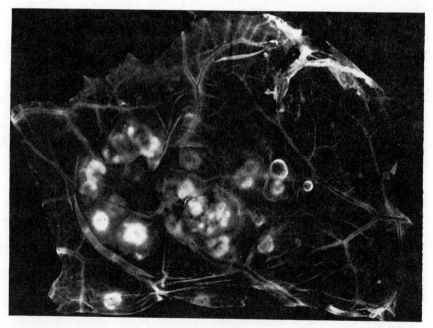

FIG. 32. Pocks on chorioallantoic membrane after vaccinia virus infection.

mental animals, consisting of qualitative, quantal, or quantitative responses, as well.

A. EMBRYONATED EGGS

1. Qualitative Responses

Kucera *et al.* (1965) studied the antiviral activity of the lemon balm plant injected into the allantoic cavity of 9–11-day-old embryonated eggs at intervals before and after infection with various viruses. The viruses were injected by the same route. The results are reported in Table XI. The statistical evaluation of data may be carried out in a manner similar to that described in Section II,B,1,*a*.

TABLE XI

ANTIVIRAL ACTIVITY OF LEMON BALM EXTRACT IN EGGS[a]

Virus dose	Extract injection[b]	Extract dose (mg/egg)				
		9.6	4.8	2.4	1.2	0.0
Newcastle;	−72	5/7	—	—	—	0/10
100 × LD₅₀	−48	12/15	2/6	1/6	0/6	0/16
	−24	23/23	4/6	2/6	0/6	0/23
	− 6	7/7	6/6	4/7	1/7	0/7
	− 3	21/24	83/96	60/96	26/92	0/79
	0	12/12	10/12	7/12	1/13	0/13
	+ 2	0 /16	—	—	—	0/16
Vaccinia;	−48	2/3	1/5	1/6	0/7	0/6
100 × LD₅₀	−24	6/11	3/12	2/13	0/12	0/12
	− 6	3/5	2/7	1/7	0/7	0/6
	− 3	12/15	9/13	3/12	2/11	0/16
	0	5/7	3/5	1/6	0/5	0/7
	+ 3	4/5	3/6	0/5	0/6	0/6
	+14	0/9	—	—	—	0/10
Herpes simplex	−24	2/4	1/5	—	—	0/5
100 × LD₅₀	− 6	5/5	4/5	3/5	3/5	0/5
	− 3	5/5	2/5	1/5	—	0/5
	0	5/5	4/5	2/5	2/5	0/5
	+ 6	2/4	2/5	0/5	—	0/5
Semliki Forest;	−24	8/13	5/12	6/12	6/12	3/11
10 × LD₅₀	−12	10/15	10/14	7/15	7/15	3/11
	− 6	8/14	8/15	5/14	2/14	3/11
	− 3	7/14	6/14	5/14	2/14	3/11
	0	10/14	10/14	6/14	4/14	3/11
	+ 1	9/13	5/13	2/14	2/13	3/11

[a] Kucera *et al.* (1965).

[b] Denotes the number of survivors divided by the total number of eggs expressed as hours before (−) or after (+) virus infection.

2. Quantal Responses

The effect of AzUR was assayed on the multiplication of *Coxiella burneti* in 7-day-old embryos inoculated into the yolk sac by Brezina *et al.* (1962). *Coxiella burneti* (strain Nine Mile) was maintained by yolk sac passages. It reached a titer of 4×10^{10} LD_{50}/ml of yolk sac suspension. The embryos were inoculated with 10^{-3} and 10^{-4} dilutions of these suspensions. The embryos were observed for 12 days after inoculation; those dead within the first 2 days were discarded. Embryos dead on the 3rd and further days were tested for the presence of rickettsiae in the yolk sac membranes and for bacterial sterility. AzUR was administered simultaneously with the inoculum, using 2.5 and 10 mg/embryo in the experiments. The volume of inoculum (rickettsial suspension + AzUR solution) per egg was 0.25 ml.

The effect of AzUR on the multiplication of *C. burneti* is illustrated in Table XII and Fig. 33. The results were evaluated by comparing the corresponding ET_{50} values, in a manner similar to that discussed in Section II,B,2,*b*. Fifty percent mortality occurred on days 5.4 and 7.6 in embryos inoculated with 10^{-3} and 10^{-4} dilutions, respectively; 2.5 mg of AzUR delayed the 50% mortality in eggs inoculated with the 10^{-3} dilution by 0.8 days, 10 mg of AzUR by 1.8 days. In eggs inoculated with a 10^{-4} dilution, this delay was 0.8 and 2 days, respectively. An interpolation of the 50% mortalities showed that embryos inoculated with a 10^{-3} dilution and receiving 2.5 or 10 mg of AzUR died

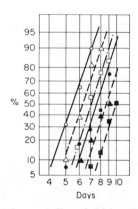

FIG. 33. Effect of AzUR on the mortality of chick embryos infected with *C. burneti*. (○) *C. burneti*, dilution 10^{-3}; (△) *C. burneti*, dilution 10^{-3} + 2.5 mg of AzUR; (□) *C. burneti*, dilution 10^{-3} + 10 mg of AzUR; (●) *C. burneti*, dilution 10^{-4}; (▲) *C. burneti*, dilution 10^{-4} + 2.5 mg of AzUR; (■) *C. burneti*, dilution 10^{-4} + 10 mg of AzUR (Brezina *et al.*, 1962).

TABLE XII

EFFECT OF AzUR ON THE MORTALITY OF CHICK EMBRYOS INFECTED WITH *C. burneti*[a]

Inoculum	No. of eggs/group	No. of embryos dead on days after inoculation						Day of 50% mortality
		5	6	7	8	9	10	
10^{-3} (control)	31	10	11	7	1	2		5.4
10^{-3} + 2.5 mg of AzUR	11	1	3	5	1	1		6.2
10^{-3} + 10 mg of AzUR	17		3	7	3	2	2	7.2
10^{-4} (control)	28	2	3	3	4	10	6	7.6
10^{-4} + 2.5 mg of AzUR	10		1	1		3	5	8.4
10^{-4} + 10 mg of AzUR	16			1	1	4	2	9.6

[a] Brezina *et al.* (1962).

as if they had been infected with doses 0.3 or 0.8 log units lower than the controls, respectively. The same holds for embryos inoculated with 10^{-4} dilutions. Administration of AzUR to eggs inoculated with a 10^{-3} dilution caused only a delay in the infection dynamics, though both in the experimental and control groups the mortality of the embryos was 100%, but the delay in the 50% mortality was significant. In embryos inoculated with a 10^{-4} dilution and given 2.5 mg of AzUR, the infection dynamics were also significantly delayed. The administration of 10 mg of AzUR, however, besides delaying the corresponding ET_{50} values, caused a significant decrease in the mortality rate, this being 51% in comparison with 100% mortality in the control group.

3. *Quantitative Responses*

The effect of virus multiplication in eggs of lemon balm extract was studied by Kucera et al. (1965). Embryonated eggs 9–11 days old were injected with various concentrations of lemon balm extract 3 hours before injection of Newcastle disease virus (NDV). After the eggs had been incubated for 48 hours, allantoic fluid was harvested, pooled, and tested for hemagglutination and for infectivity in eggs. The results (see Table XIII) indicate that virus could not be detected in eggs treated with 9.6 mg of extract. The antiviral effect was in a positive correlation with different concentrations of the extract ranging from 0.6 to 9.6 mg/egg.

TABLE XIII

EFFECT OF LEMON BALM EXTRACT ON MULTIPLICATION OF NEWCASTLE
DISEASE VIRUS[a] IN EGGS[b]

Extract[c] (mg/egg)	Titer of pooled allantoic fluids (6 eggs)[d]	
	Hemagglutinin units/0.0025 ml	Egg infectivity (negative log)
9.6	0	− 1
4.8	0	− 5.5
1.2	128	− 8.1
0.6	256	− 9.3
0.0	1024	−10.0

[a] Virus inoculum = $100 \times LD_{50}$ injected via allantoic sac of 9-day-old embryonated chick eggs.
[b] Kucera et al. (1965).
[c] Injected via allantoic sac 3 hours before injection of virus.
[d] Determined after incubation for 48 hours.

Brownlee and Hamre (1951) studied the effectiveness of p-amino-benzolaldehyd-3-thiosemicarbazone in vaccinia virus-infected embry-onated eggs by comparing the mean reciprocal survival times of treated and control embryos. The design of the experiment is similar to that described in Section II,B,2,c.

Six-day-old embryonated eggs were injected into the yolk sac of both the experimental and control groups with 0.25 ml of $10^{-5.0}$, $10^{-5.3}$, $10^{-5.6}$ dilutions of vaccinia virus, equivalent to approximately 360, 180, and 90 LD_{50}, respectively. Each group consisted of 6 eggs. The antiviral MC 2343 was injected in 0.5-ml volumes into the yolk sac in the ex-perimental group 30 minutes after infection. The eggs were incubated at 36°C and candled for death records. The tests were repeated several times and, as a representative, the results of test 4 (2/9/50) are illus-trated in Fig. 34.

We may see a linear regression of the mean reciprocal survival time in both the control and experimental groups upon the log virus dilutions. The mean reciprocal survival time of embryos in each ex-perimental group was lower than that in any control group. Thus the antiviral agent showed up an activity that was higher, as if the eggs in

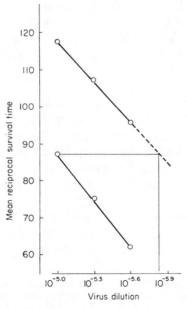

FIG. 34. Effect of MC 2343 on vaccinia virus infection of embryonated eggs. (O) Control; (●) treatment. Dotted line: extrapolation of the dose–response relation-ship of the treatment (based on data of Brownlee and Hamre, 1951).

the control group had been infected with a $10^{-5.6}$ virus dilution, instead of the original infection with a $10^{-5.0}$ virus infection. Since there is no departure from parallelism, the activity of the antiviral agent may be expressed—in this example—after extrapolating the corresponding regression lines (see dotted lines) to be as high as 0.8 log units.*

B. DEEMBRYONATED EGG

Bernkopf (1949) found that influenza viruses inoculated into embryonated eggs multiply readily in the cells of the surviving chlorioallantoic membrane, adhering also to the shell of the egg after the embryo has been discarded in a proper way. This technique, modified by Finter et al. (1954), being the missing link in antiviral testing between methods with embryonated eggs and those with chorioallantoic membrane tissue cultures, will be described here in detail.

Embryonated eggs, 14–15 days old, are recommended for deembryonating. The pointed end of the egg is cleansed with 70% alcohol, and a circular cut of about 1 inch in diameter is made in order to avoid any injury to the shell membrane and to the underlying chorioallantois. With the shell held horizontally, the shell membrane and the chorioallantois are cut with sterile scissors and the contents of the egg gently discarded. The parietal allantois should remain attached to the shell membrane, lining thus the whole inside of the egg and insuring that the virus will multiply only in the entodermal allantoic membrane cells. The allantoic fluid in the shell is then removed by draining and the egg is washed several times with 0.01 M phosphate-buffered salt solution of pH 7.0 at 37°C. As a final medium glucosol solution prepared according to Fulton and Armitage (1951) was used. This consisted of: NaCl, 8.0 gm; $CaCl_2$, 0.2 gm; $MgCl_2 \cdot 6H_2O$, 1.0 gm; glucose, 1.0 gm; and distilled water to 1000 ml, combined with phosphate buffer containing Na_2HPO_4 (4.73 gm), KH_2PO_4 (4.54 gm), and distilled water to 1000 ml. Equal volumes of these solutions are mixed shortly before use with antibiotics (penicillin, 100 units; streptomycin 100 μg/ml).

Ten milliliters of this medium warmed to 37°C are inserted into each shell, and the eggs, which are hermetically closed with sterile rubber cups, are inclined at a 20° angle from the horizontal plane and placed

---

* In biological assays, generally, no extrapolation of data is permitted. The activity of the antiviral agent under testing was therefore expressed in the test first to be merely higher than 0.6 log units. The extrapolation of the regression lines could be done in this example because of the significant parallelism of the corresponding regression lines.

in a rotating machine making about 20 revolutions per hour at 37°C. In this way the inner surface of the shell is readily bathed with the medium throughout the whole experiment. Harvests from the medium may be easily obtained by means of a sterile syringe inserted through the rubber cup at intervals. Antiviral agents may be tested by means of a combined in ovo-deembryonated egg technique, as recommended by Liu et al. (1957), who studied the effect of caprochlorone on the PR8 strain of influenza A virus. Fifteen-day-old embryos were inoculated allantoically with 0.2 ml of 10^{10} EID_{50}/ml containing infectious allantoic fluid 1 hour prior to deembryonating. The control groups were supplied with caprochlorone in modified glucosol medium or with glucosol alone. The eggs in the experimental groups were treated with caprochlorone at levels of 0.5, 1, 2, and 4 mg/egg. The fluids were removed at 2-hour intervals and replaced immediately with corresponding fresh medium. The harvests were pooled, held at 2°–4°C overnight, and titrated by standard methods for hemagglutinin content and for infectivity. The results show (Fig. 35) corresponding partial inhibition of virus multiplication in both the hemagglutination and the infectivity titrations; the effect of caprochlorone is positively correlated with levels of the antiviral agent ranging from 0.5 to 2.0 mg/egg.

IV. Experiments in Tissue Cultures

Most of the outstanding advances in virology in the last decade can be attributed to experiments in tissue cultures. After much pioneer-

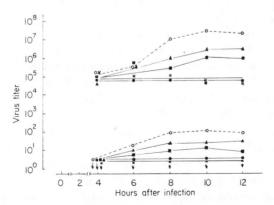

FIG. 35. The effect of different concentrations of caprochlorone on PR8 virus infection in deembryonated eggs. (○) Control; (▲) 0.5 mg/egg; (■) 1.0 mg/egg; (●) 2.0 mg/egg; (×) 4.0 mg/egg. Upper figure: infectivity titers; lower figure: hemagglutinin titers (Liu et al., 1957).

ing work on antiviral agents using chick embryo and mice, tissue cultures have now become the primary test method; they are useful not only for detection and assay of antiviral substances but also for study of the relationship of chemical structure to biological activity and for the study of their mode of action.

When testing antiviral agents in tissue cultures, as in all other systems, some general principles must be observed concerning adequate controls, reproducibility, and accuracy of the methods of analysis. The biological object answers to a specific stimulus only if the experiment is properly designed. In all biological systems, the simplest method is to test the null hypothesis with respect to two treatments. If the experimental and control groups respond differently after different treatments, then the null hypothesis is void and the observation is significant. This is the basis for the antiviral agent screening project, where the rejection of the null hypothesis leads to the selection of certain antiviral agents for further study.

In order to assure that any changes observed in the experimental group that are not present in the control can be attributed to the antiviral agent, it is essential to ascertain that the tissue cultures of both groups really owe to virus multiplication and not to toxic substances in the medium and/or in the material being tested. It is necessary on the other hand, to exclude the possibility that lack of cytopathic changes may result from the heterogeneity of the challenge virus or from the different susceptibilities of the cells. Finally, the experimenter must not rely on the results of a single assay, which could be influenced by the variability of the responses, without statistical evaluation of the data.

In general, criteria by which one can judge antiviral activity may be the inhibition of virus growth and/or the inhibition of cytopathic changes owing to multiplication of cytopathogenic viruses. The multiplication of noncytopathogenic viruses may be detected by measuring pH changes in the medium as a consequence of a decreased metabolism of virus-infected cells, by assaying hemagglutination, hemadsorption, virus neutralization, and complement fixation, or by inoculating the harvested infected medium into susceptible systems, for example, eggs and/or laboratory animals in order to determine the infectivity of the virus produced. The estimation of cytopathic changes may also differ according to the system used. The two types of tissue culture systems mainly involved in antiviral testing are chorioallantoic membrane fragments and monolayers.

A. The Use of Chorioallantoic Membrane Fragments

Until the development of tissue culture techniques, the most frequently used and the most favored system for studies on influenza virus was the allantoic cavity of the chick embryo. It was later found that only the allantoic surface in the deembryonated egg supported well virus multiplication. This observation provided the basis for the development of *in vitro* tissue culture techniques of choriallantoic membrane pieces, methods that represented an excellent, simplified system for testing antiviral agents.

Even if the infectivity titer of myxoviruses in chorioallantoic membrane fragments usually does not reach levels as high as in embryonated eggs, the former method is preferred by virologists who must carry out routine work with a large number of samples. When testing an antiviral agent, as was emphasized earlier, not only the activity of a compound but also its eventual toxicity must be taken into account. For this purpose a method described by Tamm *et al.* (1953), which makes possible the evaluation of both of these parameters, will be discussed here in detail.

The culture medium consists in this system of a glucosol solution: NaCl, 8.0 gm; $CaCl_2$ 0.2 gm; $MgCl_2 \cdot 6H_2O$, 0.5 gm; glucose, 1.0 gm; glass-distilled H_2O to 1000 ml; and, depending on the pH desired, 0.67 M phosphate buffer, for example, (1) Na_2HPO_4, 4.736 gm; KH_2PO_4, 4.539 gm; glass-distilled H_2O to 1000 ml for pH 6.8; (2) Na_2HPO_4, 7.105 gm; KH_2PO_4 2.269 gm; glass-distilled H_2O to 1000 ml for pH 7.28. Equal volumes of the glucosol solution and the phosphate buffer, either (1) or (2), are mixed according to the pH required. If necessary, the pH may be readjusted with 0.1 N NaOH or HCl. For obtaining membrane fragments, the shells of 10- or 11-day-old embryonated eggs are cut across with scissors, as indicated in Fig. 36.

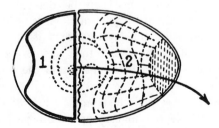

Fig. 36. Schema for preparation of chorioallantoic membrane fragments (Tamm *et al.*, 1953).

The contents of the egg are discarded except that part of the chorioallantoic membrane lining the portion of the shell that contains the air sac. The membrane is rinsed with medium from the shell and then washed with medium. The washed membrane is transferred to a Petri dish, and areas of gelatinous material found near the attachment of the allantoic vein and the cut margin are removed. The membrane is then cut into four pieces of approximately equal size (on average about 5.75 cm^2). After randomization, each piece is transferred to a large test tube (25 $\times$ 150 mm) containing 0.1 ml of culture medium or the solution of the antiviral agent to be tested. Immediately thereafter 0.1 ml of virus-infected allantoic fluid is added to the medium. It is recommended that at least six cultures be used per variable. The culture tubes are closed with rubber stoppers and incubated for 36 hours at 35°C with continuous horizontal shaking at 10–90 oscillations per minute. After the desired period of incubation, the medium is withdrawn and the concentration of virus measured by the hemagglutination technique. A significant difference between the HA titers of the experimental and control group indicates the positive antiviral activity of the compound under test.

In a screening project, however, for comparison of the therapeutic indexes of different substances, the determination of their toxic dose is also necessary. The system already described also serves for this purpose, by evaluating the morphological changes on the membrane pieces owing to the toxic effect of the antiviral agent as follows.

Intact membrane pieces undergo changes in appearance on incubation *in vitro* at 35°C with shaking (Fig. 37). This change is characterized by contraction and curving up of the membranes as early as 2 hours after incubation and becomes somewhat more marked at 36 hours. On curling up, the allantoic layers fall outward and the chorionic layer inward; even after incubation for as long as 48 hours the cellular integrity is preserved. No difference can be detected, whether or not the membranes are infected with influenza B virus.

The therapeutic index in this system may then be expressed by the ratio of the concentration of antiviral agent, decreasing by 75% the hemagglutinin titer of the control group and the concentration causing macroscopic damage to a degree of 2+. The degrees of macroscopic damage in a range of 1–4+ are illustrated in Fig. 38. Figure 39 shows the lack and the 2+ degree macroscopic damage of chorioallantoic pieces after treatment with 5,6-dichloro-1-β-D-ribofuranosylbenzimidazole in concentrations of 0.00019 and 0.00031 M, respectively. Since the 75% inhibition concentration is 0.0000375, the therapeutic index is in

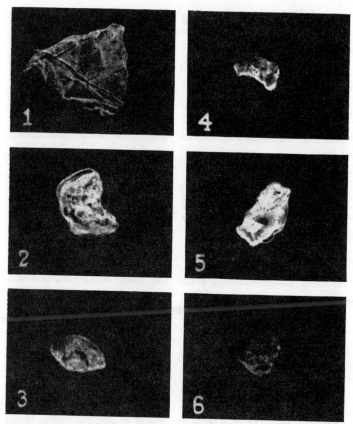

FIG. 37. Macroscopic appearance of control chorioallantoic membrane. (1) Not incubated; (2) incubated for 21 hours; (3) incubated for 36 hours; (4) incubated for 48 hours; (5) infected with Lee virus, incubated for 21 hours; (6) infected with Lee virus, incubated for 36 hours (Tamm, 1956).

this case as high as 8.2. The relationship between the inhibiting and toxic concentrations is indicated in Fig. 40.

B. The Use of Monolayers

In the foregoing paragraph an indirect method of antiviral testing was described using chorioallantoic membrane fragment tissue cultures. In this system the myxovirus group usually serves as a challenge virus; this does not cause cytopathic changes of the cells. The activity of an antiviral agent may then be assayed by comparison of either

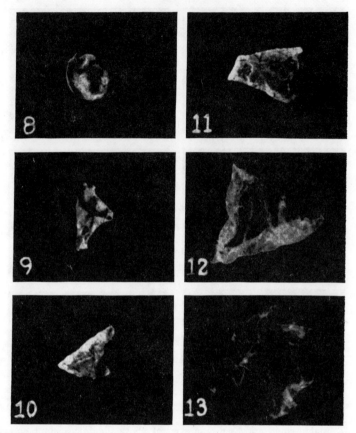

FIG. 38. Macroscopic appearance of chorioallantoic membrane in absence and presence of 2,5-dimethylbenzimidazole (MB). Membranes were infected with Lee virus and incubated for 36 hours. Vic = concentration causing 75% inhibition of Lee virus multiplication; md = macroscopic damage. (8) No compound; md = 0.9 MB, 0.0020 M, or 1.5 × vic; md: ±. (10) MB, 0.0026 M or 2 × vic; md: +. (11) MB, 0.0034 M or 2.6 × vic; md: ++. (12) MB, 0.0044 M or 3.4 × vic; md: +++. (13) MB, 0.0058 M or 4.5 × vic; md: ++++ (Tamm, 1956).

infectivity or the hemagglutinin titers of the medium of the experimental and control group, respectively.

Many viruses produce cytopathic changes in tissue cultures. Usually virus-infected cells become granular and rounded, with the sequence of degeneration occasionally leading to plaque formation. Cytopathic effects may be easily detected in monolayer cultures, and the protective effect on cells of an antiviral agent can then be directly evaluated.

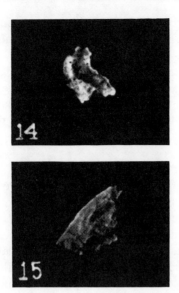

Fig. 39. Membranes infected with Lee virus and incubated for 36 hours. (14) DRB (5,6-dichloro-1-β-D-ribofuranosylbenzimidazole), 0.00019 M or 4.1 × vic; md; ±. (15) DRB, 0.00031 M or 8.2 × vic; md: ++ (Tamm, 1956).

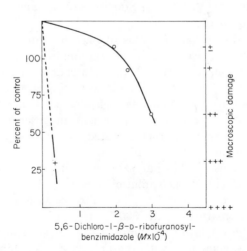

Fig. 40. Effect of 5,6-dichloro-1-β-D-ribofuranosylbenzimidazole on Lee virus multiplication and macroscopic appearance of the membrane. – + –: Virus multiplication; ○—○: macroscopic damage (Tamm, 1956).

In tissue culture antiviral testing projects, trypsinized primary animal tissue cells—the most popular being chick embryo fibroblasts and monkey kidney cells—are widely used.

The design of an antiviral project depends on the character of cytopathic changes owing to the challenge virus. Tube cultures are used in experiments with quantal responses, or glass plates, Petri dishes, or bottle cultures may be used for measuring the plaque count quantitatively.

1. Quantal Responses

The principles of the tube culture method are similar to antibody titration techniques. Serial dilutions of virus are prepared in small—usually half log—increments to an extent that would fail to cause cytopathic changes in the uniform layer of susceptible cells. The end point of the titration is then the virus dilution at which 50% of the cultures would respond alternatively. This dilution is called the $TCID_{50}$. The calculation of the end point of such quantal responses was discussed in detail in Section II,B,1,b. The activity of an antiviral agent under testing is evaluated by comparing the differences between the corresponding $TCID_{50}$ values. According to antibody titration techniques, the tube culture monolayers may be infected with constant dose (usually 100–500 $TCID_{50}$) of the virus, and the antiviral agent may be added in serial dilutions. Such an assay was proposed for interferon titration by Vilček and Stanček (1963), and will be discussed in the following example.

Ten percent suspension of brains of mice weighing 8–10 gm infected with the Hypr strain of tick-borne encephalitis virus served as the source of interferon, as antiviral agent, prepared in medium 199 with 10% horse serum. The suspension was centrifuged at 3500 rpm for 30 minutes. The supernatant fluid was then dialyzed against 20 volumes of citrate buffer at pH 2 and 4°C overnight in order to inactivate the virus. The pH 2 value was then restored by dialysis against the same volume of phosphate buffer at pH 7.4.

Twofold dilutions of the dialyzate were prepared in the tissue culture medium; 0.9 ml of each dilution was transferred into four monolayer tube cultures of L-cells. The cultures were infected 24 hours after interferon treatment with 500 $TCID_{50}$ of EMC (encephalomyocarditis) virus in 0.1 ml of medium. The inhibition and presence of cytopathic changes compared with the untreated and uninfected controls, respectively, are shown in Figs. 41 and 42. The titer of the interferon was as high as 1 : 512.

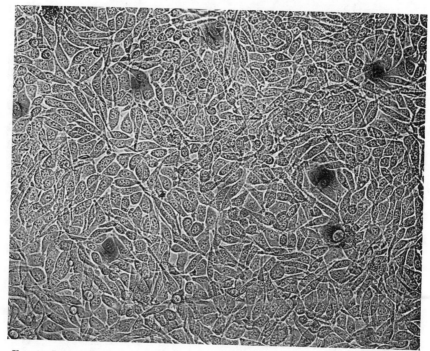

Fig. 41. Inhibition by interferon of cytopathic changes due to EMC virus inoculation into L cells. (Vilček and Stanček, 1963).

2. Quantitative Responses

A quantitative-response design serves for the same purpose if a plaque-causing virus is chosen as challenge. The plaque method was originally developed by Dulbecco and Voigt (1954). In this system, cultures showing a monolayer on glass are infected with different virus concentrations. After an adsorption period (30–120 minutes), the infected cells are covered with nutrient agar at 43°C, which solidifies within a short period of time. The cultures are then placed in an incubator and kept at 38°C for about 4 or 5 days. They are then stained with 0.02% solution of neutral red in saline containing 1% agar. The plaques, i.e., the number of cleared areas (Fig. 43), each resulting from an infective virus particle, may be easily counted 6 hours thereafter, being proportional to the concentration of virus if no more than 40–50 plaques were formed on a single Petri dish. Lorenz (1962) worked out an excellent method for statistical evaluation of the difference in plaque count between two samples. This procedure, which requires

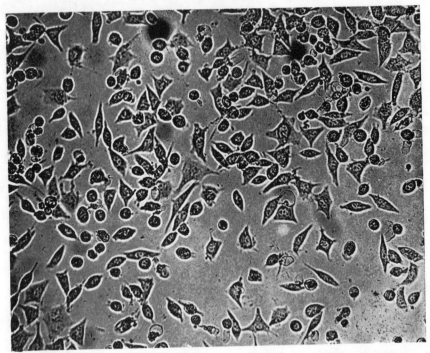

FIG. 42. Cytopathic changes in L cells owing to EMC virus infection (Vilček and Stanček, 1963).

some special training in mathematical statistics, will not be discussed here in detail; for interferon assays, usually the dilution of interferon, reducing by 50% the plaque number of the control, serves as the end point of the titration.

Antiviral activity of semipurified lemon balm plant extracts, which did not show antiviral activity in mammalian cell cultures, was assayed by Kucera *et al.* (1965) by the plaque technique in chick embryo fibroblast monolayers. The results were measured as the percentage of plaque-forming units (pfu) in treated plates compared to untreated plates. In Table XIV inhibition of virus plaque formation by pretreating chick cell monolayers with lemon balm extract is shown. Table XV represents the inhibition of virus plaque formation by simultaneous addition of lemon balm extract and virus to chick cell monolayers.

The original plaque method was further modified for antiviral testing by Herrmann *et al.* (1960) and by Rada *et al.* (1960). Both modifications serve for screening purposes, provided the monolayers are infected

TABLE XIV

INHIBITION OF VIRUS PLAQUE FORMATION BY PRETREATING CHICK CELL
MONOLAYERS WITH LEMON BALM EXTRACT[a,b]

	Plaque-forming units as % of control	
Extract (mg)	Newcastle disease	Semliki Forest
8.0	4	21
4.0	6	36
2.0	14	57
1.0	40	—
0.5	56	88
0.3	89	—
0.0 (Control)	100	100

[a] Monolayers were pretreated with 0.5 ml of extract solution for 1 hour at 36°C. The lemon balm extract was removed and the monolayers were washed twice with balanced salt solution (BSS); 0.5 ml of virus suspension (100 pfu) was added for 1 hour at 36°C. Virus was removed and the cell monolayer was washed twice with BSS and then overlaid with agar medium.

[b] Kucera et al. (1965).

with a quantity of virus that will produce numerous but not confluent plaques (Fig. 44). Filter paper discs impregnated with the antiviral agent (Herrmann et al., 1960) are then placed on the surface of agar overlay, or glass cylinders (Rada and Blaškovič, 1961) are inserted into the overlay with antiviral content, which while diffusing into the agar, suppresses the virus-induced plaque formation in monolayer. This

TABLE XV

INHIBITION OF VIRUS PLAQUE FORMATION BY SIMULTANEOUS ADDITION OF
LEMON BALM EXTRACT AND VIRUS TO CHICK EMBRYO MONOLAYER[a,b]

	Plaque-forming units as % of control			
Extract (mg)	Newcastle disease	Vaccinia	Herpes simplex	Semliki Forest
4.0	1	50	1	2
2.0	5	—	20	7
1.0	15	58	46	22
0.5	32	—	—	74
0.3	46	66	63	100
0.1	89	96	—	—
0.0 (Control)	100	100	100	100

[a] A mixture of virus (100 pfu) and lemon balm extract in 0.5 ml was added to the cell monolayer for 1 hour at 36°C. After the mixture was removed, the cell monolayer was washed twice with balanced salt solution and then overlaid with agar medium.

[b] Kucera et al. (1965).

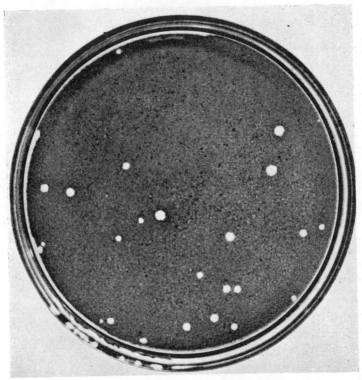

FIG. 43. Plaques in chick embryo fibroblast tissue cultures after infection with Newcastle diseases virus (Szántó, 1966).

modification makes it possible simultaneously to detect toxicity directed on the cell alone, as seen in Fig. 45, by a narrow zone of unstained cells surrounding the paper disc of the cylinder containing the antiviral agent. The wider zone of neutral red-stained, plaque-free cells indicates the antiviral effect. For the purposes of preliminary testing, the compound does not have to be tested at various dilutions, since the diffusion in agar represents a dilution gradient. A comparison of the size of the toxic zone to that of the plaque-free zone gives some idea of the tissue culture therapeutic index of the test substance.

V. Conclusion: Comments on Statistical Evaluation of the Experiment

The aim of this chapter was to systematize the principles of antiviral testing. This discipline, being a sort of applied research, profits

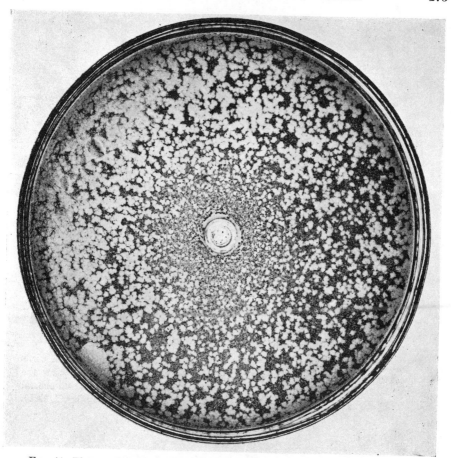

Fig. 44. Plaques in chick embryo fibroblast tissue cultures after infection with vaccinia virus (Rada *et al.*, 1960).

from almost all techniques familiar to virological laboratories. These are described in detail in other chapters of this volume. The same holds for the statistical methods, since in the testing of antiviral agents, as in all biological assays, the statistical evaluation of data cannot be avoided. Some simple statistical methods were included in this chapter, which may be used even by the virologist who has no special training in biometry, since the commoner techniques of statistical analysis should be within the competence of any scientist, however limited may be his mathematical background.

It is necessary, however, to remember that statistical analysis does not concern only the data observed but all the circumstances that may

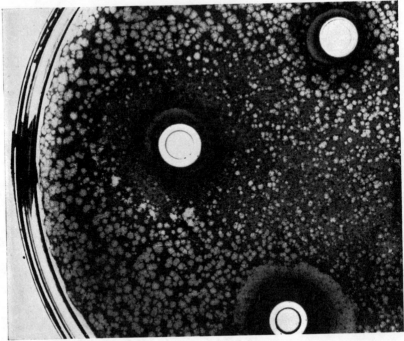

Fig. 45. Inhibition of plaque formation by chloracetyl urea after vaccinia virus infection of chick embryo cells. The narrow zone of unstained cells surrounding the cylinders shows toxicity directed at the cells alone, while the wider zone of neutral red-stained, plaque-free cells indicates the antiviral effect. (Rada and Blaškovič, 1961).

influence both their source and character. The virologist may, of course, be familiar with other statistical methods not mentioned in this chapter. These methods may be very useful, but a very severe warning must be given against the mechanical uncritical use—which may easily be a misuse—of any equation, which can lead to wrong conclusions.

In the majority of cases the evaluation of data requires the collaboration of a statistician, who is not always familiar with the problems from the virologist's point of view. When a statistician is asked to evaluate the results of an experiment for the detailed design of which he was not responsible, sometimes an enormous effort must be made to discover exactly how the experiment was assayed and conducted. Often the experimenter may fail to mention the existence of some constraint in a design, since he does not realize its relevance to the statistical analysis. In such cases, only the most careful discussion will elicit the information necessary to modify the form of analysis.

The policy of the experimenter should be, therefore, to obtain the assistance of a professional statistician, although the final responsibility for the observations always rests with the experimenter, who must decide whether or not the assay used is valid. Statistical analysis cannot enable him to evade his responsibility, but he can insure that relevant evidence is presented in a clear, objective. manner. A significant difference between two sets of responses does not itself call for rejection of an assay, but it is a danger signal, since an equally valid assay might appear to give, for example, nonparallel response curves as a result of an unsatisfactory choice of doses, and an invalid assay may give two parallel lines if tested over particular ranges of dose, giving different levels of response. If an assay shows only statistical invalidity, the analysis may be modified, using other metameters (e.g., reciprocals of survival times), or a decision between acceptance and rejection may be delayed until further information on the metameters has been accumulated. Otherwise, the statistician must be aware of the fact that execution in a laboratory of an experimental design that appears theoretically ideal may be technically difficult and may lead to errors that would destroy the expected validity of the test. A simple design can give better results than one the complexity of which defeats its own ends.

ACKNOWLEDGMENT

I am indebted to the Literary Executor of the late Sir Ronald A. Fisher, F.R.S., Cambridge, to Dr. Frank Yates, F.R.S., Rothamsted, and to Messrs. Oliver & Boyd Ltd., Edinburgh, for permission to reprint Tables III and IV from their book "Statistical Tables for Biological, Agricultural and Medical Research." In this work, data taken from Table III appears in Table I, and from Table IV in Table V.

REFERENCES

Bauer, D. J. (1958). *Brit. J. Exptl. Pathol.* **39,** 480.
Bauer, D. J. (1961). *Brit. J. Exptl. Pathol.* **42,** 201.
Bauer, D. J., and Sadler, P. W. (1960). *Brit. J. Pharmacol.* **15,** 101.
Bernkopf, H. (1949). *Proc. Soc. Exptl. Biol. Med.* **72,** 680.
Brezina, R., Kordová, N., and Link, F. (1962). *Acta Virol. (Prague)* **6,** 266.
Brownlee, K. A., and Hamre, D. (1951). *J. Bacteriol.* **61,** 127.
Dulbecco, R., and Vogt, M. (1954). *J. Exptl. Med.* **99,** 167.
Finney, D. J. (1952). "Probit Analysis: A Statistical Treatment of the Sigmoid Response Curve," 2nd ed. Cambridge Univ. Press, London and New York.
Finter, N. B., Liu, O. C., Lieberman, M., and Henle, W. (1954). *J. Exptl. Med.* **100,** 33.

Fisher, R. A., and Yates, F. (1948). "Statistical Tables for Biological, Agricultural and Medical Research." Oliver Boyd, Ltd., Edinburgh.

Fulton, F., and Armitage, P. (1951). *J. Hyg.* **49**, 247.

Gard, S. (1940). *J. Exptl. Med.* **72**, 69.

Herrmann, E. C., Jr., Gabliks, J., Engle, C., and Perlman, P. L. (1960). *Proc. Soc. Exptl. Biol. Med.* **103**, 625.

Kucera, S. L., Cohen, R. A., and Herrmann, E. C., Jr. (1965). *Ann. N.Y. Acad. Sci.* **130**, 474.

Link, F. (1959). *Physiol. Bohemoslov.* **8**, 484.

Link, F., Raus, J., and Ráthová, V. (1963). *Acta Virol. (Prague)* **7**, 465.

Link, F., Blaškovič, D., and Raus, J. (1965a). *Acta Virol. (Prague)* **9**, 381.

Link, F., Blaškovič, D., and Raus, J. (1965b). *Acta Virol. (Prague)* **9**, 553.

Link, F., Rada, B., and Blaškovič, D. (1965c). *Ann. N.Y. Acad. Sci.* **130**, 31.

Liu, O. C., Malsberger, R. G., Carter, J. E., Armand, N. deSanctis, Wiener, F. P., and Hampel, B. (1957). *J. Immunol.* **78**, 215.

Lorenz, R. J. (1962). *Arch. Ges. Virusforsch.* **12**, 108.

Rada, B., and Blaškovič, D. (1961). *Acta Virol. (Prague)* **5**, 308.

Rada, B., Blaškovič, D., Šorm, F., and Škoda, J. (1960). *Experientia* **16**, 487.

Šmejkal, F., and Šorm, F. (1962). *Acta Virol. (Prague)* **6**, 282.

Stuart-Harris, C. H., and Dickinson, L. (1965). *In* "The Background to Chemotherapy of Virus Diseases," Thomas, Springfield, Illinois.

Szántó, J., and Pristasovó, N. (1966). *Acta Virol. (Prague)* **10**, 328.

Tamm, I. (1956). *J. Bacteriol.* **72**, 42.

Tamm, I., Folkers, K., and Horsfall, F. J., Jr. (1953). *J. Exptl. Med.* **98**, 229.

Vilček, J., and Stanček, D. (1963). *Acta Virol. (Prague)* **7**, 331.

6 Techniques for Studying Defective Bacteriophages

Allan M. Campbell*

I. Induction and Detection of Defective Lysogenic Bacteria   279
   A. Definition and Scope   279
   B. Isolation of Point Mutants   282
   C. Isolation of Deletion Mutants   288
II. Detection and Properties of Defective Virus Particles   297
   A. Properties Measurable in Mixed Lysates   297
   B. Physical Separation of Defective Particles   301
III. Genetic Localization of the Defect   305
   A. Mapping of Point Mutants   305
   B. Mapping of Deletions   309
IV. Complementation   311
   A. Complementation between Defective and Conditional
      Lethal Mutants   311
   B. Complementation between Two Defectives   312
V. Definition of the Physiological Block(s)   312
   A. Genetic Pool Studies   313
   B. Accumulation of Tail-Fiber Protein   317
   C. Killing and Lysis of Cells   318
   References   319

I. Induction and Detection of Defective Lysogenic Bacteria

A. Definition and Scope

A bacterium is called lysogenic if it has the latent potential to produce bacteriophage, i.e., if it harbors and reproduces the genome of the phage along with that of the bacterium. Lysogeny is detected by the fact that this potential is occasionally expressed, so that any

*During the writing of this chapter, the author was supported by a Research Career Award from the U.S. Public Health Service. Previously unpublished work reported here was supported by grant E-2862 of the Division of Allergy and Infectious Diseases U.S.P.H.S.

culture produced by growing the progeny of a single lysogenic cell will contain some phage. A bacterium that harbors a phage genome (or a portion thereof) but that for some reason is unable to produce phage is termed a defective lysogen.

Defective lysogens are distinguished from true lysogens by their inability to produce phage. They are distinguished from nonlysogenic bacteria by the presence of some viral genes. These can be detected either (1) phenotypically, by their effect on the properties of the cell, or (2) genetically, by their ability to recombine with a genetically marked superinfecting phage. Except for certain special cases, the only known phenotypic effect of the presence of the phage genome is to render the cell immune to superinfection by phage of the carried type (and sometimes to other related phages as well). Operationally, a defective lysogen can be recognized as a strain that is immune to superinfection but that does not liberate phage. This operation discards those defective lysogens in which the immunity locus itself has been lost or rendered nonfunctional. As we shall see, such strains can occur, but only in certain special situations.

A strain that is classified as a defective lysogen by this operation might fall into that category for one of two reasons: (1) The phage genome it carries might be incomplete or altered, so that it is no longer able to perform all the viral functions necessary for phage production. We would then say that the strain is lysogenic for a defective phage. This is the most common situation. (2) It might be lysogenic in a defective or abnormal manner for a phage that is normal. We shall encounter one case below (Section I,C,4) of a strain that liberates very little phage apparently because of an abnormality in the manner of phage attachment to the bacterial chromosome rather than because of any defect in the phage genome itself.

One of our operational criteria for a defective lysogen is that it should produce no phage. In practice, a rigorous definition on this basis is complicated by two facts: (1) Like other mutants, many defective phages can revert with detectable frequency to the wild-type genotype. If this happens in the prophage, the defective lysogen will revert to an active lysogen. If it happens after induction, some active phage particles may be produced from an induced cell of a defective lysogen. In either case, the result is that a culture of a defective lysogen will produce some active, plaque-forming particles. Since reversion frequencies are typically of the order of 10^{-6} per generation, the number of such revertants is almost always vastly less than the amount of phage found in an ordinary lysogenic culture. (2) Also like other mutants, many defectives can be "leaky" to some degree. Induction of a defective lysogen or infection by a defective phage particle leads to the production of some progeny particles, still of the mutant genotype, but not of enough such particles in a short enough time to produce a visible plaque. Indeed, there is no sharp natural division between phage mutants that grow very poorly, forming tiny plaques, and those that grow a little less well and cannot be recognized as phages. The exact demarcation between the two groups will depend on the precise plating conditions employed. Except for the case of conditional lethal mutants under nonpermissive conditions, very few measurements of the leakiness of defective lysogens have been made. In principle, they could be carried out by the technique of plating on a lysogen for a heteroimmune relative of a defective phage (see Section II,B).

The mutation from normal to defective bacteriophage constitutes a lethal mutation for the phage. It survives only thanks to its ability to reproduce as a prophage. In addition to complete lethals, phages, like other organisms, can give rise to conditional lethal mutants. These are mutants that are unable to grow under certain conditions which allow the growth of wild-type phage, but are able to grow under others. The conditions under which the mutants will grow are termed "permissive." Some conditional lethal mutants function only in a restricted temperature range; others require the presence of specific suppressor mutations in the host.

If the lysogen of a conditional lethal mutant is grown under nonpermissive conditions, the mutant behaves like a defective prophage. It would be quite proper for us to include such strains in our discussion here. Indeed, we cannot assert on strictly logical grounds that there is such a thing as an "unconditional lethal." According to modern molecular genetics, there should be, but certainly some of the phage mutants isolated as "defectives" might turn out to form plaques under different conditions of growth.

For the most part, however, we shall restrict our attention to techniques that are generally applicable to defective lysogens, whether or not conditions are known under which they become nondefective. Conditional lethals play an important role in the discussion for two reasons: (1) They are handy tools for studying defective lysogens; e.g., for use in crosses or complementation tests. (2) Some measurements that can easily be made with conditional lethals suggest that other measurements could or should be made with "true" defectives, e.g., the determination of "leakiness," mentioned above.

The author's own experience is confined almost entirely to phage lambda. Most of the technical details to be given in the following discussion will therefore be those directly applicable to this phage and may require modification to be useful in other systems. Also, despite the many interesting cases of naturally occurring defective phages, we shall confine our attention to those defectives whose origin as variants of known phages is clear, because we feel that they should be understood first.

B. Isolation of Point Mutants

Point mutants in prophages can be induced by various agents. UV light and x-rays have frequently been used. These treatments induce lysis of and phage production by some of the treated population. The phage liberated by the cells that lyse can be a nuisance. If the colonies produced by the surviving bacteria arise as islands in a sea of free phage, a great deal of reinfection will occur. Also, any test of lysogeny involving printing onto a nonlysogenic indicator will be messy because of the background phage on the master plate. It is desirable to neutralize this free phage by the addition of antiphage serum, both to the liquid growth medium used immediately after induction and to the surface of the Petri plates on which the bacteria are spread.

The kinetics of induction of defective mutations in prophage has not been carefully studied. The assumption has been that, as with most mutagens, the fraction of mutants among the survivors will increase with increasing dose of the inducing agent. This assumption should hold so long as the population is homogeneous in its susceptibility to both the mutagenic and the lethal effects of the irradiation. It could fail if there were a fraction of the population that was especially easily mutagenized and also more easily killed than the remaining cells. Thus, in general, the dose that has been used is the largest one that still leaves a convenient number of viable cells to be screened; usually survival is around 10^{-5}. For phage lambda in *Escherichia coli*, the dose needed is about 6×10^4 erg/cm^2 of UV or 100,000 r of x-rays.

Under the tests usually employed, defective lysogeny behaves as "recessive" to true lysogeny. A mixed colony composed of some defective lysogens and some active lysogens would not be scored as defective. Bacterial cells are frequently multinucleate, so that a colony arising from a mutagenized cell in which a defective mutation has been induced in one nucleus might still contain some cells with good phage. Depending on the mechanism of mutagenesis, it is possible that not all the progeny from a mutagenized nucleus will be mutants. For these reasons, it is undesirable to plate the mutagenized culture immediately after irradiation. A period of growth in liquid medium sufficient to allow segregation of mutant nuclei into separate cells must be allowed. The time required for this to happen must be determined for the individual system. Especially when radiation is used as the inducing agent, there may be a long lag before the treated cells begin to multiply. Usually three or four generations of growth following irradiation is adequate to allow segregation. The exact amount of growth required has not been carefully studied.

After this growth period in liquid, the treated culture can be plated on solid medium. It may be either plated in a soft agar layer or spread with a sterile glass rod. Spreading is usually preferable if the colonies are to be tested later by printing. After overnight incubation at 37°C to allow growth of the viable cells into colonies, the plates may be printed with a sterile velvet pad or a piece of sterile coarse-textured paper onto other plates seeded with a lawn of phage-sensitive bacteria. The lawn is usually prepared in a top agar layer; printing is less messy if the layer contains 1.5–2% agar rather than the 0.7% usually used for observing plaques. These latter plates are then irradiated with an inducing dose of UV light and incubated overnight. For phage lambda, a dose of about 1.2×10^4 erg/cm^2 (one half the optimal inducing dose) works well.

The next day, these plates can be examined for the presence around each printed colony of a halo of lysis of the indicator bacteria. The majority of printed colonies will give such halos. A few (about 1 per 1000 under the best conditions) fail to produce halos. These colonies should be picked from the master plate and purified by restreaking.

The purified colonies can then be tested further to see whether they are carrying defective prophages or no prophage at all. The latter type of strain (completely "cured" of its prophage) is usually more common than the former. The presence of defective prophage can be checked by several different methods. If many isolates are to be tested, it is convenient to use some method that can be done by printing and to spot or stab all isolates on one or more master plates. The number of colonies that can be put onto one master plate without running into one another on printing depends on the technique of the investigator. The author finds 24 a convenient number.

Such a master plate can then be printed onto a suitable indicator. A variety of choices is available. The most straightforward approach is to print onto a plate spread with a lysate of phage of the same immunity type but lacking the ability to lysogenize. Although these mutants (called "clear" in lambda and "weak virulent" in phage P2) are unable to generate the phage-specific immunity, their growth is blocked in a lysogenic bacterium carrying a prophage of the same immunity type. When a nonlysogenic colony is printed onto a layer of these phage, all the cells will be lysed and no bacterial growth will occur except for perhaps a few phage-resistant mutants in the colony. A lysogenic or defective lysogenic bacterium, on the other hand, is immune to lysis; a colony of such cells will grow as well in the presence as in the absence of the background phage.

A nonlysogenic colony might also grow on this background because it carried a bacterial mutation rendering the cells resistant to phage infection. The most common type of such mutation alters the cell surface so that phage can no longer attach to it. These mutants can be distinguished from defective lysogens by the use of a phage mutant (called "virulent" in lambda and "strong virulent" in phage P2) that is insensitive to the immunity and can grow on lysogenic cells. The attachment specificity of the virulent mutant is the same as that of the temperate phage from which it came. A defective lysogen will fail to grow on a background of the strong virulent mutant, whereas a phage-resistant bacterial mutant can grow. If there were a type of defective lysogen that was immune even to the virulent mutant, it would be misclassified by this test. Such defectives are not known; but, because of the standard screening procedures, they probably would have been discarded as phage-resistant mutants.

Lysogenic strains sometimes are unable to support the growth of phages unrelated to the one they carry. This has been termed "prophage interference" and is sometimes determined by the same genetic region of the phage that controls immunity specificity (or a region very closely linked thereto). For example, the r_{II} mutants of phage T4 fail to grow on cells lysogenic for phage lambda. A layer of $T4r_{II}$ can be used as an indicator for lambda lysogeny just as lambda c can. As before, a control is needed to exclude resistant bacterial mutants. In this case, the control is $T4r^+$.

Another convenient indicator, for those phages where it is available, is a bacterial strain lysogenic for a heteroimmune relative of the tested phage. By a heteroimmune relative we mean a phage like the 434 phage that can recombine with phage lambda, but is insensitive to the specific immunity generated by the lambda prophage. Likewise, lambda is insensitive to the immunity of the 434 prophage, so that when a 434 phage recombines with a defective lambda genome, the active phage recombinants of the lambda immunity type grow freely on the background lysogenic for 434. The hybrid phage carrying the immunity of 434 and the rest of the genome of lambda (Kaiser and Jacob, 1957) is ideal. The cell density in the background should be about twice that used with a nonlysogenic indicator,* because some of the background cells will be induced by the UV used in the test. The master plate is printed onto this indicator, which is then UV'd and incubated overnight. A halo of lysis or the appearance of plaques around the colony indicates that the tested strain carries the immunity locus of lambda.

This test gives clear-cut results even when the defective phage tested has a long deletion, and the cells liberate no infectious particles of any kind after induction. This means that the recombinants are not being formed by the infection of background cells with defective particles liberated by the induced defective lysogens but rather by infection of the defective lysogens with free phage liberated by the background cells. If the defective lysogens happen to be unable to adsorb the phage, they will appear as nonlysogenic rather than as defective. Consequently, an independent test for ability to adsorb phage is necessary for this test as well as for the previous ones. The expected behavior of various types of strains is shown in Tables I and II.

If only a few isolates are to be tested, it is sometimes convenient to have them growing in liquid medium rather than to print from a master plate. The above tests can all be modified by putting a drop of the culture on the appropriate background rather than printing from

TABLE I

GROWTH OF BACTERIAL STRAINS ON LAWNS OF VARIOUS PHAGES[a]

Background phage	Tested bacteria							
	K	$K(\lambda)$	K/λ	$K(\lambda)/\lambda$	$K/4$	$K(\lambda)/4$	$K(\lambda\,def)$	$K(\lambda\,def)/\lambda$
λc	−	+	+	+	−	+	+	+
λvir	−	−	+	+	−	−	−	+
T4r_{II}	−	+	−	+	+	+	+	+
T4$r+$	−	−	−	−	+	+	−	−

[a] + = normal growth; ⇀ = little or no growth because of destruction by phage; K = nonlysogenic *Escherichia coli* K-12; $K(\lambda)$ = *E. coli* K-12 lysogenic for phage lambda; K/λ = *E. coli* K-12 mutant to which lambda is unable to attach; $K/4$ = *E. coli* K-12 mutant to which phage T4 is unable to attach.

* The exact amount is not very critical. For a nonlysogenic indicator, we usually use 0.2 ml of a fresh young culture or 0.5 ml of a culture that has been stored for a few days or weeks in the refrigerator.

TABLE II
Lysis of Background Bacteria by Various Tested Strains[a]

	Tested strain					
Bacterial layer	K	$K(\lambda)$	K/λ	$K(\lambda)/\lambda$	$K(\lambda\ def)$	$K(\lambda\ def\ /\lambda$
K	−	+	−	+	−	−
$K(\lambda\ imm^{434})$	−	+	−	+	+	−[b]

[a] Symbols for tested strains as in Table I. + = lysis of background bacteria; − = no lysis of background bacteria; $\lambda\ imm^{434}$ = lambda-434 hybrid phage of Kaiser and Jacob (1957).

[b] May be + if defective is "leaky."

a master plate. When sensitivity to a phage is tested, more clear-cut results are obtained by using cross streaks rather than spots. Instead of spreading a background of phage over the entire test plate, one streaks a loopful of lysate across the plate, allows it to dry, and then streaks the culture to be tested in a direction perpendicular to that of the streak. In streaking the cultures, care should be taken to move the loop in one direction only. Phage will be present in the phage streak and beyond it, but that part of the cross streak before the phage streak serves as control. If the strain is sensitive to the phage, a sharp demarcation is seen where the bacterial streak crosses the phage streak. The method is more reliable than using a continuous background (without considerable standardization), because the control is immediately adjacent to the test, and a strain that merely grows poorly is not confused with one that is virus sensitive. Cross streaks can also be made on a master plate and printed across test plates streaked with phage. About eight parallel streaks of bacteria can easily be put on one test plate, with two streaks of phage in the perpendicular direction.

It is also possible to test for marker rescue directly rather than to recognize defectives by means of their immunity. In principle, this is done by infecting the tested cells with a phage mutant, inducing them to remove the superinfection immunity, and observing the phage output for recombinants that carry some gene(s) of the phage from which the defective was originally derived. In practice, screening is convenient only if the recombinant in question can be selected. Conditional lethal mutants are suitable. The host-range marker can also be used, but in this case the defectives must have been made from a phage with extended host range rather than from the normal wild-type. Streaks of the tested strain can be printed onto test plates that have a bacterial lawn over which a streak of the test phage has been made. The conditions of the test plate must be selective for the recombinant sought. If the test phage is suppressor sensitive, the background bacteria must be nonpermissive. If extended host range is looked for, the host-range indicator is used. Lysis of the background layer where the bacterial and phage streaks intersect indicates the formation of recombinants. With suppressor-sensitive mutants of phage lambda, the lysate should be diluted to about 10^8 phage/ml. At higher titers, even though these mutants do not grow on the nonpermissive host, the amount of cell damage done by infection of background bacteria with the added phage is too much to allow clear scoring of recombination.

In principle, defective prophages produced and detected in the manner described here might carry either point mutations or more extended alterations of the "deletion" or "multisite" type. In practice, the author knows of no case where a deletion has been produced directly in this manner. The known deletion mutants have all occurred in special ways, which will be described in the next section.

In defective lysogens produced as described here, not only the prophage but also the rest of the bacterial genome has been subjected to a highly mutagenic treatment. It is therefore risky to attribute all the differences from the normal lysogen to the defect itself. For careful work, the defective prophage and the wild-type prophage should be compared against a common background. As will be described in Section II,A, it is frequently possible to obtain infectious defective particles by cooperation with wild-type phage, and these can then be used to lysogenize another host cell. When this is not possible, the defective phage can also be transferred to another host by conjugation or by linked transduction with a bacterial marker. These methods are less desirable in that some bacterial genes are also transferred.

After the elimination of differences in the residual bacterial genome, the residual phage genome still remains. If strains lysogenic for a defective phage show some physiological property (e.g., an abnormal level of a certain enzyme), one may ask whether this property is caused by the genetic defect itself or by some other nonlethal mutation that happened to be induced in the same phage. In principle, this can be decided by crossing the defective phage with active phage and examining recombinants. However, this can require much labor; and if the character in question fails to be separated from the defect by recombination, the possibility always remains that the two are very closely linked. If reverse mutations to active phage occur, it is easier and more conclusive to study these. Where a single mutation undoes both the defect and the abnormal properties found in association with it, it is highly probable that the two properties were also caused by the same mutation in the first place.

C. Isolation of Deletion Mutants

A "deletion" or "multisite" mutation is defined as one that fails to produce wild-type recombinants with either of two other mutants that can produce wild-type when crossed with each other. This implies that the mutation has altered more than a single nucleotide pair. We say that a defective phage has a deletion if it fails to produce wild-type recombinants after induction and superinfection by two or more recombinationally distinct phage mutants. As in other systems studied (Benzer, 1959), the deletions of defective phages can be represented on, and lend support to, a strictly linear genetic map, in which the group of mutational sites missing from any particular defective defines a connected region of the map (Campbell, 1964; Franklin et al., 1965).

As mentioned above, deletion mutations should in principle be found among defective phages occurring spontaneously or induced by agents that cause deletions in other material. In practice, we know of no well-documented case where a deletion defective mutation has been isolated in this manner. Instead, those we have have been produced by a variety of special methods.

1. Transducing Phages

Some temperate phages effect what has become known as "specialized transduction." This kind of transduction, first discovered by Morse et al. (1956) with phage lambda, differs from the "generalized transduction" found earlier by Zinder and Lederberg (1952) in that (1) specialized transduction occurs only with lysates produced from lysogenic cells, not with lytically grown phage, and (2) whereas generalized transduction can involve any marker, specialized transduction is restricted to genes very closely linked to the prophage on the bacterial chromosome.

The transduced genes are not carried by all the phage particles in the lysate but only by a small fraction of them. This fraction itself frequently consists of defective phages. When they are defective, they are always deletion defectives, which are missing a region of the phage genome rather than a point.

All the data presently available are compatible with the idea that the transducing particles of a phage showing specialized transduction contain a continuous segment of genetic material taken from the chromosome of the lysogenic cell. The genome of a transducing phage can be considered the inverse of a genetic deletion—the piece that, when thrown away, leaves behind a bacterial chromosome with a deletion in it. Because part of this piece comes from a phage genome that is capable of extracellular transmission, this piece can be recovered rather than being lost as most deleted segments are. A transducing particle carries a block of bacterial genes adjacent to the prophage and frequently misses a block from the other end of the prophage.

So far as the phage genome is concerned, the recognizable deletion consists of that part of the phage genome that was "left behind" in the bacterial chromosome. It can be seen from the above description that the deletions will always be terminal deletions, which may penetrate to various extents into the phage genome. A complication is introduced by the fact that the genetic map of the prophage is not the same as that of the phage itself, but rather a cyclic permutation thereof. Deletions that are terminal on the prophage map thus become interstitial on the vegetative map of the phage. The situation for phage lambda is diagrammed in Fig. 1. The lambda prophage lies between

A. Map of vegetative lambda phage:

$A\ B\ C\ D\ E\ F\ G\ H\ M\ L\ K\ I\ J\ h\ b_2\ c_{III}\ N\ c_I\ c_{II}\ O\ P\ Q\ R$

(imm)

B. Map of the bacterial chromosome in the region of the lambda attachment site:

$gal\quad b_2\quad bio$

C. Map of the lysogenic chromosome:

$gal\quad b_2\ c_{III}\ N\ c_I\ c_{II}\ O\ P\ Q\ R\ A\ B\ C\ D\ E\ F\ G\ H\ M\ L\ K\ I\ J\ h\ b_2\quad bio$

(imm)

Fig. 1. Mode of integration of bacteriophage lambda into the *E. coli* chromosome. Genes *A* to *R* are cistrons of conditional lethal mutants. The *h* locus determines the attachment specificity of the phage particle to the bacterial surface. The c_I locus determines immunity specificity. The c_{II} and c_{III} loci are involved in lysogenization (Kaiser, 1957.) The b_2 locus determines the ability of the phage chromosome to become integrated into the bacterial chromosome. Derivation of Fig. 1C from Figs. 1A and 1B requires that the ends of the viral chromosome become joined together and that virus and host chromosome cross over in the b_2 region.

some genes for galactose fermentation on one side and a gene for biotin synthesis on the other. Lambda exhibits specialized transduction of both *gal* and *bio,* but not of both simultaneously. Those lambda that carry *gal* are missing some genes at the end of the prophage closest to *bio.* Those that carry *bio* are sometimes active phage with the whole phage genome; others are defective and are missing genes from the end closest to lambda. Lambda that carry *gal* are called "lambda *dg*" (for defective, galactose transducing).

The possible extent of the deletion seems to be limited by the requirement that the structure formed, in order to be recognized, must be capable of infecting a recipient cell and lysogenizing it. In lambda, it is apparently necessary that the transducing particle contain the normal "end point" of the vegetative map (between R and A on Fig. 1C) but very little else. Lambda particles are known that contain *bio* but are missing some or all of the genes in region N–R (Kayajanian, 1967). Thus, the only parts of the normal lambda phage that are common to the whole collection of transducing phages are the very ends of the vegetative map, and the region labeled "b_2" in Fig. 1C (if it really is duplicated at the two ends of the prophage, as we have drawn it).

Particles with more extreme deletions may occur and may participate in transduction of bacterial genes, but they are not recoverable by the methods described below. The upper limit to the number of lambda genes contained by galactose-transducing particles probably means that the distance from *gal* through gene K represents the maximum amount of DNA that a lambda phage can contain (Kayajanian, and Campbell, 1966).

The methods for studying the position and extent of the deletion will be described in more detail in Section III,B. Here we shall only outline the method of isolation of the defective phages, using the transduction of *gal* by lambda as an example.

First, a lysate of phage is produced by induction of a gal^+ lysogenic strain, usually with UV light. Transduction is found also with free phage or with phage produced by other inducing agents (e.g., mitomycin c). Surviving bacteria in the lysate can be removed by filtration or by the addition of chloroform. In the author's experience, filtration is more reliable. For some types of experiments where many lysates are made and filtration is inconvenient, a streptomycin-sensitive donor can be used with a streptomycin-resistant recipient and streptomycin in the selection plates. This method is safe provided the donor is an F^- strain incapable of transferring genes by conjugation.

The recipient must be a gal^- strain. A stable mutant that does not revert is best. If no stable single mutant is available, double mutants can be produced by crossing. For precise quantitative studies of transduction, the phage from the donor should be allowed to attach to the recipient in liquid medium (0.01 M MgSO$_4$) and then plated in the presence of sufficient antiphage serum to prevent further cycles of growth on the plates. Merely to obtain transductants, such refinements are unnecessary. A 0.1-ml sample of a lysate with a titer between 1×10^9 and 1×10^{10} phage/ml can be mixed on the surface of the plate with 0.1 ml of a bacterial suspension at 1×10^9 cells/ml and spread with a sterile glass rod. Usually the number of colonies of transductants found per plate will be in the range 10–1000.

The transduction plates must contain some agent selective for the transduced character; in the present case, ability to ferment galactose. The most usual medium has been eosin methylene blue galactose (EMBG). It is also possible to use a synthetic medium containing the redox indicator triphenyltetrazolium chloride (TTC). The compositions of these media are given in Table III.

On the EMBG medium, colonies of galactose-fermenting bacteria

TABLE III

COMPOSITION OF MEDIA FOR TRANSDUCTION STUDIES

A. Eosin methylene blue galactose (EMBG). Per liter of water:

Agar	15 gm
Bacto tryptone	10 gm
Yeast extract	1 gm
NaCl	5 gm
Galactose	10 gm
Methylene blue	0.065 gm
Eosin	0.4 gm
K$_2$HPO$_4$	2 gm

Sugar, dyes, and phosphate are autoclaved separately and added to the medium after sterilization.

B. Triphenyltetrazolium chloride galactose agar (TTCG). Per liter of water:

K$_2$HPO$_4$	10.5 gm
KH$_2$PO$_4$	4.5 gm
MgSO$_4$	0.05 gm
(NH$_4$)$_2$SO$_4$	1 gm
Sodium citrate	0.47 gm
Galactose	4 gm
2,3,5-triphenyl-2H-tetrazolium chloride	0.1 gm

Sugar and dye are added to the medium after sterilization. Dye solution is not autoclaved but made as stock 1% solution stored in the dark.

---

appear dark purple and those of galactose-nonfermenting bacteria light pink, probably owing to a reaction between the dyes and the acid produced during fermentation. The distinction is usually clear after 16–24 hours of incubation at 37°C. However, on the primary transduction plates, the transductants appear not as isolated colonies but as foci of denser growth against a confluent background of galactose negative cells that can multiply by oxidation of the other organic components of the medium. It is usually 48–72 hours before they are clearly seen, and then they frequently do not appear darker than the background. They are recognized simply as areas of denser growth not found on control plates to which transducing phage were not added.

These transductants must be purified by restreaking on EMBG plates. Each restreaked colony will give a mixture of galactose positive (now recognizable in 16–24 hours) and galactose negative colonies.

Of the transductants found at this stage, a fraction (about one-third) are stable gal^+ strains, in which the gal^+ gene of the donor has replaced its gal^- allele in the recipient. These strains may have been produced by a defective phage, but it has been lost in the process of forming the transductant and cannot be recovered from its descendants. In the other two thirds of the colonies, the gal^+ gene, instead of replacing its homolog, has become added to the complement. The homolog is still there, as shown by the occasional segregation of gal^- cells during the growth of the culture. These persistently segregating lines (heterogenotes) are formed by lysogenization of the recipient with a lambda dg particle, which is then multiplied in the prophage form and thus found among the descendants of the original transductant.

Some of the gal^- colonies seen on the plates described above are segregants from heterogenotic transductants. However, gal^- colonies can also appear simply because the primary transductant is formed on a plate with a confluent background of the recipient culture. To distinguish the stable gal^+ transductants from the heterogenotes, it is necessary to restreak an isolated gal^+ colony from each transductant. Those that still produce mixed cultures on the second restreaking are really heterogenotes.

The heterogenotes found at this point are almost always lysogenic not only for lambda dg but for a normal lambda prophage as well. This occurs because, for reasons not yet completely understood, a cell simultaneously infected with a normal lambda and a lambda dg particle has a greater probability of giving rise to a transductant than one infected by lambda dg alone. Such a "helping effect" is not seen in all cases of specialized transduction. Defective heterogenotes (carrying only lambda *dg* but not lambda) are very occasionally found; their frequency can be augmented by centrifuging the lysate in a density gradient and using a fraction away from the density maximum of normal lambda phage (Weigle, 1961). This method has been used to demonstrate that defective particles indeed occur in the original lysate; it is not necessary for the purpose of simple isolation.

In order to produce bacterial strains lysogenic for only lambda *dg*, transduction must occur at a multiplicity of normal lambda sufficiently low so that, despite the helping effect, some of the transductants carry only the defective phage. A multiplicity lower than the reciprocal of the factor by which the normal phage "helps" will give mostly transductants carrying only the defective phage. With lambda *dg*, the helping factor is usually between 20 and 40, so the multiplicity should be less than 0.025–0.05 phage/bacterium. Suppose the multiplicity is 0.025 and the helping factor is 40. Of every 1000 cells infected with lambda *dg*, 25 will be infected also by normal lambda. However, each of these 25 has a probability of producing a transductant 40 times greater than that of the other 975. Thus the ratio of lysogenic to defective transductants will be 1000 : 975, or roughly 1 : 1.

With the original lysate prepared by induction of a *gal*+ lambda lysogen, the frequency of transducing particles is about 1 in 10^5. This is called low frequency transduction (LFT). It is generally impractical to use an LFT lysate at such a low multiplicity that many defective transductants are found. However, if the lysogenic heterogenote produced by LFT is induced, normal and defective particles are liberated in about equal amounts. This occurs because the lysogenic heterogenote is doubly lysogenic for a normal phage and a transducing phage. Such a high frequency transducing (HFT) lysate can easily be used at very low multiplicities with a new *gal*− recipient. As in LFT, the transductants must be purified by restreaking and their heterogenotic nature verified. Stable transductants also occur with HFT, but they are rarer than with LFT.

Once the heterogenotic transductants are isolated, they can be tested for lysogeny and immunity, as described in Section I,B. Those that are defective can be further characterized genetically (Section III,B).

The lysogenic heterogenote formed in LFT carries a lambda *dg* prophage as well as a normal lambda prophage. That is why it gives an HFT lysate. The lambda *dg* particles in this lysate are genetically and physically identical to each other. If one wishes a number of independent lambda *dg*'s, one must isolate a number of lysogenic heterogenotes and use each for the production of one defective strain.

2. Cryptic Prophages

We mentioned in Section I,A that the two operations for detecting defective lysogeny are immunity and genetic-marker rescue, and that the two generally give the same result. An interesting exception is the "cryptic" lambda prophage discovered by Fischer-Fantuzzi and Calef (1964). In this case, part of the phage genome is present, as seen from genetic-marker rescue, but an extensive block of genes, including the immunity locus, is absent.

There is no known case of direct induction of a cryptic prophage from a normal lambda. The cryptic prophage is derived only from lysogenic strains carrying a special phage variant (crypticogen) that happened to be the stock from which the original cryptic strain was derived. The crypticogen can be used to lysogenize any lambda-sensitive strain. When such a lysogen is "cured" by exposure to UV, about half of the nonlysogenic, nonimmune derivatives isolated are carrying the cryptic prophage (Calef, 1965).

Such cured strains can be found by following the procedure for inducing defectives described in Section I,B and looking at the nonimmune isolates. Another convenient method for recognizing the nonimmune colonies is to plate on EMB medium containing 0.1% glucose as carbohydrate (Zinder, 1958). Phage-sensitive colonies become "nibbled" at the edges by the phage produced from other cells on the test plates; on the EMB medium with low carbohydrate, the nibbled areas are easily seen because they are translucent and of a different color than the other colonies. The exact color varies with the batch of medium and must be recognized by experience. Antiphage serum should not be added to such plates, since the neutralization of background phage will prevent detection. The plates used should also be fairly crowded, so that much phage will be present. The author finds 1000–3000 colonies/plate convenient. The nibbled colonies should then be purified by two or three serial restreakings to get rid of extraneous phage and then tested for lysogeny, for immunity, and for rescue of genetic markers. The method has the disadvantage that some nonimmune cells become relysogenized on the plate and are lost to detection; but generally a sufficient number of nonimmune isolates are easily recovered.

It is also possible to cure lysogenic strains by superinfection with a related heteroimmune phage. Derivatives of the crypticogen produced by this method are completely nonlysogenic rather than cryptic.

The mechanism of formation of the cryptic from the crypticogen is not yet understood. The cryptic prophage contains the block of genes extending from A through L and also gene c_{III}. It is missing genes N through P. Some cryptic prophages contain genes Q and R, whereas others do not (Dahl and Calef, 1965). The cryptic phage is known only in the prophage form; neither vegetative replication nor the formation of infectious particles has been demonstrated, even in mixed infection with active phage.

All the cryptic prophages are derived from the one crypticogenic strain, which itself must have arisen from a normal lambda prophage somewhere in the pedigree of the particular substrain of *E. coli* K-12 from which the cryptic prophage was first isolated. The change from normal lambda to crypticogen was a unique event that has not been observed to recur in other lambda lysogens.*

3. *Bacterial Deletions Penetrating the Prophage*

According to modern theory, the prophage is part of the continuity of the bacterial chromosome, as depicted in Fig. 1. Given that deletion mutations can occur in bacterial chromosomes, it follows that a deletion might have one terminus outside of a prophage and the other within it. The remainder of the prophage that is left within the strain would then be a deletion defective. The method is convenient only if there is a bacterial gene that is (1) of such nature that bacterial mutants lacking it can be easily selected for and (2) not separated from the prophage by any other genes performing functions indispensable to the bacterium.

These requirements are met by the gene for sensitivity to phage T1. It is close to the attachment site for phage 80. Cells with the gene in its normal form make the surface receptor to which the T1 phage attaches. They are therefore able to be killed by the phage. Cells lacking the gene have no receptor; the phage cannot attach to them, and they survive infection. It is only in such a situation where the positive function of a gene creates an extreme selective disadvantage that the method is applicable. A population of cells lysogenic for phage 80 is exposed to an excess of phage T1, so that only T1-resistant mutants survive and form colonies. These colonies, after purification by restreaking, can be examined for lysogeny; and those that are nonlysogenic, for immunity and marker rescue. Franklin *et al.* (1965) used about 10^9 bacteria and 10^9 T1 phage spread on the surface of a Petri plate. It happens that there are two kinds of T1-resistant mutants of *E. coli*, determined by different genetic loci. Those at the locus near phage 80 form small colonies and can be selected on that basis.

Since the T1-resistant mutants occur spontaneously, they may arise

---

* Marchelli *et al.* (1968) have recently shown that cryptic prophages can arise from normal lambda as well as from lambda crypticogen, but at much lower frequency.

at any time during the growth of the culture before its exposure to the phage. If a mutational event occurs very early in the growth of the culture, the progeny of this first mutant may outnumber those derived from all subsequent mutations. If one wishes a series of isolates of independent origin, the safest way is to grow up a series of cultures each started from a different sensitive colony and to pick one resistant mutant from each.

Defective prophages produced by this method resemble the transducing phages in that a region has been deleted that is terminal on the prophage map. However, the two types of defectives are formed and selected in fundamentally different manners and should be expected to have different properties. The transducing phages, in order to be detected, must be able to mature into infectious particles, with the help of a normal phage to supply the necessary physiological functions. Defectives selected as bacterial deletions, on the other hand, need never have left the bacterial chromosome. The only requirement is that the block of phage genes remaining should be physiologically stable. A deletion that so deranged the normal relationships of repression among prophage genes as to lead to uncontrolled synthesis of viral components would probably be lethal to the cell and hence could not be recovered.

The transducing phages differ also in having picked up some bacterial genes in the process of losing phage genes, so that cells carrying a transducing phage have a duplication of bacterial genes, with one copy of these genes lying within the prophage. The bacterial deletion mutants, on the other hand, not only lack such a duplication of bacterial genes; but they also lack the duplication of the prophage attachment site that, according to Fig. 1, encompasses and delimits the prophage. It is indeed impossible to define, except by history, where in these strains the bacterial chromosome stops and the prophage begins.

It must be cautioned that the existence of such a duplication is one feature of prophage attachment that is not documented by any direct evidence. It is inferred from the fact that genetic exchanges usually involve homologous regions. However, if the assumption is correct, we can see that these defectives represent a situation where not only is the prophage defective but the lysogeny is defective. One can imagine such a deletion penetrating just far enough to leave all the genes of the prophage but to remove the attachment site region on one side of it. This may have occurred in some of the strains isolated by Franklin et al. (1965). These lysogens contained all known phage genes but produced very little phage following induction. This small amount might mean either that a tiny piece of the homology region remains or that some abnormal method of prophage extraction can occur rarely, similar to that which produces transducing phages from normal lysogens. One might expect that none of the deletion defectives isolated as bacterial deletions could multiply vegetatively or form mature particles, even when the cells were superinfected with a normal phage. Franklin *et al.* (1965), however, had evidence from superinfection experiments of the type discussed in Section V,A indicating that some of their deletion defectives multiply vegetatively. Whether mature defective particles are formed has not yet been carefully studied.

II. Detection and Properties of Defective Virus Particles

A. PROPERTIES MEASURABLE IN MIXED LYSATES

1. *Preparation of Lysates*

Our discussion thus far has pertained entirely to defective lysogenic bacteria; that is, to the prophage state of defective phage. Defective lysogenic bacteria generally do not produce any appreciable number of mature infectious particles. If they did, they would not be defective. But superinfection with a normal phage can allow the defective genome to multiply and/or mature into a particle that is detectable by its ability to confer defective lysogeny on another cell that it infects. Induction is necessary because the defective lysogen is immune to superinfection. Agents such as UV, which induce phage growth in normal lysogens, also cause a temporary lifting of the immunity in defective lysogens, even where the defect is at a very early stage in virus morphogenesis. The lysate thus obtained contains a mixture of defective and normal particles.

The optimal conditions for preparing such lysates have not been carefully studied. One usually would like to maximize either the total yield of defective particles or the ratio of defective to normal particles. The latter ratio should increase with decreasing multiplicities of superinfection. If we assume that (1) the total yield of mature particles produced per cell infected with at least one normal phage is fixed; (2) the ratio of defective to normal genomes produced by a cell equals the ratio of defective to normal genomes present at the time of superinfection; (3) there are exactly m prophages in each cell; and (4) the superinfecting particles are randomly distributed over the cell population, then the yield per cell of defective particles is given by

$$B \sum_{j=1}^{\infty} \left(\frac{m}{m+j} \right) \left(\frac{n^j}{j!} \right) e^{-n}$$

where B is the average burst size and n is the multiplicity of infection.

A value of $n = 1$ will give close to the maximum possible yield, regardless of the value of m.

Where the defective genome can multiply without help from the superinfecting phage (see Section V,A), the value of m can be increased by employing a late time of superinfection. Whether this will improve the yield depends on the validity of assumption (1). If the ratio of defective to normal genomes is too high, it is possible that the yield will be decreased because there are not enough normal genomes to supply the products needed by the defective ones. This probably depends on the particular defect studied.

In the author's experience (mainly with lambda dg), better lysates are usually obtained by induction of a doubly lysogenic strain carrying both normal and defective prophages rather than by induction and superinfection of the defective lysogen.

2. Presence of Defective Particles

Given a lysate prepared either from a double lysogen or a superinfected single lysogen, the first question is whether it does indeed contain defective virus particles. The simplest test is to expose a population of nonlysogenic cells to this lysate and to see whether any of these cells become defective lysogens. The test is easier if the normal phage used in preparing the lysate is itself unable to lysogenize in single infection. For phage lambda, clear mutants have been used for this purpose. The lysogenic survivors of infection by this lysate then carry either (1) defective prophage alone, (2) defective prophage and normal phage, or, rarely, (3) a recombinant normal prophage that is able to lysogenize. The occurrence of either single or double lysogens carrying the defective prophage is evidence that mature defective particles are formed. Single lysogens carrying the defective alone are obviously easiest to study and to interpret; however, because some types of defectives lysogenize very poorly in single infection (see Section II,A,3), they may be hard to find.

The double lysogens require more careful examination. If we are using as superinfecting phage the clear mutant lambda c, which cannot lysogenize by itself, the double lysogens formed must carry the c^+ allele either from a defective prophage or from a recombinant of the type lambda c^+. A good quantitative argument can usually be made that the number of lysogens formed exceeds that expected on the basis of the active lambda c^+ particles in the lysate. However, the best argument is a qualitative one. Doubly lysogenic bacteria produce singly lysogenic segregants at a certain rate, and a double lysogen carrying lambda

def^+ c and lambda def c^+ will produce some segregants carrying only lambda c^+ def. These can be found by techniques already described in Section I,B. For example, a culture of the double lysogen can be streaked out and printed onto a background of K (lambda imm^{434}). After the replica has been UV'd and incubated, colonies carrying only c^+ are easily distinguishable from those carrying both c and c^+. Some of these can be purified by restreaking and tested for lysogenicity and immunity.

The existence of defective lysogens, either produced directly or as segregants from double lysogens, demonstrates that the defect was transferred through the lysate. In principle, this could owe either to the presence of mature defective particles or to some sort of heterozygous particle carrying both the defective and normal alleles. A careful study of the effect of multiplicity on the frequency of occurrence (discussed in Section II,A,3) can provide evidence in favor of the presence of mature defective particles.

The presence of defective particles can be inferred indirectly from discrepancies between electron microscope counts and plaque counts or between the "killing titer" and the "plaque-forming titer" of a lysate. Neither method is reliable without a good deal of control data with normal lysates of the same phage. For the particular case of lambda dg, Arber et $al.$ (1957) employed an elegant method which works only for a defective phage that, like this one, is able to lyse the cells it infects but without the release of visible particles. They observed infected cells placed on a grid under the electron microscope. With a normal lambda lysate, all infected cells released visible particles on lysis. With a mixed lysate, a large proportion did not. This method again requires good control data, since normal phage particles can also give abortive infections under certain conditions.

3. Ability of Defective Particles to Lysogenize

Given the existence of defective particles, we can try to find out some of their properties. One question is whether they are able to lysogenize cells in single infection. The existence of defective lysogenic survivors of the mixed infection is in itself no proof, since these defectives might have been derived from cells infected with both an active phage and a defective one.

The question can be answered by measuring the frequency of lysogenization as a function of multiplicity of infection. If the defective phage can lysogenize by itself, the number of lysogenic survivors should be directly proportional to the multiplicity. If it requires the help of an active phage, then this number should depend on the square of the multiplicity. The argument on simple theoretical grounds is valid only in the limit as the multiplicity approaches zero. For high multiplicities, control data on the effect of multiplicity on lysogenization by the active phage are necessary. In practice, lysogenization frequencies are difficult to measure at very low multiplicities. It is convenient to compare the frequency at a multiplicity of 5 with that at a multiplicity of, say, 0.1. For some defective mutants of phage lambda, the frequency of lysogenization is proportional to the multiplicity within this range; for others, it falls off much more rapidly with decreasing multiplicity (Jacob *et al.*, 1957).

The former group is said to be able to lysogenize in single infection and the latter group is said not to. All the measurement really shows, however, is that the latter group lysogenizes less well in single than in mixed infection. If the probability of lysogenization in single infection is x and that in mixed infection is kx, the frequency of lysogenization at multiplicities much less than 1 will be approximately

$$[nkx + (1 - n)x] \, ln = (k - 1)lxn^2 + lxn$$

where n is the multiplicity of active phage particles and l is the ratio of defective to active particles in the lysate. The second term will predominate only when multiplicities less than $1/(k-1)$ are used.

The case of lambda dg is instructive. Here it is possible to measure extremely low lysogenization frequencies, because lysogenization by lambda dg converts the cell from gal^- to gal^+, and the gal^+ colonies can be scored on a galactose medium against a confluent background of gal^- cells. The value of k is about 20–40. To the author's knowledge, no measurements with other defective mutants have been made that were sensitive enough to distinguish a value of this magnitude from $k = \infty$; i.e., no lysogenization in single infection.

For lambda dg, the difference in lysogenization frequency in single versus mixed infection can be demonstrated not only from a plot of lysogenization frequency against multiplicity with a mixed lysate but also by comparing the lysogenization frequency at a low multiplicity of the mixed lysate with and without added "helper" phage. The latter method is more rigorous in that only the multiplicity of active phage is varied, and any effect of multiplicity of the defective is eliminated. To estimate the k value, this comparison must be made where the multiplicity of active phage in the lysate containing lambda dg is much less than $1/(k-1)$. However, the qualitative fact that mixed infection increases the lysogenization frequency can be shown at any multiplicity appreciably less than 1—say, 0.1. It should be possible to make this comparison with any defective phage.

4. Ability of Defective Particles To Kill and Lyse the Cells They Infect

As we anticipated in Section II,A,1, it is possible to measure differences in the killing titer and the plaque-forming titer of a mixed lysate containing defective particles (Jacob *et al.*, 1957). Cellular lysis without production of visible particles can also be observed under suitable conditions (Arber *et al.*, 1957). Figure 2 shows the measurement of killing titer for some defective lambda mutants.

Such measurements can be compared with the ability of the defective in question to kill or lyse the cell that carries it as a defective prophage, following induction (see Section V,C).

B. PHYSICAL SEPARATION OF DEFECTIVE PARTICLES

All of the arguments for the existence of defective particles given in Section II,A are indirect. Observations can be made that are most simply interpreted on the assumption that the lysate is a mixture of

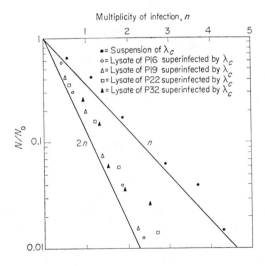

FIG. 2. Determination of the killing titer of lambda c (●) and of lysates made by superinfection of various defective lysogens with lambda c (○, △, □, ▲). The two curves are the theoretical ones for the number of uninfected bacteria, calculated on the assumption that the titer of killing particles is equal to the plaque-forming titer of each lysate (n) or to twice that number ($2n$). From Jacob *et al.* (1957).

normal and defective particles. But the defective particle is a hypothetical entity, never directly observed. More complex explanations of the results cannot be excluded. For example, one might assume that all the phage particles in the so-called mixed lysates are identical to each other and heterozygous for the defect, but that, following infection, each particle decides with a certain probability whether the normal or defective character will be expressed. Such an hypothesis can be rigorously disproved only when the mixed lysate can be physically fractionated so that the defective particles appear in one fraction and the normal particles in another.

If the amount of DNA in a defective phage is different from that in the normal phage and the amount of protein is the same, the densities of the two types of particles will be different, and they can be separated from each other by equilibrium density-gradient centrifugation. The weight will likewise be different, so that separation can also be achieved by centrifugation for a short time in a preformed gradient. In principle, the method should be applicable to any deletion defective that forms mature particles with the help of an active phage. The only known examples at present are transducing phages like lambda *dg* (Weigle *et al.*, 1959). Each isolate of lambda *dg* has a characteristic density that differs both from that of lambda and of other lambda *dg*'s (Fig. 3).

The position of the bands can be determined either by assay of biological activity or by UV absorption, which can be measured in the analytical ultracentrifuge. In any case, biological assay is desirable to be sure that a given band really contains what it is thought to contain. Lambda *dg* can be assayed by transducing activity and active lambda by plaque-forming ability. Because of the helping effect of active lambda in transduction, the assay of lambda *dg* is best performed by adding a deliberate excess of helper phage, so that the active lambda coming from the lysate itself will be inconsequential. Even where the densities of two lambda *dg*'s or of one lambda *dg* and lambda are so close that the two bands overlap, the fact that the maxima are detectably different when the two are spun in the same gradient shows that two physically different classes of particles are present.

For assay of nontransducing defective phages, the best method is probably to plate the lysate on an indicator lysogenic for a heteroimmune relative of the phage; e.g., K (lambda *imm*[434]). Judging from the results with conditional lethal mutants (Campbell and Balbinder, 1958), we expect that any kind of defective particle will give plaques on this indicator, but that the efficiency of plating will vary greatly

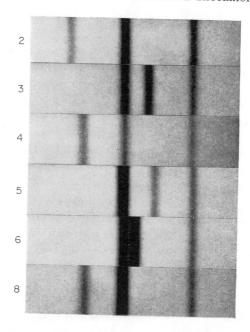

FIG. 3. Banding of normal and transducing lambda from different independent HFT lysates, as observed by UV absorption in the analytical ultracentrifuge. The band at the far right is N^{15}-labeled lambda, which was added as a density marker to aid in aligning the photographs. The central band is normal lambda. Each lambda dg bands at a different place, depending on its characteristic density. From Weigle et al. (1959).

depending on the particular mutant used. For some mutants, the observed plaques are probably the result of recombination between the defective phage and the prophage, giving active phage with the immunity type of the defective. In other cases, the prophage gene(s) will supply the function(s) for which the defective is lacking and will allow good growth of the defective genome itself (Thomas, 1966). In any case, both active and defective phage will give plaques on this indicator, so that a band of defective phage would be detectable only if well enough isolated from the band of active phage so that the absence of particles forming plaques on the nonlysogenic indicator could be demonstrated.

For biological assay, very little material is needed. For physical detection by UV absorption, it is desirable to have a final concentration in the centrifuge tube of at least 1×10^{10} phage particles/ml. For either type of assay it is valuable to have a density marker in the gradient in order to align the results of different centrifugations, as shown in Fig. 3. When biological activity is to be measured, a convenient density marker is a genetically marked phage, say lambda h, labeled with heavy isotope and/or carrying a density mutation.

There may be some phages for which no deletion defectives will show an altered density. Phage T4 seems never to form stable density variants, because any deletion is compensated by an increase in the terminal redundancy of the chromosome (Streisinger et al., 1964). Temperate phages having the same property would not be amenable to this approach. In phages like lambda, where density variants can occur, mutations are known that affect the density without rendering the phage defective. In some cases at least, this seems to owe to a deletion of DNA in a region that is not essential for phage growth (Zichichi and Kellenberger, 1963; Jordan, 1965). Density mutations can complicate the study of defective phages. If the lysate produced by induction and superinfection of a defective lysogen contains two bands, the same problem arises that we discussed in another form in Section I,B: Does the density difference owe to the defective character or to some other mutation present on the defective phage?

For example, when cells carrying the cryptic prophage are superinfected with active lambda, two bands are found (Fischer-Fantuzzi and Calef, 1964). It turns out, however, that both bands consist of active phage. This is because the cryptic prophage is derived from the original wild-type lambda prophage indigenous to E. coli K-12. On the other hand, the reference-type lambda used as a standard in most laboratories has a long history of mutation and recombination and has been deliberately selected as a variant having properties that make it more desirable for experimental purposes. Somewhere in this process a density alteration occurred. Thus the density difference is between wild-type and reference type and has nothing to do with the cryptic deletion. When a cryptic strain is superinfected, recombination between the density marker and the defect produces recombinant active phage with the wild-type density.

In the case of the cryptic prophage, this is just a complication since no mature particles of the cryptic phage are found. With defectives that form mature particles, however, the "complication" could be turned to advantage. If a preparation containing mainly defective and rather few active phages is desired, superinfection with a density variant should result in a lysate in which the defective particles are concentrated in a different band than the active phage, contaminated only by a few recombinants. The latter will be minimized if the density marker is close to the defect studied, or especially if the superinfecting phage carries several density markers and the defect is between some of them.

III. Genetic Localization of the Defect

A. MAPPING OF POINT MUTANTS

The mapping of mutations to defectivity does not differ in principle from any other kind of genetic mapping. A mutation is assumed to be closest to those genes with which it gives the least recombination. In practice, there are some technical differences from an ordinary phage cross: (1) Of the two parents in the cross, one is defective and can be propagated in pure form only as a prophage. The defective lysogen must then be induced (to lift the immunity) and superinfected with the other parent. (2) Of the types of progeny emanating from the cross, half will be defective and unable to form plaques. Occasionally it is of interest to isolate the defective progeny and to score them; but for purposes of simple mapping, it is sufficient to look among the active phage progeny.

In a simple two-factor cross, the defective phage is crossed with a mutant, m, and the active phage progeny are classified for the m character. The frequency of m^+ individuals is equal to the recombination frequency between the defect and the m gene. As in any phage cross, the frequency can depend on multiplicity, physiology of the cells, etc. Rather than standardize all these factors, it is preferable to do crosses in which the parents differ by three or more factors.

Two-factor crosses can be very useful, however, in preliminary studies to determine about where the defect is, especially if it happens to lie very close to one of the genes against which it is crossed. It is frequently convenient to use a conditional lethal mutant as the other parent in the cross. This is for two reasons: (1) The recombinants are easily scored by selective methods. (2) For some phages, e.g., lambda, many conditional lethals are known that are in different regions of the known map. Thus it is quite likely that some will be close to the defect tested.

Definitive mapping is best done by multifactor crosses. Suppose, for example, a defective lysogen of phage lambda is induced and superinfected with the double mutant lambda hc. Four types of nondefective progeny are recovered: hc, hc^+, h^+c, and h^+c^+. One of the three recombinant types will require the occurrence of two simultaneous recombinational events, whereas the other two require only one. This double recombinant class will be less frequent than the other two. If the defect is to the left of h, so that the cross is $def\ h^+c^+ \times def^+\ hc$, the double recombinant will be $def^+\ h^+c$; if it is between h and c, it will be h^+c^+; if it is to the right of c, it will be hc^+. The information can be treated in the same manner as that of any other three-factor cross. Although half of the progeny are not scored, they form four classes that are reciprocal to the ones recovered. Both gene order and map distances can be determined from the data.

It may be convenient to cross the defective mutant with various conditional lethal mutants that carry a second mutation affecting plaque morphology. The plaque morphology mutant can in principle be either on the defective parent or on the conditional lethal parent. In isolating new defective mutants where mapping experiments are contemplated, the investigator should consider in advance whether it is desirable to have any other markers on the defective stock. In referring to analogous experiments in the literature, he should bear in mind that many of these experiments were being done for the first time by people who did not have a detailed plan with respect to what they would do with their stocks once they had obtained them.

It is easy to select recombinants between the conditional lethal mutants and the h or c genes of lambda. This is because most conditional lethal mutants in common use make smaller plaques than wild-type lambda, and the h and c characters are recognizable by the appearance of the plaques. (For the h character, plating on a mixture of 10 parts of a strain that adsorbs lambda to 1 part of a strain that adsorbs only lambda h nicely discriminates between the two types.)

Given the stocks of marked conditional lethals, say lambda $h\ sus$, these can be crossed with the defective strain and the output plated under nonpermissive conditions. The ratio of $h\ sus^+\ def^+$ to $h^+\ sus^+$ def^+ progeny can then be determined. If the gene h is not between the sus and the def genes, one of the two classes will represent the double recombinant. If it is between them, both represent single recombinants. In either case, the proportion allows one to say whether h is closer to sus or to def. If it is closer to sus, the $sus^+\ def^+$ progeny will be mainly h^+; if it is closer to def, they will be mainly h.

The advantages of using the conditional lethals rather than a collection of full three-factor crosses are (1) one need not count and score the many parental particles of the superinfecting type, because only recombinants appear on the plates, and (2) the number of markers such as h and c easily scorable by plaque morphology is limited, whereas conditional lethals seem to occur in every region of the map where true defectives are found. It is thus frequently possible to localize a defective mutant between two conditional lethals that are themselves fairly close to each other.

The results of such crosses can be spurious or misleading if there is a selective advantage of one of the alleles of the "unselected marker;" e.g., h versus h^+. This is best checked by doing the cross in two different directions, $h\ def \times h^+\ sus$ and $h\ sus \times h^+\ def$. To do such crosses requires the synthesis of $h\ def$ from $h^+\ def$, or vice versa. This is a tedious process, since there is no simple way to select for the desired recombinant. The method may also fail because the unselected marker is too far away from the selected markers, or because the selected markers are so close to each other that high negative interference weakens the apparent linkage with an outside marker (Amati and Meselson, 1965); in either case, the result is that the two observed classes occur in approximately equal frequencies, and it is unclear which is larger.

In general, the most workable procedure is simply to cross a given defective with a number of marked sus mutants spaced at different positions on the map. If all the crosses agree with respect to the position of the defect, it is safe to assume that selective effects are not disrupting the results to a degree that disturbs the determination of gene order. Where the linkage to the unselected marker is too weak to detect, another unselected marker should be used.

It is sometimes helpful in locating a point mutant defective to cross it with some deletion defectives to see whether the defect of the point mutant lies within the deleted region, whose extent may be known from previous crosses. The type of deletion defectives most useful for this purpose are the transducing phages. If a defective mutant of lambda is in a gal^- strain, transduction by a known lambda dg will give a double lysogen carrying both lambda def and lambda dg. This transductant will liberate some active phage only if the defective character lies outside of the deletion of this lambda dg.

Some complications can arise. Unless the lambda dg has been physically separated from active lambda, some transductants may have been lysogenized by normal lambda as well as by lambda dg and may liberate active phage for that reason. Such results can be eliminated by examining gal^- segregants from the transductants studied. If only lambda dg has been acquired during transduction, most of the gal^- segregants should again carry the original defective. The number of such active lysogenic transductants is minimized by using as low a multiplicity as is feasible for the transduction.

A. def_{199} transduced with HFT lysates prepared from different lambda $dg's$, as shown below:

(A)(B)(C)	Map of lambda (left end)	Wild-type recombinants with def_{199}
——................................	lambda dg_2	No
——————..................	lambda dg_{11}	No
————————..............	lambda dg_{12}	Yes
——————————..........	lambda dg_{13}	Yes
————————————........	lambda dg_{15}	Yes
——————————. .—————	lambda def_{199} (location inferred from above data)	

Actual mapping data, illustrated for lambda dg_{11} and dg_{15}:

    lambda dg_{11}: of 6 transductants,   3 were haploid, not lysogenic.
                                 2 were heterogenotes, not lysogenic.
                                 1 was heterogenote, lysogenic. (Of 2 gal^- segregants tested, both were lysogenic.)

    lambda dg_{15}: of 6 transductants,   1 was haploid, not lysogenic.
                                 5 were heterogenotes, lysogenic. (3 gal^- segregants were tested from each. Of these 15, 2 were lysogenic and 13 were not.)

B. def_{25} crossed with several lambda c sus:

Map of lambda (right end)	(N)		(P)		(Q	) (	R	)
	sus_7	c	sus_3		sus_{73}	sus_{21}	sus_{54}	sus_5
Distance from def_{25}	5.1		4.3		0.7	1.1	1.2	1.7
Ratio clear to turbid among wild-type progeny	0.18 (159/881)		0.36 (98/269)		3.9 (39/10)	4.1 (148/36)	3.6 (372/103)	17 (34/2)
lambda def_{125} (location inferred from above data)	——————————————. .—————————							

Fig. 4. Mapping of two defective mutants induced by x-rays in a gal^- strain of *Escherichia coli* lysogenic for phage lambda. In part A, the defective was transduced with various lambda $dg's$, whose content of genes is known from previous crosses with sus mutants of lambda. As in Fig. 1, the capital letters A, B, C, etc., refer to cistrons defined by means of sus mutants. A solid line indicates the presence of a particular region in a lambda dg and a dotted line, its absence. Transductants are scored for lysogeny by printing or spotting on a nonlysogenic indicator and for segregation of gal^- by restreaking on EMBG. Haploid transductants (those not segregating gal^-) do not carry lambda dg and therefore are irrelevant. Of the heterogenotic transductants, those that are lysogenic are tested further for loss of lysogeny correlated with segregation of gal^-. Where lysogeny is not lost on segregation (as in one strain from lambda dg_{11}), it is likely that the heterogenote had acquired an active lambda phage from the lambda dg lysate. Where lysogeny is

It is also possible for lambda *dg* to recombine with the defective prophage in such a way that the heterogenote formed is homozygous for the defect. This will be rarer than simple addition.

In our laboratory, we usually pick six transductants and look at a *gal⁻* segregant from each heterogenotic transductant. This is generally sufficient to give a clear idea of whether the defect does or does not intersect the deletion.

The actual procedure for mapping defectives in phage lambda as it is done in the author's laboratory is illustrated in Fig. 4.

B. MAPPING OF DELETIONS

Deletions are located by marker-rescue experiments, as described earlier (Section I,B.) A given deletion is crossed in turn with a series of point mutants, and in each case the question is a qualitative one (Are there any recombinants?) rather than a quantitative one (How many recombinants?). If no recombinants are observed, one wonders whether the methods used are sensitive enough to detect them. In practice, there is little ambiguity. Many markers are efficiently rescued and are therefore clearly "outside" the deleted area. Those that appear to be deleted, if rescued at all, must have a vastly lower rescue frequency. The borderline between the two groups is very sharp even where markers quite close on both sides are available.

There is one technical point, relevant to phage lambda: When marker rescue is tested qualitatively, using conditional lethal mutants under nonpermissive conditions, the tests are sharper if the deletion mutant and the conditional lethal used for superinfection have different immunity specificities. If the conditional lethals have the lambda immunity, it is wise to start with the phage lambda imm^{434} for the isolation of different lambda *dg*'s if extensive crossing is planned. When both phages have the same immunity, superinfection is effective only during the period when the immunity has been lifted by UV. If the

---

lost on segregation, it is possible that the phage produced by the heterogenote came from recombination between lambda *dg* and lambda *def*.

In part B, the defective lysogen was induced and superinfected with several c_1 *sus* mutants of lambda. For each cross, the distance is computed as the ratio of the titer on a nonpermissive indicator to that on a permissive one, multiplied by 100; i.e., $100 \times (def^+ sus^+)/(\text{total } def^+)$. The ratio of clear (*c*): turbid (*c⁺*) changes from less than 1 to greater than 1 between sus_3 and sus_{73}, indicating that def_{25} is between these two mutants. Markers are put in the order found by Amati and Meselson (1965). Only order is indicated; distances are not drawn to scale. From del Campillo-Campbell (1965).

tests are done by mixing lysates and strains on the surface of the test plate, where attachment may be poor, the efficiency is greatly decreased. On the other hand, if the two have opposite immunities, infection at any time may produce wild-type recombinants of one or the other immunity that then can grow on the background cells.

For the type of mapping described in Section III,A, on the other hand, where a lambda *dg* is used for locating a point defect, it is preferable that the two have the same immunity. This eliminates the

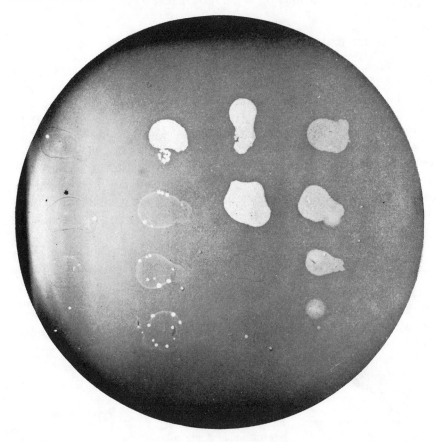

Fig. 5. Crosses between several different isolates of lambda *dg* and several different lambda *sus* mutants. On a background of nonpermissive cells have been placed loopfuls of cultures of K–12 (lambda *dg*) and of lysates of *sus* mutants. In each row is a different lambda *dg*. In each column is a different *sus* mutant. Plaques on the *pm⁻* background are wild-type lambda—either a few scattered revertants (as in column 2, rows 2, 3, and 4) or many recombinants (as in column 2, row 1.) Taken from Campbell (1964).

helping effect of free lambda phage in the transduction and thus decreases the chance that the transductants picked will have acquired an active phage from the transducing lysate.

Crossing of lambda *dg*'s with various *sus* mutants of lambda is illustrated in Fig. 5.

IV. Complementation

A. COMPLEMENTATION BETWEEN DEFECTIVE AND CONDITIONAL LETHAL MUTANTS

In this section, by "complementation" we shall mean the ability of two different mutants to cooperate with each other physiologically to allow phage production by a cell simultaneously infected with both mutants. It is of obvious interest to be able to assign each new isolate to some known group of mutants defined operationally by their inability to complement one another. Presumably this inability stems from the fact that all mutants of the group are concerned with the production of the same polypeptide chain. Mutants concerned with different polypeptides should complement one another, since a cell infected with both mutants has at least one intact "cistron" to code for each polypeptide needed for phage growth.

The suppressor-sensitive mutants of phage lambda can be put into fairly unambiguous cistrons or complementation classes on the basis of simple qualitative or semiquantitative tests. The methods can also be extended in principle to include other lethal or conditional lethal mutants. The author must immediately admit his own lack of successful experience in this area and our description must necessarily be somewhat of an idealization of how the experiments ought to work or how they seem to work in other laboratories.

To study complementation between a defective mutant and a suppressor-sensitive mutant, one should start with a culture of cells that are lysogenic for the defective and nonpermissive for the suppressor-sensitive (*sus*) mutant. If the defective mutant and the *sus* mutant cooperate, the cell should produce more phage than can be accounted for by the leakiness of the *sus* mutant on the nonlysogenic, nonpermissive strain. The phage produced can be either defective, *sus*, or recombinant. However, if many wild-type recombinants are formed, some additional argument is necessary to establish that the observed phage production is not a consequence of the physiological activity of such recombinants rather than of physiological cooperation between the parental particles.

The success of the method depends on the fact that the effects of complicating factors such as recombination, leakiness, etc., should be less important quantitatively than the physiological cooperation itself.

B. Complementation between Two Defectives

If complementation between two defective phages is to be observed, the two must be introduced into the same cell in the absence of any active phage. This has generally been achieved by bacterial crosses (Goodgal and Jacob, 1961). Especially useful are F′ strains carrying a duplication of the lambda attachment site, since this allows synthesis of persistent diploid lines, in which most cells contain both of the defective phages tested. One can then observe after induction for the production of phage particles, most of which should be defective. It seems generally agreed that complementation between two defectives is more laborious to observe and less reliable than complementation between a defective and a conditional lethal.

V. Definition of the Physiological Block(s)

One of the aims of most research on defective viruses is to determine the functions of virus genes by observing how the normal infectious cycle is altered by the mutation of a particular gene or block of genes. Mutations in many different virus genes can cause the virus to become defective, each in its own way. The infectious cycle of a defective phage is generally most conveniently studied by inducing a defective lysogen, so that every cell of the population contains a defective phage genome and none contains a good phage.

Many of the characteristics that can be looked for in such an induced defective involve techniques that are dealt with in other chapters of this volume and need not be detailed here. The culture can be observed either optically or microscopically to see whether the cells lyse at the proper time. The level of phage-specific mRNA can be measured. The lysate or the cell contents can be examined in the electron microscope for recognizable pieces of phage or aberrant forms of normal phage-specific structures. Some mutations cause the absence, or radically alter the level, of a particular enzyme; for phage lambda, mutants are known that lack the exonuclease or the phage lysozyme.

We shall discuss here only a few simple techniques that have been used extensively with defective phages.

A. Genetic Pool Studies

One important question about any defective mutation is whether it blocks any function necessary for the replication of phage DNA. Ideally, this question is answered by molecular hybridization studies of pulse-labeled DNA formed after induction. A less direct method (which we shall treat in more detail here) is to look for the accumulation of a genetic pool of defective DNA. This has been approached by two methods:

1. Superinfection Experiments

The induced defective lysogen is superinfected at various times with a nondefective phage. Two methods of analysis have been employed:

a. The output is assayed for defective as well as for normal phage. This is usually difficult to do, except for some special cases such as lambda *dg* where a selective assay for the defective is available. If we assume that the normal phage genome and the defective genome contribute equally to the progeny, then the ratio of normal phage to defective phage in the yield equals the ratio of the known input multiplicity n to the size m of the intracellular genetic pool at the time of superinfection.

The pool size calculated by this method is meaningful only if events in all cells are synchronized so that the value of m is the same throughout the population. Otherwise, it is a complicated average of the values of m for the individual cells; in particular, the observed value of m will not increase very much with time until phage replication has started in most of the cells, even if extensive replication has already occurred in some of them. The calculation also fails if there is a physiological limitation to the number of defective phage that one good phage can "rescue" and provide the missing functions for. In that case, the only cells that will produce a good yield will be those in which for some reason replication has not yet occurred at the time of superinfection; thus the calculated pool sizes will always be small, even if the defective has replicated in many of the cells.

The best check on the reliability of the estimation by this method is to use several multiplicities at each time of superinfection. The calculated pool size should be independent of the multiplicity of superinfection, if the assumptions of the method are valid.

b. Where the output can be assayed only for normal phage, the active phage used in superinfection must be genetically marked. One can then plate the phage output and tabulate the proportion that is pure super-infecting type or a recombinant between the defective prophage and the superinfecting phage. For example, if the defective phage was made from lambda h^+ and the superinfecting phage is lambda h, the proportion of h^+ among the total plaques produced is tabulated as a function of time and multiplicity of superinfection.

Calculation of the pool size from these data requires several assumptions: (1) The genetic markers employed, including the defective gene, are not selected for or against during the lytic cycle. (2) The phage yield and recombination frequency of a cell of mixed infection does not depend on the ratio of genotypes within it. (3) The amount of recombination at any time is not affected by the number of genomes introduced by superinfection. The number of observed recombinants must depend on the multiplicity of superinfection only insofar as the latter affects the ratio of phage genotypes in the cell, not their absolute number.

Given these assumptions, we can then follow the analysis of Whitfield and Appleyard (1957). At any given time, there will be some fraction, $k(t)$, which gives the probability that, for any genome in the pool, the h locus and the def locus will be separated by recombination before maturation removes the genome from the pool. The other partner in the recombination may either be genetically identical to the first, in which case no recombinant is formed, or else it may be different. The probability that it is one or the other depends on the ratio of the two genotypes in the cell.

Thus, if we consider an active phage genome $h\ def^+$, the probability p that the def^+ locus of this particle will be liberated as an $h^+\ def^+$ phage particle is given by

$$p(t) = \frac{h^+\ def^+ \text{ in output}}{\text{Total } def^+ \text{ in output}} = k(t)\frac{(h^+\ def^+)}{(h^+\ def^+) + (h\ def^+)} \tag{1}$$

where the quantities in parentheses are the number of genomes of the two types present at time t. This expression is equal to

$$p(t) = k(t)\frac{m(t)}{m(t) + n} \tag{2}$$

where, as before, n and m are the multiplicity of superinfection and the pool size, respectively.*

* The term n is here the average number of superinfecting particles per infected cell. It is related to the average multiplicity of infection, x, by the equation $n = x/(1 - e^{-x})$. This correction is important only at multiplicities where a significant fraction of the population is uninfected.

Equation (2) can be rearranged to give

$$np(t) = k(t) \, m(t) - p(t) \, m(t) \tag{3}$$

This means that if, at any given time, the quantity p is measured for several different values of the input multiplicity, n, a plot of np against p should give a straight line whose slope is the pool size m. The estimate is unaffected by how the value of k changes with time, since all measurements used to calculate one value of m are made at the same time.

In the published literature of the past few years, it has been fairly common to use a single constant superinfection multiplicity (sometimes high, sometimes low, sometimes unspecified) and to measure the change in p as a function of time. An increase in p is then taken to indicate vegetative multiplication. The treatment is not justified by any rigorous logic, since we have no basis for assuming how the value of k may be affected by a period of growth in the presence of the genetic block.

Let us assume that the amount of recombination at any given time is not affected by the physiological abnormalities of the defective. This assumption may be wrong, but it is not much worse than others we have already made. It then follows that k can only decrease with time, because whatever recombinations have already occurred at time t will no longer contribute to the recombination after that time. From Eq. (2) we see that p can increase only if the fraction $m/(m + n)$ increases more than enough to compensate for the decrease in k. However, this expression cannot increase to a value above 1. The possibility of a large increase depends, therefore, on the initial value being small, which means that the superinfection multiplicity n must be large. If n is small, no appreciable increase in p is possible, however large the change in m.

Where this procedure has been used, it should be safe to interpret an increase in p as multiplication. A failure to increase might or might not indicate a failure to multiply. Where large increases have been observed at low superinfection multiplicities, one of our primary assumptions must be in error.

The kind of results actually obtained in superinfection experiments are shown in Fig. 6 and Table IV.

2. Clonal Distribution of Revertants

Another rather ingenious method for determining whether a given defect blocks vegetative multiplication was devised by Jacob et al. (1957). Suppose we have a defective that is able to revert by mutation to the nondefective wild-type phage. Such a mutation can occur at

TABLE IV
VEGETATIVE·MULTIPLICATION OF LAMBDA[a]

Prophage	Multiplicity of superinfection	Superinfection at 0 minutes, yield			Superinfection at 40 minutes, yield			p_{40}/p_0
		c^+	c	p_0	c^+	c	p_{40}	
$\lambda dg_{30}\ imm^{434}$	15.9	36	4244	0.0084	185	3799	0.0501	5.96
$\lambda dg_1\ imm^{434}$	6.1	38	4696	0.0080	286	6573	0.0417	5.21
$\lambda dg\ imm^\lambda$	11.9	139	6134	0.0222	238	2953	0.0746	3.36

[a] Data indicate that lambda dg multiplies vegetatively. The prophages are three different independent isolates of lambda dg. Bacteria carrying these lambda dg's were induced and superinfected at 0 and 40 minutes by lambda hc. As h is deleted from lambda dg, all progeny are h, and only the c^+ recombinant can be scored. A ratio of p_{40}/p_0 greater than 1 indicates vegetative replication. From Brooks (1965).

any generation of growth, either of the prophage or of the vegetative phage.

If the defective is able to multiply, mutations can take place at any time during vegetative growth. If we look at the distribution of wild-type revertants among individual cells, it will be just like that for any mutant of a nondefective phage (Steinberg and Stahl, 1961). The most common occurrence will be that a mutation happens in the last division before maturation, so that the cell produces exactly one mutant. Cells

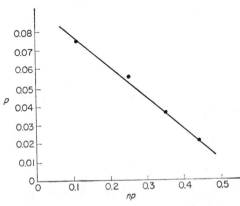

FIG. ᵃ Test of the linearity predicted by Eq. (3) for the relationship between np and p. Superinfection with lambda h of a defective lysogen 15 minutes after UV induction. From Whitfield and Appleyard (1957).

liberating exactly two mutants, three mutants, etc., are progressively less common.

On the other hand, if the defective is unable to multiply, the only way that the cell can yield any progeny is if the mutation to wild-type takes place before multiplication begins. Since the cell contains at most four prophages, at least 25% of the yield from every such cell will be wild-type revertants. Small clones of revertants will consequently be very rare in this case.

The experiment is done essentially as a "modified single-burst" experiment. A culture of the induced defective lysogen is distributed, before lysis, into aliquots of such size that most aliquots will produce no active phage. After lysis, each aliquot is then assayed for phage and the distribution tabulated.

The method has many complications and probably does not measure exactly what it is supposed to measure. Especially in the case of defectives that can multiply, what one observes is not the actual distribution of mutant genotypes but the distribution of those genotypes that become matured into nondefective particles. This probably depends in a complicated way on the number and time of appearance of wild-type revertants in the cell. Nevertheless, the method can give a fairly reliable qualitative discrimination between the two classes of mutants.

B. Accumulation of Tail-Fiber Protein

Intracellular synthesis of the substance responsible for attachment of phage to the cell surface (presumably the tail-fiber protein, by analogy with the T-even phages) can be detected in two ways:

1. Serum Blocking Power

The ability of antiphage serum to neutralize the infectivity of free phage seems to owe to its combination with the tail-fiber protein. If free tail-fiber protein is added to the phage–antiserum mixture, it should compete with the phage particles for the antibody molecules. In practice, a preparation of disrupted bacteria is first mixed with the antiserum to allow combination between antibody and free tail fibers. The residual activity of the serum is then assayed for its ability to neutralize added phage.

2. Phenotypic Mixing

The host range mutant h of phage lambda differs from wild-type in its specificity of attachment to the bacterial host. The difference is presumably located in the tail-fiber protein. The h character exhibits phenotypic mixing. A cell infected with lambda h and lambda h^+ liberates some particles with the genotype of h and the phenotype of h^+, and vice versa. If a defective lysogen is superinfected with lambda h at various times following induction, the fraction of h genotypes with the h^+ phenotype can be measured by comparing the efficiency of plating on the strain CR63 (where only those particles that are phenotypically h can attach) with the number of h plaques on a mixture of C600 and CR63 (where all genotypically h plaques can attach to the C600, and their phenotypically h progeny will then lyse the CR63).

With many defective strains, this fraction (called the ratio of phenotypic mixing) increases with later time of superinfection. The interpretation is complicated by the fact that the observed increase might come from either or both of two sources: (1) accumulation of tail-fiber protein in the induced cell before superinfection and (2) accumulation of a pool of h^+ genotypes that then contribute to phenotypic mixing owing to protein synthesized following superinfection. None of the published data really discriminates between these two possibilities.

C. KILLING AND LYSIS OF CELLS

We mentioned in Section II,A,4 that infection by defective particles can result in killing and/or lysis of the infected cell. Following exposure to agents that induce lysis of normal lysogens, some defective lysogens lyse at about the normal time. Others do not. This depends on the nature of the genetic block.

One can also ask whether induction of a defective lysogen can kill the cell, even where the cell does not lyse. The UV sensitivity of $E.$ $coli$ lysogenic for lambda is about three times that of nonlysogenic $E. coli.$ For wild-type lambda, the difference between the two sensitivities is quantitatively accounted for by the number of cells that lyse and produce phage. If a defective lysogen has the same UV sensitivity as a normal lysogen, we can say that induction of the phage kills the cell, even where lysis and vegetative multiplication do not occur.

In all defective mutants of lambda that have been tested, induction kills the cell.* There are some quantitative differences, using different strains, but the presence of the defective phage always increases the UV sensitivity above that of the nonlysogenic strain (Fig. 7). The same result has been found with conditional lethal mutants of lambda under nonpermissive conditions (Brooks and Campbell, 1964).

* The cryptic prophage is an exception to the rule.

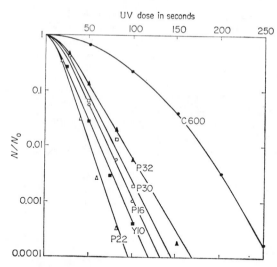

Fig. 7. UV survival curves of nonlysogenic *E. coli* K-12 (strain C600), normal lysogen (strain Y10), and various defective lysogens derived from it. From Jacob *et al.* (1957).

References

Amati, P., and Meselson, M. (1965). *Genetics* **51,** 369.

Arber, W., Kellenberger, G., and Weigle, J. J. (1957). *Schweiz. Z. Allgem. Pathol. Bakteriol.* **20,** 659.

Benzer, S. (1959). *Proc. Natl. Acad. Sci. U.S.* **45,** 1607.

Brooks, K. (1965). *Virology* **26,** 489.

Brooks, K., and Campbell, A. (1964). Unpublished data.

Calef, E. (1965). Personal communication.

Campbell, A. (1964). *In* "The Bacteria" (I. C. Gunsalus and R. Y. Stanier, eds.), Vol. 5, pp. 49–85. Academic Press. New York.

Campbell, A., and Balbinder, E. (1958). *Carnegie Inst. Wash. Year Book* **57,** 386.

Dahl, D., and Calef, E. (1965). Personal communication.

del Campillo-Campbell, A. (1965). Uupublished data.

Fischer-Fantuzzi, L., and Calef, E. (1964). *Virology* **23,** 209.

Franklin, N. C., Dove, W. F., and Yanofsky, C. (1965). *Biochem. Biophys. Res. Commun.* **18,** 910.

Goodgal, S., and Jacob, F. (1961). *Bacteriol. Proc. (Soc. Am. Bacteriologists)* p. 28.

Jacob, F., Fuerst, C., and Wollman, E. L. (1957). *Ann. Inst. Pasteur* **93,** 724.

Jordan, E. (1965). *J. Mol. Biol.* **10,** 341.

Kaiser, A. D. (1957). *Virology* **3,** 42.

Kaiser, A. D., and Jacob, F. (1957). *Virology* **4,** 509.

Kayajanian, G., and Campbell, A. (1966). *Virology* **30,** 482.

Kayajanian, G. (1967). Personal communication.

Marchelli, C., Pica, L., and Soller, A. (1968). *Virology* (in press).

320   ALLAN M. CAMPBELL

Morse, M. L., Lederberg, E. M., and Lederberg, J. (1956). *Genetics* **41,** 142.
Steinberg, C., and Stahl, F. (1961). *J. Theoret. Biol.* **1,** 488.
Streisinger, G., Edgar, R. S., and Denhardt, G. H. (1964). *Proc. Natl. Acad. Sci. U.S.* **51,** 775,
Thomas, R. (1966). *J. Mol. Biol.* **22,** 79.
Weigle, J. J. (1961). *J. Mol. Biol.* **3,** 393.
Weigle, J. J., Meselson, M., and Paigen, K. (1959). *J. Mol. Biol.* **1,** 379.
Whitfield, J. F., and Appleyard, R. K. (1957). *J. Gen. Microbiol.* **17,** 453.
Zichichi, M. L., and Kellenberger, G. (1963). *Virology* **19,** 450.
Zinder, N. D. (1958). *Virology* **5,** 291.
Zinder, N. D., and Lederberg, J. (1952). *J. Bacteriol.* **64,** 679.

7   Methods for the Study of Defective Viruses

Hidesaburo Hanafusa

I. Introduction 321
II. The Defectiveness of RSV 322
    A. Recognition 322
    B. Methods Used to Demonstrate the Defectiveness of
       RSV 326
III. Experiments with Defective RSV 332
    A. Preparation of NP Cells 332
    B. Activation of RSV from NP Cells 336
    C. Properties of Defective RSV 338
IV. Defective Plant Viruses 344
    A. Satellite Tobacco Necrosis Virus 344
    B. Unstable Variants of Plant Viruses 346
    Addendum 348
    References 348

I. Introduction

The presence of defective viruses was first detected among lysogenic bacteriophages either upon infection of sensitive bacteria with temperate phage (Jacob, 1950; Lwoff and Siminovitch, 1951) or upon exposure of normal lysogenic bacteria to heavy doses of UV light (Appleyard, 1954; Jacob and Wollman, 1956). These defective mutants of bacteriophage cannot give rise to structurally intact, infectious phage because of a block that occurs in their vegetative development at various stages (Jacob et al., 1957). Such defective viruses have also been found among some transducing phages (Arber et al., 1957; Campbell, 1957; Luria et al., 1960; Matsushiro, 1963). In the case of these defective transducing phages, the defectiveness stems from the replacement of a portion of the phage genome, which is essential for its own growth, with a fragment of the host cell's chromosome.

Despite the reproductive inability of these defective phage, their presence in infected bacteria can be detected in one of three ways: (1) by the specific immunity conferred on the lysogenic bacteria against superinfection by homologous, active phage, (2) by the issue of defective phage itself, or its genetic markers in recombinants, following superinfection of the UV-induced defective cultures with homologous, active phage, or (3) by the transduction of specific genetic characters of the host from one cell to another.

Among animal and plant viruses, three types of defective viruses have been isolated: certain strains of Rous sarcoma virus, satellite tobacco necrosis virus, and unstable variants of plant viruses. Although these viruses are all defective in that they are unable to produce complete, infectious virus particles in their natural hosts, they differ in the details of the mechanism that prevents them from becoming complete virus. They also differ in the way they manifest their presence in infected cells. For example, Rous sarcoma virus can be seen to cause transformation in its host chick embryo cells, whereas satellite tobacco necrosis virus does not cause any lesions in infected cells and can be detected only on the basis of its small size.

In this chapter, the three types of defective animal and plant viruses will be discussed, and an attempt will be made to stress the methods used to detect their defectiveness and their mechanical deficiencies. The methods used in studying defective Rous sarcoma virus will be taken as an example and considered in detail.

II. Defectiveness of Rous Sarcoma Virus

A. RECOGNITION

Rous sarcoma virus (RSV), a medium-sized RNA virus, has been studied as an example of RNA tumor viruses since its isolation from a chicken tumor (Rous, 1911). It consistently produces sarcomas in chickens and transforms cultivated chick embryo cells into Rous sarcoma cells that have the same morphological characteristics as the tumor cells in chickens. These transformed cells, elicited by infection with high doses of RSV, always release RSV progenies. Virus synthesis and cellular transformation can coexist in the same cell (Rubin, 1960b). However, cellular transformation in the absence of concomitant virus production has been found under certain conditions with the Bryan strain of RSV (Temin, 1962, 1963; Hanafusa et al., 1963). Studies on this transformed, nonvirus-producing state of RSV-infected cells have led to the concept of the defectiveness of RSV.

The recognition of this defectiveness of RSV stemmed from the discovery of the existence of another virus, designated Rous associated virus (RAV)*, in the Bryan high-titer strain of RSV (Rubin and Vogt, 1962). RAV is a typical avian leukosis virus. It causes visceral lymphomatosis and erythroblastosis in infected chickens (Rubin and Vogt, 1962), but does not cause detectable morphological changes in chick embryo cells, as contrasted with the efficient transformation resulting from RSV infection. However, RAV does grow in chick embryo cells, from which viruses are released continuously without drastically impairing the cell's viability. The presence of RAV in these infected cells is demonstrated by the strong interference that it induces with superinfection by RSV. RAV, aside from lack of transforming ability and interference with RSV, is identical to RSV in all other physical and biological properties tested: sensitivity to heat or UV light, buoyant density in RbCl, growth rate in chick embryo cells, and antigenicity (Hanafusa et al., 1964a). The fact that RAV is present in all stocks of the Bryan high-titer strain of RSV in higher concentration than RSV itself and that RAV is indistinguishable from RSV in many characteristics suggested a very close relationship between the two viruses.

While it was easy to obtain a stock of RAV free of RSV using the end-point dilution procedure, all attempts to obtain RSV free of RAV failed. Since there was no available physical means to separate RSV from RAV, clonal isolation of RSV-infected cells was attempted (Hanafusa et al., 1963). Individual Rous sarcoma foci were isolated from chick embryo cultures infected with only one or two infectious units of RSV. These foci were planted in a new plate containing normal chick embryo cells. With continuing transfer of the cultures, transformed cells isolated in this way from single foci continued to multiply and formed an increasingly larger fraction of the population. Some of these transformed cells produced RSV, but RSV production in this case was always accompanied by production of RAV. However, the majority of the cultures produced neither RSV nor RAV, even when they contained more than 10^5 transformed cells. Despite the lack of virus production, the transformed cells retained their characteristic morphology and proved highly malignant upon being transplanted into young chicks. These nonvirus producing, transformed cells, referred to as NP cells, can be maintained indefinitely without the release of mature virus particles.

* RAV isolated from the Bryan high-titer RSV by Rubin and Vogt (1962) is referred to as RAV-1, since other helper viruses, designated as RAV-2 and RAV-3, have been isolated from stocks of the same RSV strain.

Failure to obtain RSV free of RAV strongly suggested that RAV is in some way essential for production of RSV. This suggestion was confirmed by the fact that deliberate infection of NP cells with RAV infallibly resulted in the release of infectious RSV. In addition to RAV, all viruses of the avian leukosis complex thus far tested are capable of activating RSV production from NP cells where they act as "helper viruses." Newcastle disease and influenza viruses, which are similar to RAV in their physical properties, are ineffective as helper virus. Activation of RSV from NP cells can be achieved only by superinfecting with helper virus. Irradiation of NP cells by x-ray or UV light is totally ineffective in inducing RSV production. These findings led to the conclusion that RSV lacks some genetic information necessary for the reproduction of complete virus and depends on the complementary helper virus to provide the missing information (Hanafusa *et al.*, 1963). On the other hand, the ability of RSV to cause malignant transformation is continuously present and therefore independent of the production of mature virus. Since, even after many cell divisions, NP cells retain the potential of producing RSV upon addition of helper virus, the genome of RSV must replicate in the infected cells and be transmitted to daughter cells.

The occurrence of replication of RSV genome in NP cells without the aid of helper virus suggested that there is a defect in the maturation process of the RSV genome. Indeed, subsequent studies showed that RSV cannot produce its own coat in infected cells. First, no detectable RSV-neutralizing antigen was found in NP cells. This was demonstrated by the failure to detect a serum-blocking power for RSV in disrupted NP cells and by the failure to demonstrate RSV-neutralizing antibodies in NP cell-bearing chickens. Second, by using different helper viruses to activate RSV from NP cells of the same origin, the antigenicity of RSV was shown to be indistinguishable from that of the helper virus used (Hanafusa *et al.*, 1964b). Furthermore, there was no cross-neutralization between two RSV stocks activated by two distantly related helper viruses (Vogt, 1965a; Hanafusa, 1965). Since neutralizing antigen is a structure borne in the outer coat of virus particles, these results indicate that RSV depends on the helper virus for production of this antigen specific portion of its coat.

Other properties of RSV, such as the host range of RSV among the genetically different chick embryo cells and the sensitivity of RSV to interference induced by helper viruses, are also found to be controlled by helper virus (Hanafusa *et al.*, 1964c; Vogt, 1965a; Hanafusa, 1965). The rate of RSV production is also determined by helper virus (Hanafusa, 1964; Hanafusa and Hanafusa, 1966a). When helper viruses that differ in their growth rates are added to separate cultures of NP cells, infectious RSV are produced at a rate corresponding to the growth rate of the respective helper virus. All these findings are consistent with the idea that RSV depends on helper virus for production of the viral envelope, this dependency being the main cause of the defectiveness of RSV.

Control of the properties of RSV by helper virus has thus far been observed only for properties of the virus where the phenotype depends in some way on the character of the viral envelope. There is as yet no evidence that the helper virus controls the properties of RSV, which seems to depend only on some aspect of early functions induced by its own genome, such as the morphology of foci of transformed cells.

Thus far, clear evidence for the defectiveness of RSV has been provided only with the Bryan high-titer strain. There are several different strains of RSV that have been maintained for over 50 years in different laboratories, and they are considered to be derived from a single isolate of RSV. Among them, Bryan standard RSV seems to be defective (Shimizu, personal communication). Vogt (1965b) suggested that Fujinami sarcoma virus, which is similar to RSV in many respects, may also be defective.

However, recent observations in several laboratories suggest that at least one strain, called Schmidt–Ruppin strain, is not defective. No helper virus has been found in purified stocks of this RSV, and all attempts to isolate NP' cells have failed (Dougherty and Rasmussen, 1964; Hanafusa, 1964; Goldé, 1966). Foci formed by this strain of RSV always contain viral antigen even in low multiplicity of infection (Vogt, 1965b). The occurrence of a nondefective strain of RSV may suggest that the defective strains are particular variants of RSV which might have emerged by the mutation of active RSV.

Studies of defective RSV have had the important consequence of showing that viral multiplication can be separated from malignant transformation. Recently, however, Goldé and Latarjet (1966) showed this separation of phenomena using the nondefective Schmidt–Ruppin strain. After Schmidt–Ruppin RSV were irradiated with heavy doses of cobalt-60, a significant proportion of the survivors induced nonvirus-producing pocks on chorioallantoic membranes. The proportion of such pocks rose with the dose of irradiation. About 37% of the pocks produced by a stock of this RSV irradiated by 3200 kr of γ-ray were isolated as nonvirus-producing cells. These nonproducing cells differ from those obtained using nonirradiated Bryan RSV in their inability to produce RSV even after superinfection with avian leukosis virus. Production of such nonvirus-producing transformed cells by irradiation of nondefective RSV further implies that mutation of the RSV genome might cause RSV defectiveness. It is hoped that future genetic studies of RSV may lead to an understanding of the molecular basis of defectiveness.

Notation

In order to distinguish between RSV variants that differ in their envelope characteristics, the helper virus endowing RSV with these characteristics will be noted in parentheses after "RSV." For example, RSV(RAV-1) means RSV obtained from NP cells by activation with RAV-1 (see footnote on p. 323), and consequently, whose envelope-dependent properties are controlled by RAV-1.

Unless otherwise stated, RSV will refer to the Bryan high-titer strain of RSV, since the present discussion is based largely on this strain.

B. Methods Used To Demonstrate the Defectiveness of RSV

The following are the methods used to demonstrate the defectiveness of the Bryan high-titer strain of RSV. These methods may serve as useful criteria in tests for the defectiveness of other viruses.

1. Isolation of Nonvirus Producing Cells (NP Cells) *

Demonstration of the absence of virus production in cells infected with RSV is the most essential proof of their defectiveness. In order to arrive at such a demonstration, it is necessary to have cells uniquely infected with RSV. But the problem is that because of the dependency of RSV on helper virus, stocks of RSV inevitably contain helper virus in concentrations somewhat higher than RSV itself. Therefore, to obtain cells infected only with RSV, clonal isolation of foci from cultures infected with very low doses of RSV must be made in order to avoid superinfection with helper virus and consequent RSV production. The ratio of helper virus to RSV in the initial inoculum is also important: the greater this ratio, the more difficult to obtain NP cells. Yet, to prevent superinfection of RSV-infected cells by helper virus, rigorous precautions must be taken during the manipulation of infected cells. In the case of defective Bryan high-titer strain of RSV, where the ratio of RAV-1 to RSV is 10 : 1, about 80%, on

* The technical details for isolation of NP cells are given in Section III,A.

the average, of foci were isolated as NP cells from cultures infected with 1–2 focus-forming units (ffu) of RSV (Hanafusa et al., 1963).

In order to apply these criteria to the examination of the possible defectiveness of other strains of RSV, the conditions for minimizing the contamination of RSV-infected cells by helper virus have to be satisfied. Failure to isolate NP cells would be meaningful only if the various obstacles involved in this endeavor had been carefully eliminated. On the contrary, success in obtaining NP cells would immediately indicate the defectiveness of at least some proportion of RSV particles in the original stock.

2. Detection of Helper Virus in RSV Stocks

The isolation of a helper virus, which is essential for reproduction of RSV, from a stock of RSV may be considered supporting evidence for defectiveness.

In stocks of the Bryan high-titer strain of RSV, which contain both RSV and RAV-1, the concentrations of RAV-1 are generally about 10-fold higher than those on RSV. Therefore, helper virus could be isolated by using a simple end-point dilution technique, as indicated below (Rubin and Vogt, 1962). Cultures of chick embryo cells were infected with 3-fold serial dilutions of RSV stocks, and the cultures were transferred serially at 3- or 4-day intervals. At each transfer, each dilution was examined for the presence of RSV and RAV-1, respectively, by focus formation and by interference to challenge infection with RSV. After two or three transfers, the cultures inoculated with the dilutions beyond the end point of RSV developed strong interference to RSV, indicating the presence of helper virus in these dilutions. A representative result appears in Table I.

Three different methods may be used for the detection of helper viruses. They are based on the capacities of the helper virus (1) to induce interference to RSV infection in the infected chick embryo cells, (2) to activate RSV from NP cells, and (3) to produce virus-specific antigens in infected cells. The capacity to induce leukosis in infected chickens is characteristic of helper viruses, but it cannot be directly applied in the detection of an unknown virus in a given RSV stock, since manifestation of disease is different with different leukosis viruses, and its development usually takes a long time. The interfering capacity of helper virus is most frequently used for detection. The rate of establishment of interference depends on the growth rate of the helper virus present in the original RSV stock. For example, the cultures infected with one infectious unit of RAV-1 and resistance-

TABLE I
PRESENCE OF RAV-1 IN THE RSV STOCK

Dilution of the RSV stock	Number of RSV foci at 7 days	Relative sensitivity to RSV after passage number[a]		
		1	2	3
$10^{-3.0}$	314	NT[b]	NT	NT
$10^{-4.0}$	30	NT	NT	NT
$10^{-5.0}$	2	~0.02[c]	<0.01[c]	<0.01[c]
$10^{-5.5}$	0	0.64	0.0005	0.00002
$10^{-6.0}$	0	0.90	0.0012	0.00003
$10^{-6.5}$	0	1.0	1.0	1.0
$10^{-7.0}$	0	1.0	1.0	1.0
Control	0	1.0	1.0	1.0

[a] All cultures were challenged with RSV (RAV-1). The ratio of the number of RSV foci on each culture to the number on the control cultures was recorded.

[b] NT = not tested; confluent RSV foci in the unchallenged cultures.

[c] Foci initiated by RSV in the original inoculum made accurate measurement of resistance to RSV challenge impossible.

inducing factor [RIF, a field strain of avian leukosis virus (Rubin, 1960a)] develop significant interference after two and four transfers, respectively. Since it is known that interference to RSV by helper virus is specifically determined by their relatedness in characters of the viral envelope structure, a proper RSV variant must be chosen as a challenge virus (see Section III,C,3). In general, a helper virus induces the strongest interference to RSV coated with the same helper virus. The production of viral-specific antigen in helper virus-infected cells may be detected either by complement fixation (Huebner et al., 1964; Sarma et al., 1964) or by staining with fluorescent antibodies (Rubin and Vogt, 1962; Vogt, 1964).

Of course, the presence of helper virus in a given stock of RSV does not necessarily indicate that that RSV is defective; it could be a mere contaminant. Conversely, a consistent failure to detect helper virus in a stock of RSV could be considered as evidence that the RSV is not defective.

3. Demonstration of the Necessity of Double Infection of Cells with RSV and Helper Virus for RSV Production

It was established that the production of RSV occurs only in cells doubly infected with RSV and helper virus and that infection with one infectious unit of helper virus is enough to activate RSV from NP cells

(Hanafusa *et al.*, 1963; Hanafusa and Hanafusa, 1966a). Therefore, the number of RSV-producing cells and, hence, the early yield of RSV from infected cultures, would be proportional to the square of concentration of RSV inoculum, unless the amount of helper virus in the RSV stock largely exceeds that of RSV. In fact, it was shown that a 10-fold dilution of the original inoculum containing RSV and RAV-1 resulted in about a 100-fold reduction in the RSV yield at 1 and 2 days after infection (Hanafusa and Hanafusa, 1966a).

This principle was applied to prove that cells infected only with RSV do not produce RSV even in early days after infection (Hanafusa *et al.*, 1963). Monolayers of chick embryo cells containing 10^6 cells were infected with 50 ffu of RSV for 1 hour. Under this condition, about 500 infectious units of RAV-1 present in the RSV stock would be adsorbed to the same cultures, but most RSV are considered to establish solitary infection at the cellular level. Half of the cultures were then infected with an excess (10^7 infectious units) of RAV-1 so that each RSV-infected cell would be superinfected with RAV-1. All cultures were washed and overlaid with agar medium containing antiserum to RAV-1. Each day thereafter the agar was removed from one of each group of cultures and the cells suspended with trypsin containing the antiserum to RAV-1. An aliquot of the suspended cells from the RSV-infected culture and the excess RAV-1 superinfected culture were irradiated with 5000 r of x-ray. Irradiated and unirradiated cells were centrifuged, resuspended in medium, and plated for evaluation of focus formation on chick embryo cells, in which the antiserum was continually present, until they were overlaid with agar. An example of this type of experiment is shown in Table II.

TABLE II

EFFECT OF X-IRRADIATION ON FOCUS FORMATION BY CELLS INFECTED WITH LOW DOSES OF RSV

Inoculum		Days after infection				
		0 (2 hours)	1	2	3	4
RSV (50 ffu)	Unirradiated	55[a]	48	152	712	1600
	Irradiated	0	0	0	0	18
RSV (50 ffu) and 1 hour later RAV (10^7 IU[b])	Unirradiated	49	45	208	2520	2000
	Irradiated	50	54	128	2780	1860

[a] Calculated number of foci produced by plating cells from a single infected culture.
[b] IU = infectious unit.

X-ray irradiation inhibits division of transformed cells but does not affect the release of RSV from virus-producing cells. The unirradiated RSV-infected cells would thus register as focus formers regardless of whether or not they produced virus because they could multiply to form foci. The irradiated RSV-infected cells could initiate foci only if they released virus. The results show that the number of foci produced by the RSV-infected culture was sharply reduced by x-irradiation. On the other hand, almost the same number of foci was registered before and after x-irradiation of the RAV-1 superinfected cells, indicating that irradiation did not suppress the initiation of foci by RSV-producing cells. Therefore, the results show that the vast majority of cells infected only with RSV fail to release RSV.

When this technique is used to test the defectiveness of other strains of RSV, one should take into consideration the rate of RSV production and the suitable dose of x-ray for the cells infected with a given strain of RSV. Focus formation by x-irradiated transformed cells owes to the infection of indicator cells by RSV released from x-rayed cells. If RSV production occurs very slowly from infected cells, some x-rayed cells may lose the capacity to support the RSV production before they can release virus, which might result in a reduction in the number of foci even though the RSV is nondefective. The dose of x-ray should be large enough to block division of infected cells but not large enough to affect the production of RSV from helper superinfected cells. The proper dosage may differ for the cells infected with different strains of RSV. If the above conditions are satisfied, this technique could be used as a simple preliminary test for the defectiveness of RSV.

4. Cytological Methods

Although the helper viruses generally do not produce detectable morphological changes in infected cultures, their presence can be demonstrated by staining the infected cells with fluorescein-conjugated antibodies against the helper viruses (Rubin and Vogt, 1962). Vogt and Rubin (1963) showed that avian myeloblastosis virus could be assayed by counting the fluorescent foci on the infected cultures. Since the staining of infected cells with fluorescent antibodies depends on the production of virus-specific antigens by the infected cells, the cells infected with RSV alone, which do not produce specific virus-coat antigens, may remain unstained. However, if an RSV is not defective, every RSV-infected cell would produce antigens and therefore be able to bind specific fluorescent antibodies. When chick embryo cells were infected with a low multiplicity of Bryan RSV(RAV-1), besides the fibroblastic areas infected with RAV-1, some proportion of RSV foci bound the fluorescent RSV antibodies (which are equivalent to RAV-1 antibodies in this case; see Section III,C,1), but a significant proportion of RSV foci remained free of stain. The proportion of unstained RSV foci increased as the multiplicity of infection to RSV was lowered (Vogt, 1964). This finding is consistent with the idea of the necessity of double infection by RSV and helper virus for virus production from RSV-infected cells. Vogt (1964) also showed more than 50 lines of NP cells that failed to bind the fluorescent antibodies.

Electron microscope examination for the presence of virus particles on the surface of RSV-infected cells could be one possible means to determine the defectiveness of RSV. In order to apply this method, uninfected chick embryo cells used to prepare NP cultures must be free of any virus particles, and the technique must be satisfactory to demonstrate virus particles released from every virus-producing cell. Dougherty and Di Stefano (1965) examined isolated NP cells under such conditions and found about 50 virus particles per NP cell. Although the number of particles they found was about 10- to 100-fold less than that seen on RSV-producing cells, this observation raised the possibility that NP cells release intact, apparently mature, virus particles that are, however, lacking some structural component of their viral envelope. The presence of virus particles in NP cultures was also observed by Haguenau (personal communication). The real meaning of the presence of virus particles in some NP cells remains unsolved.

5. Helper Control of Some Properties of RSV

As already mentioned, RSV depends on helper virus for the production of the viral envelope. Therefore, several envelope-dependent properties are entirely determined by helper virus (see Section III,C). If a defective virus depends on its helper virus in a way similar to RSV, two different viruses having the same surface properties may occur in a single virus stock. However, it should be stressed that the dependency of one virus on another must be complete. If the production of the viral coat of one virus is in some way hindered, but its genome can be enclosed in the viral envelope of another, the majority of the progenies may have an envelope produced by the latter, even if the former is not defective. Actually, such an interaction between two viruses has been found between nondefective Schmidt–Ruppin RSV and RAV-1 (Hanafusa, 1964; Hanafusa and Hanafusa, 1966b). In this case, the yield of Schmidt–Ruppin RSV from infected cultures increased 50- to 100-fold upon addition of RAV-1, and 98–99% of the resulting progeny virus had the same envelope characters as RAV-1, and only 1–2% had those of the Schmidt–Ruppin RSV itself.

III. Experiments with Defective RSV

A. PREPARATION OF NP CELLS

The following procedures are used to prepare NP cells from foci formed by RSV of the Bryan high-titer strain (Hanafusa et al., 1963, 1964b). Monolayer cultures containing about 1.2×10^6 secondary chick embryo cells are infected with 1–2 ffu of RSV(RAV-1) per plate. The RSV preparation has been sonicated at 9 kc for 3 minutes before infection in order to disperse possible virus aggregates. After an adsorption period of 1 hour, the cultures are overlaid with an 0.8% agar medium containing antiserum to RAV-1 in concentrations large enough to inactivate RSV(RAV-1) to less than $\frac{1}{1000}$ within 40 minutes. Following incubation at 38°C for 7 days, fully developed RSV foci are marked, and the agar is removed after being softened for 2 hours by the addition of 2 ml of culture medium containing the RAV-1 antiserum. The cell sheet is washed with antiserum-containing medium to remove floating cells, and 2 ml of solution containing both 0.05% trypsin and the antiserum is added. The culture plate is placed under the stereomicroscope (dissecting microscope), and a few minutes later, when the cells of the sheet begin to round up prior to detachment from the dish, the transformed cells in one focus are isolated in a glass capillary tube and transferred to a culture containing 1×10^6 chick embryo cells. Henceforth the cultures are transferred serially at 4–5-day intervals. They are maintained in the 0.4% agar medium except for one plate of each NP line, which is kept in a fluid medium to test the RSV production after each transfer. When the cultures are transferred more than four times without RSV production, they are considered to be NP cultures. The media of cultures containing more than 10^5 transformed cells become rapidly acidified, making it difficult to maintain such cultures for extended periods of time. It is therefore necessary, from time to time, to dilute transformed cells upon transfer of the cultures by adding them to 10^6 normal chick embryo cells. The number of NP cells in any one culture is determined by the number of foci produced when the NP cells from that culture are plated on a background of normal chick embryo cells.

1. Conditions for Isolation of NP Cells

The most critical factor in successfully obtaining NP cells is the prevention of contamination of RSV-infected cells with helper viruses.

Two different sources of helper viruses are conceivable: those from chick embryo cells used as feeder cells for NP cells and those from the original RSV inoculum.

The first type of contamination occurs naturally in chick embryos congenitally infected with avian leukosis viruses. The incidence of such congenitally infected embryos varies with different chicken strains and with the conditions under which they are bred. Chick embryo cells prepared from such infected embryos manifest strong interference with RSV (Rubin, 1960a). To avoid using such embryos, therefore, chick embryo cells are prepared separately from individual embryos, and their sensitivity to RSV is routinely tested before their use. Since the interference induced is restricted to the RSV that is closely related to the interfering helper virus in its viral envelope properties (see Section III,C,3), the interference test must be made with various RSV bearing different envelopes. Usually most of the chick embryo cultures that prove to be sensitive to RSV by this interference test do not contain helper virus capable of activating RSV from NP cells. Yet one cannot preclude the existence of some unknown helper virus that, while not interfering with known RSV variants, does activate RSV from NP cells. Probably the only assured way to eliminate the congenitally infected chick embryo cells would be to use frozen chick embryo cells that had been previously examined for absence of helper virus by various tests, including the inability to activate RSV from NP cells. Techniques for preserving chick embryo cells in a frozen state have recently been developed (Dougherty, 1962; Dougherty and Rasmussen, 1964). Cells derived from individual embryos can be stored with dimethyl sulfoxide in liquid nitrogen, and cultures can be prepared as needed by thawing these frozen cells.

Various precautions are taken to prevent the contamination of NP cells by helper viruses derived from the orignal RSV inoculum. The use of antiserum against helper virus during the isolation of foci has proved to be a very effective means. To prevent the spread of helper virus in a culture containing foci to be isolated, some technical modifications have been proposed. Instead of removing agar, the transformed cells can be isolated by inserting a capillary pipet through the agar (Vogt, 1964; Hanafusa, 1965) or by cutting and removing the agar only in the very small area over the foci and trypsinizing the cells located only in this hole (Dougherty and Di Stefano, 1965). Sometimes the transformed cells come off the plate selectively, since they adhere to the removed agar as a focus when the agar is not soft enough. Transformed cells from such an isolated focus often grow as NP cells.

Temin (1962, 1963) showed that RSV infection of cultures containing 10^6 x-irradiated chick embryo cells (to 10% survival) or containing both 10^3 chick cells and 10^5 mouse cells gives rise to NP foci more than does infection of unirradiated chick embryo cells. One of the merits of this technique is the suppression of growth of helper virus by the use of x-rayed chick cells or mouse cells as a feeder for RSV-infected cells. Similar techniques may be used to reduce the chance of helper virus infection in isolated NP cells during their maintenance. For instance, foci produced by infection of K-type cells (chick cells susceptible to RAV-1 and RAV-2 and their cognate RSV) with RSV(RAV-2) can be maintained with the feeder chick cells of the K/2 type, which are resistant to infection by RAV-2.

Isolation of NP cells from pocks induced by RSV on chorioallantoic membranes was described by Goldé (1964). The advantage of this system is evident in that a high proportion of the pocks could be isolated as NP cells. About 60% of the pocks were isolated as NP cells from membranes containing 10 pocks, and about 40–50% from membranes with 30 pocks. Compared with chick embryo cultures containing similar numbers of foci per plate, the rate of successful isolation is strikingly higher. Probably the spread of helper virus is more restricted in some way on the chorioallantoic membranes than on the *in vitro* cultivated chick embryo cells.

2. *Test for RSV Production*

The presence of infectious RSV in the culture fluid of NP cells may be tested by focus formation on chick embryo cells. Certain chick embryo cells are known to be genetically resistant to certain variants of RSV. For example, as will be discussed later (Section III,C,2), RSV(RAV-2) produce foci on two genetically different types of chick embryo cells: K (or C/O) and C/A, but not on K/2 (or C/B) and C/AB cells. Therefore, the infectivity test must be done with the K (or C/O) type of chick embryo cells, which are known to be susceptible to all variants of RSV so far isolated.

A more sensitive test for RSV production is the detection of virus-producing cells by plating cells on K- (or C/O) type normal chick embryo cells following irradiation by 5000 r of x-ray (Hanafusa et al., 1963). As discussed earlier (Section II,B,3), under such conditions the x-rayed cells cannot multiply to form foci, but any virus released from them could initiate focus formation upon plating the x-rayed cells on normal chick embryo cells.

3. Maintenance of NP Cells

Besides morphological transformation, infection with RSV results in an alteration of some of the other properties of chick embryo cells. The transformed cells grow more rapidly than do the normal cells, especially when overlaid with agar. The contact-inhibition mechanism (Abercrombie and Heaysman, 1953, 1954), which normally inhibits the division of cells upon their contact with neighboring cells, is modified or lost in transformed cells, so that they can continuously divide even after contact with one another and can pile up to form foci. Both these traits of transformed cells may be turned to advantage in the maintenance of NP cells. NP cells predominate over normal cells when they are serially transferred at 4- and 5-day intervals in an agar medium.

Another irregularity of transformed cells is a rise in the production of acidic substances such as lactic acid and acidic mucopolysaccharides. Therefore, the media of cultures containing more than 10^5 NP cells become rapidly acidified and must be replaced frequently. NP cells may be maintained in a healthy state only when they are plated in relatively few numbers (about 10^4) on normal chick embryo cells at each transfer, as already described. Probably for the same reason cultures containing more than 10^4 transformed cells can generally be maintained better in fluid medium than in an agar medium. The by-products of NP cells, localized and accumulated under the agar, may hurt the NP cells themselves. Sometimes addition of beef embryo extract (about 1%) to the fluid medium enhances the growth of NP cells.

However, even under carefully controlled conditions, NP cells maintained for long periods of time gradually tend to lose their ability to multiply and begin to exhibit some degenerative changes such as granularization of the cytoplasm, thus becoming giant cells. The fate of NP cells seems to depend largely on the type of cell that has been transformed originally by infection with RSV. Generally speaking, NP cells derived from compact foci made of relatively small-sized transformed cells can be maintained for a long time. When the cultures begin to deteriorate, selection and transfer of actively growing transformed cells sometimes recover the activity of the NP cells. For this purpose, several foci, consisting of large numbers of small transformed cells, are isolated from cultures of NP cells and transferred to cultures containing 10^6 normal chick cells.

Recently we kept NP cells in a frozen state in the presence of dimethyl sulfoxide. About 5% of the frozen cells kept in a Dry Ice chest for over 1 month could be recovered as living transformed cells. These surviving NP cells retained their accelerated growth rate as compared with normal cells and produced RSV upon the addition of helper virus. Better preservation of transformed cells might be had by freezing and storing at lower temperatures.

B. Activation of RSV from NP Cells

1. Kinetics of RSV Production

The rate of RSV production from NP cells upon superinfection with helper virus was found to be the same as the growth rate of the superinfecting helper virus (Hanafusa and Hanafusa, 1966a). When NP cells were superinfected with a fast-growing helper virus such as RAV-1, RSV(RAV-1) was produced rapidly and its titer reached its maximum in 36 hours, while infection of NP cells with a slow-growing helper such as RIF resulted in a slow production of RSV(RIF), with the maximum titer being reached only after 72 hours. These findings are consistent with the idea that the final process in the assembly of progeny virus, probably the synthesis of the viral envelope by helper virus, is the rate-limiting step in the production of RSV.

After 1.5–3 days' postinfection, depending on helper viruses, the titer of RSV reaches its maximum, thereafter staying constant, provided the cells are maintained under healthy conditions by repeated transfers and by frequent medium changes. The plateau of maximum RSV production represents, in all likelihood, the establishment of an equilibrium between continuous virus production and heat inactivation of free virus in the medium. The yield of RSV at the plateau also depends on the helper virus, for example, between 8 and 25 ffu of RSV(RAV-1), and 0.5–3 ffu of RSV(RIF) are produced every hour from an RSV-producing cell superinfected with RAV-1 or RIF, respectively (Hanafusa and Hanafusa, 1966a).

It has been confirmed that the number of virus-producing cells and/or the early yield of RSV from NP cultures, is proportional to both the number of NP cells in a culture and the amount of helper virus added (Hanafusa, 1964; Hanafusa and Hanafusa, 1966a). This observation indicates that helper virus can be assayed by its capacity to activate RSV from NP cells.

2. Preparation of RSV

The discovery that helper viruses control several properties of defective RSV has illustrated the importance of preparing RSV whose envelope characteristics are under the control of a single kind of helper virus. This can be assured only by activating RSV from NP cells with a biologically purified helper virus.

Because helper virus does not generally produce any lesions in infected culture, the clonal purification of helper virus, in its strict sense, is almost impossible. The only practical means of purifying helper viruses would be repeated end-point dilution passages in chick embryo cells. In such a case, the use of 2- or 3-fold serial dilutions is desirable in order to minimize the number of infectious virus in the terminal dilution. The presence of helper virus in infected cultures is usually evidenced by its interference to RSV, as has been described for the isolation of helper virus from RSV stocks (see Section II,B,2). The purity of helper virus can best be examined by studying the various properties of RSV activated from NP cells with that purified helper virus. The following techniques were used in the preparation of RSV(RAV-1) and RSV(RIF). Monolayer cultures containing about 3×10^5 NP cells and 1×10^6 normal chick embryo cells are exposed for 1 hour to 0.5 ml of viral preparation containing about 10^7 infectious units of RAV-1 or RIF. The cultures are then incubated at 37°C with 5 ml of fluid medium. The medium is replaced with fresh medium every 12–15 hours, and all the culture fluids harvested are stored at −70°C. The cultures are transferred twice at 3-day intervals, and the culture medium is harvested until the transformed cells begin to degenerate. The titers of RSV in the daily harvests are shown in Table III. Testing

TABLE III

ACTIVATION OF RSV FROM NP CELLS

Days after infection with helper virus	Titer of RSV (ffu/ml)		
	RSV (RIF)	RSV (RAV-1)	NP control culture
1	5.4×10^4	9.6×10^6	
2	2.8×10^5	3.7×10^7	<10
Transfer			
3	1.1×10^6	2.4×10^7	
4	4.2×10^6	8.2×10^7	
5	5.7×10^6	5.1×10^7	<10
Transfer			
6	2.6×10^6	1.9×10^7	
7	5.3×10^6	4.2×10^7	
8	7.5×10^6	6.6×10^7	<10
9	6.1×10^6	7.1×10^7	

the envelope-specific properties of the two RSV preparations confirmed that the respective stocks consisted of pure helper viruses and their RSV cognates.

The ratio of the concentration of helper virus to that of RSV among virus progeny is chiefly determined by the proportion of transformed cells in a culture, because helper virus can be produced from both transformed and nontransformed cells, whereas RSV can be produced only from transformed cells. Since excess amounts of helper virus in the RSV stocks can cause simultaneous interference with RSV infection (see Section III,C,3), it is desirable to use cultures containing NP cells in high proportion. The ratios of helper virus to RSV in the stocks of RSV(RAV-1) and RSV(RIF) obtained above were both about 10 : 1.

Once RSV stocks contain more than one variant, one of them may be selected by combining several different techniques, such as the end-point dilution technique, selective neutralization by specific antiserum (see Section III,C,1) and selection of virus by passage in genetically resistant cultures (see Section II,C,2). Generally these selective purifications can be made more readily with a mixture of RSV and helper virus than with helper virus alone. If the proportion of contaminating helper virus is reduced, the proportion of its RSV cognate would simultaneously be reduced, resulting in an alteration of the phenotypic expression of the RSV stock. Therefore, success in purification becomes apparent immediately. After a certain extent of purification, a helper virus can be isolated by the terminal-dilution passages and used to activate RSV. The best examples of such purification can be seen in studies on the isolation of RAV-2 (Hanafusa, 1965; Vogt, 1965a).

C. PROPERTIES OF DEFECTIVE RSV

Although production of complete RSV particles occurs only in the presence of helper virus, certain functions of RSV can be carried out without the aid of helper virus. For example, malignant transformation takes place in cells infected with RSV alone. Some properties of RSV are therefore independent of the helper virus and cannot be affected by changing the helper virus. Since the viral envelope of RSV is the only structure known to be determined by helper virus, the helper-independent properties must be determined by internal viral components. Examples of helper-independent properties of RSV are the morphology of the cells it transforms, the morphology of foci made of these transformed cells, and the production of a complement-fixing antigen. The first two properties are specific for each strain of RSV.

For example, Bryan high-titer RSV and Schmidt–Ruppin RSV can be distinguished on the basis of these properties. The third characteristic, production of complement-fixing antigen, is common to all avian tumor viruses (Huebner *et al.*, 1964). The antisera produced in hamsters by immune response to Schmidt–Ruppin RSV-induced tumors do not neutralize the virus but fix the complement to infected cells and sub-cellular components (Huebner *et al.*, 1964; Sarma *et al.*, 1964). Specific complement-fixing antigens are also found in NP cells (Vogt *et al.*, 1965). It is likely that these antigens represent either some internal viral components of RSV or virus-specific products produced in NP cells.

Three properties of RSV, antigenicity, host range, and sensitivity to interference induced by helper virus, are known to be helper-dependent and, therefore, envelope-dependent properties. It has been proved that all these properties are entirely determined by which helper virus is used to activate RSV and not by the phenotypic properties of the original RSV with which NP cells have been prepared (Hanafusa, 1965; Vogt, 1965a). Because full knowledge on these phenotypic proper-ties of RSV is required for the proper choice of RSV–cell systems or for standardization of the biological purity of RSV, and because com-plete dependence of phenotypic properties of one virus on another is a unique consequence of the virus defectiveness, these phenotypic char-acters will be discussed in the following sections.

1. *Antigenic Specificity*

The fact that RSV bears the antigenic stamp of helper virus was first demonstrated with RSV(RIF) and RSV(RAV-1) that were de-rived from the same line of NP cells superinfected with RIF and RAV-1 (Hanafusa *et al.*, 1964b). These two helper viruses cross-react antigenically to a considerable degree, but they can be distinguished by cross-absorption. Upon being absorbed by RIF, antiserum to RAV-1 completely lost anti-RIF activity yet retained full activity against RAV-1. Neutralization test using such absorbed sera showed that the RSV activated by RAV-1 or RIF had the same antigenic specificity as its respective helper virus. When RSV was activated by RAV-1 or RAV-2, which are more distantly related to each other, no detectable cross-neutralization was observed between two resulting RSV (Vogt, 1965a; Hanafusa, 1965). This lack of cross-neutralization between RSV derived from the same NP cells confirms the hypothesis that no RSV-specific antigen is present in the viral envelope.

More recently, Vogt and Ishizaki (1966) extensively examined the antigenic specificities of various avian tumor viruses. Their studies allowed them to classify most of the avian tumor virus group into two major subgroups, A and B, a classification based on their host range (Vogt and Ishizaki, 1965) (see Section III,C,2 and Table IV). Antigenic cross-reactions are almost entirely limited to viruses belonging to the same subgroup. However, it should be stressed that this is a general classification and that antigenic cross-reaction may not even occur between viruses belonging to the same subgroup.

The concept of helper control of RSV antigenicity has been demonstrably useful in studies on the antigenic specificity of various avian tumor viruses (Vogt, 1965a; Hanafusa, 1965; Vogt and Ishizaki, 1965). By using a variety of leukosis viruses as helpers, it is now possible to prepare RSV having the antigenic characteristics of each variety of leukosis virus. Neutralization studies of avian leukosis virus can be greatly simplified by the use of such "tailor-made" RSV, since these are carriers of the avian leukosis viral coat, and accurate assay can be made by focus formation.

2. Host Range

It is known that different strains of chickens have different degrees of susceptibility to avian tumor viruses. The genetic resistance to RSV seen in the whole animal is also found at the cellular level (Crittenden et al., 1963). Recently, genetic resistance to RSV has been found to be highly selective for certain virus strains. Chick embryo cells derived from certain embryos (designated as K/2) are resistant to RAV-2 but not to RAV-1. RSV activated by one of these helper viruses has the same limited host range as its respective helper. Chick embryo cells derived from other embryos (designated as K), are susceptible to both RSV(RAV-1) and RSV(RAV-2) (Hanafusa, 1965; Vogt, 1965a).

The genetic basis of the cellular susceptibility to RSV infection was studied by Crittenden et al. (1964) and Rubin (1965). They showed that the susceptibility of cells is controlled by a single gene with two known alleles, of which susceptibility to RSV infection is dominant and resistance is recessive.

More recent studies on genetic susceptibility and resistance of various chicken strains to RSV have shown that there are four genetically different types of chick embryo cells (Vogt and Ishizaki, 1965). The first type, designated C/O, which is equal to K, is susceptible to all variants of RSV, including RSV(RAV-1) and RSV(RAV-2). The second type, C/A, is susceptible to RSV(RAV-2) and resistant to RSV

(RAV-1). The third type, C/B, which is equal to K/2, is susceptible to RSV(RAV-1) and resistant to RSV(RAV-2). The fourth type, C/AB, is resistant to both RSV(RAV-1) and RSV(RAV-2). Based on their ability to infect these four cell types, avian tumor viruses were classified into two subgroups (Vogt and Ishizaki, 1965), subgroup A represented by RSV(RAV-1) and subgroup B represented by RSV(RAV-2). Some avian tumor viruses falling into these two groups are listed in Table IV. More extensive characterization of various avian tumor viruses may lead to the discovery of viruses belonging to still a third subgroup. But, at present, the genetic status of chick embryo cultures may be determined by measuring the susceptibility of primary cultures to RSV (RAV-1) and RSV(RAV-2).

Several findings provide evidence that such cellular resistance is due to a block at some early stage in the infectious cycle of RSV (Hanafusa, 1965; Vogt, 1965a). First, the host range of RSV is determined by helper virus. The viral envelope of RSV, which participates only in the initial steps of virus–cell interaction, is the only structure of RSV known to be controlled by the helper virus. Second, RSV(RAV-2) fails to transform K/2 cells. Cellular transformation by RSV is a helper-independent process and probably, therefore, depends on some early process induced by RSV. Third, no RSV progeny can be recovered from K/2 cells mixedly infected with RSV(RAV-2) and RAV-1. If RSV (RAV-2) in such mixed infection penetrates the K/2 cells but is

TABLE IV
LIST OF SOME HELPER VIRUS AND RSV

Subgroup A	Subgroup B
RAV-1[a], RAV-3[b]	RAV-2[a], AMV-2[c]
RAV-4[b], RAV-5[b]	RIF-2[d]
AMV-1[c], RIF-1[d]	RSV activated with
RSV activated with	these helper
these helper	viruses
viruses	

[a] RAV-1 and RAV-3 are Rous-associated viruses isolated from stocks of the Bryan hightiter strain of RSV (Rubin and Vogt, 1962; Vogt, 1965a; Hanafusa, 1965; Vogt and Ishizaki, 1965).

[b] RAV-4 and RAV-5 are Rous-associated viruses isolated from stocks of the Bryan standard strain of RSV (Vogt and Ishizaki, 1966).

[c] AMV-1 and AMV-2 are avian myeloblastosis virus 1 and 2 isolated from strain BAI-A of AMV (Vogt, 1965a).

[d] RIF-1 and RIF-2 are field strains of avian leukosis virus (Rubin,1960a; Vogt and Ishizaki, 1966).

blocked at a subsequent stage, RAV-1 might rescue the focus-forming property of RSV.

Determination by helper virus of the RSV host range among chicken cells raised the question as to whether the ability of certain strains of RSV to infect mammals is also due to a change in the virus coat. This has been shown to be true (Hanafusa and Hanafusa, 1966b). When the genome of Schmidt–Ruppin RSV, which is capable of inducing tumors in hamsters, is enclosed in the viral envelope of RAV-1, it loses the tumor-producing capacity. On the other hand, Bryan RSV coated by RAV-1 or RAV-2 is inactive in hamsters, whereas the same Bryan RSV coated by a newly isolated helper virus, designated as RAV-50, can effectively produce tumors in hamsters. Probably, as in the case of genetically resistant chick embryo cells it is the viral envelope that determines the ability of RSV to attach to or penetrate the hamster cell membranes.

It becomes evident from these studies that characterization of both the genetic status of host cells and the envelope characters of the RSV to be used is a prerequisite for quantitative studies on RSV.

3. Sensitivity to Interference Induced by Helper Viruses

Multiplication of avian leukosis viruses in chick embryo cells induces in these cells a resistance to infection by RSV that is manifested by a marked reduction in the number of RSV foci formed by challenge infection with RSV (Rubin, 1960a; Rubin and Vogt, 1962; Vogt and Rubin, 1963). The nature of this interference has been studied to a considerable degree. The resistance does not extend to other viruses such as Newcastle disease, vesicular stomatitis, Western equine encephalomyelitis, and vaccinia virus (Rubin, 1961; Hanafusa et al., 1964a). This specificity of resistance to RSV distinguishes it from the nonspecific resistance produced by interferon. The resistance induced by leukosis virus is not absolute; even after prolonged cultivation of the leukosis virus-infected cells, RSV can still induce some foci in these cultures, provided a high concentration of RSV is used to challenge. The resistant cultures are homogeneous, however, in their susceptibility to RSV, and the probability of successful RSV infection is greatly and equally reduced in each cell. The rate of resistance buildup in a culture depends, of course, on the dose and growth rate of the leukosis virus used for infection of that culture. However, no matter how small the dose of leukosis virus inoculated, the culture eventually reaches the same maximum level of resistance as a culture initially infected with a large dose of helper virus. This maximum level is characteristic for a given combination of interfering leukosis virus and challenging RSV and remains constant through successive transfers of leukosis virus-infected cultures. Thus, infection of a culture by a single infectious unit of RAV-1 develops maximum resistance in the cultures after two to three transfers, or in 6–9 days after infection, and the focus formation by RSV(RAV-1) is reduced by factor of about 10^4.

Maximum resistance can be obtained only when leukosis virus is given several days ahead of the secondary infection by RSV. But, if high concentrations of leukosis virus are given concomitantly, the simultaneous interference can also take place. When a culture is simultaneously infected with RSV and a multiplicity of infection of about 10 of RAV-1, both focus formation and RSV yield are reduced about 10-fold (Hanafusa et al., 1964a; Hanafusa and Hanafusa, 1966a). Simultaneous interference must be taken into consideration in interpreting the results obtained by infecting cells with high concentrations of RSV, since the stocks of defective RSV always contain helper virus in concentrations higher than RSV. However, this does not affect focus assay of RSV, since this must be carried out with relatively low concentrations of RSV stock, in which the concentration of helper virus is usually too low to induce simultaneous interference.

The specificity of this interference has been shown to be more exact than suspected. The sensitivity of RSV to interference induced by leukosis viruses appears to be determined by the helper virus used in the activation of the RSV (Hanafusa et al., 1964c; Hanafusa, 1964, 1965; Vogt, 1965a). For example, RSV activated by RAV-1 is highly sensitive to interference by RAV-1, but it is completely insensitive to interference by RAV-2, and vice versa (Table V). These interference patterns between RSV and helper viruses are extended to various combinations of different RSV and helper viruses (Vogt and Ishizaki, 1966). A helper virus can induce interference only to RSV belonging to the same subgroup in the classification of avian tumor viruses based on their host range (see Table IV).

The dependence on helper virus of RSV sensitivity to the specific interference suggests that this property of RSV is also determined by its viral envelope. Thus, it is likely that interference, like restriction in host range, owes to a blocking of some early stage of infection. Cells infected with helper viruses might release enough viral coat protein to saturate the cell receptors, which would otherwise be used in adsorption or penetration by RSV bearing a similar coat. This explanation is consistent with the finding that NP cells, which produce no viral coat antigen, are fully susceptible to infection by leukosis virus.

TABLE V

INFECTIVITY OF RSV ASSAYED ON VARIOUS CULTURES

Cells		Relative sensitivity of cells to infection with[a]	
Phenotype	Preinfected with	RSV(RAV-1)	RSV(RAV-2)
K	Uninfected	1.0	1.0
	RAV-1	0.00012	$\sim 20^{b}$
	RAV-2	1.0	0.0002
K/2	Uninfected	1.0	$<0.00004^{c}$
	RAV-1	0.00015	<0.00004
	RAV-2	1.0	<0.00004

[a] Infectivity of RSV on various cultures was compared with that on uninfected K cells.
[b] Focus formation of RSV(RAV-2) was enhanced by preinfection with RAV-1 (Hanafusa, 1965).
[c] No foci were detected on K/2 cells infected with RSV(RAV-2).

The main practical importance of the above-mentioned facts comes in the choice of proper RSV variants for challenge infection in the detection or assay of avian leukosis viruses based on their interfering capacity. For example, to detect an unknown helper virus by its interference, at least two variants representing two subgroups must be used as challenge virus. The degree of sensitivity of RSV to this interference is a good measure of the purity of RSV because the maximum level of resistance is characteristic of each combination of interfering leukosis virus and challenge RSV.

IV. Defective Plant Viruses

A. SATELLITE TOBACCO NECROSIS VIRUS

It is known that a stock of tobacco necrosis virus (TNV) maintained in the Rothamsted Experimental Station in England differed from other members of the TNV group, particularly in that the purified preparations always contained particles of two sizes (Bawden and Pirie, 1945, 1950). Partially purified preparations were highly infective and always contained two types of particles, whereas preparations purified to the point where they consisted almost entirely of small particles have relatively little infectivity. Bawden and Pirie (1950), therefore, made the suggestion that only the large particles are infectious and that the small particles might be derivatives, or by-products, of the replication of the large particles.

Further investigations by Kassanis and Nixon (1961) of these two particles led to the discovery of a peculiar defective nature of the small particles. In line with the suggestion made by Bawden and Pirie, examination of the cultures derived from single lesions induced by the Rothamsted TNV showed that few cultures contained only large particles, but that most contained both. An attempt was then made to study the nature of both particles after separating them by density-gradient centrifugation in sucrose. The preparations, consisting only of large particles, produced typical TNV lesions in host plants from which only large particles could be isolated. From their pathogenicity and antigenicity, the large particles were identified as TNV itself. On the other hand, the purified small particles were not infectious; leaves inoculated with them produced no lesions and yielded no detectable small particles. However, when small particles were inoculated into leaves together with TNV (large particles), both particles were produced. These two particles had no serological relationship. From these observations, Kassanis and Nixon (1961) concluded that the small particles represent a virus that is different from the large particles of TNV and unable to multiply in the absence of TNV. Because of its dependency, the small-sized virus was called "satellite virus," or "satellite tobacco necrosis virus" (STNV) (Kassanis, 1962).

The defective STNV is the smallest of all plant viruses reported. It is polyhedral, with a diameter of about 17 mμ and a molecular weight of about 1.9×10^6, 20% of which is RNA (Kassanis, 1962; Reichmann, 1964). It can be crystallized as rhombic plates (Kassanis, 1962; Fridborg et al., 1965). Although serologically unrelated to TNV, STNV can be activated only by co-infection with TNV. All other plant viruses so far tested, such as tobacco mosaic, lucerne mosaic, carnation ringspot, and tomato bushy stunt, failed to activate STNV (Kassanis and Nixon, 1961). That STNV causes slight interference with the development of lesions formed by TNV is known, but no characteristic lesion is produced in leaves infected with STNV, and, therefore, its existence can be recognized chiefly by its characteristic physical attributes.

Important information concerning the nature of the defectiveness of STNV has been obtained through studies of its structure and composition (Reichmann et al., 1962a,b; Reichmann, 1964). The defectiveness of STNV is due to the unusually small size of its RNA. The molecular weight of its RNA is in the order of 4×10^5, which corresponds to only about 1200 nucleotide residues. Assuming a nonoverlapping triplet code, this RNA could code for a maximum of 400 amino acid residues. This figure coincides very well with 372 amino acid residues (except tryptophane) found in a subunit of the viral coat protein of STNV

(Reichmann, 1964). No serological relationship between TNV and STNV suggests that TNV does not code for the STNV coat protein. Reichmann (1964) therefore concluded that the genome of STNV contains just enough information to code for its coat protein. This conclusion has received strong support from the demonstration of *in vitro* enzymatic synthesis of STNV coat protein using STNV RNA as a template (Clark *et al.*, 1965). In contrast with the fact that STNV RNA can code for only a single protein, the viral RNA of most other plant viruses can code for as many as 10–12 proteins. It seems very obvious now that STNV is defective because its RNA cannot code for several of the functional proteins that are essential in the synthesis of viral components in infected cells. This conclusion is also compatible with the finding that an unstable variant of TNV, which induces synthesis of infectious RNA but not coat protein in infected plants (see Section IV,B), is capable of assisting in the multiplication of STNV (Babos and Kassanis, 1962).

B. Unstable Variants of Plant Viruses

Other classes of defective plant viruses have been described as variants of tobacco rattle virus (TRV) (Sänger and Brandenburg, 1961; Cadman, 1962), tobacco mosaic virus (TMV) (Siegel *et al.*, 1962), and TNV (Babos and Kassanis, 1962). The RNA genome of these variants can replicate in infected plants, but the functional capsid protein of virus cannot be made. As a result, they occur in plants as free infectious RNA, which are less stable *in vitro* than are intact complete virus. Obviously, these unstable variants differ from the defective RSV and STNV described above in their ability to give rise to infectious entities and in their independence with respect to intervention of another virus. However, they are still defective in that the reproduction of complete virus particles does not occur.

Köhler (1956) and Cadman and Harrison (1959) described some isolates of TRV as being much more difficult to transmit than other isolates. Sänger and Brandenburg (1961) and Cadman (1962) found that those isolates of TRV which were difficult to transmit by inoculation with leaf sap became readily transmissible when they were extracted from infected plants with phenol. It was suggested that these isolates exist largely in infected plants as naked nucleic acid and not as fully formed virus particles. Similar unstable variants were isolated from TMV treated with nitrous acid (Siegel *et al.*, 1962) and from two strains of TNV (Babos and Kassanis, 1962).

Some characteristics of these unstable variants may be summarized as follows: (1) The unstable variants are less stable in aqueous solution than the complete viruses. (2) They are highly sensitive to the action of RNase, to which intact viruses are resistant. (3) Infectivity of the unstable variants increases or is unaffected by phenol treatment, whereas that of complete viruses is markedly reduced. (4) In sucrose density-gradient centrifugation, the unstable variants band at the same position as RNA extracted from complete viruses. These characteristics leave little doubt that the unstable variants exist as free RNA.

Although complete virus particles cannot be formed, production of virus-specific protein has been shown to occur in leaves infected with unstable variants of TMV (Zaitlin and Ferris, 1964; Bald, 1964; Zaitlin and McCaughery, 1965). One of the unstable variants of TMV, designated as PM2, produces in infected leaves a protein that aggregates into unusual open helical structures rather than the compact rods produced by intact TMV (Zaitlin and Ferris, 1964). This PM2 protein has an amino acid composition similar to the protein of the common strain. But, one threonine residue and one glutamic acid or glutamine residue in the common strain are replaced by one isoleucine and one aspartic acid or asparagine respectively, in PM2 (Zaitlin and McCaughery, 1965). Therefore, it seems likely that the replacement of either one or two of these amino acid residues causes inhibition of proper aggregation of protein subunits into rods. Cytological observation on infected leaf cells showed that another TMV variant, PM1, also induces, in infected cells, an accumulation of protein, which forms a network of featureless gel instead of striate needles and/or loops, as seen in PM2-infected cells (Bald, 1964). Bald (1964) suggested that viral proteins are made in both PM1- and PM2-infected cells but that PM1 protein chains are more poorly folded to make compact tertiary structures than are the chains of PM2 protein.

One may conclude from these facts that the unstable variants of plant viruses are defective in their ability to synthesize properly the viral protein necessary for the coating of the replicated viral genomes. The process of blocked protein synthesis would be different for each unstable variant, as has been shown for PM1 and PM2. It should be pointed out that the unstable variants of TMV are the only two variants whose origins are known. Both PM1 and PM2 resulted from the mutation of TMV following nitrous acid treatment, while the variants of TRV and TNV were isolated from untreated stocks. Furthermore, no spontaneous mutant could be isolated from untreated stocks of TMV (Siegel et al., 1962). In this respect, these TMV variants may be compared with some defective mutants of lysogenic phage that have been produced by irradiating lysogenic bacteria with large doses of UV light (Appleyard, 1954; Jacob and Wollman, 1956).

Addendum

Since this article was written, important findings have been made on the nature of the defectiveness of RSV. The existence of virus particles in NP cells first revealed by electron microscopy (Dougherty and Di Stefano, 1965) was confirmed by other investigators (Courington and Vogt, 1967; F. Haguenau and H. Hanafusa, unpublished). By exposing NP cells to a radioactively labeled RNA precursor, Robinson found labeled virus particles in the culture fluid (Robinson, 1967). RNA was extracted from these virus particles and was shown to have the same buoyant density as that derived from the standard RSV preparation (RSV + RAV). Further, these particles were found to be infectious to certain host cells (Weiss, 1967; Vogt, 1967). Although no helper virus has been detected in the RSV preparation released from the NP cells, it has not yet been established whether this RSV is produced by activation with unknown helper virus. Extensive investigation into the release of infectious RSV in many NP cell lines is being made. It seems likely that there are two variants of Bryan RSV, one of which releases RSV progeny from NP cells, while the other does not produce RSV, the infectivity of which is detectable in chicken or quail cells (T. Hanafusa and H. Hanafusa, unpublished). Both RSV variants can be recovered from NP cells by activation with helper virus. The RSV spontaneously produced from NP cells induced by the productive variant of RSV is infectious to Japanese quail cells and to cells derived from a certain proportion of C/O and C/A type chick embryos. Therefore, a conclusion described in this article, that is the absolute absence of infectious RSV in NP cells, must be modified. At least with the productive variant of RSV, its apparent defectiveness is reflected in the restricted host range.

A new defective virus was found in the stock of human and simian adenoviruses (Hoggan, 1965; Hull et al., 1965; Mayor et al., 1965; Melnick, et al., 1965; Atchison, et al., 1965). These viruses, which are smaller in size than adenovirus, were named adeno-associated viruses (AAV), and they replicate only in the presence of an adenovirus as helper. The mechanisms by which adenovirus exerts its helper function on AAV is not known.

References

Abercrombie, M., and Heaysman, J. E. M. (1953). *Exptl. Cell Res.* **5,** 111.
Abercrombie, M., and Heaysman, J. E. M. (1954). *Exptl. Cell Res.* **6,** 293.
Appleyard, R. K. (1954). *Genetics* **39,** 440.
Arber, W., Kellenberger, G., and Weigle, J. J. (1957). *Schweiz. Z. Allgem. Pathol. Bakteriol.* **20,** 659.
Atchison, R. W., Casto, B. C., and Hammon, W. McD. (1965). *Science* **149,** 754.
Babos, P., and Kassanis, B. (1962). *Virology* **18,** 206.
Bald, J. G. (1964). *Virology* **22,** 388.
Bawden, F. C., and Pirie, N. W. (1945). *Brit. J. Exptl.* **26,** 277.

Bawden, F. C., and Pirie, N. W. (1950). *J. Gen. Microbiol.* **4**, 464.

Cadman, C. H. (1962). *Nature* **193**, 49.

Cadman, C. H., and Harrison, B. D. (1959). *Ann. Appl. Biol.* **47**, 542.

Campbell, A. (1957). *Virology* **4**, 366.

Clark, J. M., Jr., Chang, A. Y., Spiegelman, S., and Reichmann, M. E. (1965). *Proc. Natl. Acad. Sci. U.S.* **54**, 1193.

Courington, D., and Vogt, P. K. (1967). *J. Virol.* **1**, 400.

Crittenden, L. B., Okazaki, W., and Reamer, R. (1963). *Virology* **20**, 541.

Crittenden, L. B., Okazaki, W., and Reamer, R. (1964). *Natl. Cancer Inst. Monograph* **17**, 161.

Dougherty, R. M. (1962). *Nature* **193**, 550.

Dougherty, R. M., and Di Stefano, H. S. (1965). *Virology* **27**, 351.

Dougherty, R. M., and Rasmussen, R. (1964). *Natl. Cancer Inst. Monograph* **17**, 337.

Fridborg, K., Hjertén, S., Höglund, S., Liljas, A., Lindberg, B. K. S., Oxelfelt, P., Philipson, L., and Strandberg, B. (1965). *Proc. Natl. Acad. Sci. U.S.* **54**, 513.

Goldé, A. (1964). *Compt. Rend.* **260**, 3507.

Goldé, A (1966). *Compt. Rend.* **262**, 329.

Goldé, A., and Latarjet, R. (1966). *Compt. Rend.* **262**, 420.

Hanafusa, H. (1964). *Natl. Cancer Inst. Monograph* **17**, 543.

Hanafusa, H. (1965). *Virology* **25**, 248.

Hanafusa, H., and Hanafusa, T. (1966a). *Virology* **28**, 369.

Hanafusa, H., and Hanafusa, T. (1966b). *Proc. Natl. Acad. Sci. U.S.* **55**, 532.

Hanafusa, H., Hanafusa, T., and Rubin, H. (1963). *Proc. Natl. Acad. Sci. U.S.* **49**, 572.

Hanafusa, H., Hanafusa, T., and Rubin, H. (1964a). *Virology* **22**, 591.

Hanafusa, H., Hanafusa, T., and Rubin, H. (1964b). *Proc. Natl. Acad. Sci. U.S.* **51**, 41.

Hanafusa, T., Hanafusa H., and Rubin, H. (1964c). *Virology* **22**, 643.

Hoggan, M. D. (1965). *Fed. Proc.* **24**, 248.

Huebner, R. J., Armstrong, D., Okuyan, M., Sarma, P. S., and Turner, H. C. (1964). *Proc. Natl. Acad. Sci. U.S.* **51**, 742.

Hull, R. N., Johnson, I. S., Culbertson, C. G., Reimer, C. B., and Wright, H. F. (1965). *Science*, **150**, 1044.

Jacob, F. (1950). *Compt. Rend.* **231**, 1585.

Jacob, F., and Wollman, E. L. (1956). *Ann. Inst. Pasteur* **90**, 282.

Jacob, F., Fuerst, C., and Wollman, E. L. (1957). *Ann. Inst. Pasteur* **93**, 724.

Kassanis, B. (1962). *J. Gen. Microbiol.* **27**, 477.

Kassanis, B., and Nixon, H. L. (1961). *J. Gen. Microbiol.* **25**, 459.

Köhler, E. (1956). *Nachrbl. Deut. Pflanzenschutzdienstes (Stuttgart)* **8**, 93.

Luria, S. E., Adams, J. N., and Ting, R. C. (1960). *Virology* **12**, 348.

Lwoff, A., and Siminovitch, L. (1951). *Compt. Rend.* **233**, 1397.

Matsushiro, A. (1963). *Virology* **19**, 475.

Mayor, H. D., Jamison, R. M., Jordan, L. E., and Melnick, J. L. (1965). *J. Bacteriol.* **90**, 235.

Melnick, J. L., Mayor, H. D., Smith, K. D., and Rapp, F. (1965). *Bacteriol.* **90**, 271.

Reichmann, M. E. (1964). *Proc. Natl. Acad. Sci. U.S.* **52**, 1009.

Reichmann, M. E., Reese, M., Symons, R., and Markham, R. (1962a). *Nature* **195**, 999.

Reichmann, M. E., Reese, M., and Markham, R. (1962b). *Biochem. J.* **84,** 86p.

Robinson, H. L. (1967). *Proc. Natl. Acad. Sci. U.S.* **57,** 1655.

Rous, P. (1911). *J. Exptl. Med.* **13,** 397.

Rubin, H. (1960a). *Proc. Natl. Acad. Sci. U.S.* **46,** 1105.

Rubin, H. (1960b). *Virology* **10,** 29.

Rubin, H. (1961). *Virology* **13,** 200.

Rubin, H. (1965). *Virology* **26,** 270.

Rubin, H., and Vogt, P. K. (1962). *Virology* **17,** 184.

Sänger, H. L., and Brandenburg, E. (1961). *Naturwissenschaften* **48,** 391.

Sarma, P. S., Turner, H. C., and Huebner, R. J. (1964). *Virology* **23,** 312.

Siegel, A., Zaitlin, M., and Sehgal, O. P. (1962). *Proc. Natl. Acad. Sci. U.S.* **48,** 1845.

Temin, H. M. (1962). *Cold Spring Harbor Symp. Quant. Biol.* **27,** 407.

Temin, H. M. (1963). *Virology* **20,** 235.

Vogt, P. K. (1964). *Natl. Cancer Inst. Monograph* **17,** 523.

Vogt, P. K. (1965a). *Virology* **25,** 237.

Vogt, P. K. (1965b). *Advan. Virus Res.* **11,** 293.

Vogt, P. K. (1967). *Proc. Natl. Acad. Sci. U.S.* **58,** 801.

Vogt, P. K., and Ishizaki, R. (1965). *Virology* **26,** 664.

Vogt, P. K., and Ishizaki, R. (1966). *In* "Viruses Inducing Cancer—Implications for Therapy." (W. J. Burdette, ed.) p. 71. Univ. of Utah Press, Salt Lake City.

Vogt, P. K., and Rubin, H. (1963). *Virology* **19,** 92.

Vogt, P. K., Sarma, P. S., and Huebner, R. J. (1965). *Virology* **27,** 233.

Weiss, R. (1967). *Virology* **32,** 719.

Zaitlin, M., and Ferris, W. R. (1964). *Science* **143,** 1451.

Zaitlin, M., and McCaughery, W. F. (1965). *Virology* **26,** 500

8 Cell Cultures and Pure Animal Virus in Quantity

Howard L. Bachrach and Sydney S. Breese, Jr.

I. Introduction 351
II. Production and Purification of Centigram Quantities of
FMDV 352
   A. Assay and Production of FMDV in Cell Cultures 352
   B. Stability and Other Properties of FMDV 358
   C. Protocol for Concentration and Purification 359
   D. Efficacy of Purification Steps 364
   E. State of Purity and Viral Parameters 364
III. Large-Scale Purification of Other Animal Viruses 366
References 368

I. Introduction

A large number of articles dealing with the growth of animal viruses as well as extraction and purification of viruses from their hosts have appeared both in original publications and in reviews. The original papers usually describe methods applied on a small scale, and the reviews, the general principles that have emerged. For example, Brakke in the present treatise (Vol. II) and Cramer (1964) have adequately discussed the selection of hosts, methods of infection and harvest, methods for extraction of virus, variables in viral stability, purification procedures, and criteria for virus purity. Less information is available, however, on methods for preparing the amounts of pure animal viruses required for precise and extensive studies of their physical and chemical compositions. In contrast, plant viruses, which often constitute a substantial proportion of the total protein of infected plants, can be readily isolated in milligram and even gram quantities. Because of the nature of their hosts, bacteriophages are also plentiful. With animal viruses, however, there is usually no more than one part of virus per 10^8–10^9 parts of wet host tissue (Cramer, 1964). Thus, the primary task becomes one of producing sufficient animal virus. Solution of this problem usually introduces another difficulty, one concerned with concentration of the virus down to workable volumes. During the purification procedure itself, a first consideration is to achieve purification factors of at least 5- to 10-fold during each stage, concomitant with recovery of a major portion of the virus.

A protocol for the routine production on a weekly basis of large quantities of animal cell cultures and of pure animal virus may find extensive use. We have devised, and have in constant use, such a procedure for foot-and-mouth disease virus (FMDV). This virus, which possesses seven immunologically distinct types, is naturally infective for cattle, swine, sheep, and other cloven-hoofed animals. Types A, O, and C occur frequently in Europe, Asia, and South America. South African types—SAT I, II, and III—and Asia I are usually confined to the indicated continental areas. A procedure for the preparation of FMDV in centigram quantities will be described in sufficient detail for application elsewhere or as a basis for similar work with other animal viruses. Large-scale production and purification procedures that have been developed for other animal viruses will also be mentioned briefly provided that they, too, yield a pure product in large amounts.

Several conditions are essential to the successful production and purification of animal viruses in quantity. Among these are: (1) readily accessible and inexpensive hosts in which virus multiplies to high concentrations, (2) precise, reproducible, and inexpensive assays for infectivity and specific infectivity, (3) knowledge of stability of the virus to biological, chemical, and physical stresses, (4) availability of concentration and purification methods for the virus that can be readily scaled up, and (5) tests for purity of the virus product. These essential elements will first be discussed below in conjunction with a procedure for the routine production of pure FMDV.

II. Production and Purification of Centigram Quantities of FMDV

A. ASSAY AND PRODUCTION OF FMDV IN CELL CULTURES

FMDV can be produced and assayed in its natural hosts, as well as in a number of small animals, including guinea pigs, chickens, and unweaned mice. Suckling mice are widely used for the experimental assay of FMDV infectivity. Nevertheless, for large-scale work, cell cultures are the preferred substrate for FMDV. Their ease of production, together with the high precision of the plaque assay compared with extinction end point methods, makes cell cultures preferable to animals for infectivity measurements of FMDV during purification studies. Primary calf kidney (CK) cultures for plaque assay of FMDV are prepared in 4-ounce prescription bottles (Bachrach *et al.*, 1957a). The assay has proved reliable and precise. Ninety-five percent of replicate assays for FMDV (at levels of about 60 plaques) yield plaque counts that deviate from the mean by less than 25%. Primary CK cultures are equally useful for the detection and assay of FMDV RNA provided they are washed free of serum prior to use (Bachrach, 1960).

Cell cultures that are suitable for assay of infectivity are usually also suitable for the production of virus. This, initially, was the case for FMDV; CK cultures served both purposes. (As will be discussed below, virus can be produced more effectively in a baby hamster kidney cell line.) The CK cultures were prepared inexpensively in relatively large numbers from calf kidneys obtained at an abattoir. The kidneys were chilled and brought to Plum Island within 3 hours of excision. Methods for trypsinization, media preparation, and seeding were quite standard and have been described in detail (Bachrach *et al.*, 1962). However, the preparation of 2000 or more cultures for plaque assay in a single day necessitated some innovations in equipment. Sixty-four 4-ounce bottles were inserted into racks like the one shown in Fig. 1 prior to sterilization in an autoclave. The grill-type cover (shown detached) holds the bottles securely in place so that the racks can be inverted for draining on a rotating platform situated over a collecting container. This equipment allows 64 bottles to be treated as a unit for the original seeding of cells and for fluid changes on the 4th and 6th days of incubation at 37°C. The cultures reach confluency and are used for plaque assays of FMDV after the second fluid change. Those not used immediately are stored at 30°C for as long as 9 days without loss in sensitivity to FMDV or its RNA. A 15-tray floor cart holding 38 cultures per tray is used for this storage. Each tray has one open side. This permits rapid transfer of all cultures to the work bench in a single sliding motion.

Initially, CK cultures for virus production were prepared in 5-liter Povitsky bottles. When the amount of virus produced in this manner proved insufficient for our needs, an improved method of culturing CK cells was devised (Ubertini *et al.*, 1963; Bachrach *et al.*, 1964). It employs cultures in 2-liter, cylindrical Baxter bottles on a three-tiered roller mill (Fig. 2). Enough trypsin-dispersed cells could be prepared in about 4 hours to seed 228 bottles. Nineteen bottles are held as a

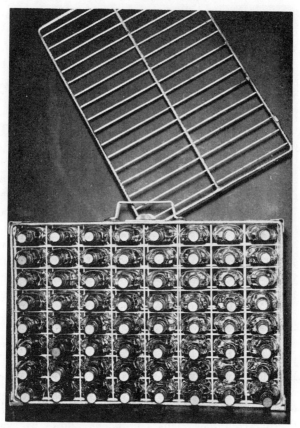

Fig. 1. Calf kidney cultures for plaque assays in 4-ounce prescription bottles with grill-type cover removed. From Bachrach *et al.* (1962).

single unit in a cylindrical wire cage. To distribute the cells evenly on the glass and to insure their attachment, the cage is rotated at 3 rpm for an initial 2-hour period of culturing. The speed is then automatically decreased to 2 rph. The CK cultures reach confluency on the 6th day after seeding. During growth, the cultures contain 100 ml of growth medium, which is removed just prior to infection with virus. During infection with FMDV, only 15 ml of growth medium, buffered with 0.02 M tris(hydroxymethyl)aminomethane (Tris) at pH 7.5, is present. The Tris buffer is required to neutralize acid produced during virus infection. The acid, if released, would otherwise split FMDV into its protein and nucleic acid constituents. This system yielded, each week, about 3 liters of FMDV containing approximately

FIG. 2. Three-tiered roller mill for culturing calf kidney and BHK cells. Capacity:
19 Baxter bottles (2-liter) per cylindrical cage. From Polatnick and Bachrach (1964).

$10^{8.8}$ plaque-forming units (pfu) of infectivity/ml. About 1 mg of
pure virus was obtained from such harvests. However, this quantity of
virus did not satisfy our requirements, and it was not practical to
trypsinize more kidneys.

These difficulties in producing enough susceptible cultures and virus
were overcome by using a baby hamster kidney (BHK) cell line isolated by Macpherson and Stoker (1962). The BHK cell line, either
cloned or uncloned, grows rapidly and supports the multiplication of
many animal viruses, including FMDV (Mowat and Chapman, 1962).
The resulting virus should be used with discretion, since BHK cells
are tumorigenic (Gotlieb-Stematsky and Shilo, 1964). (Cells derived
from clone 13 of this line are now available from the American Type

Culture Collection, Rockville, Maryland.) The BHK cell was grown by Macpherson and Stoker in a medium containing Eagle's salts, purified amino acids, and serum. In this medium, the BHK cells require continuous gassing with CO_2 to hold the pH constant. Obviously, such media and methods, in particular the purified amino acids and CO_2, are not adaptable to mass culturing. Fortunately, the BHK cell grows well in a medium (Table I) consisting of 80% modified Eagle's solution, 10% tryptose phosphate broth, and 10% bovine serum (Polatnick and Bachrach, 1964). As shown, the medium is buffered with 0.02 M Tris. Additional NaCl is added to maintain isotonicity, and lactalbumin hydrolyzate fortified with histidine is used as a substitute for the purified amino acids. The BHK cells are grown on a roller mill in 2-liter Baxter bottles, as described above for CK cultures.

Passage of BHK cells is rapid and uncomplicated. One Baxter bottle culture contains enough cells to seed 20 new ones. Growth medium is removed from 7-day-old cultures, as shown in Fig. 3, by inverting an entire rack of bottles. Twenty milliliters of 0.25% trypsin in phosphate-buffered saline at pH 7.5 is then introduced into each bottle. After 20-minutes' rotation at room temperature, the loosened cells are diluted, without prior removal of the trypsin, into fresh growth medium. The concentration and viability of cells is determined by

TABLE I

GROWTH MEDIUM FOR BHK CELL LINE[a]

Constituents	Amount	Volume (ml)
Modified Eagle's solution[b]		800
NaCl	6.85 gm	
KCl	0.4 gm	
CaCl$_2$	0.2 gm	
MgSO$_4$·7H$_2$O	0.2 gm	
NaH$_2$PO$_4$·H$_2$O	0.12 gm	
Fe(NO$_3$)$_3$·9H$_2$O	0.0001 gm	
Glucose	4.5 gm	
L-Glutamine	0.292 gm	
NaHCO$_3$	0.35 gm	
Tris buffer, 0.16 M, pH 7.5	125.0 ml	
Lactalbumin hydrolyzate	5.0 gm	
L-Histidine·HCl	0.05 gm	
Vitamins (Difco, HeLa)	0.2 gm	
Phenol red (10% solution)	0.15 ml	
Tryptose phosphate broth (Difco)		100
Bovine serum		100

[a] Containing penicillin, dihydrostreptomycin, and mycostatin, each at 100 units/ml.

[b] Modified Eagle's solution is diluted to 800 ml with distilled or demineralized water.

counting and by trypan blue staining, respectively. One hundred-milliliter volumes containing 300,000–400,000 cells/ml are then dispersed into Baxter bottles. Without changing fluids, a confluent, multilayered sheet of approximately 0.75 billion BHK cells is produced within 6 days. At this time, growth medium is decanted, as shown in Fig. 3, from those BHK cell cultures that are to be used for virus production.

Virus is produced as follows. The cultures are inoculated with FMDV in 40 ml of Tris-buffered growth medium (Table I) containing 1.5% serum. This is the least quantity of medium that effectively neutralizes the acid produced during infection of BHK cells with

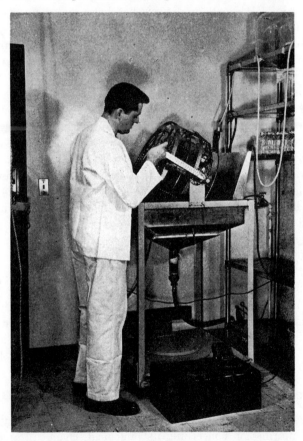

FIG. 3. Stainless-steel funnel with rotatable mount for decanting fluids from 19 cultures in Baxter bottles. The tubing connected to the funnel carries spent culture fluids directly to a drain. This is replaced with chilled carboy for harvesting infectious fluids. From Polatnick and Bachrach (1964).

FMDV. Virus concentration in the inoculum is sufficient to give a multiplicity of infection of 0.01–0.05 pfu/cell. Infectious fluids are collected after 22 hours when the inoculum is type A119 virus and at 18 hours for type C3-Canefa (Polatnick and Bachrach, 1964). The viral fluids are poured from the Baxter bottles (Fig. 3) into a chilled 5-gallon carboy. (Residual FMDV in the emptied bottles is inactivated by immersing the wire cages in an acetic acid solution at pH 3.) Approximately 7.6 liters of infectious fluid are collected from 190 cultures. This fluid contains about $10^{8.2}$ and $10^{8.9}$ pfu/ml for virus types A119 and C3-Canefa, respectively. From 7 to 17 mg of pure virus can be obtained from these harvests.

Production of BHK cells and virus has been scaled up even further. A special laboratory for this purpose has a capacity for producing approximately 150 mg of pure virus per week. Two roller mills, much longer than the one shown in Fig. 2, accommodate 2052 Baxter bottle cultures in 108 cylindrical cages. Lifting of the cages onto the upper tiers is done with the aid of an overhead electric hoist. Since it is impractical to stopper this number of bottles, closure is effected by placing a sheet of sterile aluminum foil over the top of the bottles in each cage. The foil is pressed against the bottle tops by a 0.5-inch thick sheet of polyurethane foam bonded to the underside of a circular metal lid.* With the lid locked in place, the pressure of the foam is sufficient to provide an effective seal between bottle and foil. A special bottle washer accommodates four of the cylindrical wire cages filled with Baxter bottles. Using these procedures, cages are opened only to replace a broken or chipped bottle.

Although BHK cells have permitted the production of increasing amounts of virus, they must be used with caution. Specifically, while early cell passages produce the desired quantities of virus, successive passages may gradually or suddenly fail to do so. When this occurs, it is necessary to return to an earlier BHK cell passage. For this purpose, cells from early passages, which have been frozen at a controlled rate in dimethyl sulfoxide to −196°C, are kept on hand.

B. STABILITY AND OTHER PROPERTIES OF FMDV

The concentration and purification of virus in quantity requires some prior information concerning its biological, chemical, and physical

---

* Similar to one in use at the Instituto Zooprofilattico Sperimentale delle Province Lombarde, Brescia, Italy.

properties. Several of these were known or determined for FMDV. This virus has a much narrower range of pH stability (Bachrach *et al.*, 1957b) than other animal viruses. It is especially sensitive to even weakly acidic conditions, e.g., pH 6.5, and should be maintained between pH 7.0 and 8.0. Extended exposure between pH 8.0 and 9.0 and at higher values is not advisable. Acid degrades the virus to its protein and RNA components (Mussgay, 1959). The latter is infectious and is stable in the cold for at least 5 minutes at pH values as low as 4.0 in the absence of RNase (Bachrach, 1960). Crude virus preparations withstand freezing and thawing. Purified virus in phosphate buffer is inactivated by freezing, except in the presence of 1% disodium ethylenediaminetetraacetate (EDTA) (Trautman *et al.*, 1962) or 50% glycerine (H. L. Bachrach and R. Trautman, unpublished data). Like many other viruses, liquid suspensions of FMDV store best at $0°-4°C$; in crude culture media at $37°C$, FMDV is inactivated at a rate of about 90% per day (Bachrach *et al.*, 1957b). It is not affected by high molar concentrations of cesium chloride, possesses an isodensity therein of 1.43 gm/ml, and can be centrifuged through a mixture of chloroform and Octoil-S of density 1.09 gm/ml (Trautman *et al.*, 1962).

In small-scale purification experiments (Bachrach and Breese, 1958), the virus could be precipitated from culture fluids by the addition of methanol to a concentration of 20% at or below $0°C$. It then withstood homogenization in the cold with *n*-butanol, chloroform, and trichlorotrifluoroethane. The virus could be further purified by differential ultracentrifugation, but was difficult to recover from the high-speed pellets. Enough virus of sufficient purity was obtained by these procedures for its electron microscopic identification. It proved to be 23 ± 2 mμ in diameter and became aggregated in the presence of specific antibody (Bachrach and Breese, 1958; Breese and Bachrach, 1960).

The information just described concerning the properties of FMDV was utilized in devising the following scheme for the preparation of centigram amounts of pure FMDV.

C. Protocol for Concentration and Purification

Figure 4 is a flow diagram of the procedure for concentrating and purifying FMDV from the 7.6 liters of infectious fluid harvested from 190 BHK cell cultures in Baxter bottles (see Section II,A).

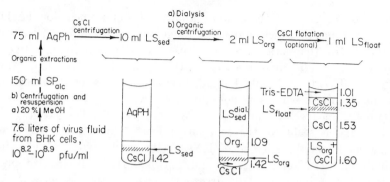

FIG. 4. Flow diagram for purifying FMDV from cell culture fluids in five steps. Conditions for the initial loading of liquids into the centrifuge tubes are shown. The final viral light-scattering (LS) zones are depicted by the diagonal lines. Modified from Bachrach *et al.* (1964).

1. *Concentration: Formation and Collection of Virus Precipitate*

Infectious cell culture fluid (virus fluid) in a 5-gallon carboy is chilled to 0°C. One-fourth volume of methanol precooled to −12°C is added to the virus dropwise and stirred mechanically so that the temperature remains at or below 0°C at all times. After addition of methanol, the stirring is stopped, and the precipitate is allowed to accumulate at −12°C overnight or for several days. Without disturbing the precipitate, all but the lower 4 liters of supernatant fluid are removed by aspiration. (The aspirated fluid should be held at −12°C until it is determined by plaque assay that it contains negligible virus, e.g., 5% or less of total.) The precipitate is swirled up into the remaining 4 liters of mother liquor, and the suspension is centrifuged in four 1-liter, alcohol-decontaminated, prechilled polyethylene bottles at 2000 rpm for 1 hour at −5°C in a PR2 International centrifuge. (The metal buckets for the above bottles are filled with 85 ml of ethyl alcohol and precooled overnight to −12°C prior to their use.) Without disturbing the pellets, the supernatant fluids are carefully decanted and pooled; these may also be held until assayed. The four bottles containing the pellets are placed on cracked ice in a 4°C walk-in refrigerator. With a 30-ml syringe fitted with an 8-inch cannula, all pellets are pooled into one of the four bottles with 75 ml of cold 0.16 M Tris at pH 7.5 containing 1% EDTA (0.16 M Tris + 1% EDTA). Three 25-ml aliquots are used, and the pellets are successively washed from bottle 4 through 3 and 2 into bottle 1. The final volume of the pellet suspension (SP_{alc}) will be about 115 ml.

2. Purification by Extraction with Organic Solvents

The SP_{alc} fraction is distributed in 10-ml amounts into plastic tubes of the No. 30 Spinco centrifuge rotor. To each tube is then added 20 ml of a 1 : 1 mixture of n-butanol–chloroform prechilled to $-12°C$. Each tube is shaken intermittently for 30 minutes, keeping the temperature near $0°C$ by frequent immersion in an ice bath. The tubes are then centrifuged at 7000 rpm for 10 minutes in the Model L Spinco centrifuge with refrigerant pressure set at 8 psi. The top phases are aspirated and then pooled in a chilled beaker. This fluid is redistributed in 10-ml amounts into clean plastic tubes, and the extraction is repeated with the n-butanol–chloroform mixture. After centrifugation, the upper phases are aspirated and then pooled in an ice cold beaker. The pooled fluids are redistributed in 15-ml amounts into clean centrifuge tubes, and an equal volume of prechilled ($-12°C$) trichlorotrifluoroethane is added to each. The tubes are shaken and centrifuged as before. The supernatant fluids are pooled and clarified at 20,000 rpm for 20 minutes. The clarified fluids (AqPh) are then decanted and pooled. If not used immediately in an LS_{sed} run (see below), this approximately 75-ml AqPh fraction may be frozen at $-60°C$.

3. Purification by Density-Gradient Centrifugation

a. *Preparation of Cesium Chloride Solutions.* It is necessary to prepare a buffered solution of CsCl of known density. A CsCl stock solution of density (ρ) 1.8 is prepared as follows: Dissolve 5.4 gm of dry CsCl and 0.05 gm of EDTA in 3.6 ml of 0.16 M Tris and adjust to pH 7.5. Clarify this solution by vacuum filtration through collodion-type bags of porosity 5 mμ. Store the $\rho_{1.8}$ CsCl stock at $4°C$ in vials with rubber-lined screw caps. Make a CsCl solution of approximately $\rho_{1.419}$ by appropriate dilution with 0.16 M Tris containing 1% EDTA. Adjust to this value by using an organic density-calibration column.

A density-calibration column ranging in density from 1.3 to 1.5 gm/ml is prepared and used as follows: Pour 50 ml of bromobenzene ($\rho_{1.50}$) into a 100-ml graduate and, using a 10-ml pipet, carefully overlay with 50 ml of a 15.6 : 34.4 mixture of m-xylene–bromobenzene. Starting at the liquid–liquid interface, slowly move a wire plunger back and forth across the interface. The plunger is formed by bending one end of a straight wire into the form of a loose, flat spiral. Gradually increase the excursions on either side until the final excursion traverses the whole liquid column. With practice, a linear gradient will be obtained. Aqueous salt solutions of known density are used to calibrate this column. Water saturated with NaNO$_3$ plus KCl of density 1.427 gm/ml and water saturated with KBr of density 1.383 gm/ml are useful for the $\rho_{1.3-1.5}$ gm/ml column. These standards, overlaid with mineral oil, are stored in vials closed by rubber-lined screw caps.

The testing and adjustment of density is carried out as follows: With Pasteur pipets, introduce fixed droplets of the standards and CsCl solution just through the meniscus of the organic gradient in the 100-ml graduate, and then raise the pipet upward to release the droplets. Let them settle to their isodense positions. If the droplets of the NaNO$_3$ + KCl and KBr standards and of the diluted CsCl solution settle to the graduation marks, X_{NaNO_3+KCl}, X_{KBr}, and X_{CsCl}, respectively, then

$$\rho_{CsCl} = 1.383 + 0.044 \, \frac{X_{KBr} - X_{CsCl}}{X_{KBr} - X_{NaNO_3+KCl}}.$$

If the density is not 1.419 ± 0.001 gm/ml, add $\rho_{1.8}$ CsCl or 0.16 M Tris + 1% EDTA as required until it falls within this range.

b. *Short-Column Density-Gradient Centrifugation.* Pipet 5 ml of 0.15 M Tris + 1% EDTA containing CsCl at ρ1.419 into each of three plastic tubes of a Spinco SW 25.1 rotor. Carefully pipet 25 ml of the AqPh fraction down the wall of each tube so that it layers over the CsCl solution without producing any disturbance at the interface. Watch for and avoid the transient formation of schlieren lines below the junction. To avoid mixing, lower the tubes into their Spinco buckets until they come to rest; do not let them fall into place. Centrifuge at 25,000 rpm for 3.5 hours with the brake in the on position. [This method of density-gradient centrifugation conserves CsCl. Moreover, near-equilibrium conditions are reached in 3.5 hours rather than in 24 hours when CsCl is added directly to the AqPh, because the time (Trautman *et al.*, 1962) required for equilibrium to be attained is approximately proportional to the square of the depth of the CsCl solution.] Remove the rotor to a darkened 4°C room, and with a high-intensity narrow beam of light determine the position and character of the light-scattering zones. Three zones will generally be seen—one just above the level of the original interface (lipoprotein), one just below (protein), and a lower one (FMDV). Puncture the bottom of the tubes with a solid stainless-steel needle. Remove the light-scattering virus zones (LS$_{sed}$), about 3.25 ml from each tube, dropwise directly into thin-walled dialysis casing. This casing is previously autoclaved, once with distilled demineralized water and three times with 0.16 M Tris $+1\%$ EDTA. Dialyze with agitation at 4°C for 2 hours against two 1-liter volumes of 0.16 M Tris $+1\%$ EDTA at pH 7.5. Change to the second liter after 45 minutes.

c. *Aqueous–Organic Interface and Short-Column Density-Gradient Centrifugation.* Set up an aqueous–organic short-column density-gradient centrifuge run as follows: Pipet 0.5 ml of $\rho_{1.419}$ CsCl in 0.16 M Tris $+1\%$ EDTA into the bottom of each of three SW 39 Spinco tubes without wetting the upper walls. Onto the center of the CsCl surface, layer 1 ml of a mixture (v/v) of 30% chloroform and 70% di-2-ethylhexyl sebacate (Octoil-S) at specific gravity 1.09. (Owing to the imperfect miscibility of these solvents and the high volatility of chloroform, it is important to make separate mixtures for each tube as follows: Into the bottom of 12×75 mm test tubes, place 0.6 ml of $CHCl_3$ and overlay with 1.4 ml of Octoil-S. Mix exactly four times with a 2-ml pipet just prior to layering over the CsCl solution.) Immediately after introducing the organic mixture, layer onto its center 3.5–3.7 ml of the dialyzed LS_{sed} fraction. Centrifuge at 37,000 rpm for 3.5 hours with the brake off. [If this step is used routinely, it can be greatly facilitated in a Model L centrifuge that has been automatically programed (Bachrach *et al.*, 1964) for temperature changes and delayed operation.]

Remove the bottom 0.5 ml (LS_{org} fraction) from each tube dropwise into a dialysis bag (previously autoclaved, once with water and three times with 0.05 M sodium phosphate at pH 7.5) and dialyze overnight at 4°C against two changes of 0.05 M sodium phosphate buffer containing 0.2 M NaCl at pH 7.5. Store in plastic tubes at 0.5°C or freeze at −60°C after adding EDTA to 1% or an equal volume of glycerine. This LS_{org} fraction is pure by all criteria (see below), but before this was known, it was further subjected to an ultracentrifugal flotation step.

d. *Density-Gradient Flotation (Optional).* Adjust the density of the undialyzed LS_{org} fraction to 1.6 gm/ml with sufficient CsCl solution in Tris $+$ EDTA of density 1.8 gm/ml. After adjustment, pipet the LS_{org} fraction into an SW 39 tube and overlay consecutively with 1.5- and 1.0-ml columns of CsCl in Tris $+$ EDTA of density 1.53 and 1.35 gm/ml, respectively. Top off with 0.5 ml of Tris $+$ EDTA. During 3 hours' centrifugation at 37,000 rpm, the virus floats upward to its isodense position, whereas nucleic acids, if present, settle downward. The virus zone (LS_{float}) is collected by aspiration and is dialyzed against 0.05 M sodium phosphate containing 0.2 M NaCl at pH 7.5.

D. EFFICACY OF PURIFICATION STEPS

Measurements of specific infectivity and of infectivity recovery are reliable indicators of the effectiveness of a virus purification procedure. Infectivity is measured as pfu/ml in CK cultures in 4-ounce prescription bottles (Bachrach *et al.*, 1957a). Specific infectivity is the logarithm of the pfu/gm of nucleic acid plus protein in the isolated fraction. The amounts of RNA and DNA are determined quantitatively with orcinol and diphenylamine, respectively (Schneider, 1957), and protein with the Folin–phenol reagent (Lowry *et al.*, 1951). Standard calibration curves employing purified yeast RNA, calf thymus DNA, and crystallized bovine serum albumin (BSA) are prepared for analysis of the unknown samples. The standard BSA concentration is checked by digestion and nesslerization according to a modification of a procedure of Vanselow (1940). It has an error of about 5% in the range 5–16 μg of nitrogen/sample.

Infectivity, specific infectivity, and cumulative recovery for each of the fractions in Fig. 4 are shown in Table II. The average cumulative recoveries for SP_{alc}, AqPh, LS_{sed}, LS_{org}, and LS_{float} fractions across the three groups are 62, 32, 25.6, 15.1, and 4.5%, respectively. This corresponds to an average recovery of about 0.6 for each of the first four steps of about 0.3 during flotation. The specific infectivity increased gradually during the first two stages of purification and markedly during the LS_{sed} stage, reaching $10^{13.3}$ pfu/gm at this stage. It did not increase appreciably thereafter, indicating that purification, at least by density-gradient methods, had been achieved. The average specific infectivity for the LS_{sed} and LS_{float} fractions was $10^{13.4}$ pfu/gm, but individual values were as high as 10^{14}. For FMDV weighing approximately 6 million daltons, a specific infectivity of 10^{17} pfu/gm, i.e., Avogadro's number/6×10^6, could be reached if every virion were capable of initiating a plaque. The fact that the highest specific infectivity values fell 10^3 pfu/gm short of this could be accounted for by the observation that 100–2,500 virions enumerated by analytical electron microscopy are required to produce a plaque in CK cultures (Bachrach *et al.*, 1964). As in many other virus–host interactions, both components undoubtedly contribute to the low pfu-to-virion ratios.

E. STATE OF PURITY AND VIRAL PARAMETERS

Extensive examination of LS_{org} and LS_{float} fractions by critical biological, chemical, and physical tests (see Chapter 3, Vol. II) indicates that

TABLE II

PURIFICATION OF FMDV: INFECTIVITY, SPECIFIC INFECTIVITY, CUMULATIVE RECOVERY OF INFECTIVITY, AND MASS

Experimental group	Parameter	Virus fluid	SP$_{alc}$	AqPh	LS$_{sed}$	LS$_{org}$	LS$_{float}$
1[a]	log pfu/ml	7.4	9.2	9.3	10.2	10.4	10.2
	log pfu/gm	10.9	11.2	11.7	13.3	—	13.5
	% recovery	100.0	48.0	39.0	21.0	12.0	4.5
	Centigrams	—	—	—	—	—	0.1
2[b]	log pfu/ml	8.2	9.5	9.6	10.5	11.3	—
	log pfu/gm	—	—	—	—	13.4	—
	% recovery	100.0	90.4	33.3	35.2	25.3	—
	Centigrams	—	—	—	—	1.1	—
3[b]	log pfu/ml	8.9	10.9	10.3	11.1	11.4	—
	log pfu/gm	—	—	—	—	13.3	—
	% recovery	100.0	48.0	25.0	20.5	8.0	—
	Centigrams	—	—	—	—	1.4	—

[a] Group 1: average of 23 runs of type A119 virus from 20 liters of CK culture fluid.
[b] Groups 2 and 3: average of 6 and 2 runs of virus types A119 and C3, respectively, from 7.6 liters of fluid harvested from BHK cell cultures.

FMDV therein is monodisperse. The following evidence supports this view (Bachrach et al., 1964):

1. The single light-scattering zones comprising the LS_{org} and LS_{float} fractions contain, except for sampling errors, all virus infectivity, virus mass and 23-$m\mu$ virions; fluids above and below these zones are negative for protein, nucleic acid, and nucleoproteins.

2. Specific infectivities reach 10^{14} pfu/gm of virus, which is the theoretical value for pure FMDV having a virion pfu ratio of 10^3. Experimentally determined ratios range from 10^2 to 2.5×10^3.

3. Analytical ultracentrifugation shows a single schlieren peak with the known 140-S sedimentation rate of FMDV.

4. Masses determined for the monodisperse virus by chemical and centrifugal analyses agree to within 6%. A value of about 0.158 ml/gm is tentatively calculated for the specific refractive increment of the virus.

5. The ratio of protein to RNA, 69 : 31, is essentially constant in different strains of FMDV purified from both animal and tissue culture sources, and this prevails in experiments that yield 10- to 20-fold varying amounts of virus. No DNA is present.

6. Spectral diagrams of the virus are reproducible with $\text{max}_{259 \ m\mu}/\text{min}_{239 \ m\mu}$ values of 1.4, indicative of nucleoprotein. The virus extinction coefficient corrected for light scattering, $E^{1\%\ \text{FMDV}}_{259\ m\mu}$, is 76.0.

7. $\text{Max}_{258 \ m\mu}/\text{min}_{230 \ m\mu}$ values of 2.1 for FMDV RNA prepared from the virus by phenol extraction are obtained reproducibly. The extinction coefficient for viral RNA, $E^{1\%\ \text{FMDV RNA}}_{258\ m\mu}$, averages 220. The purine–pyrimidine content of this RNA is constant and is the same as that found by direct analysis of virus in the LS_{org} and LS_{float} fractions. Guanine, adenine, cytosine, and uracil are present in the molar proportions 0.24 : 0.26 : 0.28 : 0.22. No thymidylic acid spots are present.

8. The virus gives reproducible absorbance–temperature profiles in 0.01 M sodium phosphate at pH 7.5, in which the relative absorbance at 259 $m\mu$ remains constant up to 52°C, at which point the RNA is released and thereafter undergoes reversible heat denaturation (Bachrach, 1964). The viral RNA reveals a single-stranded profile, with considerable intramolecular folding, and a T_m of about 54°C.

9. Virus in LS_{org} fractions moves in carrier-free, zone electrophoresis in a glucose density gradient as an infectious, monodisperse component (Matheka et al., 1966).

III. Large-Scale Purification of Other Animal Viruses

Purified poliovirus for use in Salk vaccine is prepared (Charney et al., 1957, 1961a,b) using methods based on earlier research by

Bachrach and Schwerdt (1954) and Schwerdt and Schaffer (1955). Charney and co-workers added nucleic acid precipitation of poliovirus to the earlier procedures in order to produce vaccines containing known quantities of purified virus.

Type I (Parker), type II (MEF 1), and type III (Saukett) viruses were grown in monkey kidney tissue cultures. Crude virus fluids were filtered through Horman D6 or D8 filter pads. The filtered fluid was treated with 200 μg/ml of yeast nucleic acid to aid in the precipitation of virus at pH 3.5 at 0°–5°C. The precipitate was collected by low-speed centrifugation and the pellet washed twice with 0.063 M potassium phosphate buffer at pH 3.5. The washed precipitate was dissolved in 0.063 M potassium phosphate buffer at pH 8.5 containing 2% NaCl and adjusted to pH 7.0 by the addition of 1% NaOH. The fluid volume at this stage was 1/500 of the original. This virus concentrate was digested with RNAse and DNAse (10 μg/ml plus 1 mg/ml of $MgSO_4 \cdot 7H_2O$) for 3 hours at 37°C to degrade nonviral nucleic acid. The enzyme-treated virus concentrate was treated with 7.5% NaCl at pH 4.5 and 0°–5°C to precipitate extraneous protein and was then clarified by low-speed centrifugation and adjusted to pH 7.0. One or two cycles of differential centrifugation at 30,000–40,000 rpm for 2–5 hours at 2°C were used to concentrate the virus into pellets, which were then washed with cold distilled water. The washed pellets were resuspended to 1/4000 of the original tissue culture fluid volume in saline–phosphate buffer of pH 7.0 containing 20 gm of NaCl/liter of 1% phosphate. This final concentrate was then clarified by centrifugation at 10,000 rpm for 20 minutes.

The virus produced by this method was checked for purity by optical density measurements, by ultracentrifugal boundary analysis, and by assay for total nitrogen. The absorbance spectra (Hilleman et al., 1960; Charney et al., 1961b) were identical to those found by Schwerdt and Schaffer (1955). Ultracentrifugal patterns showed a single sedimenting boundary for the type II and type III strains of virus. The type I strain showed small amounts of two additional components, one of which sedimented at one-half the rate of the virus and was shown to be the virus-associated C protein component (LeBouvier et al., 1957). Nitrogen determinations for all three types of virus were in agreement to within about 10% with the other two methods of purity assay. When virus purity was calculated in terms of virus nitrogen after correction for the C component, the virus was found to be essentially pure. The concentration of monkey kidney CF antigen was also substantially reduced, being 60- and 300-fold less for types I and II, respectively. This determination could not be made for type III virus because the level of monkey kidney CF antigen was below the sensitivity of the CF test both at the start and after a 129-fold concentration of virus. Electron microscopy and light microscopy were used to demonstrate close-packed virus in a crystal face and a macrocrystal, respectively.

This method provided poliovirus of a purity and in the gram amounts required for further physical and chemical determinations. However, the basic purpose was for the production of potent vaccines containing a standard weight of pure poliovirus. The purification steps, while similar to those for FMDV in some respects, differ most strikingly in the steps that allow poliovirus to be manipulated at low pH and low salt concentrations.

Other large-scale methods have been used to produce animal viruses in a partially purified form for the manufacture of vaccines. These include Sharples centrifugation in the manufacture of influenza vaccines (Stanley, 1946), alum precipitation in the preparation of inactivated measles vaccines (Warren and Gallian, 1962), and isoelectric precipitation of adenoviruses (Brandt et al., 1963). The details of these methods are not discussed here, since the products are for use in vaccines, and data concerning purity are usually insufficient to allow their use in biochemical and physical studies that require essentially pure virus.

REFERENCES

Bachrach, H. L. (1960). *Virology* **12**, 258.
Bachrach, H. L. (1964). *J. Mol. Biol.* **8**, 348.
Bachrach, H. L., and Breese, S. S., Jr. (1958). *Proc. Soc. Exptl. Biol. Med.* **97**, 659.
Bachrach, H. L., and Schwerdt, C. E. (1954). *J. Immunol.* **72**, 30.
Bachrach, H. L., Callis, J. J., Hess, W. R., and Patty, R. E. (1957a). *Virology* **4**, 224.
Bachrach, H. L., Breese, S. S., Jr., Callis, J. J., Hess, W. R., and Patty, R. E. (1957b). *Proc. Soc. Exptl. Biol. Med.* **95**, 147.
Bachrach, H. L., Callis, J. J., Hess, W. R., Patty, R. E., DeBoer, C. J., and Hamblet, F. E. (1962). *Am. J. Vet. Res.* **23**, 608.
Bachrach, H. L., Trautman, R., and Breese, S. S., Jr. (1964). *Am. J. Vet. Res.* **25**, 333.
Brandt, C. D., Neal, A. L., Owens, R. E., and Jensen, K. E. (1963). *Proc. Soc. Exptl. Biol. Med.* **113**, 281.
Breese, S. S., Jr., and Bachrach, H. L. (1960). *Proc. 4th Intern. Conf. Electron Microscopy, Berlin, 1958* Vol. II, pp. 619–621. Springer, Berlin.
Charney, J., Fisher, W. P., and Machlowitz, R. A. (1957). *Proc. Soc. Exptl. Biol. Med.* **96**, 601.

Charney, J., Machlowitz, R. A., Tytell, A. A., Sagin, J. F., and Spicer, D. S. (1961a). *Virology* **15**, 269.

Charney, J. Tytell, A. A., Machlowitz, R. A., and Hilleman, M. R. (1961b). *J.A.M.A.* **177**, 591.

Cramer, R. (1964). *In* "Techniques in Experimental Virology" (R. J. C. Harris, ed.), pp. 145–168. Academic Press, New York.

Gotlieb-Stematsky, T., and Shilo, R. (1964). *Virology* **22**, 314.

Hilleman, M. R., Charney, J., Tytell, A. A., Weihl, C., Cornfeld, D., Ichter, J. T., Riley, H. D., Jr., and Huang, N. (1960). *Acad. Med. of New Jersey, Spec. Bull.* **6**, No. 3, 1.

LeBouvier, G. L., Schwerdt, C. E., and Schaffer, F. L. (1957). *Virology* **4**, 590.

Lowry, O. H., Rosebrough, N. J., Farr, A. L., and Randall, R. J. (1951). *J. Biol. Chem.* **193**, 265.

Macpherson, I. A., and Stoker, M. (1962). *Virology* **16**, 147.

Matheka, H. D., Bachrach, H. L., and Trautman, R. (1966). *Z. Naturforsch.* 21b, 774.

Mowat, G., and Chapman, W. G. (1962). *Nature* **194**, 253.

Mussgay, M. (1959). *Monatsh. Tierheilk.* **11**, 185.

Polatnick, J., and Bachrach, H. L. (1964). *Appl. Microbiol.* **12**, 368.

Schneider, W. C. (1957). *In* "Methods in Enzymology" (S. P. Colowick and N. O. Kaplan, eds.), Vol. 3, pp. 680–684. Academic Press, New York.

Schwerdt, C. E., and Schaffer, F. L. (1955). *Ann. N.Y. Acad. Sci.* **61**, 740.

Stanley, W. M. (1946). *J. Immunol.* **53**, 179.

Trautman, R., Breese, S. S., Jr., and Bachrach, H. L. (1962). *J. Phys. Chem.* **66**, 1976.

Ubertini, B., Nardelli, L., Dal Prato, A., Panina, G., and Santero, G. (1963). *Zentr. Veterinaermed.* **10**, 93.

Vanselow, A. P. (1940). *Ind. Eng. Chem., Anal. Ed.* **12**, 516.

Warren, J., and Gallian, M. J. (1962). *Am. J. Diseases Children* **103**, 418.

9 Methods in Human Virus Vaccine Preparation

Louis Potash

I. Introduction 372
II. Historical Development of Human Viral Vaccines 373
   A. Pre-Cell-Culture Technology 373
   B. The Modern Age of Cell Cultures 379
   C. Experimental Vaccines 385
   D. Future Virus Vaccines 390
III. Virus Vaccine Manufacturing Standards 393
   A. Establishment Standards 394
   B. Production Standards 398
IV. Killed Virus Vaccine Production—Licensed Biologicals .. 402
   A. Production—Additional Standards 402
   B. Testing—Additional Standards 409
   C. General Requirements 413
   D. Equivalent Methods 416
V. Live Virus Vaccine Production—Licensed Biologicals ... 416
   A. Production—Additional Standards 416
   B. Testing—Additional Standards 421
   C. General Requirements 426
   D. Clinical Trials to Qualify for License 427
   E. Equivalent Methods 428
VI. Virus Vaccines—General Considerations 429
   A. Live- versus Killed-Virus Vaccines 429
   B. Methods of Inactivation 430
   C. Vaccine Formulations 435
   D. Methods of Mass Immunization 439
VII. Production of Experimental Vaccines—General Principles 443
   A. Production 443
   B. Testing Procedures 447
   C. Clinical Trials in Man—Field Assessment 449
   D. General Requirements 450
VIII. Vaccine Production—Special Problems 451
   A. Choice of Propagation System 451
   B. Adventitious Agents—Overt and Latent 454
IX. Summary 458
   References 458

I. Introduction

Centuries before viruses were identified as a distinct group of micro-organisms or were etiologically related to specific infectious diseases, man had been aware that second attacks of certain diseases, such as smallpox and measles, were rare if not unknown. This knowledge led to the principle of artifically inducing active immunity for protection against smallpox as originally practiced by the ancient Chinese. They applied the crusts from lesions of very mild cases of smallpox to the skin or nasal mucous membranes of their children to protect them from severe cases of smallpox. The same principle was employed by the Turks, who scratched the arms of the persons to be immunized with crusts from lesions of mild cases of smallpox. This procedure, known as variolation, did result sometimes in generalized vaccinia and, sub-sequently, death.

It was Edward Jenner (1798) who first observed that the use of fully virulent pathogens was not necessary to induce immunity. He had noticed that farm workers who had contracted cowpox seldom had second attacks and were usually resistant to smallpox. By deliberately inoculating infectious material (vaccinia virus) from lesions of cowpox (vaccinia) into the skin of individuals, he artificially immunized these persons so that they became immune to subsequent challenge with variolous material. Thus the terms vaccination ("en-cowing") and vac-cine (an adjective meaning "of the cow") were employed originally in relation to immunization against smallpox with vaccinia virus.

Louis Pasteur, in homage to Jenner, used the terms vaccination and vaccine for his prophylactic immunizations. His work led to the widen-ing of the meaning of the word "vaccination" until it now has become identical with "inoculation" and the term "vaccine" has been applied not only to the use of live, attenuated but also of dead infectious agents or their antigenic components. Thus the principle of immuniza-tion or the vaccination of individuals through the use of vaccines has made available to man a means for combating infectious disease and, in particular, those of viral etiology.

With advances in the methodology of viral propagation together with the development of newer and more sophisticated techniques in related fields, a more profound understanding of the nature and properties of viruses resulted. These discoveries have led to the recent rapid progress in the development and production of safe and effective human viral vaccines. However, as knowledge of the art increases, new problems constantly arise which can markedly affect the future course of events with respect to the use of laboratory-developed biologicals as immunizing agents in the prophylaxis of specific virus-induced infectious diseases. Thus, the standards that have been rigidly applied to the manufacture and testing of these biologicals are of utmost concern and the comprehensive reevaluation of these standards in the light of the newer developments is an integral part of the present and future status of viral vaccines.

II. Historical Development of Human Viral Vaccines

A. PRE-CELL-CULTURE TECHNOLOGY

1. *Smallpox*

For nearly 100 years, the Jennerian prophylaxis proved to be not only the first but the only successful immunizing procedure against any disease other than by inoculation or direct contact with the actual disease itself.

The smallpox vaccine, now commonly used, is prepared from the vaccinal lesions of the skin of inoculated calves or sheep and contains live infective virus in the form of glycerinated lymph pulp. It often has been necessary to passage the virus seed used in vaccination through other animal species, such as rabbits, to aid in maintaining the purity and potency of the virus. Methods to be employed in the preparation, preservation, and storage of these vaccines are carefully controlled, and the requirements for smallpox vaccine are set forth in the World Health Organization (WHO) Technical Report Series, No. 323 (1966d).

One major disadvantage of these vaccines prepared in animals is that they cannot be produced completely free of bacterial contaminants. In an effort to produce bacteriologically sterile vaccines, two other methods of production have been employed: vaccinia virus grown in the chorioallantois of chick embryos (Jackson *et al.*, 1956) and in tissue cultures of bovine embryo skin (Wesslen, 1955) and chick embryos (Kaplan and Micklem, 1961). It has been recommended that the seed virus employed for smallpox vaccine production in tissue culture or chick embryos, because of the possibility of the lessening of immunizing potency of the vaccinia virus for man, should not be more than five passages removed from the animal host (WHO Technical Report Series, No. 323, 1966d).

2. Rabies

The next development in human viral vaccines occurred when the true infective agent of rabies was isolated from the brain of an animal that died of the disease and its pathogenicity for its natural host was successfully modified by serial intracerebral passage in rabbits (Pasteur *et al.*, 1881). This treatment resulted in the development of an infection characterized by a short, fixed incubation period (fixed virus in contrast to natural or so-called street virus). After 100 serial passages, this fixed virus had little capacity to infect dogs when administered subcutaneously. Pasteur and his associates (1884) were able to immunize dogs with this fixed virus material—a series of 10 daily subcutaneous injections of rabbit spinal cords dried at room temperature for varying periods of time in order to obtain preparations graded to contain no infectivity to maximum infectivity—and to subsequently show that they were immune to challenge with the street virus. In 1885, the same regimen first was applied to a peasant boy severely bitten by a rabid dog. Since the boy remained well and suffered no ill effects related to the immunization schedule (Pasteur, 1885), this vaccine treatment for rabies soon received widespread acclaim and was adopted as routine procedure throughout the world.

The use of chemical treatment (phenol) of suspensions of fixed virus for vaccines was introduced by Fermi (1908); hence, the Fermi vaccine. Semple (1919) modified Fermi's technique by incubating the phenol-treated material at 37°C to render the tissue–virus suspension noninfectious, but still retain its immunogenicity; hence, the Semple vaccine. The latter two vaccine types have been standard for postexposure treatment. They are packaged in 7–14 doses of 2 ml of 5% rabbit brain tissue infected with Pasteur brain-fixed virus suspended in physiologic saline containing 0.25% phenol with or without the addition of such preservatives as phenylmercuric borate (1 : 12,500) or thimerosal (1 : 10,000).

More recent vaccines have been prepared in avian embryos as well as tissue cultures in an effort to avoid the demyelinating reactions occasionally associated with the use of central nervous system (CNS) tissue of infected animals. An avian vaccine studied rather extensively in man has been that produced in chick embryos infected with high egg passage (HEP) Flury strain of virus (Koprowski and Cox, 1948; Koprowski *et al.*, 1954). This attenuated live virus vaccine has had extensive clinical trials for preexposure immunization without any serious reactions (Schwab *et al.*, 1954; Fox *et al.*, 1957; Sharpless *et al.*, 1957; Ruegsegger *et al.*, 1961; Ruegsegger and Sharpless, 1962). Another avian vaccine is prepared in duck embryos infected with the Pasteur brain-fixed virus. This preparation is inactivated with β-propiolactone and each dose originally consisted of 1 ml of rehydrated 10% duck embryo tissue virus preserved with 1 : 10,000 thimerosal (Peck et al., 1955, 1956). The protein content of this vaccine, in order to meet potency test requirements, has been increased to a level equivalent to that of brain tissue vaccines.

The use of tissue cultures for vaccine production has been a more recent development. The preparation of a Formalin-inactivated concentrated rabies vaccine grown in hamster kidney tissue cultures that met the NIH standards was reported by Kissling and Reese (1963). Wiktor et al. (1964) published on the propagation of rabies virus in human diploid cells (WI-38), suggesting a possible source of a new, attenuated, live virus vaccine.

It is quite apparent that a truly effective and safe vaccine for rabies is still in the developmental stage in spite of the advances made in the field of virology and the number of years that have elapsed since the recovery of the causative agent by Pasteur and his associates. The present state of knowledge relating to rabies virus and rabies vaccines is reviewed in the "Symposia Series in Immunobiological Standardization," Vol. I (1966) and the WHO Technical Report Series No. 321 (1966).

3. Yellow Fever

One of the more effective and safe viral vaccines for human use has been that produced against yellow fever. There are two strains of attenuated yellow fever virus now employed for human vaccination.

a. *Strain 17D.* Employing the Maitland-type of tissue culture, Lloyd et al. (1936) successfully grew the Asibi strain of neurotropic yellow fever virus in a medium containing minced mouse embryo tissue. After a number of passages, the virus was adapted to growth in a medium containing minced whole chick embryo and finally in a medium containing minced chick embryo minus brain and spinal cord, resulting in a marked modification of both viscerotropic and neurotropic affinities (Theiler and Smith, 1937a). This variant known as strain 17D is the seed virus employed in the production of vaccine (Theiler and Smith, 1937b).

The present production method employed is essentially that described by Hargett et al. (1943) and Fox et al. (1943) utilizing chick embryos. The acceptable passage level of the seed virus and its characteristics, determined by monkey inoculation, are well standardized (Theiler and Smith, 1937a; Fox and Penna, 1943; and Hargett and

Burruss, 1945). The finished vaccine is an aqueous-base (serum-free), chick embryo pulp in the lyophilized state.

b. *The French Neurotropic Strain.* This strain of virus was originally isolated from a Syrian in Dakar in 1929. It was shown to be pathogenic for mice inoculated intracerebrally; however, on serial passage, this strain became more pathogenic for the rodents but, at the same time, entirely lost its capacity for producing fatal visceral yellow fever in rhesus monkeys.

Both vaccines originated from the studies of Theiler and his associates (Theiler, 1951). The French vaccine prepared in mouse brains is administered primarily by the scratch technique, whereas the 17D vaccine prepared in chick embryos is inoculated subcutaneously. A disadvantage of the former vaccine has been the significant incidence of adverse reactions in the inoculated population.

Methods to be employed in the preparation, preservation, and storage of these vaccines are carefully controlled, and the requirements for yellow fever vaccine are set forth in the WHO Technical Report Series Nos. 179 (1959) and 323 (1966a).

4. *Influenza*

The discovery of two major distinct immunologically unrelated serologic types, influenza A (W. Smith *et al.*, 1933) and influenza B (Francis, 1940a; Magill, 1940), together with their propagation in the extraembryonic fluid of infected chick embryos were important contributions in the practical development of influenza virus vaccines. These events were followed by the observation that influenza viruses possessed the capacity of agglutinating chicken erythrocytes (Hirst, 1941; McClelland and Hare, 1941). However, it was Stanley (1944) who demonstrated that these viruses grown in the extraembryonic fluids could be purified and concentrated by means of the Sharples centrifuge. This method, because of its efficiency, ease of process, and particularly because of the purity of the product, was adopted for commercial production of purified influenza virus for use in vaccines (Stanley, 1945).

The prophylactic value of inactivated influenza virus vaccines has been well documented, particularly when the vaccines were composed of those viral strains involved in the specific epidemics studied. Unfortunately, the periodic occurrence of strain variation especially among the influenza A serotypes (type A of the 1930's and 1940's; type A-1, 1947–1957; type A-2, 1957 on) has necessitated the frequent alterations in the composition of the vaccine strains in an effort to include a variant that is most broadly related antigenically to those circulating in the most recent epidemic. The many problems encountered by commercial firms in attempting to produce a vaccine against a newly isolated major antigenic variant of influenza virus within a given period of time to be an effective prophylactic during the ensuing epidemic are discussed by McLean (1961). These problems include: need for haste; logistic problems of staff, equipment, materials; choice of candidate strain; production of new strain; concentration and purification studies; and potency testing.

By applying the knowledge of strain variation and variation in the antibody patterns of the different age groups in the population, continued efforts are being made to create a compound vaccine containing antigens that have been prominent in past and recent epidemic strains of influenza virus. This type of vaccine may provide immunity to current strains and, in addition, lay a foundation of resistance to future strains against which a great portion of the population would not be prepared.

The influenza virus vaccines presently being produced are generally in the form of Formalin-inactivated aqueous preparations that have been concentrated and purified by the Sharples centrifuge. Experimental vaccines employing mineral oil adjuvants have been studied and have resulted in higher, more sustained, and broader antibody responses against influenza virus than those obtained employing an equal amount of antigen in aqueous preparations (Salk et al., 1952; Hennessy and Davenport, 1961; Davenport et al., 1962). In addition, the use of mineral oil adjuvant has indicated that the amounts of antigen required for adequate stimulus can be reduced; thus permitting both economical and practical incorporation of multiple strains of virus.

A more recent advance in influenza virus vaccines has been the use of purified viral hemagglutinins (Davenport et al., 1964). Studies indicated that these preparations were as effective as whole virus in stimulating antibody in both children and adults and, in addition, failed to induce febrile responses in children in contrast to intact virus vaccines.

Another approach to influenza virus vaccines has been the use of live virus vaccination performed largely by Soviet investigators. Their results have indicated effectiveness comparable to that obtained with inactivated vaccines. The principles involved in the preparation and administration of live influenza vaccines as well as problems involved in the selection of vaccine strains are discussed by Zhdanov (1961).

5. *Other Vaccines*

The early 1930s saw the extensive use of the developing chick embryo for the propagation of viral and rickettsial agents based on the studies of Goodpasture (1933) and Goodpasture and his associates (1931). In the years that followed, tissues from the infected intact host such as the white mouse and the developing chick embryo were utilized for the preparation of vaccines against a host of viral diseases including smallpox, rabies, yellow fever, influenza A and B (see Section II,A,1,2,3 and 4 above), Japanese and Russian spring–summer encephalitis, as well as against epidemic typhus and spotted fevers caused by rickettsia. The latter group of vaccines were administered primarily to those populations at risk or in specific need. In addition, experimental vaccines against a number of other agents (equine encephalitis, dengue, psittacosis, measles, mumps) were produced, but were either ineffective or had limited application.

a. Encephalitis Viruses. Among the group A arboviruses, vaccines for the equine population are commercially available for both Eastern and Western but not for the Venezuelan equine encephalitis. Although clinical infection with these viruses can cause encephalitis of variable severity in man, there are, as yet, no vaccines for routine human use. The vaccines now in commercial production consist of Formalin-inactivated virus grown in chick embryos (J. W. Beard *et al.*, 1940). The development of a chick embryo cell culture vaccine against Western equine encephalitis has been reported by Robinson *et al.* (1966).

Of the group B arboviruses, the Japanese and the tick-borne encephalitis (Russian spring–summer encephalitis) viruses have been studied most intensely. A Formalin-inactivated mouse brain vaccine against Japanese encephalitis for use in man was developed by Sabin and collaborators (1943) and has seen widespread use in Japan (Sabin and Tigertt, 1956). It is thought that the vaccine resulted in a significant reduction in the incidence of the disease although no control studies were made ("Seminar on Japanese Encephalitis and Other Arbovirus Infections," 1962; Matsuda, 1962). Recently, Darwish and Hammon (1966) have reported the development of a hamster kidney-grown inactivated vaccine for man against Japanese B encephalitis.

A vaccine for human use against the group B tick-borne encephalitis viruses consisting of Formalin-inactivated virus in mouse brain suspensions was developed by Smorodintsev (1944). The effectiveness of this vaccine, determined by field trials, is reported by Smorodintsev (1958).

b. Rickettsial Agents. Antityphus vaccines containing killed *Rickettsia prowazeki* have been prepared from a variety of sources including the intestines of human lice, rodent lungs, agar-slant tissue cultures and from the yolk-sac membrane of developing chick embryos. The latter vaccine, known as the Cox-type (Cox, 1938, 1941, 1948; Craigie, 1945) was widely used during World War II to immunize troops and certain civilian populations. It is believed to reduce the incidence of disease in exposed persons and is known to reduce mortality from typhus to practically zero. Immunized persons who subsequently become infected undergo a milder and shorter course of disease and suffer fewer serious complications.

A more promising antityphus vaccine is that prepared from "Strain E," a variant of epidemic typhus. This strain originated in Spain in the laboratory of Clavero and Perez Gallardo (1943) during routine serial passages in the chick-embryo yolk sac of one of several strains isolated during an epidemic in Madrid in 1941. This strain, during its eleventh passage, abruptly changed its character in the direction of lesser virulence for laboratory animals. Although this change has not been reproducible, the newly acquired characteristic of the strain has persisted. The extensive studies carried out with this live avirulent vaccine have been reviewed by Fox (1956). The ability of Strain E to immunize man against a direct challenge with a virulent epidemic strain is known; however, what protection it will afford in the face of naturally occurring epidemic typhus is under study.

Effective vaccines (inactivated) against Rocky Mountain Spotted Fever Rickettsia (*Rickettsia rickettsi*) have been made from tissues of the infected ticks (*Dermacentor andersoni*) and from the yolk-sac tissue of developing chick embryos (Cox, 1938, 1941). The latter type is now the standard preparation (Smadel, 1960). The vaccine has definite protective value with the degree and duration of immunity being variable and probably dependent on the vaccinee, the virulence of the regional strains, and the dose of infection.

B. THE MODERN AGE OF CELL CULTURES

The modern era of tissue culture methodology was ushered in when Enders and his associates (Enders *et al.,* 1949; Robbins *et al.,* 1950) successfully demonstrated the practicality of cell cultures for the propagation of viruses. This *in vitro* host system provided the virologist with a novel tool for isolating, propagating, and studying viral agents both "old" and "new" and, as a result, marked a new age in vaccine development. The tissue culture system together with the important advances made in related fields have resulted in a more profound understanding of the nature and properties of viruses. With the isolation of a large number of previously unknown viral agents and the establishment of their etiologic relationship to acute human diseases, the demand for new vaccines has been overwhelming. This past decade has seen the development and world-wide use of tissue propagated vaccines against polioviruses, adenoviruses, and measles as killed and/ or live, attenuated preparations.

1. *Poliovirus*

The published literature relating to poliovirus vaccines is extensive and no attempt will be made to refer to all the studies on the subject. The ability to propagate poliovirus in non-nervous tissue cultures of primate cells (Enders *et al.*, 1949), and the separation of polioviruses into three antigenic types (Bodian *et al.*, 1949; Kessel and Pait, 1949) set the stage for the development of poliovirus vaccines.

a. Killed Virus Vaccine. Salk (1953) first introduced a Formalin-inactivated vaccine of the three types of poliovirus grown in monkey kidney tissue culture cells. Following a number of small trials that demonstrated its effectiveness in inducing antibody responses in susceptible individuals, the inactivated vaccine was put on test on a national scale in the United States in 1954 (Francis *et al.*, 1957). The safety and the effectiveness of this vaccine in reducing paralytic poliomyletis determined from this control study led to the commercial licensing of the preparation in 1955. Outbreaks of poliomyelitis occurred following the use of specific vaccine lots that subsequently were shown to contain residual amounts of live virus (Nathanson and Langmuir, 1963). This unfortunate event resulted in the formulation of more stringent regulations for manufacturing and safety testing. In 1960, it was reported that many lots of vaccine produced in primary monkey kidney tissue cultures contained a live adventitious agent, SV40 (Sweet and Hilleman, 1960a, 1960b), which since has been shown to produce tumors in hamsters (Eddy, 1962; Girardi *et al.*, 1962) and to transform tissue culture cells *in vitro* (Shein and Enders, 1962; Koprowski *et al.*, 1962). This discovery resulted in the inclusion of still more rigid tests for safety in the commercial preparation of killed as well as live virus vaccines prepared in monkey kidney tissue cultures.

During the past decade, there have been numerous publications relating to the production and inactivation of polioviruses as used in vaccines including newer methods for evaluating antigenic potency (Gard et al., 1956; Timm et al., 1958; Ghendon and Marchenko, 1959; Van Frank et al., 1965) and safety testing (Beardmore et al., 1957; Van Hoosier et al., 1961; Baron et al., 1961). The results of mass vaccination studies have indicated that the inactivated vaccine has been and is a reliable and effective means for poliomyelitis control. However, vaccination with killed poliovirus vaccines produces only humoral immunity, wherein the development of the paralytic form of the disease is prevented, but not the proliferation of the poliovirus in the intestines, thus permitting the spread of wild strains of poliovirus in a given community on a par with the nonvaccinated individuals in the same community. These shortcomings intensified the search for and subsequent development of a live virus vaccine against poliomyelitis.

Specific manufacturing and killed virus vaccine production standards based on the United States Public Health Service Regulations (1965) and the WHO Technical Report Series No. 323 (1966a, 1966b) are described in Sections III and IV.

b. Live Virus Vaccine. The first attenuated strain of poliovirus administered to humans was developed by Koprowski et al. (1952). They employed a strain of type 2 poliovirus (TN) that had been attenuated (as measured by its reduced virulence for the CNS of monkeys) by serial passages in cotton rat CNS. The oral feeding of this vaccine resulted in asymptomatic infections and antibody rises comparable to those following natural inapparent infection. Subsequently, tissue culture-attenuated strains were developed by Sabin (1955, 1957), by Koprowski et al. (1956), and Cox et al. (1959). Detailed accounts relating to the development of oral poliovirus vaccines have been reviewed by Sabin (1959), Koprowski (1961), and Paul (1961).

These vaccines have been shown to simulate inapparent infections similar to those induced by the naturally occurring wild strains of poliovirus and, as a result, to immunize the intestines against reinfection with wild strains. Numerous and extensive studies have confirmed the safety as well as the effectiveness of the vaccines in preventing paralytic poliomyelitis. Although the attenuated vaccines have the capacity of contact spread, there has been no confirmation of the plausible theory that repeated human passage might result in mutation, enhanced virulence, and potential danger of paralytic disease.

The major advantages of the live virus vaccine in preference to the killed one include the ease of administration (orally as liquid or in candy) and the high immunogenicity of the vaccine and its ability to prevent reinfection. These aspects have permitted mass immunization of the order of magnitude not realized with the killed vaccine; and, in addition, the speed of the immune response in the vaccinees makes this vaccine effective in controlling epidemics.

Standards for the manufacture, the selection of attenuated strains, the production, and the testing of live poliovirus vaccines based on the United States Public Health Service Regulations (1965) and the WHO Technical Report Series No. 323 (1966a, 1966c) are described in Sections III and V.

2. Adenovirus

Numerous studies have indicated that adenoviruses were responsible for a major portion of the acute febrile respiratory tract disease in military recruits (Huebner et al., 1958; van der Veen, 1963). Of the serotypes involved, type 4 appears to be the major causal agent followed by types 3 and 7. Because of the tremendous impact of adenovirus infection in recruits, involving high respiratory tract disease morbidity, hospitalization, and costly disruption of military training, concentrated efforts were extended for the development of effective prophylactic vaccines.

In 1956, experimental inactivated adenovirus vaccines prepared in monkey kidney tissue cultures were studied in military populations and proved to be very effective in preventing adenovirus disease (Bell et al., 1956; Hilleman et al., 1956, 1957; Stallones et al., 1957). Problems arose when subsequent production lots exhibited variable degrees of potency (Sherwood et al., 1961) and were found to be contaminated with simian viruses, SV40 in particular (see Section II,B,1,a). The status of adenovirus vaccines was further complicated when it was discovered that a portion of the SV40 virus genome could become incorporated into the type 7 adenovirus virion resulting in the formation of a "virus hybrid" possessing the oncogenic potential of SV40 virus (Huebner et al., 1964; Rowe and Baum, 1964).

Although the vast experience of immunizations with poliovirus vaccines known to contain viable SV40 virus has not indicated, to date, any harmful effects in man, the potential danger to man, nevertheless, exists. This awareness of the problem of oncogenic infectious viruses and of oncogenic viral genome, not only on behalf of SV40 but of the adenoviruses themselves, has greatly hindered the development of adenovirus vaccines. Possible means of bypassing the dangers of SV40 contamination may be the development of vaccines grown in human diploid tissue culture and administered live in the form of enteric coated capsules (Chanock et al., 1966; Edmondson et al., 1966) or vaccines composed of the soluble antigens of adenoviruses (Kasel et al., 1966). The present standards for the production and testing of killed adenovirus vaccines based on the United States Public Health Service Regulations (1965) are described in Sections III and IV.

3. Measles

The measles vaccines, both live attenuated and Formalin-inactivated, now licensed for use in the United States, were derived from the Edmonston strain originally supplied by Enders. This strain was isolated in 1954 from the blood of a measles patient and underwent a number of passages (24) in primary human kidney tissue cultures and then primary amnion cell cultures (28) before adaptation to growth in the chick embryo (Enders and Peebles, 1954; Milovanovic et al., 1957). Subsequently, Katz et al. (1958) adapted the virus to growth in monolayer cultures of chick embryo cells and it is this chick-adapted virus that has served as the basis for the commercially produced vaccines. Employing the method described above, Smorodintsev et al. (1960) obtained a strain of measles virus with characteristics similar to the Edmonston strain. Studies relating to measles virus and measles virus vaccines are reviewed in the publications of the International Conference on Measles Immunization (1963), the World Health Organization Scientific Group on Measles Vaccines (1963), and the Seminar on the Epidemiology and Prevention of Measles and Rubella (1965). Since the literature relating to measles virus vaccines, both killed and live, is so extensive, it would be impractical to cite all the individual publications.

a. *Killed Virus Vaccines.* Formalin-killed alum-adsorbed measles virus vaccines have been produced employing as original seed the Edmonston strain of virus. These vaccines have been prepared in chick embryo, monkey kidney, and canine kidney cell cultures. These types of vaccines require three monthly injections in order to induce high levels of protective antibody; however, this immunity is short-lived and within 6–12 months may no longer be detectable. Along with the loss of measureable antibody there occurs a decrease in protective efficacy against natural measles. Studies have indicated that the combination of killed followed by live attenuated vaccine can result in a successful immunization procedure (Guinee et al., 1963; WHO Technical Report Series No. 263, 1963).

Standards for the production and safety testing of inactivated mea-

sles virus vaccines based on the United States Public Health Service
Regulations (1965) and the WHO Technical Report Series No. 329
(1966) are described in Sections III and IV.

b. *Live Attenuated Vaccines.* The first successful attenuated measles
virus vaccine was developed by Enders *et al.* (1960) employing chick
embryo cell cultures. A comparison of the properties of the virulent
and attenuated strains are shown in Table I. Subsequently, additional

TABLE I

VARIANTS OF MEASLES VIRUS (EDMONSTON STRAIN)[a]

Property	Virulent	Attenuated
Growth in cell cultures		
Primary human or simian	Good	Poor
Continuous stable lines	Questionable	Excellent
Primary chick embryo	None	Excellent
Production of interferon	Minimal	Moderate
Formation of plaques		
Human amnion	"Large"	"Small"
Monkey kidney	None	Elongated
Chick embryo	None	Punctate
Effects in monkey and man		
Viremia	Nearly always	Almost never
Reactivity	Severe	Mild
Communicability	Extreme	None
CNS involvement	About 0.1%	None

[a] From Katz, S. L., and Enders, J. F. (1965).

vaccines were prepared in chick embryo, monkey kidney, canine kidney,
and bovine kidney cell cultures. Numerous studies have proven not
only the safety but the efficacy of these Enders' live measles virus
vaccines. The solid immunity resulting following vaccination and the
persistence of antibody levels show a similarity to that found after the
natural disease and suggests that a single inoculation may result in
life-long immunity. The first vaccine licensed in the United States in
1963 was the chick cell-adapted measles virus and was generally given
together with a small volume of immune globulin (0.02 ml/kg) to
modify the clinical reactions which may occur. Subsequently, more
attenuated measles virus vaccines have been developed and have been
shown to be as immunogenic as the initial type but, at the same
time, they cause fewer clinical reactions in the absence of immune
globulin. Standards for the production and safety testing of live attenuated measles virus vaccines based on the United States Public

Health Service Regulations (1965) and the WHO Technical Report Series No. 329 (1966) are described in Sections III and V.

C. EXPERIMENTAL VACCINES

Although vaccines for human and/or animal use against a variety of viral and rickettsial diseases now are produced commercially (see Section II,A and B), continued efforts are being made to improve these biologicals in the areas of immunogenicity, safety, and efficacy. As with any newly developed vaccines, major changes in production, virus seed, and cell culture–propagation systems of "licensed" biologicals often cause these vaccines to be reevaluated and necessitate their undergoing the required tests for safety and efficacy (see Section VII,C). In addition to the refinement of "old" vaccines, the development of prophylactic immunizing agents against rubella, mumps, the virus-induced respiratory disease complex, and arboviruses is being investigated by private industry as well as by United States government-financed grants and contracts. These studies involve the preparation of both killed and live attenuated vaccines with the specific formulations based, to a great extent, on the following: The particular disease manifestations caused by these viruses; the nature of immunity that must be induced for the vaccine to be effective; and the safety of the live vaccine, not only in reference to the vaccinee, but also to the possible spread of infection to contacts, both familial and community-wide.

1. Rubella

It is commonly believed that rubella is a mild and generally harmless childhood disease, but, in association with the first trimester of pregnancy, the infection may result in congenital malformations, stillbirths, and abortions. Because of these manifestations, e.g., teratogenesis, which the epidemic of 1963–1964 brought into sharp focus, studies leading to the development of a rubella vaccine are being intensified. It was the successful propagation of rubella virus in cell cultures by Weller and Neva (1962) and by Parkman and associates (1962) that opened the door for the biological characterization of this agent and the present studies leading to experimental vaccines.

The first report of the development and characterization of an attenuated rubella virus vaccine was made by Parkman et al. (1966). By repeated serial passages in African green monkey kidney tissue cultures, two strains of rubella virus (M33 and ML) were obtained that exhibited modified biological characteristics as determined by several laboratory test systems. Among these changes were the increased cytopathic effect obtained on back-titration in the RK13 tissue culture system as well as the formation of plaques in RK13 cells; the increased production of interferon, a phenomenon previously described as characteristic of attenuated measles and polioviruses (Enders, 1960); and the experimental infection of simians without subsequent viremia, virus shedding, or communicability, but with immunogenicity that was evidenced by antibody formation and resistance to reinfection.

The preparation of the M33 strain as an experimental vaccine and its application in a clinical trial is described by Meyer *et al.* (1966). The standards and requirements for the commercial production of live measles and poliovirus vaccines were applied to the production and testing of the live rubella vaccine (see Section V). The vaccine proved to be safe and immunogenic in the institutionalized children inoculated with this preparation, and, in addition, there was no evidence of spread to intimate contacts although some virus shedding did occur. However, the efficacy of the vaccine in the face of natural exposure to rubella still must be determined. Other vaccines, both killed and live attenuated, are presently in the developmental stage (Hilleman, 1966a) and it is anticipated that the near future will bring many publications relating to these experimental preparations.

2. *Mumps*

A commercial preparation of a killed, concentrated, mumps vaccine propagated in the extraembryonic fluid of the infected chick embryo has been licensed in the United States for about 16 years, but has not received widespread use. The lack of enthusiasm for this type of vaccine can be traced to the transitory nature of the induced antibody responses, the probable need of booster inoculations, and the occurrence of cases of mumps in spite of immunization within a few months following administration. These disadvantages soon led to attempts to develop a live attenuated vaccine.

However, one of the major problems facing investigators in attempting to develop a mumps vaccine is that the virus after 30 or more passages in the chick embryo becomes so altered that it is no longer pathogenic for man and, at the same time, poorly immunogenic. In addition, prolonged chick embryo passage results in the inability of the virus to propagate in human or simian cell cultures. Thus the problem of determining the proper level of attenuation for the production of a safe and effective vaccine requires investigation.

Soviet investigators have vigorously pursued the development of a live mumps vaccine. The original production method involved the use of the virus propagated in the intraamniotic cavity of chick embryos (Smorodintsev and Klyachko, 1958; Smorodintsev, 1961). Subsequently, the same strain of virus, after prolonged adaption to embryonated eggs, was employed as seed to prepare a live vaccine in chick embryo cell cultures (Luzyanina et al., 1963; Smorodintsev et al., 1965). This experimental vaccine, administered parenterally, was immunogenic and effective in protecting vaccinees from infection following natural exposure and, in addition, appeared to cause no obvious clinical reactions.

More recently, Buynak and Hilleman (1966) have reported on the development of a live attenuated mumps vaccine. The virus, Jeryl Lynn strain (B level), was attenuated by passage in chick embryos and then adapted to growth in chick cell cultures. The vaccine is prepared as a dried product that has undergone the same rigid production and testing standards applied to the live attenuated measles virus vaccine. Clinical field trials have indicated the immunogenicity and the efficacy of the vaccine, and the absence of viral excretion in the vaccinees (Stokes et al., 1967; Weibel et al., 1967; Hilleman et al., 1967).

3. Respiratory Virus Complex

The various agents responsible for the majority of the respiratory disease syndromes include influenza, parainfluenza, respiratory syncytial, adeno-, rhino-, respiratory entero-, and reoviruses as well as *Mycoplasma pneumoniae*. Influenza and adenovirus vaccines have been discussed previously (Sections II,A,4 and II,B,2). Although the rhinoviruses are known to be a principal cause of common colds in adults and of both upper and lower respiratory illness in children, the development of vaccines against these agents is complicated by the number of distinct serotypes identified to date (over 50 types with the number increasing rapidly) and by the lack of knowledge relative to the clinical significance of the various types. Many of the enteroviruses appear to play a significant role in acute respiratory disease, but the multiplicity of serotypes is a limiting factor in vaccine development. The reoviruses, at the present time, do not seem to be of major importance as human pathogens. Eaton agent or *M. pneumoniae* is of prime concern as a cause of primary atypical pneumonia and vaccines both killed and live have been experimentally produced. However, major interest now is being focused on the parainfluenza and respiratory syncytial viruses.

The parainfluenza viruses (types 1, 2, 3, 4A, and 4B) have been shown to be etiologically responsible for a significant portion of both upper and lower respiratory tract diseases in children and infants. The respiratory syncytial virus is probably the most important cause of acute febrile respiratory tract illness in children and infants, particularly during the first 6 months of life. The importance of these agents in pediatric medicine has fostered vigorous efforts toward the development of safe and effective vaccines.

Employing virus preparations grown in African monkey kidney cell cultures, killed concentrated alum-adsorbed experimental vaccines have been developed against parainfluenza types 1, 2, and 3 and respiratory syncytial virus (Potash et al., 1966; Sweet et al., 1966; Woodhour et al., 1966). Although these vaccines have been found to elicit antibody responses in animals and man, their protective efficacy remains to be determined.

Other inactivated experimental vaccines against the parainfluenza viruses have been prepared in embryonated hens' eggs (Jensen et al., 1962; DeMeio and DeSanctis, 1966; Kim et al., 1966). As with the tissue culture vaccines, both man and animals responded to the antigenic stimulus, but the efficacy of the immunologic response to protect against natural exposure is not as yet known.

A recent development has indicated that the use of inactivated vaccines to protect against the parainfluenza and probably the respiratory syncytial viral induced diseases may not be ideal. A study by C. B. Smith et al. (1966) showed that the presence of antibody in nasal secretions (immunoglobulin type A) proved to be more indicative of host resistance to infection to parainfluenza type 1 virus than did the level of serum antibody (immunoglobulin type G). Of a group of adult volunteers all possessing serum-neutralizing antibody to type 1 parainfluenza virus, a high proportion of those also possessing specific IgA antibody in their nasal secretions were resistant to reinfection. In contrast, men who were immunized with an inactivated type 1 parainfluenza virus vaccine and failed to demonstrate antibody production in their nasal secretions, remained susceptible to reinfection when challenged with live virus. This phenomenon wherein antibody present at the initial site of infection (respiratory tract) might be more effective than serum antibody in protecting against reinfection was suggested some time ago by Francis (1940b, 1943), Francis and Brightman (1941), and Smorodintsev and Chalkina (1955). Recently, Artenstein et al. (1964) and Bellanti et al. (1965) reported on the association of virus-neutralizing substances in nasal secretions with antibody of the immunoglobulin type A, further supporting the view that what

C. B. Smith *et al.* (1966) measured was antibody. These findings suggest that future respiratory vaccines, live attenuated or possibly killed, be administered via the intranasal route by some type of aerosol in order to stimulate the appearance of antibody in the respiratory tract secretions. The use of killed vaccines applied to the respiratory tract to elicit this type of antibody response was reported by Fazekas de St. Groth and Donnelley (1950a, 1950b) in experimental influenza infection in mice. Furthermore, the measurement of nasal antibody may provide a more meaningful yardstick of the potential efficacy of the parainfluenza and respiratory syncytial virus vaccines to protect against natural reinfection than the measurement of serum antibody.

4. *Other Experimental Vaccines*

Although the number of virus-induced diseases is quite large, the development of vaccines has been pursued mainly against those agents that have been shown to be highly pathogenic for man and/or animals or whose infection often results in serious complications or sequelae. Listed among these viruses are those that have been discussed previously in Section II and include smallpox, rabies, yellow fever, influenza, members of the arbovirus group (Japanese B encephalitis, Russian spring–summer encephalitis, Western and Eastern equine encephalitis), poliovirus, adenovirus, measles, rubella, mumps, and the respiratory virus complex.

In addition to the above vaccines presently licensed or being tested experimentally in man and animals, a number of additional formulations may be mentioned. With respect to rabies virus vaccines, studies on a modified live virus (chick embryo cell culture-grown) preparation have shown promise in dogs (Dean *et al.*, 1964; Cabasso *et al.*, 1965). In 1965, Russian workers (Svet-Moldavsky *et al.*, 1965) reported on the development of a killed allergen-free rabies vaccine prepared in the brains of suckling rats that produced very few clinical reactions in humans even in those groups considered especially at risk because of previous antirabies vaccination or with histories of trauma or CNS disease. Wiktor and Koprowski (1965) successfully immunized primates with a rabies vaccine prepared in human diploid cells (strain WI 38).

Attempts to develop vaccines against a number of the arboviruses have been stressed because of their economic importance as pathogens for livestock as well as their disease-producing effect in man. One of the experimental preparations is a live attenuated Western equine encephalitis vaccine developed by Johnson (1963) as a clone 15 variant in chick embryo cell cultures. Mouse-adapted strains of dengue virus

are being investigated for use as live attenuated vaccines (Wisseman
et al., 1963). Immunization against Rift Valley fever has involved the
use of killed vaccines prepared from pantropic virus grown in monkey
kidney tissue culture (Randall et al., 1963) as well as in lamb kidney
and hamster kidney primary cell cultures (Binn et al., 1963).

For monkey handlers faced with the potentially fatal occupational
hazard of B virus infection, an experimental killed vaccine prepared
in rabbit kidney cell cultures has been developed, although its protective efficacy is unknown (Hull and Nash, 1960; Hull et al., 1962).

In addition to the above-mentioned viral agents, investigators have
been interested in the development of vaccines against those groups
of agents causing trachoma and Q fever. Since trachoma appears to be
the greatest single cause of progressive loss of sight in the world, a
truly effective vaccine could serve as a prophylactic and possibly as
a therapeutic measure. Experimental vaccines that have been studied
have consisted of killed yolk sac-grown preparations (Grayston et al.,
1962, 1963); unfortunately, they have not been shown to be fully
effective.

Q fever is an occupational disease wherein infection is derived from
infected livestock. Since there is no apparent economic importance to
the infection in livestock, the prophylactic immunization of man is the
major means of control. Protective vaccines have been prepared using
killed rickettsia grown in the yolk sacs of embryonated eggs, but a
high incidence of local reactions have usually accompanied its administration. In addition, studies have indicated that there are marked
differences in immunogenicity between vaccines prepared with phase I
or phase II rickettsiae (Ormsbee et al., 1964). In an effort to overcome the local reactions related to the earlier vaccines, purified and
concentrated preparations have been produced (Berman et al., 1961;
Ormsbee, 1962), but their practical use has not been determined. Russian workers have developed a live attenuated vaccine (strain M) by
passage in embryonated egg cultures; however, this material does produce some reactions in vaccinees (Genig, 1960; Zdrodovskii and Genig,
1962).

D. Future Virus Vaccines

The rapid developments in virology and in closely related fields
and the new techniques in vaccine production have uncovered and
can be expected to continue to uncover previously unforeseen problems.
These unexpected complications, though at present not too clearly

defined, can impede the present and the future progress in the development of effective viral vaccines.

The first hazard that has been encountered and recognized has been the contamination of rhesus monkey kidney tissue cultures with an indigenous virus, SV40, that has the capacity to multiply without producing any cytopathic or other changes. This agent has been shown to produce tumors in hamsters, to transform human skin and kidney cell cultures, and to enter in genetic recombination with other viruses producing highly oncogenic "hybrids." Although large numbers of individuals have received live and dead poliovirus vaccines containing this contaminant, its oncogenic potential for man has not as yet been determined. However, since it is anticipated that the incubation period may be very long, 15–25 years or more, it may be too soon at this time to rule out any adverse effects relating to this virus. Furthermore, with the rapidly increasing attack rates of neoplastic disease, it may not be possible, even in long term followup studies, to specifically implicate any virus as the causal agent for a given tumor unless methods for differentiating tumors on etiological grounds become available. The SV40 virus is but one of many simian viruses that have been isolated from monkey kidney and it required a subculture from one species (rhesus) to another (grivet) for initial detection. The possibility, therefore, exists that other agents with similar potentials may be latent not only in monkey kidney but in other tissues, and that means for their detection have not been developed in spite of the highly sophisticated equipment and techniques now available.

Potential hazards also exist in most live virus vaccines, particularly those prepared in the intact animal host such as the arboviruses in mouse brain, smallpox in calf lymph, and yellow fever in chick embryos. Those vaccines prepared in chick embryos are believed to have contained fowl leukosis viruses. The significance of the murine leukosis viruses is now being brought to light and the presence of bovine leukosis virus is expected. In fact, it is anticipated that with the appropriate techniques, leukosis viruses could be detected in nearly any animal studied. Although no untoward reactions have been reported in individuals receiving vaccines containing these extraneous agents, the potential danger nevertheless exists. The problem of adventitious agents will be discussed more extensively in Section VIII. One possible method of bypassing the potential danger of extraneous agents would be the use of killed vaccines wherein both RNA and DNA have been separated from the immunogenic protein. However, safety could be assured only if the viral proteins could be proven to be unassociated with the induction of neoplasia. The present state of knowledge would indicate that this type of vaccine should be a reasonably safe product.

There have been two vaccines experimentally produced which could fit into the above category. Davenport and co-workers (1964) reported on the preparation of inactivated influenza A vaccines composed of isolated hemagglutinins liberated by ether treatment and further purified by chemical and physical means. The vaccines proved to be as immunogenic as the intact virus vaccine, and in addition, failed to induce febrile responses in children in contrast to the pyrogenic effect observed with intact virus vaccines administered in equal or even smaller doses. This development could alleviate the concern relating to the commercial production of intact influenza virus vaccines produced in chick embryos known to be infected with the avian leukosis viruses. Furthermore, the elimination of the undesirable side reactions that often attend influenza virus vaccination indicate that the prospects for wider use of such vaccination may be enhanced.

Kasel and associates (1966) summarized their progress in the use of soluble antigens derived from adenoviruses for the immunization of man. The excess formation of at least three virus-specific soluble antigens generally accompanies the proliferation of adenoviruses in tissue cultures. These noninfectious antigens appear to be structural subunits of the outer virus coat or capsid of the virion and include the hexon, the penton, and the fiber (an incomplete penton subunit) antigens. By means of column chromatography following ultracentrifugation it has been possible to successfully isolate and concentrate the soluble antigen fractions. Employing as immunizing agents the fiber and hexon fractions derived from adenoviruses types 1, 2, and 4 and administered either individually or in combination, these investigators were able to induce homotypic and heterotypic neutralizing-antibody responses (type 7S) in man. The importance of this development cannot be minimized in the light of the problems associated with the production of whole virus vaccines. Other than the difficulty in obtaining adenovirus seed material free of both adventitious agents and genetic material from known oncogenic agents (SV40), the discovery that certain serotypes have the capacity to induce tumors in newborn hamsters has further hindered vaccine development. The possibility of preparing effective adenovirus vaccines without any oncogenic potential may be the immediate answer to the needs of the military population and a future prophylactic measure in children and infants.

A report by Neurath (1966) on the soluble antigens of rabies virus suggests the possibility of the development of a new type of antirabies vaccine consisting of subunits. Cohen and Wilcox (1960) described the separation of the soluble antigens of vaccinia virus into two classes, high and low molecular weight antigens. The former class was found to induce the production of virus-neutralizing antibody in rabbits.

Thus with the newer and more sophisticated techniques available in the related fields of biochemistry and biophysics, it would appear that the development of viral vaccines consisting of noninfectious immunogenic subunits lacking any viral genome and possessing little of the host protein may be realized in the not too distant future. However, this form of vaccine may be an effective prophylactic for only some of the virus-induced diseases; whereas, others may still require the administration of either live attenuated or killed whole virus preparations.

III. Virus Vaccine Manufacturing Standards

The standards to be discussed in this section have been extracted from The United States Public Health Service Regulations, Title 42, Part 73, Sections 73.35–38, 73.50–55, 73.70–85 (1965) and the World Health Organization Requirements for Biological Substances in Technical Report Series No. 323, Annex 1, pp. 11–19 (1966a). In the latter case, the requirements are presented as recommendations for individual countries to adopt as they wish as the basis for their own national regulations concerning general requirements for the manufacture and control of biological products. For more detailed information, refer to the specific regulations and requirements.

In the United States two forms of licenses are required for biological products: establishment and product. The procedures for obtaining these licenses are described in Section 73.2 through 73.16. In general, an establishment license is issued only after the establishment has been inspected and it has been determined that it complies with the applicable standards prescribed in the regulations. In addition, no establishment license is issued unless a product is available not only for examination, but also for inspection during all stages of manufacture, and a product license is requested and issued simultaneously with the establishment license. A product license is issued only when the examination of the product complies with the standards prescribed in the regulations, and provided that the establishment complies with the establishment standards as prescribed in the regulations and applicable to the manufacture of the specific product.

A. ESTABLISHMENT STANDARDS

1. *Personnel*

The manufacturing establishment shall be headed by a person who has been trained in the techniques used in manufacturing biological substances and who has an understanding of the scientific principles upon which the manufacture of these products are based. He shall have the authority to represent the manufacturer before the national control authority and to enforce discipline among employees. In addition, he shall be responsible for the training of all personnel in manufacturing methods and of informing them of the specific provisions relating to their respective duties. All senior personnel responsible for signing protocols shall be registered with the national control authority.

Unauthorized personnel shall be excluded from the manufacturing area. All necessary precautions shall be taken to prevent cross-contamination or the introduction of outside contamination by movement of personnel through different manufacturing areas or from animal quarters to areas in which products are being manufactured.

2. *Physical Plant, Equipment, Animals, and Care*

a. Work Areas. Laboratories, operating rooms, animal rooms, and all other rooms and buildings used for the manufacture of biological products shall be so designed and constructed of such materials that the highest standards of cleanliness and sanitation can be maintained and freedom from dust, insects, and vermin ensured. All such buildings and rooms shall be equipped with hot and cold running water, drainage, and all necessary electrical and other services. Adequate precautions shall be taken to avoid airborne dissemination of pathogenic microbes, viruses, smoke, and other deleterious substances. Staff changing rooms, etc., shall be provided as needed. All buildings and rooms shall be clean and sanitary at all times. If rooms intended for the manufacture of biological substances are used for other purposes, they shall be cleaned thoroughly and, if necessary, sterilized prior to resumption of manufacture of biological substances in them. Any persons not concerned with the production process who enter the production area for the purpose of inspection shall be supplied with sterile protective clothing.

Specific space for live vaccine processing may be individual or multiple units set aside for each live vaccine. Such space shall not be used for any other purpose during the processing period for that vaccine.

Each such unit shall be isolated either in a separate building, in a separate wing of a building, or in quarters at the blind end of a corridor so situated as to be an independent unit. The separate unit or units in which live vaccine is processed shall include adequate space and equipment for all processing steps up to filling into final containers. Test procedures that potentially involve the presence of microorganisms other than the vaccine strains, or the use of tissue culture cell lines other than primary cultures, shall not be conducted in live-vaccine processing areas.

At any one time, manufacture of each biological product shall take place in a separate area using separate equipment. Only strains of microorganisms or viruses used for the production of the particular biological product shall be permitted in the manufacturing area.

All procedures with spore-forming microorganisms or viruses shall be confined to separate areas with complete equipment used exclusively in those areas. Separate facilities shall be provided for work with each virus and care shall be taken to prevent aerosol formation (especially by centrifugation and blending), which might lead to transfer of virus from one production unit to another. Adequate staff shall be provided to avoid the necessity for staff to work in any one working day in areas in which different biological products are being manufactured. Sequential manufacture of different products in the same area shall be allowed provided that the method of sterilization of the area between manufacture of the different products is shown to be satisfactory and has the approval of the national control authority. Pathological specimens sent in for diagnosis shall be permitted only in separate areas not used for manufacturing biological substances.

Filling shall be performed in rooms reserved for this purpose. These shall be sterile rooms equipped specifically for transferring measured quantities of finished biological substances from bulk containers to the final containers. Strict dust control measures and aseptic techniques shall be enforced to ensure that the product is not contaminated during the filling process. Filling operations shall be conducted in such a way that any contamination or alteration of the product is avoided. They shall take place in areas that are completely separate from those in which living microorganisms, including viruses, are handled.

The final container shall be sealed as soon as possible after filling. Closures shall be of material that does not have a deleterious effect upon the biological substances, and shall be designed to maintain a hermetic seal throughout the dating period. In addition, final containers and closures for products intended for use by injection shall be sterile and free from pyrogens. Final containers for products intended for use by injection shall be colorless and sufficiently transparent to permit visual examination of the contents under normal light.

   b. *Equipment.* Work areas shall contain adequate refrigerator space, as well as incubators or warm rooms, capable of being maintained at a uniform temperature within any required range and shall be free of extraneous material which might affect the safety of the product. In addition, it is recommended that refrigerators and incubators should maintain a uniform temperature in all parts of the interior and should preferably be equipped with recording thermometers and with appropriately placed alarm signals to ensure that an early repair can be effected in case of breakdown.

   Adequate facilities shall be available for washing apparatus. Steam autoclaves, dry-heat sterilizers, and bacteria-retaining filters shall be available for sterilizing supplies, media, and apparatus and the method of operation shall be such as to insure the destruction of contaminating microorganisms. Processing vessels, storage containers, filters, filling apparatus, and other pieces of apparatus and accessory equipment, including pipes and tubing, shall be designed and constructed to permit thorough cleaning and, where possible, inspection for cleanliness. All surfaces that come in contact with products shall be clean and free of extraneous material. For products for which sterility is a factor, equipment shall be sterile unless sterility of the product is assured by subsequent procedures.

   c. *Animal Quarters and Care.* Quarters for animals shall be designed in a manner and constructed of materials that permit maintenance in a clean and sanitary condition free from insects and vermin, and shall be adequately lighted and ventilated. It is recommended that the facilities provide for the disinfection of cages, if possible by steam, and for an incinerator for disposing of waste and of dead animals. Facilities for animal care shall include isolation units for quarantine of incoming animals, and vermin-free food storage. Provision shall be made for animal inoculation rooms which shall be separate from the postmortem rooms.

   Animals used for production purposes or test purposes shall have been kept under competent daily inspection and preliminary quarantine for a period of at least 7 days before use. They shall be provided with a well-balanced diet, adequately housed, and be kept clean and sanitary. Animals on production shall be inspected daily to observe response to production procedures. Animals that become ill for reasons not related to production shall be isolated from other animals and shall not be used for production until recovery is complete. Caretakers and attendants for animals used for the manufacture of products shall be sufficient in number and have adequate experience to insure adequate care. Competent veterinary care shall be provided as needed.

3. Records

Records shall be made, concurrently with the performance, of each step in the manufacture and distribution of products, in such a manner that at any time successive steps in the manufacture and distribution of any lot may be traced by an inspector. Such records shall be legible and indelible, shall identify the person immediately responsible, shall include dates of the various steps, and be as detailed as necessary for clear understanding of each step by one experienced in the manufacture of products. Distribution records must be kept in a manner that permits rapid recall of any particular batch, if necessary.

Records shall be retained for such interval beyond the expiration date as is necessary to permit the return of any clinical report of unfavorable reactions for the individual product.

Records relating to the mode of sterilization, date, duration, temperature, and other conditions relating to each sterilization of equipment and supplies used in the processing of products shall be made by means of automatic recording devices or by means of a system of recording that gives equivalent assurance of the accuracy and reliability of the record. Such records shall be maintained in a manner that permits an identification of the product with the particular manufacturing process to which the sterilization relates. A necropsy record shall be kept on each animal from which a biological product has been obtained and which dies or is sacrificed while being so used. Records shall be maintained of the complete passage history of all cultures kept in the establishment. Cultures shall be labeled and stored in a safe, orderly manner.

4. Retention Samples

Samples from each lot shall be taken in a sufficient amount to satisfy the requirements for samples of the national control laboratory. In addition, manufacturers shall retain for a period of at least 6 months after the expiration date a quantity of representative material of each lot of each product sufficient for examination and testing for safety and potency. Such sample material shall be stored at temperatures and under conditions that will maintain the identity and integrity of the product.

B. Product Standards

1. Labels

All products shall be clearly identified by labels. The information given on the label on the container or the label on the package shall be determined by the national control authority.

a. Container Labels. The following items shall appear on the label affixed to each container of a product capable of bearing a full label:

(1) The proper name of the product.

(2) Name, address, and license number of manufacturer.

(3) Lot number.

(4) The expiration date.

b. Package Labels. The label on the package shall, in addition to the information shown on the label on the container, include the following:

(1) The preservative used and its concentration.

(2) The volume of the contents, if a liquid, or the weight, if a solid, and the potency or dosage if more than one strength is dispensed.

(3) The recommended human dose and route of administration.

(4) The condition of storage and expiry date.

It is further recommended that the label on the package or the leaflet in the package should indicate the stability under different storage conditions, contain instructions for the use of the product, and give information about reactions that may follow administration of the product.

2. Release Requirements

A lot of a biological substance shall not be released until all the required tests for conformity with standards applicable to such product have been performed. No new biological substance shall be released until consistency of production has been established. In routine production, failure of a single batch to meet the requirements for safety shall be considered as a breakdown in production, and consistency shall be reestablished to the satisfaction of the national control authority before any further batches are released.

3. Potency

The word "potency" is interpreted to mean the specific ability or capacity of the product, indicated by appropriate laboratory tests or by adequately controlled clinical data obtained through the administration of the product in the manner intended, to effect a given result.

Tests for potency shall consist of either *in vitro* or *in vivo* tests, or both, that have been specifically designed for each product to indicate its potency in a manner adequate to satisfy the interpretation of potency given above.

4. General Safety

In addition to specified safety tests prescribed for individual products, a general safety test shall be performed in final container material, from each filling of each lot of all products intended for administration to man, after the labels have been affixed to the final container. The general safety test shall consist of the parenteral injection of the maximum volume tolerated into each of two mice weighing approximately 20 gm each, and into each of two guinea pigs weighing approximately 350 gm each, but no more than 0.5 ml need be inoculated into each mouse and no more than 5.0 ml need be inoculated into each guinea pig. After injection the animals shall be observed for a period of no less than 7 days and if neither significant symptoms nor death results during the observation period, the product meets the requirements for general safety. Variations of this test, either in the volume injected or in the species of test animal used, shall be made whenever required because of the human dose level demanded of the product or because of any individual demands of the product itself.

5. Sterility

A volume of at least 10 ml of bulk material, representative of the bulk container material, shall be tested for bacterial and mycotic sterility. A percentage of the final containers (Sec. 73.73) shall be similarly tested. In addition, it is recommended that tests for mycoplasma employing both solid and liquid media also be included.

The ratio of the volume of the inoculum to the volume of culture medium shall be such as will dilute the preservative in the inoculum to a level that does not inhibit growth of contaminating microorganisms. The growth-promoting qualities and conditions of the culture medium shall be such as to provide conditions favorable to aerobic and anaerobic growth of microorganisms throughout the test period.

a. Fluid Thioglycollate Medium. The inoculum and the medium shall be mixed thoroughly and incubated at a temperature of 30°–32°C for a period of at least 7 days with intermittent examination for bacterial growth. If two temperatures are chosen, these shall be in the ranges of 18°–22°C and 35°–37°C.

b. Fluid Sabouraud Medium. The inoculum and the medium shall be mixed thoroughly and incubated at a temperature of 20°–25°C for a period of at least 14 days with intermittent examination for mycotic growth. The formulas for the preparation of these media are given in the PHS Regulations 73.73 (e) and WHO Technical Report Series No. 200, Appendix 1, page 22 (1960).

6. Purity and Identity

a. *Purity*. The products shall be free from extraneous material and shall be tested for residual moisture, if a dried product, and for pyrogenic substances by intravenous injection into rabbits, if product is intended for use by injection. The test for dried products shall consist of measuring the maximum loss of weight in a weighed sample equilibrated over anhydrous P_2O_5 at a pressure of not more than 1 mm of mercury, and at a temperature of 20°–30°C for as long as it has been established is sufficient to result in a constant weight. The residual moisture and other volatile substances shall not exceed 1% except for measles virus vaccine (live attenuated) which shall not exceed 2%. The test dose for each rabbit shall be at least 3 ml/kg of body weight of the rabbit and also shall be at least equivalent proportionately, on a body weight basis, to the maximum single human dose recommended. Three or more rabbits in overt good health shall receive this test dose intravenously. Temperatures shall be taken 1 hour prior to and 1, 2, and 3 hours post injection. The product fails to meet test requirements if half or more of all rabbits show a temperature rise of 0.6°C or more or if the average temperature rise of all rabbits is 0.5°C or more.

b. *Identity*. The contents of a final container of each filling of each lot shall be tested for identity after all labeling operations shall have been completed. The identity test shall be specific for each product in a manner that will adequately identify it as the product designated on final container and package labels and circulars and distinguish it from any other product being processed in the same laboratory. Identity may be established either through the physical or chemical characteristics of the product, inspection by macroscopic or microscopic methods, specific cultural tests, or *in vitro* or *in vivo* immunological tests.

7. Release Protocols

A lot of a biological substance shall be released only if it fulfills the requirements adopted by the national control laboratory. Samples of any lot of any licensed product, together with the protocols showing results of applicable tests, may at any time be required if the safety, purity, or potency of the product is in question.

8. Cultures

Cultures used in the manufacture of products shall be stored in a secure and orderly manner at a temperature and by a method that will retain the initial characteristics of the organisms and insure freedom from contamination and deterioration. Each culture shall be clearly identified with respect to source strain. A complete identification of the strain shall be made for each new stock culture preparation. Primary and subsequent seed lots shall be identified by lot number and date of preparation. Periodic tests shall be performed as often as necessary to verify the integrity of the strain characteristics and freedom from extraneous organisms. Results of all periodic tests for verification of cultures and determination of freedom from extraneous organisms shall be recorded and retained.

9. Ingredients, Preservatives, Diluents

All ingredients used in a licensed product and any diluent provided as an aid in the administration of the product shall meet generally accepted standards of purity and quality. Any preservative used shall be sufficiently nontoxic so that the amount present in the recommended dose of the product will not be toxic to the recipient and in the combination used shall not denature the specific substances in the product below the minimum acceptable potency within the dating period when stored at the recommended temperature.

10. Dating and Storage

The dating period of a product kept at the manufacturer's recommended storage temperature shall begin on the date of manufacture, i.e., the date of initiation by the manufacturer of the last valid potency test. In general, products may be held by the manufacturer in cold storage after the date of manufacture without decreasing the dating period, for the following periods: at a temperature not above 10°C for 6 months; at a temperature not above 5°C for 1 year; at a temperature not above 0°C for 2 years; or as stipulated in Section 73.86 of the Public Health Service Regulations (Amendment No. 3).

The dating period for each biological shall be based on data relating to usage, clinical experience, or laboratory tests that establish the period beyond which the product cannot be expected beyond reasonable doubt to yield its specific results and retain its safety, purity, and potency, provided the product is maintained at the recommended temperatures.

IV. Killed Virus Vaccine Production—Licensed Biologicals

The standards to be described for the manufacture of killed virus vaccines (poliovirus, adenovirus, and measles) have been extracted from the United States Public Health Service Regulations Title 42, Part 73, Sections 73.100–105, 73.130–135, and 73.150–155 (1965) as well as from the WHO Technical Report Series No. 323, Annex 2, pp. 23–36 (1966b) and No. 329, Annex 2, pp. 74–90 (1966). The requirements in the latter instances are in the form of recommendations that may constitute the basis for definitive national requirements. For more detailed information, refer to the specific regulations or requirements mentioned above.

A. PRODUCTION—ADDITIONAL STANDARDS

1. The Product

a. Inactivated Poliomyelitis Vaccine. Inactivated virus vaccine shall consist of an aqueous suspension of poliovirus types 1, 2, and 3 grown in monkey kidney tissue cultures and inactivated by a suitable method.

b. Inactivated Adenovirus Vaccine. Inactivated virus vaccine shall consist of an aqueous preparation of one or more adenoviruses grown in monkey kidney tissue cultures inactivated by a suitable method. When more than one type of virus is used in the manufacture of the vaccine, equal proportions of each type shall be combined with a tolerance for each component of 5% of the total volume.

c. Inactivated Measles Virus Vaccine. Inactivated virus vaccine shall be a preparation of measles virus grown in various types of primary tissue cultures and inactivated by an appropriate method.

2. Strains of Virus

Strains of virus used in the manufacture of vaccine shall be identified by historical records, infectivity tests, and immunological methods, and shall produce a vaccine meeting the safety and potency requirements described below. In addition, seed virus employed for vaccine manufacture shall be free of all demonstrable extraneous viable microbial agents and shall at no time have been passed in malignant cells of human or animal origin.

a. Adenovirus. Only those strains of virus may be employed that have been maintained in monkey kidney cultures for at least 10 passages prior to use.

b. Measles Virus. Strains used shall have been shown to be safe and potent in man by field studies with experimental vaccines. Vaccine prepared from measles virus strains propagated in chick embryo tissue cultures, monkey kidney tissue cultures, or canine renal tissue cultures, shall have been demonstrated as safe and potent in at least 10,000 susceptible persons. (Susceptibility shall be shown by the absence of neutralizing or other antibodies against measles virus, or by other appropriate methods.) Vaccine prepared from measles virus strains propagated in canine renal tissue cultures shall also have been demonstrated to be free from harmful effects in not less than 100,000 persons. Virus in the final vaccine shall represent no more than 10 tissue culture passages beyond the passage used to perform the clinical trials that qualified the vaccine strain for license.

3. *Tissue Cultures for Virus Propagation*

a. Monkey Kidney Tissue. Only cynomolgus or rhesus monkeys or other species of equal suitability, in overt good health, that have reacted negatively to tuberculin within 2 weeks prior to use shall be used as a source of kidney tissue for the production of virus. Each animal shall be examined at necropsy under the supervision of a qualified pathologist for gross signs of disease. If there is any gross pathological lesion of any significance to their use in the manufacture of vaccine, the kidneys shall be discarded. Kidney tissue from monkeys that have been used previously for experimental purposes shall not be used, except that monkeys in overt good health, used for the safety or potency tests with negative clinical findings that have reacted negatively to tuberculin prior to such test, may be used within 2 weeks of the end of the test period. The monkeys shall not at any time have been housed in the same building in which monkeys actually infected with or exposed to poliovirus are housed, and due precautions shall be taken to prevent cross-infection from any infected or potentially infected monkeys on the premises.

Virus for manufacturing vaccine shall be grown with aseptic technique in monkey kidney cell cultures using a synthetic medium. Suitable antibiotics in the minimum concentration required may be used; however, penicillin shall not be used. Phenol red may not exceed a concentration of 0.002%.

b. Chick Embryo Tissue Cultures. Embryonated chicken eggs used as a source of chick embryo tissue for the propagation of measles virus shall be derived from flocks certified to be free of *Salmonella pullorum* and avian tuberculosis, fowl pox, Rous sarcoma, avian leukosis, and other adventitious agents pathogenic for chickens. If eggs are procured from flocks that are not so certified, tests shall be performed to demonstrate that the virus pool be free from such agents prior to inactivation.

c. *Canine Renal Tissue Cultures.* Only dogs in overt good health that have been maintained in quarantine in vermin-proof quarters for a minimum of 6 months, having had no exposure to other dogs or animals throughout the quarantine period, or dogs born to dogs while so quarantined, provided the progeny have been kept in the same type of quarantine continuously from birth, shall be used as a source of kidney tissue for the propagation of measles virus. Dogs that have been used previously for experimental or testing purposes with microbiological agents shall not be used as a source of kidney tissue in the manufacture of vaccine.

Each dog shall be examined periodically during the quarantine period as well as at the time of necropsy under the direction of a qualified pathologist, physician, or veterinarian having experience with diseases of dogs, for the presence of signs or symptoms of ill health, particularly for evidence of tuberculosis, infectious canine hepatitis, canine distemper, rabies, leptospirosis, and other diseases indigenous to dogs. If there are any such signs, symptoms, or other significant pathological lesions observed, the kidneys from such animals shall be discarded.

4. *Clarification*

After harvesting, the virus fluids shall be clarified by centrifugation, by passage through filters of sufficiently small porosity, or by any other method that will assure removal of all intact tissue cells which may have been collected in the harvesting process.

a. *Poliovirus.* After filtration or clarification and before the initiation of inactivation, a sample shall be taken of each monovalent pool for titration of infective poliovirus using tissue culture methods. This titration shall be carried out in 10-fold dilution steps using 10 tubes per dilution, or any other arrangement of tubes and dilutions yielding equal precision.

Each monovalent pool should show a titer of not less than 10^6 $TCID_{50}$/ml using a batch of tissue culture of normal sensitivity compared to a reference standard. The main purpose of determining the titer of virus pools destined for inactivation is to select pools which can be expected to meet potency requirements after inactivation.

b. Adenovirus. The titer of each virus pool after filtration shall be determined by a suitable method. It shall also be demonstrated that each virus pool possesses adenovirus group antigen by the complement-fixation test.

An identity test shall be done on each virus pool using monovalent adenovirus serums free from poliomyelitis antibodies. Such serums shall have been prepared from animals immunized with virus grown in other than the tissue used for the neutralization test. The identity tests shall be done (1) in monkey kidney and (2) in HeLa or other equally susceptible cells. The tissue cultures shall be observed for 7 days. Those showing cytopathogenic effect in the presence of type specific serum shall be subcultured in monkey kidney cells or HeLa cells. The subcultures shall be maintained for 7 days and observed for cytopathogenic effect. Only virus pools free of unidentified cytopathogenic agents and free of all viruses pathogenic to man other than adenoviruses may be used for vaccine manufacture.

c. Measles Virus. The virus content of each single harvest shall be determined by a suitable method which may consist of infectivity titrations and/or the measurement of hemagglutinating activity.

5. *Inactivation*

In general, inactivation shall be initiated as soon as possible and not later than 72 hours after filtration or clarification. The virus shall be inactivated through the use of an agent or method that the manufacturer has demonstrated to be effective in inactivating a series of at least 5 consecutive lots of vaccine. If formaldehyde is used for inactivation, it shall be added to the virus suspension to a final concentration of USP formaldehyde solution of at least 1 : 4000. The inactivation shall be conducted under controlled conditions of pH and time at a temperature of 36°–38°C.

As an indication of inactivation, not less than two samples shall be removed at the time of inactivation, and titrated in an appropriate tissue cell culture for viable virus. Regardless of the concentration of formaldehyde or other inactivating agent used, the total inactivation period shall be not less than three times the period demonstrated by the manufacturer to be necessary to reduce the concentration of live virus to a point where no virus is detectable in a 5.0-ml sample.

6. *Detection of Residual Live Virus*

a. Poliovirus. Two samples of at least 500 ml from each monovalent pool shall be tested, after removal or neutralization of the formaldehyde, by inoculation into tissue cultures for the absence of infective poliovirus. One sample shall be taken at the end of the inactivation period and the other before the end of this period separated by an interval of at least 3 days during inactivation at 36°–38°C. Each sample shall be inoculated into bottles of monkey kidney tissue cultures derived from at least two different monkeys. Not more than 100 ml shall be inoculated into each bottle. The dilution of the vaccine in the nutrient fluid shall not exceed 1 : 4 and the area of the cell sheet shall be at least 3 cm²/ml of vaccine. One or more bottles of each batch of cultures shall be set aside to serve as uninoculated control bottles with the same medium.

The primary tissue culture bottles shall be observed for at least 2 weeks. Not less than two subcultures shall be made from each original bottle, one at the end of the observation period and the other 1 week earlier. The subcultures shall be observed for at least 2 weeks. The inoculum for these subcultures shall be a volume of at least 2% of the original fluid studied.

Cultures can be maintained in good condition for long periods of time by the addition to the medium of serum, albumin preparations, amniotic fluid, etc. Any such additional components of the medium should have first been shown to be free from virus inhibitors and antibodies. Maintenance of the cultures in good condition may require frequent changes of culture medium. However, it should be borne in mind that by early changes of fluid unadsorbed virus might be removed and the validity of the test thus impaired.

If cytopathogenic effects occur in any of the cultures, the decision regarding the further use of the pool shall be deferred until the matter is resolved. If active poliovirus is isolated, the monovalent pool shall not be used unless effectively reprocessed. If viruses other than poliovirus are present, the pool shall not be used unless it can be demonstrated that such viruses have originated from a source other than the monovalent pool being tested.

No less than 1500 ml of the trivalent vaccine pool, without final preservative, prepared by pooling the three type pools, each of which has passed all tests described above, shall be subjected to similar complete tissue culture tests consisting of at least two approximately equal tests in separate monkey kidney tissue culture preparations.

b. Adenovirus. The samples removed during inactivation shall be placed immediately after sampling in contact with sodium bisulfite or a similar formaldehyde-neutralizing substance that will stop the inactivation process. Each sample shall be dialyzed or rendered nontoxic to tissue culture cells by an appropriate method that does not affect the detection of live virus. An amount of fluid representing at least 5 ml of the original virus pool shall be inoculated into monkey kidney or other equally susceptible tissue cultures. The tissue cultures shall be maintained for 7–12 days and examined at intervals. At the end of the above period, the cell sheet shall be removed from each culture vessel, broken up by an appropriate means, suspended in a portion of its culture fluid equal to at least 10% of the volume that was present during incubation, and inoculated into corresponding fresh tissue culture preparations. Any fluids recovered prior to refeeding during original observation period shall be held at 2°–5°C. A volume of each fluid representing at least 10% of the total volume shall be subcultured to fresh tissue culture. All subcultures shall be examined for at least 7 days. This test shall be considered negative only if no cellular degeneration occurs attributable to any virus.

In addition, a sample of at least 500 ml of each single strain pool shall be fully subjected to the following testing procedure in tissue culture cells, with half the sample in monkey kidney cells and half in suitable human cells of demonstrated high susceptibility to adenovirus and poliovirus. The entire sample shall be dialyzed and rendered nontoxic for tissue culture cells. Each half of the samples shall be inoculated into four or more tissue culture bottles of suitable capacity so that direct observation of the culture cells is possible under conditions that assure the growth of adenovirus, poliovirus, or simian viruses should infective particles of any one of these viruses be present in the vaccine. The monkey kidney cell cultures shall be handled as described above for poliovirus except that a third subculture shall be included after 21 days of incubation of the initial culture and that this subculture shall be made by suspending the cell sheet. The initial human cell cultures shall be observed for at least 12 days. A subculture shall be made on each fluid at each refeeding and on the suspension of each cell sheet in the culture fluid removed at the end of the observation period. The inoculum for the subcultures shall be a volume of at least 2% of that of the fluid being studied. The subculture shall be examined frequently, refed as required, and maintained for a period of at least 12 days. If a cytopathogenic effect occurs during the test, the vaccine pool shall be held until the matter is resolved.

If active poliomyelitis virus or adenovirus is indicated, the strain pool shall not be used for inclusion in a final vaccine. If other viruses are present, the pool shall not be used unless it can be demonstrated that such viruses did not originate from the strain pool being tested. No less than 1500 ml of the final vaccine pool without final preservative, prepared by pooling the individual single strain preparations, shall be tested as described above for the trivalent poliovirus vaccine pool.

c. *Measles virus.* A sample representing the equivalent of at least 500 doses of final vaccine of each lot shall be rendered nontoxic for tissue culture cells and tested as follows: One half of the sample shall be tested in the same tissue culture system used for propagating the virus vaccine and one half of the sample shall be tested in primary cercopithecus monkey kidney tissue or another suitable cell line of demonstrated high susceptibility to measles virus, poliovirus, and SV40 or other adventitious viral agents. Each half of the sample shall be inoculated so that direct microscopic observation of the culture cells is possible under conditions that assure the growth of measles virus, poliovirus, and simian viruses which might have survived the inactivation procedure. After inoculation of the test sample, the tissue cultures shall be observed for at least 14 days. At the end of the observation period the fluids from all the culture bottles in a system shall be removed and pooled. At least 2% of each pool shall be subinoculated in the same cell system as that from which the pooled sample was drawn. The subcultures shall be observed for a period of at least 14 days and examined for cell changes indicative of viral growth. The lot of final vaccine is satisfactory for measles virus vaccine only if none of the tissue culture tests show evidence of viable measles virus or any extraneous transmissible agents attributable to the vaccine.

For vaccine produced in chick embryo tissue culture, the equivalent of at least 100 doses of each vaccine lot shall be tested in embryonated eggs by the allantoic cavity route and of 100 doses by the yolk sac-route of inoculation using 0.5 ml of inoculum per egg. The lot of final fluid is satisfactory for measles virus vaccine only if there is no evidence of the presence of extraneous agents in the vaccine.

7. Preservatives

Preservatives or other substances that might be added to or combined with the vaccine shall have been shown to have no deleterious effect on the product.

B. TESTING—ADDITIONAL STANDARDS

1. Tests for Safety

All tests for safety shall be performed on each virus pool prior to inactivation.

a. *Microbial Sterility.* Each virus pool shall be tested for bacteriological sterility in accordance with the procedures prescribed in Section III,B,5. Each virus pool also shall be tested for the presence of *M. tuberculosis*, human and/or avian, by appropriate culture methods.

In addition, each virus pool shall be tested for the presence of PPLO (Mycoplasma). Samples of the virus for this test shall be stored either (1) at 2°–5°C for not longer than 24 hours, or (2) at −20°C or lower if stored for longer than 24 hours. The PPLO test shall be performed both on samples of viral harvests and control fluids as follows: No less than 2.0 ml of a sample shall be inoculated in no less than 0.1-ml amounts evenly distributed over the surface of 20 agar plates. No less than 1.0 ml of sample shall be inoculated into each of four tubes of 10 ml each of broth. Ten agar plates and two tube cultures shall be incubated aerobically at 36°C ± 1°C and the remaining agar plates and tube cultures shall be incubated anaerobically at 36°C ± 1°C in an environment of 5% CO_2 and 95% N_2. The aerobic broth cultures shall be incubated for no less than 3 days and no more than 5 days, at which time 0.5 ml from each of two tubes shall be combined and the 1.0 ml subinoculated to 10 additional agar plates. The anaerobic broth cultures shall be tested in the same manner. All inoculated agar plate cultures shall be incubated for no less than 14 days when observation for PPLO growth shall be made at a magnification of no less than 300 ×.

If the Dienes methylene blue–azure dye or equivalent staining procedure is used, no less than a 1-cm^2 plug of the agar shall be excised from the inoculated area and examined for the presence of PPLO colonies. Control cultures of known strains of PPLO shall be included in the test. Identification of the PPLO shall be made by comparison of the growth obtained from the test sample with the controls with respect to typical colonial and microscopic morphology. The virus pool is satisfactory for vaccine only if none of the tests on the samples of viral harvests show evidence of the presence of the pleuropneumonia-like organism (Mycoplasma).

b. *Tissue Culture—Purity.* (i) *Virus propagation in monkey kidney tissue cultures.* Each individual harvest or virus pool, or a pool of tissue culture fluids from corresponding control vessels, shall be tested for the presence of SV40 either as follows or by a test producing equally reliable results: 5 ml of the virus pool shall be neutralized by high titer antiserum of an origin other than human, chicken, or simian. The sample shall be tested in the same tissue culture system used for propagating the virus vaccine, and in primary cercopithecus tissue cultures or in a cell line of demonstrated equal susceptibility to SV40. The tissue cultures shall be observed for at least 14 days and at the end of the observation period at least one subculture of fluid shall be made in the same tissue culture system and the test continued for an additional 14 days. The virus harvest or virus pool is satisfactory for virus vaccine only if the test produces no evidence of the presence of SV40.

(*ii*) *Virus propagated in chick embryo tissue cultures.* The equivalent of at least 50 doses of final vaccine from each undiluted virus pool, or in proportionate amounts from individual harvests or subpools, shall be tested and found negative for avian leukosis, using either Rubin's procedure for detecting Resistance Inducing Factor (RIF) or a procedure of equivalent effectiveness. These tests may be performed on corresponding amounts of fluids from control vessels instead of on the undiluted virus pool or individual harvests of subpools.

In addition, similar volumes of each virus pool shall be tested for avian adenovirus by inoculation of chicken-liver cell cultures and for Rous virus by inoculation of the chorioallantois membrane of embryonated hens eggs known to be sensitive to Rous virus. The virus pool passes the test if there is no evidence of the presence of avian leukosis viruses, avian adenovirus, or Rous virus.

(*iii*) *Virus propagated in canine renal tissue cultures.* (a) Inoculation of monkey tissue and other cell cultures. A volume of each virus pool, equivalent to at least 500 human doses or 50 ml, whichever represents a greater volume, shall be tested for adventitious agents in cercopithecus, rhesus, or cynomolgus monkey kidney, chick embryo, and human tissue culture preparations, after neutralization of the virus by a high titer antiserum of nonhuman, nonsimian, and nonchicken origin. The immunizing antigen used for the preparation of the antiserum shall be grown in tissue culture cells that shall be free of extraneous viruses which might elicit antibodies which could inhibit growth of extraneous viruses present in the virus pool. The tissue cultures of the virus pool shall be observed for no less than 14 days. The virus pool is satisfactory for virus vaccine only if all the tissue culture tests fail to show evidence of any extraneous transmissible agent other than virus attributable to the vaccine.

(b) Inoculation of embryonated chicken eggs. A volume of virus suspension of each undiluted virus pool, equivalent to at least 100 doses or 10 ml, whichever represents a greater volume, after neutralization of the virus shall be tested in embryonated eggs by the allantoic cavity route of inoculation and a separate group tested by the yolk sac-route of inoculation, using 0.5 ml of inoculum per egg. The virus pool is satisfactory if there is no evidence of adventitious agents.

(c) Tests for infectious agents of dogs. Each virus pool shall be tested for the presence of such adventitious agents as canine distemper virus, canine hepatitis virus, leptospira, and toxoplasma and the following fungi: coccidiomyces, histoplasma, and blastomyces. The virus pool is satisfactory only if the results of all tests show no evidence of any extraneous agent attributable to the canine renal tissue or the vaccine.

c. Animal Purity. (i) Inoculation of guinea pigs—test for M. tuberculosis. Each of at least five guinea pigs, each weighing 350–450 gm, shall be inoculated intracerebrally with 0.1 ml and intraperitoneally with 5.0 ml of the virus pool to be tested. The animals shall be observed for at least 42 days and daily rectal temperatures recorded for the last 3 weeks of the test. Each animal that dies after the first 24 hours of the test, or is sacrificed because of illness, shall be necropsied. The tissues shall be examined both microscopically and culturally for evidence of tubercle bacilli, and by passage of tissue suspensions into at least three other guinea pigs by the intracerebral and intraperitoneal routes of inoculation for evidence of viral infection. If clinical symptoms suggest infection with lymphocytic choriomeningitis virus, serological tests shall be performed on blood samples of the test guinea pigs to confirm the clinical observations. Animals that die or are sacrificed during the first 3 weeks after inoculation with poliovirus shall be examined for infection with lymphocytic choriomeningitis virus. Animals that die in the final 3 weeks shall be examined both microscopically and culturally for M. tuberculosis. The virus pool is satisfactory for vaccine only if at least 80% of all animals remain healthy and survive the observation period and if all the animals used in the test fail to show evidence of infection with M. tuberculosis, or any viral infection.

(ii) Inoculation of rabbits—test for B virus and other adventitious agents. A minimum of 100 ml of each virus pool shall be tested by inoculation into at least 10 healthy rabbits, each weighing 1500–2500 gm. Each rabbit shall be injected intradermally at multiple sites with a total of 1.0 ml and subcutaneously with 9.0 ml of the virus, and the animals observed for at least 3 weeks. Each rabbit that dies after the first 24 hours of the test or is sacrificed because of illness shall be necropsied and the brain and organs removed and examined. The virus pool may be used for vaccine only if at least 80% of the rabbits remain healthy and survive the entire period and if none of the rabbits used in the test shows lesions of any kind at the sites of inoculation or shows evidence of B virus or any other transmissible agent attributable to the vaccine.

(iii) *Inoculation of adult mice—test for adventitious agents.* Each virus pool shall be shown to be free of contaminating agents pathogenic for mice by the intracerebral inoculation of 0.03 ml and intraperitoneal inoculation of 0.5-ml amounts of the pool into each of 10 or more adult mice (15–20 gm). The mice shall be observed for at least 21 days. All mice that die after the first 24 hours of the test or that show signs of illness shall be autopsied and examined for evidence of viral infection, both macroscopically by direct observation and by subinoculation of appropriate tissue suspension by the intracerebral and intraperitoneal routes into at least five additional mice which shall be observed for 21 days. The virus pool is satisfactory for vaccine only if at least 80% of the inoculated animals survive the observation period and none of the animals inoculated shows evidence of infection with extraneous transmissible agents attributable to the vaccine.

(iv) *Inoculation of suckling mice.* Each of at least 20 suckling mice less than 24 hours old shall be inoculated intracerebrally with 0.01 ml and intraperitoneally with 0.1 ml of the virus pool to be tested. The mice shall be observed daily for at least 14 days. Each mouse that dies after the first 24 hours of the test, or is sacrificed because of illness, shall be necropsied and examined for evidence of viral infection. Such examination shall include subinoculation of appropriate tissue suspensions into an additional group of at least five suckling mice by intracerebral and intraperitoneal routes and observed daily for 14 days. In addition, a blind passage shall be made of a single pool of the emulsified tissue (minus skin and viscera) of all mice surviving the original 14-day test. The virus pool is satisfactory only if at least 80% of the original inoculated mice remain healthy and survive the entire observation period, and if none of the mice used in the test show evidence of a transmissible agent or viral infection, other than virus, attributable to the vaccine.

2. Potency

a. Poliovirus Vaccine. Each final vaccine shall be tested for immunizing potency by a test approved by the national control authority. Such a test shall be done in suitable animals (monkeys, guinea pigs, or chicks) by a method that measures either the titer of antibody response or the limit of dilution at which the vaccine fails to give a response in 50% of the animals. The preparation under test shall meet the potency requirements of the national control authority.

b. Adenovirus Vaccine. Each lot of vaccine shall be subjected to a potency test that permits an estimation of the antigenic capacity of the vaccine in comparison with a reference vaccine. This shall be done using at least six animals for each dilution of each vaccine tested and measuring the neutralizing antibody response of the animals receiving test vaccine and others receiving reference vaccine in simultaneous tests. The average antibody level for each type shall equal or exceed the corresponding value of the reference vaccine.

c. Measles Virus Vaccine. A potency test shall be performed on each lot of vaccine by determining the antigenic capacity of the vaccine under tests in comparison with a reference vaccine of antigenic capacity at least equal to that required for the clinical trials specified in Section IV,A,2,b. The test shall be performed using at least 10 animals for each dilution of the test vaccine and of the reference vaccine. The average antibody levels of the animals injected with the vaccine under test shall equal or exceed the average antibody levels of the animals injected with the reference vaccine.

C. GENERAL REQUIREMENTS

1. Final Container Tests

a. Final Vaccine Test for Active Virus in Monkeys. (i) *Poliovirus vaccines.* A test shall be made in Macaca or equally susceptible monkeys for the absence of infective poliovirus in vaccine from the final containers, if this test has not been performed on the trivalent bulk product. A total of not less than 20 monkeys in overt good health shall be used. A preinjection serum sample from each animal must contain no neutralizing antibody against any of the three poliovirus types in a dilution of 1 : 4 when tested against not more than 500 $TCID_{50}$ of virus.

Vaccine shall be injected, under deep anesthesia, by combined intracerebral, intraspinal, and intramuscular routes into monkeys. The intracerebral injection shall consist of 0.5 ml into the thalamic region of each hemisphere. The intraspinal injection shall consist of 0.5 ml of vaccine, or of vaccine suitably concentrated, into the lumbar spinal cord enlargement and may be divided between more than one site. The intramuscular injection shall consist of 1.0 ml into the right leg.

At the time of inoculation of vaccine, an intramuscular injection of 200 mg of cortisone acetate shall be given, as well as an intramuscular injection of 300,000 IU of procaine penicillin. The cortisone acetate may be given in divided doses over a period of several days, starting 2 days before the inoculation of vaccine. The monkeys shall be observed for 17–19 days and symptoms suggesting poliomyelitis shall be recorded. Provided that at least 60% of the animals survive the first 48 hours after injection, those animals that do not survive this 48-hour period may be replaced by an equal number of test animals. If less than 60% of the original test animals survive the first 48 hours, or if the number of animals that survive the entire test period without significant weight loss is less than 80% of the initial number, the test must be repeated.

At the end of the observation period, samples of nervous tissue shall be taken for virus recovery and identification. Histological sections from both spinal cord enlargements shall be examined. Doubtful histopathological findings necessitate (a) examination of samples of sections from several regions of the brain and spinal cord, and (b) attempts at virus recovery from the nervous tissues previously removed from the animal. Evidence of intraspinal and intrathalamic trauma arising from injection must be observed in at least 80% of the animals. The final lot passes the test if the histological and other studies show no evidence of poliomyelitis infection.

(ii) *Adenovirus vaccines.* Final bulk vaccine shall be tested in monkeys as prescribed above except that the test may be applied to vaccine before it is placed in final containers, and the sample may be dialyzed in order to remove sodium bisulfite or the sodium bisulfite–formaldehyde complex before injection intraspinally and intracerebrally into monkeys. In no case, however, shall dialyzed vaccine be used for the intramuscular injection of the monkeys. The test is considered negative if the histological and other studies leave no doubt that virus infections attributable to the vaccine did not occur.

(iii) *Measles virus vaccines.* Each lot of vaccine shall be tested for neurotropic agents following the procedure prescribed above except that antibody determinations for measles need not be performed. The test shall be performed before the product is placed in final containers and prior to the addition of an adjuvant, and that symptoms suggestive of all neurotropic agents shall be recorded during the observation period of 17–19 days. The lot is satisfactory only if the histological and other studies produce no clinical or histological evidence of central nervous system involvement attributable to the presence of a neurotropic agent in the vaccine.

b. *Tests for Safety, Sterility, and Identity.* Tests shall be made on final containers for safety, sterility, and identity in accordance with the general standards set forth in Section III,B,4,5 and 6b, respectively. In addition, no lot of final vaccine shall be released unless it is one of a series of five consecutive lots produced by the same manufacturing process, all of which have shown negative results with respect to all tests for the presence of live poliovirus, and unless each of the monovalent pools of which a polyvalent final vaccine is composed similarly is one of a series of five consecutive monovalent pools of the same type of inactivated poliovirus, all of which have shown negative results in all tests for the presence of live poliovirus.

2. Extraneous Protein

Extraneous protein capable of producing allergenic effects on injection into human subjects shall not be added to the final virus medium. If serum is used at any stage, its calculated concentration in the final medium shall not exceed 1 : 1,000,000. The final vaccine shall have a protein nitrogen content of less than 0.02 mg/individual human dose.

3. Dosage and Labeling

a. *Dose.* These standards are based on an individual human dose of 1.0 ml for a single injection.

b. *Labeling.* Labeling shall be in compliance with the requirements set forth in Section III,B,1. In addition, the label or package enclosure shall include an appropriate statement indicating the type and amount of each antibiotic added, if any. The preservative used shall be stated on the label, as well as allergenic substances added, if any, and the source, composition, and method of inactivation of the viruses.

4. Adjuvants in the Final Vaccine

An adjuvant shall not be introduced into the product unless there is satisfactory evidence that it does not adversely affect the safety or potency of the vaccine. In no event shall an individual human injection contain more aluminum than that contained in 15 mg by assay, or 20 mg by calculation, of $AlK(SO_4) \cdot 12H_2O$. Aluminum in another form may be used, provided the amount of aluminum does not exceed the amount permitted as $AlK(SO_4) \cdot 12H_2O$.

5. *Requirements for Samples and Reports*

From each lot of vaccine the following samples shall be taken.

1. A large sample (1500–2500 ml) of bulk vaccine taken at the latest possible stage of manufacture, but before final preservatives, adjuvants, or other substances are added. The formaldehyde may be neutralized at the time of sampling by the addition of bisulfite.

2. A sample of 100–200 ml of final vaccine containing preservatives.

3. A sample of 200 ml of final vaccine in final labeled containers.

Together with the above samples shall be protocols showing the history of the lot and the results of all of the tests prescribed in these additional standards and carried out by the manufacturer.

D. EQUIVALENT METHODS

Modification of any particular method or process or the conditions under which it is conducted as set forth in the additional standards relating to the inactivated virus vaccines shall be permitted whenever the manufacturer presents evidence to demonstrate that such modification will provide equal or greater assurance of the safety, purity, and potency of the vaccine as the assurances provided by such standards, and the national authority so finds and makes such findings a matter of official record.

V. Live Virus Vaccine Production—Licensed Biologicals

The standards to be discussed relating to the manufacture of live virus vaccine (poliovirus and measles) have been extracted from the United States Public Health Service Regulations, Title 42, Part 73, Sections 73.110–118 and 73.140–146 as well as from the WHO Technical Report Series No. 323, Annex 3, pp. 37–55 (1966c) and No. 329, Annex 2, pp. 58–73 (1966). The requirements in the latter instances are in the form of recommendations that may constitute the basis for definitive national requirements. For more detailed information refer to the specific regulations or requirements mentioned above.

A. PRODUCTION—ADDITIONAL STANDARDS

1. *The Product*

a. *Live Oral Poliovirus Vaccine.* This vaccine shall be a preparation of one or more live attenuated polioviruses grown in monkey kidney cell cultures and prepared in a form suitable for oral administration.

b. *Live Attenuated Measles Virus Vaccine.* This vaccine shall be a preparation of a live attenuated measles virus grown in various types of primary tissue culture.

2. Virus Strains and Seed Virus

a. *Polioviruses.* Strains of attenuated poliovirus types 1, 2 and 3 used in the manufacture of the vaccine shall be identified by: (1) Historical records including origin and techniques of attenuation, (2) antigenic properties, (3) neurovirulence for monkeys, (4) pathogenicity for other animals and tissue cultures of various cell types, and (5) established virus markers including rct/40, d, MS. In addition, it must be established that each such strain is free of harmful effect upon administration in the recommended dosage to at least 100,000 people susceptible to poliomyelitis, under circumstances in which adequate epidemiological surveillance of neurological illness has been maintained and that each such strain produces a vaccine meeting the safety and potency requirements to be described below. Susceptibility shall be demonstrated by blood tests, stool examinations, and other appropriate methods. Each seed virus used for vaccine manufacture shall be free of all demonstrable extraneous viable microbial agents and shall be assayed for its neurovirulence in Macaca monkeys.

b. *Measles Virus.* Strains of attenuated measles virus used in the manufacture of vaccine shall be identified by (1) historical records including origin and manipulation during attenuation, (2) antigenic specificity as measles virus as demonstrated by tissue culture neutralization tests. In addition, they shall have been shown to be safe and potent in man by field studies with experimental vaccines.

Each seed virus used in manufacture shall be demonstrated to be free of extraneous microbial agents. The seed strain shall be shown to be lacking in neurotropic properties as determined by neurovirulence tests in susceptible monkeys.

3. Animal Conditioning, Personnel, and Facilities

a. *Poliovirus Vaccine.* (i) Monkeys of a suitable species, in good health, that have reacted negatively to tuberculin at the start of the prescribed quarantine period, shall be used as the source of kidney tissue for the production of seed virus and the manufacture of poliovirus vaccine. Monkeys that have been used previously for experimental purposes shall not be used.

Monkeys shall be maintained in quarantine for at least 6 weeks prior to use in cages closed on all sides with solid materials except the front, which shall be screened. Not more than two monkeys shall be housed in one cage and cage mates shall not be interchanged.

Each animal at necropsy shall be examined under the direction of a qualified pathologist, physician, or veterinarian having experience with diseases of monkeys, for the presence of signs or symptoms of ill health, particularly for (a) evidence of tuberculosis, (b) presence of herpeslike lesions, including eruptions or plaques on or around the lips, in the buccal cavity, or on the gums, and (c) signs of conjunctivitis. If there are any such signs or other significant gross pathological lesions, the kidneys shall not be used in the manufacture of vaccine.

(*ii*) Steps shall be taken to ensure that all persons in the production areas and monkey quarters are immune against poliomyelitis and do not excrete poliovirus or other microorganisms of significance to the safety of the vaccine.

(*iii*) The space set aside for work with the live poliovirus vaccine shall not be used for any other purpose during the vaccine processing period. All areas used for live poliovirus vaccine processing shall be decontaminated prior to the initiation of such processing. Test procedures that potentially involve the presence of microorganisms including viruses other than the vaccine strains, or the use of tissue culture cell lines other than primary cultures, shall not be conducted in live poliovirus vaccine manufacturing areas.

b. Measles Virus Vaccine. (*i*) For regulations concerning the use of embryonated chicken eggs as a source of chick embryo tissue and the care and handling of dogs to be used as a source of canine renal tissue refer to Section IV,A,3,b and c.

(*ii*) If guinea pig tissue is used for the propagation of measles virus, only guinea pigs of a strain approved by the national control authority shall be used as a source of tissue. The animal stock shall be free from infection with mycoplasma, tuberculosis, lymphocytic choriomeningitis virus, reovirus, cytomegalovirus, and microorganisms pathogenic for guinea pigs. The animals parent to those used as a source of tissue shall be maintained in quarantine in vermin-proof quarters for a minimum of 3 months. Their progeny shall be used for the preparation of tissue cultures within 1 week of birth. Neither the animal stock nor their progeny shall have been used for experimental purposes with microbiological agents.

(*iii*) Only calves that are in overt good health and have been maintained in quarantine in vermin-proof quarters for a minimum of 3 months shall be used as a source of kidney tissue for the propagation of measles virus. Animals previously used for experimental or testing purposes with infectious agents shall not be used. Each calf shall be examined periodically during the quarantine period and at the time of necropsy by a pathologist, physician, or veterinarian having experience with diseases of cattle for signs of disease indigenous to cattle.

(iv) All personnel in production areas and animal quarters shall be immune against measles virus and steps shall be taken to ensure that they do not excrete measles virus or other microorganisms of significance to the safety of the vaccine.

(v) The facilities used for measles virus production shall be separate and independent of all other manufacturing processes.

4. Virus Propagation

a. Poliovirus Vaccine. Virus seed for the preparation of vaccine shall be not more than four tissue culture passages from the original strain and shall be grown with aseptic technique in primary monkey kidney cell cultures using a synthetic medium. Suitable antibiotics, other than penicillin, may be used in the minimum concentration required. Phenol red may not exceed a concentration of 0.002%.

Prior to inoculation with the seed virus, the tissue culture growth in vessels representing each pair of kidneys shall be examined microscopically for evidence of cell degeneration at least 3 days after complete formation of the tissue sheet. If such evidence is observed, the tissue from that pair of kidneys shall not be used for poliovirus vaccine manufacture. To test the tissue found free of cell degeneration for further evidence of freedom from demonstrable viable microbial agents, the fluid shall be removed from the cell cultures immediately prior to virus inoculation and tested in each of four culture systems; (1) Macaca monkey kidney cells, (2) cercopithecus monkey kidney cells, (3) primary rabbit kidney cells, and (4) human cells in the following manner: Aliquots of fluid from each vessel shall be pooled and at least 10 ml of the pool inoculated into each system, with ratios of inoculum to medium being 1 : 1 to 1 : 3 and with the area of surface growth of cells at least 3 cm^2/ml of test inoculum. The cultures shall be observed for at least 14 days. If these tests indicate the presence in the tissue culture preparation of any viable microbial agent the tissue cultures so implicated shall not be used for poliovirus vaccine manufacture.

Before inoculation with seed virus, sufficient tissue culture vessels to represent at least 25% of the cell suspension from each pair of kidneys shall be set aside as controls. The control vessels shall be examined microscopically for cell degeneration for an additional 14 days. The cell fluids from such control vessels shall be tested, both at the time of virus harvest and at the end of the additional observation period, by the same method prescribed for testing of fluids in the preceding paragraph.

In addition the cell sheet in each control vessel shall be examined for presence of hemadsorption viruses by the addition of guinea pig red blood cells.

At least 80% of the control vessels shall successfully complete the additional 14-day observation period without microscopic evidence of cell degeneration of the tissue sheets. If less than 80% of the control vessels fail to complete satisfactorily the observation period, no tissue from the kidneys implicated shall be used for poliovirus vaccine manufacture. If the test results of the control vessels indicate the presence of any extraneous agent at the time of virus harvest, the entire virus harvest from that tissue culture preparation shall not be used for poliovirus vaccine manufacture. If any of the tests or observations described above demonstrate the presence in the tissue culture preparation of any microbial agent known to be capable of producing human disease, the virus grown in such tissue culture preparation shall not be used for poliovirus vaccine manufacture. After virus inoculation, production vessels shall be maintained at a temperature not to exceed 35.0°C during the course of virus propagation.

b. Measles Virus Vaccine. Virus in the final vaccine shall represent no more than 10 tissue culture passages beyond the passage used to perform the clinical trials that qualified the manufacturer's vaccine strain for license. The primary tissue cultures for vaccine production shall be grown under aseptic conditions using synthetic medium containing minimum concentrations of suitable antibiotics other than penicillin.

From the tissue used for the preparation of tissue cultures for growing attenuated measles virus, an amount of processed cell suspension equivalent to that used to prepare 500 ml of tissue culture shall be used to prepare uninfected tissue control materials. This material shall be distributed in control vessels and observed microscopically for a period of no less than 14 days beyond the time of inoculation of the production vessels with measles virus; but if the production vessels are held for use in vaccine manufacture for more than 14 days, the control vessels shall be held and observed for the additional period. At the end of the observation period or at the time of virus harvest, whichever is later, fluids from the control cultures shall be tested for the presence of adventitious agents as follows.

Samples of fluid from each control vessel shall be collected at the same time as fluid is harvested from the corresponding vessels. If multiple virus harvests are made from the same cell suspension, the control samples for each harvest shall be frozen and stored at −60°C until the last viral harvest for that cell suspension is completed. The fluid from all the control samples from that suspension shall be pooled in proportionate amounts and at least 5 ml inoculated into human and simian cell tissue culture systems and in the tissue culture system used for virus production. The cultures shall be observed for the presence of changes attributable to growth of adventitious viral agents including hemadsorption viral agents.

The cell sheets of one quarter to one third of the control vessels shall be examined at the end of the observation period (14 days or longer) for the presence of hemadsorption viruses by the addition of guinea pig red blood cells. If the chick embryo cultures were not derived from a certified source, the remaining tissue culture controls may be used to test for avian leukosis virus using either Rubin's procedure for detecting Resistance Inducing Factor (RIF) or a method of equivalent effectiveness. The test is satisfactory only if there is no evidence of adventitious viral agents and if at least 80% of the control vessels are available for observation at the end of the observation period (14 days or longer).

5. Clarification

After harvesting and removal of samples for safety testing to be described below, the pool, in the case of poliovirus, shall be passed through sterile filters with sufficiently small porosity to assure bacteriologically sterile filtrates. The measles virus pools, on the other hand may be clarified by centrifugation, by passage through filters of sufficiently small porosity, or by any other method that will assure removal of all intact tissue cells which may have been collected in the harvesting process.

B. TESTING—ADDITIONAL STANDARDS

1. Tests for Safety Prior to Filtration or Clarification

a. *Microbial Sterility.* Each virus pool shall be tested for bacteriological sterility in accordance with the procedures prescribed in Section III,B,5. The presence of *M. tuberculosis,* human and/or avian, shall be tested for by appropriate culture methods. Furthermore, each virus pool shall be tested for the presence of PPLO (Mycoplasma) as prescribed in Section IV,B,1,a.

b. *Tissue Culture Purity.* (i) *Poliovirus vaccines.* Wherever indicated, the virus pool shall be neutralized by type specific high titered antiserum of nonsimian derivation. The immunizing antigens used for the preparation of antisera shall be grown in a human tissue culture

cell line. The material shall be tested in a ratio of inoculum to medium of 1 : 1–1 : 3, and with the area of surface growth of cells at
least 3 cm²/ml of test inoculum. Cultures shall be observed for no less
than 14 days.

(a) Inoculation of monkey kidney tissue cultures. At least 500 doses
or 50 ml, whichever represents a greater volume of virus, of each undiluted monovalent virus pool or in equal proportions from individual
harvests or subpools after neutralization, shall be tested for simian viruses in Macaca, and the same volume in cercopithecus, monkey kidney
tissue culture preparations. The monovalent virus pool is satisfactory
for poliovirus vaccine only if all the tissue cultures fail to show evidence of the presence of simian viruses.

(b) Inoculation of human cell cultures. At least 500 doses or 50 ml,
whichever represents a greater volume of virus, taken from either a
single monovalent pool or in equal proportions from individual harvests
or subpools, shall be tested after neutralization for the presence of
measles virus in either (1) primary human amnion cells, (2) primary
human kidney cells, or (3) any other cell system of comparable susceptibility to unmodified measles virus. The monovalent virus pool is
satisfactory for poliovirus vaccine only if all tissue cultures fail to show
evidence of the presence of measles virus.

(c) Inoculation of rabbit kidney tissue cultures. At least 500 ml of
virus pool taken from either a single monovalent pool or in equal proportions from individual harvests or subpools, shall be tested in primary
rabbit kidney tissue culture preparations for evidence of B virus. The
monovalent virus pool is satisfactory for poliovirus vaccine only if all
tissue cultures fail to show evidence of the presence of B virus.

(ii) Measles virus vaccines. Vaccine manufactured in chick embryo
tissue cultures or canine renal tissue cultures shall be tested for adventitious agents in cercopithecus monkey kidney tissue cultures,
rhesus or cynomolgus monkey kidney, chick embryo, canine renal, and
human tissue cell cultures as prescribed in Section III,B,1,b,iii. The
virus pools also shall be tested by the inoculation of embryonated
chicken eggs as prescribed in the same section.

c. Animal Purity. The tests for safety and purity in animals are
similar to those prescribed in Section IV,B,1,c, except that the number
of adult mice shall be increased to at least 20 animals and the observation of the suckling mice shall be extended to 28 days both for
the original inoculation and the subinoculation (blind passage unnecessary).

d. Additional Tests. (i) Test for avian leukosis (chick embryo tissue *vaccine*). If the cultures were not derived from a certified source and the control fluids were not tested for avian leukosis, at least 500 doses or 50 ml, whichever represents a greater volume of each undiluted vaccine pool, shall be tested and found negative for avian leukosis, using either Rubin's procedure for detecting Resistance Inducing Factor (RIF) or another method of equivalent effectiveness.

(*ii*) *Tests for adventitious agents (canine renal tissue vaccine).* Each virus pool shall be tested for the presence of such adventitious agents as canine distemper virus, canine hepatitis virus, leptospira, and toxoplasma and the following fungi: coccidiomyces, histoplasma, and blastomyces. The virus pool is satisfactory only if the results show no evidence of any extraneous agents attributable to the canine renal tissue or the vaccine.

(*iii*) *Guinea pig tissue vaccine.* Each virus pool shall be tested for the presence of adventitious agents known to be indigenous to guinea pigs, such as leptospira, toxoplasma, and various viruses. The virus pool is satisfactory only if there is no evidence of the presence of any extraneous agents attributable to the tissue culture or vaccine.

(*iv*) *Bovine kidney tissue vaccine.* Each virus pool shall be tested for the presence of adventitious agents known to be indigenous to cattle, such as leptospira, toxoplasma, and the viruses of foot-and-mouth disease, Q fever, and rinderpest. The virus pool is satisfactory only if there is no evidence of the presence of any extraneous agents attributable to the tissue culture or vaccine.

2. *Tests for Safety Post Filtration or Clarification*

a. *Microbial Sterility.* Tests are the same as described previously in Section V,B,1,a.

b. *Neurovirulence in Monkeys.* (*i*) *Measles virus vaccines.* Before final dilution for standardization, these vaccines shall be tested for neurotropic agents following the procedure prescribed in Section IV,C, 1,a,iii.

(*ii*) *Poliovirus vaccines.* Each monovalent virus pool or monovalent lot shall be tested in comparison with the reference attenuated poliovirus for neurovirulence in Macaca monkeys by both the intrathalamic and intraspinal routes of injection. A preinjection serum sample obtained from each monkey must be shown to contain no neutralizing antibody in a dilution of 1 : 4 when tested against no more than 1000 $TCID_{50}$ of each of the three types of poliovirus. The neurovirulence tests are not valid unless the sample contains at least $10^{7.0}$ $TCID_{50}/ml$ when titrated in comparison with the reference poliovirus (live attenuated) of the appropriate type. All monkeys shall be observed for 17–21 days, under the supervision of a qualified pathologist, physician, or veterinarian, and any evidence of physical abnormalities indicative of poliomyelitis or other viral infections shall be recorded.

(a) Intrathalamic inoculation. Each of at least 10 Macaca monkeys shall be injected intrathalamically with 1.0 ml of virus pool material containing at least $10^{7.0}$ $TCID_{50}$/ml and each of at least 10 additional Macaca monkeys shall be injected intrathalamically with 1.0 ml of a 10^{-1} dilution thereof. Comparative evaluations shall be made with the virus pool under test and the reference material. Only monkeys that show evidence of inoculation into the thalamus shall be considered as having been injected satisfactorily.

(b) Intraspinal inoculation. Each of a group of at least five Macaca monkeys shall be injected intraspinally with 0.2 ml of virus pool material containing at least $10^{7.0}$ $TCID_{50}$/ml and each monkey in four additional groups of at least five Macaca monkeys shall be injected intraspinally with 0.2 ml of 10^{-1}, 10^{-2}, 10^{-3}, and 10^{-4} dilutions thereof, respectively. Comparative evaluations shall be made with the virus pool under test and the reference material. Only monkeys that show microscopic evidence of inoculation into the gray matter of the lumbar cord shall be considered to have been injected satisfactorily.

(c) Determination of neurovirulence. At the conclusion of the observation period comparative histopathological examinations shall be made of the lumbar cord, cervical cord, lower medulla, upper medulla, and mesencephalon of each monkey in the groups injected with virus under test and those injected with the reference attenuated poliovirus, except that for animals dying during the test period, these examinations shall be made immediately after death. The animals shall be examined to ascertain whether the distribution and histological nature of the lesions are characteristic of poliovirus infection. A comparative evaluation shall be made of the evidence of neurovirulence of the virus under test and the reference attenuated poliovirus with respect to (1) the number of animals showing lesions characteristic of poliovirus infection, (2) the number of animals showing lesions other than those characteristic of poliovirus infection, (3) the severity of the lesions, (4) the degree of dissemination of the lesions, and (5) the rate of occurrence of paralysis not attributable to the mechanical injury resulting from inoculation trauma. The virus pool under test is satisfactory for poliovirus vaccine manufacture only if at least 80% of the animals in each group survive the observation period and if a comparative analysis of the test results demonstrate that the neurovirulence of the test virus pool does not exceed that of the reference attenuated poliovirus.

c. *Virus Titer.* The determination of the amount of infective virus per milliliter of filtered or clarified bulk suspension shall be made in cell cultures. This determination shall be made in terms of pfu per milliliter and/or in terms of $TCID_{50}$ per milliliter, in parallel with the determination of the virus concentration of a known reference preparation of the same measles or poliovirus type. The determination of the number of pfu per milliliter shall be based on a total count of at least 100 clearly defined plaques on at least five different cell sheets. The determination of the number of $TCID_{50}$ per milliliter shall be based on the use of 10-fold dilution steps with 10 tubes/dilution, or on any other arrangement of dilutions and tubes yielding equal precision.

d. *Tests for in Vitro Markers.* A test shall be performed on each monovalent poliovirus pool or each monovalent lot resulting therefrom, using the rct/40 marker and at least one of the other marker methods described below. The test results shall demonstrate that the virus under test and the seed virus have substantially the same marker characteristics.

(*i*) *rct/40 Marker.* Attenuated strains that grow readily at 40°C (± 0.5°C) are classified as rct/40 positive (+) in contrast to the rct/40 negative (−) strains that show an increased growth of at least 100,000-fold at 36°C over that obtained at 40°C. Comparative determinations shall be made in either tube or bottle cultures.

(*ii*) *d Marker.* Attenuated strains that grow readily at low concentrations of bicarbonate under agar are classified as d positive (+) in contrast to the d negative (−) strains which exhibit delayed growth under the same conditions. The cultures shall be grown in a 36°C incubator either in stoppered bottles or in plates in an environment of 5% CO_2 in air.

(*iii*) *MS Markers.* Attenuated strains that grow more readily on monkey stable (MS) cells are classified as MS positive (+) in contrast to the MS negative (−) strains. Comparative determinations shall be made in either tube cultures or in bottle cultures under agar.

3. *Potency*

a. *Poliovirus Vaccines.* The concentration of live virus expressed as $TCID_{50}$ of each type in the vaccine shall constitute the measure of its potency. The accuracy of the titration to determine the concentration of live virus in the lot under test shall be confirmed by performing a titration with the reference poliovirus (live attenuated) of the appropriate type as a check on titration technique. The concentration of each type of live virus contained in the vaccine of the lot under test shall be between 200,000 and 500,000 $TCID_{50}$ per human dose.

b. *Measles Virus Vaccines.* The concentration of live measles virus shall constitute the measure of potency. The titration shall be performed in a suitable cell culture system, free of wild viruses, using either the reference measles virus (live attenuated) or a calibrated equivalent strain as a titration control. The concentration of live measles virus contained in the vaccine of each lot under test shall be no less than the equivalent of 1000 $TCID_{50}$ of the reference per human dose.

C. General Requirements

1. *Final Container Tests*

Tests shall be made on final containers for safety, sterility, and identity in accordance with the general standards set forth in Section III,B,4,5 and 6b, respectively.

2. *Production Consistency*

No lot of poliovirus vaccine shall be released unless each monovalent pool contained therein is one of a series of five consecutive pools of the same type, each pool having been manufactured by the same procedures, and each having met the criteria of neurovirulence for monkeys prescribed in Section V,B,2,b, and of *in vitro* markers prescribed in Section V,B,2,d.

3. *Extraneous Protein*

Extraneous protein, capable of producing allergenic effects on injection into human subjects, shall not be added to the vaccine at any time. If animal serum is used at any manufacturing stage, its calculated concentration in the final medium shall not exceed 1 : 1,000,000.

4. *Dried Vaccine*

Measles vaccine (live attenuated) may be dried immediately after completion of processing to final bulk material and stored in the dried state, provided its residual moisture and other volatile substances content is not in excess of 2%.

5. Dosage and Labeling

a. Dose. The individual human dose of poliovirus vaccine shall contain from 200,000 to 500,000 $TCID_{50}$ of each type of virus that is in the final product. The individual human dose of measles virus vaccine shall contain no less than 1000 $TCID_{50}$ of the live, attenuated virus in the final product.

b. Labeling. Labeling shall comply with the requirements set forth in Section III,B,1. In addition the label or a package enclosure shall include the identification and source of the virus or viruses contained in the vaccine, the tissue medium on which the virus or viruses were propagated, stabilizers and preservatives if any, and the type and calculated maximum amount of antibiotics. For poliovirus vaccines the information also shall include the fact that the vaccine is for oral administration only and that the liquid vaccine shall not be used for more than 7 days after opening the container. For measles virus vaccines, the information also shall include a statement concerning the photosensitivity of the vaccine, cautioning that both lyophilized and reconstituted vaccine should be protected from light; the volume and nature of diluent to be added for reconstitution; and a statement to the effect that reconstituted vaccine should be stored between 0° and 10°C for a period not exceeding eight hours.

6. Requirements for Samples and Protocols

From each lot of vaccine the following samples shall be taken.

1. A 500–1000-ml bulk sample of each final vaccine pool prior to the addition of any preservative, stabilizer, or adjuvant, in the frozen state (−60°C) and prior to filling into final containers.

2. A total of no less than 200 ml or 200 recommended human doses of the vaccine in final labeled containers.

Together with the above samples shall be protocols relating to the history of manufacture of each lot of vaccine and the results of all tests prescribed in these additional standards as performed by the manufacturer.

D. CLINICAL TRIALS TO QUALIFY FOR LICENSE

1. Poliovirus Vaccines

To qualify for license, the antigenicity of the vaccine shall have been determined by clinical trials of adequate statistical design by oral administration of the product. Such clinical trials shall be conducted with five consecutive lots of poliovirus vaccine that have been manufactured by the same methods, each of which has shown satisfactory results in all prescribed tests. Type-specific neutralizing antibody (from less than 1 : 4 before vaccine treatment, to 1 : 16 or greater after treatment) shall be induced in 80% or more of susceptibles when administered orally as a single dose or in excess of 90% of susceptibles when administered orally after a series of doses. A separate clinical trial shall have been conducted for each monovalent and each polyvalent vaccine for which license application is made.

2. Measles Virus Vaccines

To qualify for license, the antigenicity of the vaccine shall have been determined by clinical trials of adequate statistical design, by subcutaneous administration of the product. Such clinical trials shall be conducted with five consecutive lots of measles virus vaccine that have been manufactured by the same methods, each of which has shown satisfactory results in all prescribed tests. There shall be a demonstration under circumstances wherein adequate clinical and epidemiological surveillance of illness has been maintained to show that the measles virus vaccine, when administered as recommended by the manufacturer, i.e., either with or without human gamma-globulin, is free of harmful effect upon administration to approximately 1000 susceptible individuals in that there were no detectable neutralizing antibodies before vaccination and there was serological conversion after vaccination. The five lots of vaccine used to qualify for consistency of vaccine manufacture shall be distributed as evenly as possible among the 1000 individuals tested. Demonstration shall be made of immunogenic effect by the production of specific measles neutralizing antibodies (i.e., seroconversion less than 1 : 4 to 1 : 8 or greater) in at least 90% of each of five groups of measles susceptible individuals, each having received the parenteral administration of a virus vaccine dose that is not greater than that which was demonstrated to be safe in field studies (Section V,A,2,b) when used under comparable conditions.

E. EQUIVALENT METHODS

Modification of any particular manufacturing method or process or the conditions under which it is conducted as set forth in the additional standards relating to live virus vaccines shall be permitted whenever the manufacturer presents evidence that demonstrates the modification will provide assurances of the safety, purity, and potency of the vaccine that are equal to or greater than the assurances provided by such standards and the national authority so finds and makes such findings a matter of official record.

VI. Virus Vaccines—General Considerations

A. LIVE- VERSUS KILLED-VIRUS VACCINES

The relative merits of live, attenuated virus vaccines and inactivated virus vaccines frequently have been debated. If immunity to viral infection and disease is dependent on the presence of neutralizing antibody, both types of vaccine would be equally effective. A series of injections of killed vaccine often results in higher antibody levels than those attained from natural infections or from live vaccine administration; however, the resulting immunity may neither be as durable nor as lasting.

Because live virus multiplies in the host, it is thought to result in a more "natural" form of immunity since the infection would produce the whole range of antigens and stimulate the production of appropriate antibodies; in contrast, some of the antigens may not be present in sufficient concentrations in killed virus vaccines to stimulate the necessary antibody formation. Furthermore, the mechanism of local production of antibody as in the case of polioviruses and possibly some members of the respiratory viral disease complex indicate that live virus vaccines, which can induce this type of local resistance, would be more effective than killed vaccines, despite the equal or higher circulating antibody levels evoked by the killed vaccines.

Therefore, based on immunological grounds, the use of live virus vaccines may prove more advantageous for those viral diseases wherein local immunity is of prime importance and where there is an extensive systemic invasion of the host. Often these viral diseases are caused by a single or a few antigenic types and result in lasting or lifelong immunity (smallpox, measles, mumps, rubella, varicella, poliomyelitis, and yellow fever). However, many of the more recently discovered etiologic agents (members of the viral respiratory disease complex) cause diseases wherein the infection is more superficial, the number of antigenic types is extensive, and the resulting immunity is short-lived. Against these viral diseases, multivalent killed virus vaccines prepared from purified, accurately measured antigens devoid of their nucleic acid may be more advantageous and, in addition, may be more readily controlled with respect to potency and safety.

In general, live vaccines require less viral substance and often confer long-lasting immunity after only a single dose. In some instances, they can be administered by the same route by which natural infection occurs; thus, conferring the desired local immunity, e.g., live oral poliovirus vaccine. However, the problem of viral interference may prevent the establishment of the live vaccine virus in the host (concurrent nonpolio enterovirus infection at time of administration of live oral poliovirus vaccine), indicating a potential difficulty with the use of multiple live virus vaccines.

Irrespective of the merits and theoretical advantages of either type of vaccine, the final choice must depend on the particular disease situation and the evaluation of the effectiveness of the specific vaccine in preventing disease if not infection, both under experimental and natural conditions.

B. Methods of Inactivation

Various methods have been studied in efforts to inactivate virus preparations and have included both chemical and physical means. The techniques most commonly employed for the inactivation of virus fluids for use as human vaccines have been formaldehyde, β-propiolactone, and ultraviolet irradiation either alone or in combinations. Irrespective of the method used, the sensitivity of the tests for the detection of viable virus after inactivation is of prime importance. In addition, it must be shown that the inactivation has had no adverse affect on the immunogenicity of the product and, furthermore, has neither denatured nor altered the vaccine so as to render it toxic for the recipient.

The published literature relating to the inactivation of viral fluid for use as human vaccines is extensive and no effort will be made to include all references. Of general interest is the monograph published by the New York Academy of Sciences entitled "Inactivation of Viruses" (1960).

1. Formaldehyde

This chemical is a typical tanning agent and its action on proteins appears to be extremely complex, suggesting, in turn, that the formaldehyde inactivation of viruses must be a highly complicated process. The theoretical aspects of this method of inactivation will not be discussed, but the practical use of formaldehyde, which has been well-documented in the literature, will be described.

The specific kinetics of the Formalin inactivation must be determined for each virus studied. In general, a final concentration of a USP solution of formaldehyde of 1 : 2000 to 1 : 4000 is added to the filtered or clarified virus suspension (nonviral matter, present in tissue culture fluid, consisting of amino acids, protein-degradation products, and cell debris reacts with formaldehyde, reversibly as well as irreversibly, thus interfering with the inactivation of the virus) and the inactivation is allowed to proceed under controlled conditions of pH and temperature (36°–38°C). The total time of inactivation will depend on the "in process" testing performed during the inactivation period to determine the intercept time or that point where no viable virus is detected in a 5-ml sample. The usual rule has been an incubation period no less than 3 times that required for a 5-ml sample to be tested and found to be negative for live virus or a minimum of 20 hours, whichever is longer.

The "in process" testing and intercept time determination may be performed as follows: the desired concentration of formaldehyde is added to the viral fluid prewarmed to 37°C, well mixed, and incubated at 36°–38°C after adjustment of the pH, if necessary. Samples are removed immediately after Formalin addition and periodically during the inactivation period. Preliminary inactivation studies often require frequent sampling in order to establish the rate at which the specific virus under study is being inactivated. These samples are treated with sodium bisulfite to immediately neutralize the free formaldehyde and then dialyzed to remove the sodium formaldehyde–bisulfite complex formed. When employing a final concentration of 1 : 4000 formaldehyde, samples have been neutralized by the addition of a 1 : 16 dilution of a 35% solution of sodium bisulfite at the rate of 0.1 ml/5 ml of sample. This provides an excess of bisulfite sufficient to completely neutralize all free formaldehyde present in the sample. Stock solutions of 35% sodium bisulfite should not be exposed to light to prevent photoinactivation or degradation.

Dialysis is carried out at 4°C for approximately 24 hours against a volume of dialyzing fluid at least 40 times greater than the sample dialyzed with a minimum of one change of fluid. Dialyzing fluid may consist of any solution that has been shown to have no adverse affect on the viability of the virus under study. In preliminary studies appropriate controls should be included: virus incubated at 36°–38°C at the same pH but in the absence of Formalin to serve as a control on thermal inactivation; untreated virus dialyzed under the same conditions to serve as a control on the dialysis procedure; virus without Formalin but with sodium bisulfite dialyzed under the same conditions to serve as a control on the possible antiviral affect of the bisulfite. Following dialysis, infectivity titers or plaque-forming units (pfu) should be determined employing the most sensitive tissue culture system available.

The intercept time or that point wherein no viable virus can be detected in a 5-ml sample may be determined by use of Eqs. (1)–(5), where $X =$ hours of sampling postaddition of formaldehyde, $Y =$ infectivity or pfu titer of sample, and $N =$ number of samples with calculable titers. Also to be calculated are: $\overline{Y}$, $\overline{Y}$, X^2, XY, ΣX, and ΣY.

$$\Sigma x^2 = \Sigma X^2 - (\Sigma X)^2/N \tag{1}$$

$$\Sigma xy = \Sigma XY - (\Sigma X)(\Sigma Y)/N \tag{2}$$

$$b = \Sigma xy/\Sigma x^2 \qquad \text{[values obtained from Eqs.}$$
$$\text{(1) and (2) above]} \tag{3}$$

$$\text{Intercept time} = \overline{X} - \overline{Y}/b \tag{4}$$

$$\text{Adjusted titers: } Y' = \overline{Y} + b(X - \overline{X}) \tag{5}$$

Employing the above formulas, the time at which no viable virus should be detectable can be calculated. Based on this information, 5-ml samples taken around this intercept time can be tested as described in Section IV,A,6. The inactivation should be continued for a time equal to at least 3 times that initial incubation period for a 5-ml sample to be found devoid of viable virus.

2. Beta-Propiolactone (BPL)

This chemical is a colorless, stable liquid in its concentrated form, but quite unstable in aqueous solutions. It is best stored at $-20°$ to $-30°$C in plastic or neutraglass sealed containers. It has a specific gravity of 1.149 and is 37.5% soluble in water at 25°C. It reacts readily with hydroxyl, amino, carboxyl, sulfhydryl, and phenolic groups. It hydrolyzes rapidly and completely within 2 hours at 37°C in aqueous solutions breaking down into β-propionic acid and hydracrylic acid derivatives. These acid products have not been found to be toxic or to cause allergic reactions in recipients.

The major human viral vaccine presently in use that has been inactivated with β-propiolactone is the duck embryo rabies vaccine (see Section II,A,2). Other studies have shown that BPL can inactivate certain viruses within 2 hours at 37°C resulting in a higher degree of antigenicity than that obtained with the same viruses inactivated for longer periods of time with Formalin or phenol (LoGrippo and Hartman, 1955; Hartman and LoGrippo, 1957; Polley and Guerin, 1957).

The conditions necessary for the inactivation of a given virus preparation must be determined and include: the concentration of BPL; the pH; the temperature of inactivation and the medium in which the virus is suspended. Any or all of these factors may play an important role in the successful inactivation of a virus preparation resulting in a safe, immunogenic, and effective product. It must be emphasized that only the "Specially Purified" brand of BPL be used as this product contains at least 99% of the lactone or active form of the drug.

3. Ultraviolet Irradiation

The use of ultraviolet irradiation in the inactivation of virus for the preparation of vaccines has received a great deal of attention within the past decade. The lethal effect of the biologically effective wavelength of 2537 Å upon microorganisms suspended in liquid media is considered to result from the absorption of the ultraviolet photons within the nucleic acid or nucleoproteins.

The major problem in the use of ultraviolet energy has been to inactivate the viruses without seriously changing or altering the media and the associated constituents. At the same time, the antigenic potency of the inactivated product must not be affected. Conditions must be established for each given virus preparation so that a safe minimum of ultraviolet energy can effect, consistently, the desired biological action. A certain amount of energy, sufficiently intense to affect the viruses, must reach every portion of the suspension, and the net photon density throughout the fluid should demonstrate only a small range of variation.

Because of the need to effectively sterilize or inactivate large volumes of fluid, i.e., plasma, blood serum, or virus fluids, a centrifugal device was developed wherein uniformly thin-flowing films of any desired thickness could be produced and exposed to incident ultraviolet energy of controllable intensity. The development of this precision instrument, the "Centrifilmer" and its practical use have been reported by Oppenheimer et al. (1959).

The primary component of the filmer is a vertical 15-inch stainless-steel bowl that rotates at a fixed speed (1750 rpm). The inner wall of the bowl is inclined outward at a 1° angle so that fluid fed in the bottom of the rotating bowl is spread centrifugally into an extremely thin film as it flows upward (Fig. 1). Six ultraviolet lamps in a special water-cooled holder (30°C) are suspended inside the rotating bowl so that 750 cm² of area of the inside surface of the bowl with its flowing film of fluid receives incident ultraviolet energy of controllable intensity. The effective energy can be varied from 5 to over 30 W by varying the number and the input current of the lamps. Variable ultraviolet exposures can be obtained by combining the variations in the effective incident ultraviolet energy with different flow rates of the fluid being irradiated. The thickness of the fluid film is proportional to the flow rate; at 100 ml/minute the average film thickness is approximately

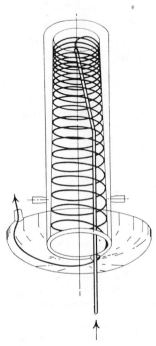

Fig. 1. Diagramatic illustration of the spiral characteristics of the flowing film. Fluid introduced on the bottom of the bowl is spread by centrifugal force. Acceleration upward progressively increases rapidly in the lower third of the bowl as fluid friction and the mass inertia are overcome and balanced. Under the influence of the continually increasing outward component of the gravitational field, the flow in the upper two thirds of the bowl is relatively uniform (Oppenheimer et al., 1959).

75 μ. A schematic diagram showing the relation of the various components in a typical irradiation setup is shown in Fig. 2.

4. Combination of Inactivation Methods

The application of the Centrifilmer for the inactivation of viruses by ultraviolet irradiation alone was not found to be practical for all viruses. However, studies have shown that irradiation used in combina-

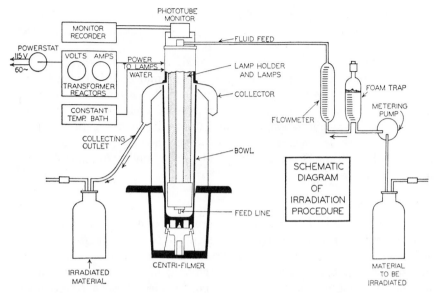

FIG. 2. Schematic diagram showing relation of various components in a typical irradiation setup. In large-scale operation, the bottles illustrated are replaced by stainless-steel tanks (Oppenheimer *et al.*, 1959).

tion with other inactivating agents (formaldehyde and/or β-propiolactone) resulted not only in more highly antigenic vaccines, but also in more consistent and reliable inactivation (Taylor *et al.*, 1957; LoGrippo, 1958).

C. Vaccine Formulations

The form in which vaccines are packaged depends, to a great extent, on whether they are live (attenuated or nonattenuated), killed (whole virus or antigenic subunits), monovalent, or polyvalent preparations. The formulations to be described refer not only to licensed biologicals but also to the many experimental vaccines that have been recently tested for safety and efficacy in human field trials.

1. *Aqueous Vaccines*

Killed virus vaccines, irrespective of method of inactivation, are usually packaged in the aqueous form in the liquid state in single or multiple dose containers. It is strongly recommended that this type of vaccine, composed of either whole intact virus or antigenic subunits as monovalent or mixed polyvalent forms, be stored at 4°C and never undergo freeze–thaw cycles. Section II has described a number of these vaccines including rabies, influenza, poliovirus, adenovirus, and measles in monovalent and/or polyvalent form.

Live virus vaccines, usually attenuated, may be packaged in the aqueous form in the frozen state in single or multiple dose containers. This type of vaccine must be stored frozen and once thawed should be used immediately or within a short time period and the remainder discarded. These vaccines should not undergo multiple freeze–thaw cycles. A number of these vaccines, monovalent and/or polyvalent, have been discussed in Section II (smallpox, yellow fever, poliovirus, measles, rubella, and mumps).

2. *Lyophilized Vaccines*

Certain viruses can be safely dried provided that the remaining moisture content is of a sufficiently low percentage to have no adverse affect on viability. This is extremely important since the potency of the live virus vaccine is often determined by the titer of the preparation and a loss in titer would indicate a loss in potency or effectiveness. Lyophilized live virus vaccines may be stored at 4°C until reconstituted with the prescribed diluent. Generally, dried preparations are packaged in single dose containers, i.e., smallpox, rabies, yellow fever, and measles.

3. *Enteric Coated Capsules*

The use of encapsulated live virus for immunization has been employed in experimental studies with adenovirus and rhinovirus vaccines (Couch *et al.*, 1963; Chanock *et al.*, 1966; Edmondson *et al.*, 1966; Mascoli *et al.*, 1966). Basically, the virus either in the liquid or lyophilized state is placed in gelatin capsules and then enteric coated by ordinary procedures employing a solution of cellulose acetate–hydrogen phthalate in acetone. By this vehicle it is hoped to bypass the high acidity of the stomach and permit the virus to multiply in the intestine. This technique may be ideal for those viruses known to proliferate naturally in the lower alimentary tract.

4. *Adjuvants*

The desire to achieve greater efficiency of immunization from a given amount of inactivated antigen led to the development of immunological adjuvants capable of enhancing the immune response. All such substances appear to act by stimulation or facilitation of body mechanisms essential to antibody production and include: localization and proliferation of antibody producing cells; increased particle size facilitating phagocytosis; provision of a vehicle for transport of antigen to distant sites or slow release from an insoluble depot. Substances employed as adjuvants are varied and have included aluminum compounds, calcium phosphate, protamine, acrylamide gel, gram-negative bacteria, endotoxins, cholesterol, fatty acids, aliphatic amines, and water-in-oil and water-in-oil-in-water emulsions of paraffinic and vegetable oils.

For human use, aluminum compounds have been found to be acceptable and efficient. The emulsified water-in-oil adjuvants (Hilleman, 1966b), though more effective in eliciting higher levels of antibody persisting for longer periods of time, have been used only experimentally and have, as yet, not received acceptance for routine human use.

As with other formulations of killed virus vaccines, the antigenic components included in the adjuvant preparation must be of sufficient potency to elicit an antibody response with the aid of the vehicle employed. One of the major advantages of the use of adjuvants is that single or multiple antigens in smaller antigenic masses could be incorporated in an adjuvant vaccine and be administered in fewer doses than the corresponding aqueous material and still result in a more durable and higher level of immunity.

a. Alum Adjuvant. The use of alum or aluminum compounds in an effort to enhance the immunogenicity of the antigenic components may involve either the direct flocculation of the alum in the antigen preparations or the addition of preformed alum to a given virus preparation. In either case the adjuvant is so prepared that an individual human dose does not contain more aluminum than that contained in 15 mg by assay or 20 mg by calculation of $AlK(SO_4) \cdot 12H_2O$. Other forms of aluminum may be employed provided that the amount of aluminum does not exceed that permitted as $AlK(SO_4) \cdot 12H_2O$. Mono- or polyvalent vaccine formulations may easily be prepared by means of alum adsorption; however, the efficacy of the preparation is directly dependent on the immunogenicity of the specific components adsorbed.

Alum-adsorbed vaccines are usually packaged in multiple dose containers. These preparations are stored at 4°C and never permitted to undergo freeze–thaw cycles. Because of the nature of the final product, the vaccine must be well shaken prior to use.

b. Emulsified Oil Adjuvants. (i) Freund's emulsified mineral oil adjuvants are of two kinds—complete and incomplete. Though both consist of a water-in-oil emulsion of aqueous vaccine in light mineral oil employing mannide monooleate (Arlacel A) as the emulsifier, only the complete adjuvant also contains *M. tuberculosis* to further potentiate the immunological response. This latter adjuvant form is not used in man because of its danger. The mechanism of action of Freund's adjuvants appears to be associated principally with three phenomena: (1) the establishment of the antigens in a persistent form or repository at the site of injection with gradual and continuous release of antigen for antibody stimulation; (2) the adjuvant acts as a vehicle for the transport of the emulsified antigen throughout the lymphatic system to distant sites such as lymph nodes and spleen where new foci of antibody formation could be established; and (3) the adjuvant evokes the formation of cells of the mononuclear series appropriate to the production of antibody at local and distal sites.

In general, Freund's incomplete adjuvant is a water-in-oil emulsion composed of 1 part aqueous vaccine and 1 part of a mixture of 90% light mineral oil (Drakeol 6VR or Bayol F) and 10% Arlacel A as emulsifier. Both the mineral oil and Arlacel A must meet certain specifications for use in man (Hilleman, 1966b).

Though Freund's incomplete mineral oil adjuvant has been tested and given some evidence of safety in man in influenza, poliovirus, adenovirus, and trachoma vaccines and in a variety of allergenic preparations, its widespread use has been hindered by the lack of long-term chronic toxicity data in animals and by the lack of information relating to the metabolic fate of the components of the adjuvant administered under conditions similar to those used in man. In addition, the possible long-term irritant effect of the retention of the mineral oil on the tissues is of some concern.

(ii) Emulsified peanut oil adjuvant, Adjuvant 65 (Woodhour et al., 1964), is a water-in-oil emulsion composed of 1 part aqueous vaccine and 1 part oil vehicle consisting of 86% peanut oil, 10% Arlacel A (emulsifier), and 4% aluminum monostearate (stabilizer). All components of the adjuvant are nontoxic, readily metabolized, and have had long-term use in products in man without any apparent harmful effects.

This adjuvant has been found to effect a degree of immunogenic potentiation and duration roughly equivalent to that obtained with Freund's adjuvant. In addition, no significant adverse clinical reactions have been reported in persons receiving this preparation. Both short- and long-term toxicity studies carried out in a variety of animals have failed to reveal evidence of any immunopathological process or tissue alteration.

Adjuvant 65 may be the means of providing a safe and effective vehicle for increasing the efficacy of a variety of vaccines for use in man, particularly the multivalent, killed, respiratory virus vaccines. However, the main difficulty may be in preparing the individual antigenic components possessing sufficient potency for the adjuvant vehicle to be effective.

Because of the nature of the vaccine formulation, the experimental preparations have been packaged in syringes ready for use with storage at 4°C. Water-in-oil emulsions should never be allowed to undergo freeze–thaw cycles.

D. Methods of Mass Immunization

In the past, mass immunization campaigns were carried out in cases of epidemic emergencies such as the danger of spread of infectious disease from other countries or from other areas of the same country, during natural catastrophes or mass migrations. However, with the more recent developments in vaccine production and the increased knowledge of the pathogenesis of both "old" and "new" viruses, attempts are being made not only to markedly decrease specific virus-induced disease morbidities, but to completely eradicate certain viruses from a given population. Because of the large numbers of people necessarily involved in mass vaccination, the use of individual needles and syringes becomes not only time consuming but expensive. For the purpose of speed, economy and efficiency, jet guns have been developed for the parenteral administration and aerosols for the oral administration of vaccines.

1. Jet Guns

The basic principle of a jet injector is the development of a high velocity jet of the liquid projected through microorifices under great pressure. The necessary pressure is obtained from either an electrically driven hydraulic pump as in the Hypospray Jet Injector, Model K-3 (R. P. Scherer Corp., Detroit, Mich.) (Figs. 3 and 4) and the Automatic Hypodermic Jet Injection Apparatus (Scientific Equipment Manufacturing Corp., N.Y.) or through the compression of springs as in the Hypospray, Professional Model (R. P. Scherer Corp., Detroit, Mich.) (Fig. 5). The vaccine delivered through the microorifices travels at relatively high speed (ca. 700 mph) and penetrates the skin with little or no pain. These multidose injectors can often be regulated to deliver between 0.1 and 1.0 ml in graduated steps and have the advantage of being easily dismantled and sterilized for maximum safety.

With the electrically driven jet guns it is possible to inject approximately 1000 individuals/hour and with the spring compression model, approximately 250 individuals/hour. The practical use of jet guns for mass immunization has been reported by Towle (1960) for cholera and

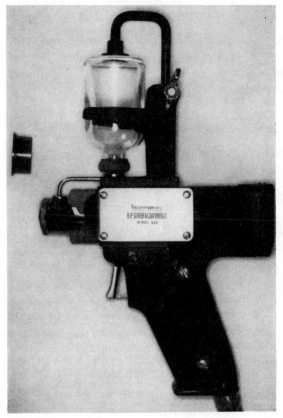

FIG. 3. Hypospray Jet-Injector, Model K-3; electrically driven hydraulic pump (R. P. Scherer Corp., Detroit, Mich.).

typhoid vaccination in Pakistan and by Meyer *et al.* (1964) for combined live measles, smallpox, and yellow fever in Volta.

2. Aerosols

Since many of the infectious diseases afflicting man are acquired via the respiratory tract, it is possible that the immunizing antigen might be more effective in inducing a high-grade host defense if the route of administration were identical to the natural portal of entry of the infecting agent rather than the unnatural route generally employed, i.e., subcutaneous or intramuscular inoculation.

The immunization of man by aerogenic vaccination with single or combined live vaccines has been studied extensively by Russian investi-

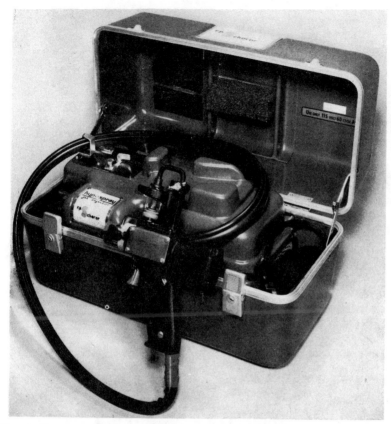

FIG. 4. Hypospray Jet-Injector, Model K-3; electrically driven hydraulic pump (R. P. Scherer Corp., Detroit, Mich.).

gators. In the United States, only small pilot studies have been performed, to date. Live influenza virus (liquid or powder) administered intranasally by the spray method has been employed by Soviet workers for many years not only on an experimental basis, but also in efforts to abort epidemics (Smorodintsev and Zhdanov, 1957; Smorodintsev et al., 1961). In addition, the immunization of man with dust vaccines against brucella and anthrax has been described by Aleksandrov and associates (1961). In these studies immunization was achieved by the inhalation of the dried vaccines upon exposure to the dust cloud in a closed room. Based on the room size (5–160 m³), it was possible to immunize 4–200 persons at one time.

It would appear that aerogenic immunization, though potentially a

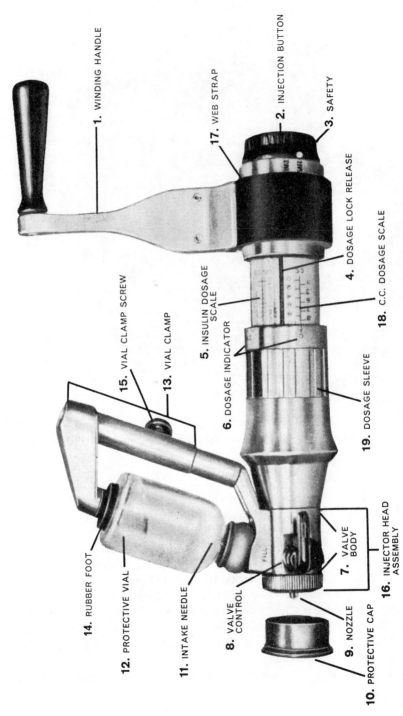

1. WINDING HANDLE
2. INJECTION BUTTON
3. SAFETY
4. DOSAGE LOCK RELEASE
5. INSULIN DOSAGE SCALE
6. DOSAGE INDICATOR
7. VALVE BODY
8. VALVE CONTROL
9. NOZZLE
10. PROTECTIVE CAP
11. INTAKE NEEDLE
12. PROTECTIVE VIAL
13. VIAL CLAMP
14. RUBBER FOOT
15. VIAL CLAMP SCREW
16. INJECTOR HEAD ASSEMBLY
17. WEB STRAP
18. C.C. DOSAGE SCALE
19. DOSAGE SLEEVE

FIG. 5. Hypospray, Professional Model (R. P. Scherer Corp., Detroit, Mich.).

sound and effective method, is not as practical or economical as the jet guns, especially for widespread use particularly among the masses of population in the underdeveloped areas of the world. Furthermore, the development of live vaccines (liquid or dried) for administration by aerosols has not reached the level presently achieved by those vaccines administered parenterally as concerns safety, potency and efficacy.

VII. Production of Experimental Vaccines—General Principles

The standards prescribed in Sections III, IV, and V should be applied to the production of any experimental vaccine. In addition, there are a number of general principles which can facilitate the preparation of such a vaccine and their presentation and discussion is the purpose of this section. Many of the recommendations have been extracted from the WHO Technical Report Series No. 325 (1966).

A. PRODUCTION

1. *Virus Seed Strain*

The selection of the strain of virus to be employed for vaccine production is generally dictated by its ability to result in a product with high immunogenicity. When utilizing inactivated vaccines, the strain of virus yielding maximum viral titer in the tissue culture system of choice determines the method of selection, since infectivity and antigenicity are often directly related.

As a rule, the seed lot system should be employed in any vaccine production. Following a number of serial passages to establish the optimal conditions for growth and virus yield, preprimary, primary, and secondary seed pools in increasing volumes should be produced. The secondary seed pool should serve as the master seed for vaccine production and should be of sufficient volume to permit multiple use. This method makes it possible to reproduce a given vaccine at the same passage level necessary for demonstrating consistency. The rationale for the preparation of the preprimary and primary pools is to serve as sources for replenishing the secondary seed pool.

Each virus seed strain must be carefully documented with respect to source, to passage history prior to and subsequent to receipt, and to strain designation. It must be identified with respect to growth, host range, and serological findings both at the secondary seed level and at the vaccine level. In no instance shall the virus strain employed for vaccine production have been propagated in malignant cells of human or animal origin.

2. Propagation System

The selection of the tissue culture system employed for the propagation of a particular virus generally is based on precedence. The most widely used systems have been primary monkey kidney tissue cultures derived from rhesus, cynomolgus, and cercopithecus monkeys, and chick embryo cell cultures. Other primary cell systems that have been utilized are tissues from domestic or laboratory animals such as dogs, calves, bovine embryos, and guinea pigs.

Since the safety of the tissue employed for virus growth and vaccine production is as important as the safety of the virus itself, the propagation system must be carefully screened for the presence of extraneous agents. The importance of control bottles, either uninoculated or inoculated with serially passaged control fluids, performed in parallel with virus passages, cannot be overemphasized. The detection of extraneous agents either directly or after subpassages, as prescribed in Section V,A,5, will preclude the use of the virus fluid for vaccine purposes. Unfortunately, the lack of accurate knowledge relating both to the sensitivity and the inclusiveness of the tests, particularly for nonprimate cell cultures, raises the question of safety. This problem of propagation system will be fully discussed in Section VIII,A.

In general, the tissue culture system of choice is one that has been shown to: (1) be devoid of any detectable extraneous agents by the techniques available; (2) support the optimum growth of the specific virus; and (3) result in a product that is both safe and highly immunogenic in man.

3. Vaccine Production

Any vaccine produced for parenteral administration should be grown in a synthetic medium in the absence of any animal or human serum. Since penicillin cannot be employed, the use of antibiotics such as neomycin (50 μg/ml) and aureomycin (10–20 μg/ml) have been found to be satisfactory. It is advisable to omit penicillin not only from the final maintenance medium but also from the growth medium as well.

The optimal conditions for the growth of the virus for vaccine production should include inoculum size, inoculum concentration, medium composition and pH, temperature, and length of time of incubation. Since primary cell cultures are grown in the presence of serum, it is necessary to wash the cultures either prior to infection or 24–72 hours postinfection with a medium such as Hanks' Balanced Salt Solution.

The cell films should be washed at least 2 times with a volume of medium sufficient to dilute the serum to a concentration not exceeding 1 ppm. The time of wash will depend on the specific virus, its volume and concentration, and the rapidity of growth and/or demonstration of cytopathic effects. Fluids should be harvested at time of maximum CPE or when experience has indicated that the resulting viral yield is optimal for vaccine purposes.

4. Clarification

Viral fluids should be clarified soon after harvesting in order to remove the cellular debris. Centrifugation may be the simplest method depending on volume but generally is not considered as effective as filtration. Preliminary studies should be performed to determine the ideal conditions for filtration such as type of filters (Millipore, fritted glass, and Selas candles), porosity, filter aids, and effect of such treatment on the various parameters (infectivity, CF activity, antigenicity) of the virus preparation.

A technique found to be both useful and effective for the clarification of some of the myxoviruses (parainfluenza and respiratory syncytial viruses) has been the use of 1 × 8 inch coarse fritted glass candles primed with Celite #503 and gelatin (10 gm of Celite #503 plus 0.05% Kind and Knox pharmaceutical gelatin in 800 ml of distilled water). The filtration set-up consists of a completely closed system (the filter candle is enclosed in a glass mantle) which can be sterilized in situ. Vacuum is applied to the candle followed by the addition of the filter aid (Celite–gelatin mixture) under positive air pressure (3–5 psi). After the candle has been primed, vacuum is reapplied and then the harvest fluid to which Celite #503 has been added at the rate of 1 gm/liter of fluid is filtered under positive air pressure (the Celite is mixed in a small volume of distilled water and added as a suspension). Each 1 × 8 inch candle can effectively filter approximately 7 liters of fluid within 15–30 minutes with little or no loss in measurable parameters.

5. Inactivation

Methods of inactivation have been discussed in Section VI,B and tests for the detection of residual live virus have been described in Section IV,A,6.

6. Concentration and Purification

The present state of knowledge in virology and closely related fields has made available a wide variety of chemical and physical procedures for the concentration and purification of viruses. These techniques include: (1) preferential precipitation by the addition of chemicals such as zinc salts, manganese salts, protamines, and nucleic acid, or by the pH adjustment to the isoelectric point; (2) the use of adsorbents such as charcoal, Celite, or kaolin; (3) adsorption and elution from chemical substances such as alum, zinc sulfate, and calcium phosphate, or from biological materials such as red blood cells; (4) column chromatography on various ion-exchange substances or resins; (5) extraction and partition of aqueous suspensions utilizing diethyl ether or fluorocarbon; (6) partition in aqueous polymer two-phase systems such as sodium dextran sulfate and polyethylene glycol; (7) enzymatic digestion with trypsin, papain, and similar substances; (8) physical separation utilizing filters of graded pore size or preferential absorptive capacity; (9) filtration through molecular sieves of specified pore size such as crosslinked dextran; (10) physical separation by means of differential centrifugation or the use of density gradients. In addition, the viral capsid or envelope antigens may be separated and purified. The recently developed zonal centrifuge that permits continuous flow separation in a density gradient may offer the most efficient method for viral purification.

In the past, infectivity was employed as the measure of virus quantification but this procedure was of limited value as it often failed to indicate the true measure of the total viral mass or viral antigen present in a given preparation. The measurement of other parameters such as CF and/or hemagglutinin activity afforded additional information as did tests for immunogenicity that were quantitated serologically. However, accuracy in viral antigen determination is achieved by using highly purified virus which can be quantified by ultraviolet adsorption, by measurement of the sedimenting boundary in an ultra-centrifugal field, or by direct particle count in the electron microscope aided by negative staining with phosphotungstic acid.

Since the immunizing capacity of killed virus vaccines is dependent on the amount of antigenic material present in the vaccines, the use of concentrated and purified preparations containing precise quantities of viral antigen is desired. Furthermore, purified viral fractions would be ideal for use in multivalent vaccines wherein the volume of each dose would be small but, at the same time, contain a sufficient quantity of each type of antigen to give an adequate response, particularly if incorporated in a safe and effective immunological adjuvant (see Section VI,C,4).

B. Testing Procedures

1. *Safety Testing*

These tests are concerned with the safety of the vaccine virus harvest as well as with the absence of potentially dangerous contaminants. In the case of killed vaccines, the tests employed should be sufficiently sensitive to detect any residual live virus that has escaped inactivation. With a live attenuated vaccine, it is necessary to ensure that the characteristics of the vaccine virus do not differ from those of the seed virus that had been tested previously and found to be safe and immunogenic in man.

The most time-consuming and costly part of the safety testing is the search for adventitious agents (applicable to the seed virus as well as to the vaccine preparation). Extraneous agents can be detected by a cytopathic effect in cell cultures, by an interference effect, or by clinical and/or histopathological signs in animals. In an effort to increase the chances of detecting an unknown extraneous virus contaminant, it is advisable to subpass the test fluids in a number of different tissue culture systems. These cell cultures should include both primary and serial passage lines of types known to support the growth of a number of varied agents, e.g., homologous tissue cultures employed in the vaccine production, primary kidney cultures derived from simian, rabbit, and human embryonic sources, human diploid, and one of a number of stable line cells such as HeLa, H.Ep-2, or KB.

Tests for extraneous viruses should be performed prior to inactivation. Preferably, the search should be made employing the control cultures of the tissues used for the virus propagation. In addition, the virus fluid should be tested following neutralization by a serum prepared by infection or by hyperimmunization with a viral antigen grown in an immunologically unrelated tissue culture system. All breakthroughs following serum neutralization must be identified.

Noncytopathic contaminants and/or latent viruses may be uncovered by the interference effect in which a known cytopathogenic virus when inoculated into the cell culture is inhibited by the presence of the "undetectable" agent. This technique has been employed to detect the fowl leukosis viruses and rubella virus. Additional methods involve the staining of infected or control cell cultures and the screening for hemadsorbing agents by the use of guinea pig erythrocytes. Of greatest concern is the possibility that an undetected oncogenic virus may be present and for this purpose both virus harvest and control fluids should be inoculated into newborn hamsters. It should be noted that none of the methods described can eliminate all risk of the presence of an unknown virus.

2. Sterility Testing

All viral vaccines, whether killed or live attenuated preparations, should be thoroughly tested for the presence of bacterial and mycotic contaminants, PPLO, and M. tuberculosis of human, avian, or bovine source depending on the tissue culture propagation system employed in production.

3. Potency Testing

The potency of live virus vaccines is determined by the infectivity titers of the final product. Since immunity is conferred by establishing infection in the host, the vaccine must contain a sufficient concentration of viable virus particles to establish infection in the vaccinee.

For killed virus vaccines, either crude, concentrated, and/or purified, the only measure of potency is that of the serological response of an animal. The animal potency test must be standardized and shown to be reproducible both within and between laboratories. It is recommended that the antigenic extinction-limit titration test be employed and that, wherever possible, single versus multiple injections of antigen be administered. Single inoculations lessen the risk of a broad antibody response and of host tissue response. However, a test that measures an antigenic stimulus in animals will not necessarily indicate that man will react in a similar manner; therefore, the response in animals to a number of batches of vaccine must be correlated with the responses in man.

4. Stability Testing

In the absence of data on long-term low temperature storage, the stability of the vaccine may be determined by storage at 18°–37°C for varying periods of time and then testing for potency as discussed above. Though this method will not necessarily reflect the behavior of the product at +4°C or −20°C, it will provide preliminary information on the "shelf life" of the vaccine.

5. Assessment of Testing Procedures

Basically, the safety of live virus vaccines depends on their lack of pathogenicity and freedom from extraneous agents. All such vaccines currently licensed or being studied experimentally have standard laboratory tests for the determination of attenuation or loss of pathogenicity and immunogenicity; however, there are no laboratory tests for assessing the safety of the virus strain which can be determined only by clinical studies in man. Laboratory tests can help ensure that the vaccine strain has the same characteristics as the seed strain shown to be safe in man. This may be achieved by cloning the specific virus strain in order to obtain a homogeneous population with the desired characteristics.

For killed virus vaccines, it is necessary to demonstrate that the product is devoid of any residual viable virus, free of extraneous agents and will elicit a high antibody response in animals without producing any untoward reactions. A product that is highly immunogenic in animals will often elicit a similar response in man.

C. Clinical Trials in Man—Field Assessment

The final assessment of the value of a given human vaccine can only be made by studies in man. The validity of the laboratory tests are dependent on the comparable results obtained by performing controlled trials employing the newer statistical and epidemiological methods now available.

1. Safety

The first stage in the study of a new vaccine in man is the field assessment of safety. Often early trials are conducted in selected volunteers who, by reason of age, immunity status, and other conditions, can be expected to be in no danger from the procedure. All participants must be kept under close clinical observation for an appropriate period of time to detect possible local or general reactions. In the case of live virus vaccines, surveillance must be made concerning the occurrence of clinical manifestations of infection with the vaccine and of viremia and the excretion of virus. If excretion occurs, the possibility of contact transmission must be investigated and the reisolated virus must be studied for possible reversion of the attenuated characteristics to the more dangerous pathogenic traits.

Subsequent trials, provided no untoward clinical effects are observed, would include volunteers from susceptible groups in whom information could be obtained regarding route of inoculation; optimal dosage (volume and schedule) and serological response. All this data is necessary to confirm some of the laboratory tests and before large-scale studies can be undertaken to evaluate the effectiveness of a given vaccine.

2. Efficacy

The second stage in the assessment of a new vaccine is the test for efficacy in a natural epidemiological situation. These studies tend to offer additional information on the occurrence or absence of side effects and to determine whether the laboratory tests regarding potency and protection can be correlated with the results in human vaccinees.

The principles in planning and executing controlled trials for efficacy will be mentioned only briefly. They include the composition of the study populations with respect to age, sex, presumed susceptibility, risk of exposure to the relevant infection, the background experience of the investigators, standard criteria for diagnosis to prevent bias, and to ensure the highest degree of uniformity of procedures. The trials should be designed as double-blind studies again to prevent any suspicion of bias. Serological and virological observations should be carried out on at least a representative proportion of the study population and all cases of infection and/or disease should be thoroughly investigated. Whether the trials are to be made in the general population or in special groups will largely depend on the age incidence of the disease and its epidemiological behavior.

D. GENERAL REQUIREMENTS

In the United States, any new drug or vaccine product subject to the licensing provisions of the Public Health Service Act of July 1, 1944, requires the submission of a "Notice of claimed investigational exemption for a new drug" to the Division of Biologics Standards, National Institutes of Health, Public Health Service. This notice is submitted under the provision of Section 505 (i) of the Federal Food, Drug and Cosmetic Act and Section 130.3 of Title 21 of the Code of Federal Regulations.

In general, these forms submitted by the product sponsor and by the clinical investigators deal with the product itself and the qualifications of the investigator(s) responsible for the clinical trials. A sample of an outline of a release protocol relating to the preparation and testing of a potential virus vaccine (live or killed) is presented below:

1. Virus seed strain
   a. Designation

    b. History prior to receipt
    c. History at manufacturing facility
    d. Identification
  2. Vaccine pool preparation
    a. Tissue culture system and medium
    b. Inoculation and pool preparation
    c. Clarification
    d. Inactivation
    e. Tests for residual live virus
  3. Testing procedures and results
    a. Microbial sterility
    b. Identity and purity (safety) tests in tissue cultures
    c. Animal safety tests
    d. Viral quantification and immunogenicity (potency)
  4. Inventory and storage

VIII. Vaccine Production—Special Problems

A. Choice of Propagation System

In general, cell cultures may be divided into two types: first, the mixed population of cells freshly explanted from normal animal tissues and cultured in artificial medium usually containing serum and used without further passage, i.e., primary cell cultures; second, mixed or cloned cell lines derived from normal or malignant tissues that can be serially propagated in artificial medium with or without serum or other proteins, i.e., cell lines or cell strains. The pros and cons relating to the use of primary or continuously cultured tissue cells for the production of viral vaccines has been discussed rather extensively in the literature (Hayflick, 1963; Scherp et al., 1963; Perkins and Hayflick, 1967).

1. Primary Cell Cultures

Tissue cultures prepared directly from animal organs are customarily referred to as primary cultures. However, this term is a misnomer since only a very small proportion of the original trypsinized suspension of cells actually takes part in the initiation of the confluent cell sheet and the film employed for vaccine production consists of a population of mixed age, with some cells representing the tenth to fifteenth generation. Because the cells have not been subcultured, they are referred to as primary tissue.

There apparently are no compelling advantages for employing primary cell cultures for viral vaccine production. On the other hand, there are a number of disadvantages associated with their use of which the most important has been the emergence of a multitude of adventitious agents. The occurrence of these agents, which are discussed below, has given rise to serious production and testing problems. However, since the present Federal Government Regulations (1965) forbid the use of any serially propagated cell, the sole choice remaining for viral vaccine production is the primary cell culture.

a. *Primate Tissues.* Several species of monkeys (rhesus, cynomolgus, and cercopithecus) have been employed as sources of primary tissue cultures with the prototype vaccine being that of poliovirus grown in rhesus monkey kidney cells. These tissues have seen wide-scale use for a number of years in spite of the large number of simian agents isolated from kidney and other organs, as well as from fecal and throat specimens. The extent to which the monkeys are infected with these viruses varies widely between species. This, in turn, may be a reflection of the degree of human and/or other animal contact both in their natural habitat as well as during the time period between capture and sacrifice for use as tissue culture.

Attempts at overcoming this problem of viral contamination have included special arrangements for trapping, transporting, and caging of monkeys so that animals can be received by the user within 48–72 hours postarrival into the supplier's main compound. In addition, monkeys are kept in individual cages to prevent contact with animals of the same or different species. Past experience has shown that monkeys, irrespective of species, when captured during the rainy seasons within their natural habitat, consistently demonstrate a much higher incidence of simian contamination than those trapped during the dry season. Animals should be conditioned in quarantine for a minimum of 6–8 weeks prior to sacrifice for tissue culture. Though these procedures help markedly to reduce the incidence of simian virus contamination, the establishment of primate colonies in a strictly controlled environment would be much more satisfactory. Unfortunately, the practical problems involved in such an undertaking are formidable and costly especially since the monkey species generally employed in vaccine production breed very poorly in captivity.

b. *Nonprimate Tissues.* Tissues derived from chick embryos, dogs, bovine animals, and guinea pigs have been the other major source of primary cell cultures. The requirements for the substrate for measles vaccine have set the modern trend for the use of chick embryo tissue. The flock producing the embryos for use in the vaccine production must be pretested and known to be free from disease, including fowl leukosis.

The use of primary kidney cultures obtained from dogs, bovine animals, and guinea pigs has been advocated because these animals can be bred under controlled conditions and contact with many viruses is thought to be preventable. To date, they have been found to be relatively free of extraneous agents; however, since extensive use of these animal tissues has not been made, further experience and the application of newer technology may bring to light hitherto undetected contaminants.

2. Continuous Cell Cultures

Continuous cell lines or cell strains generally consist of two types: (1) those derived by serial subculture from normal primary tissue cultures, and (2) those derived from explants of neoplastic mammalian tissues, e.g., the HeLa line originating from a human cervical carcinoma. The latter cell lines have been expressly forbidden for use in routine vaccine production because of their frankly malignant origin and of the possible presence of undetectable oncogenic viruses or transmissible nucleic acid which might induce cancer in the recipient. Strains of cells derived originally from normal tissues may be divided into two categories; those that on serial subculture develop characteristics suggesting malignant transformation and possible oncogenic activity and those such as diploid cells that retain all measurable properties of normalcy.

There are a number of advantages associated with the use of continuous cell cultures in viral vaccine production and they include: independence from a continual supply of fresh tissue, which often varies genetically, nutritionally, immunologically, and in viral susceptibility from one batch to another; greater assurance of freedom from adventitious agents since repeated subculture greatly increases the probability that hidden viruses harbored by the original tissue will become manifest; accumulation and storage of certified seed stock in the frozen state for indefinite periods of time. In addition, it is possible to establish clonal populations and to adapt the cloned lines to a chemically defined medium free from serum and protein.

The use of a cell system composed of human diploid cell strains derived from embryonic tissue holds promise as an acceptable source of virus in the future. The practical application of these cell strains for human viral vaccines has been reported in a Symposium on the Characterization and Uses of Human Diploid Cell Strains (1963).

Over 200,000 individuals have received vaccines produced in the human diploid cell strain WI38 with no adverse effects reported in those persons receiving vaccines against poliovirus, adenovirus type 4, measles, rubella, and rhinoviruses whether administered orally or parenterally.

The major features of this human diploid cell strain are: (1) retention of normal human diploid karyotype and other characteristics associated with normal cells (Hayflick and Moorhead, 1961); (2) apparent freedom from latent viruses (Trlifajova and Strizova, 1966), and (3) capability of supporting the growth of a wide variety of viruses, including those associated with the common cold that are not readily propagated in any animal cell (Hayflick, 1963). Very stringent criteria of acceptability have been suggested for these cell strains prior to their use in vaccine production.

1. The strain should be derived from normal human fetal tissue in order to lessen the possibility of viral contamination.

2. During the period of active growth, there should be no significant deviation from the normal karyotype.

3. During the period of active growth, there should be no changes in the morphological or biochemical characteristics.

4. The cell strain must be free of all extraneous microorganisms.

5. When inoculated into the hamster cheek pouch or tested by another equally sensitive *in vivo* test, the strain must not induce tumors.

6. The strain must be preserved in the frozen state in sufficient quantity and at a passage low enough to make it available for a "cell seed" system.

7. The cells must produce a high yield of human viruses for vaccine production.

8. The strain must be approved by the National Control Authority.

The methodology for selecting cell strains based on these criteria has been described in the standards drafted by a subcommittee of the Symposium on The Characterization and Uses of Human Diploid Cell Strains (1963).

B. Adventitious Agents: Overt and Latent

A major problem encountered in the course of tissue culture studies and, particularly, vaccine production has been the detection of a great many adventitious agents. Although there had been speculation that cultures derived from tissues of a variety of animal species might contain indigenous viruses, the extent of this contamination was unexpected. This has been especially true of the Macacus monkey kidney, which has been most extensively studied since it was the tissue chosen to prepare poliovirus vaccines.

Subsequently, cytopathic agents were isolated not only from cell cultures but from stools, throat specimens, and various tissues of all the monkey species employed in virus and/or vaccine preparations. A number of these agents have been detected only by subpassage of cell cultures derived from one species to another (SV40 in rhesus kidney cultures detected only after subpassage to renal cells derived from cercopithecus monkeys) or to a completely unrelated animal species (B virus in rhesus kidney cultures detected after subpassage to renal cells derived from rabbits).

The use of tissue cultures derived from other laboratory and/or domestic animals such as dogs, bovines, and guinea pigs has not been fully investigated and the total spectrum of indigenous viruses in these animals is yet to be uncovered. The major difficulty does not lie with those adventitious agents that produce or cause cytopathic effects in one or more tissue culture systems, since their ready detection during the testing or production of vaccines can actually assure that the final product is free from such contamination, but rather with those agents whose presence can be detected only indirectly such as by an interference effect.

The newer developments in virology, especially in relation to the phenomenon of hybridization and the part played by "helper" viruses, have clearly indicated that this problem of adventitious virus contamination (overt or latent) of the substrate employed for virus propagation and virus vaccine production is of utmost concern.

1. *Known Indigenous Viruses*

a. Simian Contaminants. There are a large number of viruses known to be harbored by monkeys which may be detected during the production of vaccines prepared from monkey tissues. These agents have been isolated either from the intact animals (stools and throat specimens) or from cell cultures prepared from their tissues. The problem lies not only with the tissue culture contamination of potential virus vaccines, but also in the possible transmission of some of these viruses from monkey to man either by direct contact or by aerosol. It may be added that this is not a one way street and that the monkeys, in turn, may be readily infected by human agents such as parainfluenza virus types 1, 2, and 3.

The agents that may be encountered include B virus, SV40 virus, miscellaneous simian viruses, foamy viruses, hemadsorption viruses, and possibly LCM and arboviruses. Of prime importance is B virus, which is a definite human pathogen and has invariably resulted in death upon infection. The SV40 virus raises a special problem in that it has been shown to (1) produce tumors in hamsters; (2) to cause a malignant type of transformation in cells of human origin as well as in a variety of other cells in culture; (3) to enter into genetic recombination with other viruses to produce "hybrids"; and (4) to fail to be completely inactivated by formaldehyde with the result that trace amounts of live virus could be detected in certain killed vaccines prepared in rhesus kidney cultures.

The remaining simian contaminants including the foamy and hemadsorption viruses are probably not infectious for man although the isolation of SV5 virus from man has been reported.

b. *Avian Contaminants.* Although chickens are known to be infected with various viral agents such as infectious laryngotracheitis virus (ILT), infectious bronchitis virus (IBV), avian orphan virus (GAL), chicken embryo lethal orphan virus (CELO), myxovirus Yucaipa (MVY), and particularly avian leukosis virus, a number of vaccines both live and killed continue to be produced in chick embryo tissues without any extensive efforts to examine the product for adventitious agents. These "grandfather" vaccines include smallpox, rabies, yellow fever, influenza, and rickettsial agents. To date, no adverse reactions or human oncogenesis attributable to extraneous agents that may have been present in the vaccines have been reported.

Nevertheless, it is important that these human virus vaccines be produced in chick embryo tissue known to be free from avian leukosis viruses. The standards set forth for the production of measles virus vaccine clearly indicate the direction that must be taken in producing any human viral vaccine in tissues derived from chick embryo.

c. *Bovine, Canine, and Guinea Pig Contaminants.* The number of viruses recovered from bovines has been quite extensive, but no attempt will be made to list them. Other than the use of calf lymph smallpox vaccine, bovine tissues have not been extensively employed for vaccine purposes. In spite of the lack of safety testing procedures for viral contaminants in smallpox vaccines, no evidence has been advanced relating to untoward reactions that could be attributable to the presence of foreign viral agents. The major canine contaminants are the viruses of canine infectious hepatitis and canine distemper, and the present regulations make provision for the testing of these agents.

Little is known of the viral contaminants of guinea pigs and the use of tissues derived from these animals for vaccine purposes has been minimal. It is believed that more extensive use of these tissue culture sources will reveal the presence of extraneous agents, both known and new, and standard methods for detection and safety testing will need to be devised.

2. *Unknown Adventitious Agents—Oncogenic Potential*

Concentrated efforts are presently underway on studies of leukemia, lymphoma, and sarcoma of the following species: avian, bovine, canine, human, murine, and others. Interest in this area of investigation has been fostered by the possible occurrence of leukosis viruses in vaccines prepared from the tissues of animals that may be so infected. The present state of knowledge suggests that probably all animal species possess leukosis viruses even though the etiologic agents have not been recovered because means for their detection have not been developed as yet.

The fact that live vaccines, produced in chick embryos that must have contained fowl leukosis virus (smallpox and yellow fever), have been administered to hundreds of thousands of persons without any reported untoward reactions and no statistically or epidemiological evidence of increased incidence of leukemia, strongly indicates that the avian leukosis complex probably has little or no oncogenic potential for man. However, very little is known of the bovine and canine leukemia, lymphoma, and sarcoma agents. It is in this area that the potential danger lies, particularly if live vaccines, derived from the tissues of these animals, are to be administered to infants within the first 6–9 months of life. The hypothetical hazard associated with these types of vaccines is believed to be greater if given by parenteral inoculation rather than orally.

Recent studies have shown that oncogenic capacity and the characteristic of inducing the production of specific antigens in the resulting tumor cells may pass from one virus to another in the course of mixed infections. This phenomenon can be explained by genetic recombination(s) wherein a significant fragment of the genome of one virus is incorporated in the genome of the other. It is thus theoretically possible for the seed virus and/or vaccine virus pools to become "hybridized" with foreign genetic material of an undetected adventitious agent and, in this way, emerge as potentially oncogenic human viruses. In addition, the possibility of genetic recombination has been hypothesized for viruses grown in frankly malignant cell lines even though the release of viruses or other genetically active materials from such transformed cells has not been confirmed experimentally.

IX. Summary

With the discovery and standardization of the *in vitro* tissue culture techniques for the study and propagation of viruses, much progress has been made in the development of safe and effective human viral vaccines. These advances, aided by the new methodology and sophisticated techniques developed in closely related fields, have greatly increased our knowledge relating to the nature and properties of viruses and of cells in culture.

Although rigid criteria for the safety and potency testing of virus vaccines are now either enforced or recommended for use, more recent information has indicated that unexpected problems and potential hazards, principally the risk of carcinogenesis, have increased the anxiety about the safety of tissue culture propagated human vaccines. It is apparent that the standards employed in biological control require periodic revision and reevaluation as knowledge expands and new tests are developed.

The phenomenon of genetic recombination and the part played by "helper" viruses demonstrated among the avian leukosis viruses have emphasized the importance of the substrate employed for virus propagation and vaccine production. These discoveries also have suggested that the use of viral antigens, devoid of their nucleic acid, concentrated and purified by one or more of the many methods now available may be the answer to the danger of hybridization and potential oncogenicity. By employing known and measurable amounts of antigen and incorporating these fractions into an adjuvant formulation, it may be possible to safely and effectively immunize man against multiple viral diseases using smaller volumes of antigen and fewer doses of vaccine.

The final decision to prepare any new viral vaccine, either live or killed, and its final formulation is dependent on the specific agent, the inherent risk associated with natural infection, and the safety and efficacy of the product when measured in field trial assessments.

REFERENCES

Aleksandrov, N. I., Gefen, N. E., Gapochko, K. G., Garin, N. S., Sergeyev, V. M., and Smirnov, M. S. (1961). *J. Microbiol. Epidemiol. Immunobiol.* **32**, 1567.

Artenstein, M. S., Bellanti, J. A., and Buescher, E. L. (1964). *Proc. Soc. Exptl. Biol. Med.* **117**, 558.

Baron, S., Kirschstein, R. L., Van Hoosier, G. L., Jr., Abinanti, F. R., and Hottle, G. A. (1961). *Am. J. Hyg.* **74,** 220.

Beard, J. W., Beard, D., and Finkelstein, H. (1940). *J. Immunol.* **38,** 117.

Beardmore, W. B., Hook, A. E., Sarber, R. W., McLean, I. W., Jr., and Taylor, A. R. (1957). *J. Immunol.* **79,** 489.

Bell, J. A., Hantover, M. J., Huebner, R. J., and Loosli, C. G. (1956). *J. Am. Med. Assoc.* **161,** 1521.

Bellanti, J. A., Artenstein, M. S., and Buescher, E. L. (1965). *J. Immunol.* **94,** 344.

Berman, S., Gochenour, R. B., Cole, G., Lowenthal, J. P., and Benenson, A. S. (1961). *J. Bacteriol.* **81,** 794.

Binn, L. N., Randall, R., Harrison, V. R., Gibbs, C. J., Jr., and Aulisio, C. G. (1963). *Am. J. Hyg.* **77,** 160.

Bodian, D., Morgan, I. M., and Howe, H. A. (1949). *Am. J. Hyg.* **49,** 234.

Buynak, E. B., and Hilleman, M. R. (1966). *Proc. Soc. Exptl. Biol. Med.* **123,** 768.

Cabasso, V. J., Stebbins, M. R., Douglas, A., and Sharpless, G. R. (1965). *Am. J. Vet. Res.* **26,** 24.

Chanock, R. M., Ludwig, W., Huebner, R. J., Cate, T. R., and Chu, L. W. (1966). *J. Am. Med. Assoc.* **195,** 445.

Clavero, G., and Perez Gallardo, F. (1943). *Rev. Sanidad Hig. Pub.* **17,** 1.

Cohen, G. H., and Wilcox, W. C. (1960). *J. Bacteriol.* **92,** 676.

Couch, R. B., Chanock, R. M., Cate, T. R., Lang, D. J., Knight, V., and Huebner, R. J. (1963). *Am. Rev. Respirat. Diseases* 88 (Suppl.), 394.

Cox, H. R. (1938). *Public Health Rept.* **53,** 2241.

Cox, H. R. (1941). *Science* **94,** 399.

Cox, H. R. (1948). *In* "Symposium on Rickettsial Diseases, Dec. 1946," Am. Assoc. Advancement Science, Boston.

Cox, H. R., Cabasso, V. J., Markham, F. S., Moses, M. J., Moyer, A. W., Roca-Garcia, M., and Ruegsegger, J. M. (1959). *Brit. Med. J.* **2,** 591.

Craigie, J. (1945). *Can. J. Res. Sect. E* **23,** 104.

Darwish, M., and Hammon, W. McD. (1966). *Am. J. Trop. Med. Hyg.* **15,** 765.

Davenport, F. M., Hennessy, A. V., and Bell, J. A. (1962). *Military Med.* **127,** 95.

Davenport, F. M., Hennessy, A. V., Brandon, F. M., Webster, R. G., Barrett, C. D., Jr., and Lease, G. O. (1964). *J. Lab. Clin. Med.* **63,** 5.

Dean, D. J., Evans, W. M., and Thompson, W. R. (1964). *Am. J. Vet. Res.* **25,** 756.

DeMeio, J. L., and DeSanctis, A. M. (1966). *Appl. Microbiol.* **14,** 558.

Edmondson, W. P., Purcell, R. H., Gundelfinger, B. F., Love, J. W. P., Ludwig, W., and Chanock, R. M. (1966). *J. Am. Med. Assoc.* **195,** 453.

Eddy, B. E. (1962). *Federation Proc.* **21,** 930.

Enders, J. F. (1960). *Trans. Coll. Physicians Phila.* **28,** 68.

Enders, J. F., and Peebles, T. C. (1954). *Proc. Soc. Exptl. Biol. Med.* **86,** 277.

Enders, J. F., Weller, T. H., and Robbins, F. C. (1949). *Science* **109,** 85.

Enders, J. F., Katz, S. L., Milovanovic, M. V., and Holloway, A. (1960). *New Engl. J. Med.* **263,** 153.

Fazekas de St. Groth, S., and Donnelley, M. (1950a). *Australian J. Exptl. Biol. Med. Sci.* **28,** 45.

Fazekas de St. Groth, S., and Donnelley, M. (1950b). *Australian J. Exptl. Biol. Med. Sci.* **28,** 61.

Fermi, C. (1908). *Z. Hyg. Infektionskr.* **58,** 233.

Fox, J. P. (1956). *Am. J. Trop. Med. Hyg.* **5**, 464.

Fox, J. P., and Penna, H. A. (1943). *Am. J. Hyg.* **38**, 152.

Fox, J. P., Kossobudzki, S. L., and Fonseca da Cunha, J. (1943). *Am. J. Hyg.* **38**, 113.

Fox, J. P., Koprowski, H., Conwell, D. P., Black, J., and Gelfand, H. M. (1957). *Bull. World Health Organ.* **17**, 869.

Francis, T., Jr. (1940a). *Science* **92**, 405.

Francis, T., Jr. (1940b). *Science* **91**, 198.

Francis, T., Jr. (1943). *Science* **97**, 229.

Francis, T., Jr., and Brightman, I. J. (1941). *Proc. Soc. Exptl. Biol. Med.* **48**, 116.

Francis, T., Jr., Napier, J. A., Voight, R. B., Hemphill, F. M., Wenner, H. A., Korns, R. F., Boisen, M., Tolchinsky, E., and Diamond, E. L. (1957). *In* "Evaluation of the 1954 Field Trial of Poliomyelitis Vaccine (Final Report)." Michigan Univ. Poliomyelitis Vaccine Evaluation Center, Ann Arbor, Michigan.

Gard, S., Wesslen, T., Fagraeus, A., Svedmyr, A., and Olin, G. (1956). *Arch. Ges. Virusforsch.* **6**, 401.

Genig, V. A. (1960). *Vestn. Akad. Med. Nauk, USSR* **15**, 46 (in Russian).

Ghendon, I. Z., and Marchenko, A. T. (1959). *Acta Virol. (Prague)* **3**, 250.

Girardi, A. J., Sweet, B. H., Slotnick, V. B., and Hilleman, M. R. (1962). *Proc. Soc. Exptl. Biol. Med.* **109**, 649.

Goodpasture, E. W. (1933). *Southern Med. J.* **26**, 418.

Goodpasture, E. W., Woodruff, A. M., and Buddingh, G. J. (1931). *Science* **74**, 371.

Grayston, J. T., Woolridge, R. L., and Wang, S. P. (1962). *Ann. N.Y. Acad. Sci.* **98**, 352.

Grayston, J. T., Woolridge, R. L., Wang, S. P., Yen, C. H., and Chang, I. (1963). *Proc. Soc. Exptl. Biol. Med.* **112**, 589.

Guinee, V. F., Casey, H. L., Ruthig, D. W., Henderson, D. A., Wingo, S. T., Cockburn, T. A., Nave, F., Thomas, R. E., Vinson, T. O., Calafiore, D. C., Bryan, J. A., Winkelstein, W., Jr., Karzon, D. T., Cox, L. M., Crowley, A. M., Rathbun, M. L., Font, W. F., Alexander, E. R., Peterson, D. R., and Fremont, J. C. (1963). *Am. J. Public Health* **53**, 645.

Hargett, M. V., and Burruss, H. W. (1945). *Am. J. Trop. Med.* **25**, 19.

Hargett, M. V., Burruss, H. W., and Donovan, A. (1943). *Public Health Rept.* **58**, 505.

Hartman, F. W., and LoGrippo, G. A. (1957). *J. Am. Med. Assoc.* **164**, 258.

Hayflick, L. (1963). *Am. Rev. Respirat. Diseases* **88** (Suppl.), 387.

Hayflick, L., and Moorhead, P. S. (1961). *Exptl. Cell Res.* **25**, 585.

Hennessy, A. V., and Davenport, F. M. (1961). *Public Health Rept.* **76**, 411.

Hilleman, M. R. (1966a). *Clin. Pharmacol. Therap.* **7**, 752.

Hilleman, M. R. (1966b). *Progr. Med. Virol.* **8**, 131.

Hilleman, M. R., Stallones, R. A., Gauld, R. L., Warfield, M. S., and Anderson, S. A. (1956). *Proc. Soc. Exptl. Biol. Med.* **92**, 377.

Hilleman, M. R., Warfield, M. S., Anderson, S. A., and Werner, J. H. (1957). *J. Am. Med. Assoc.* **163**, 4.

Hilleman, M. R., Weibel, R. E., Buynak, E. B., Stokes, J., Jr., and Whitman, J. E., Jr. (1967). *New Engl. J. Med.* **276**, 252.

Hirst, G. K. (1941). *Science* **94**, 22.

Huebner, R. J., Rowe, W. P., and Chanock, R. M. (1958). *Ann. Rev. Microbiol.* **12**, 49.

Huebner, R. J., Chanock, R. M., Rubin, B. A., and Casey, M. J. (1964). *Proc. Natl. Acad. Sci. U.S.* **52**, 1333.

Hull, R. N., and Nash, J. C. (1960). *Am. J. Hyg.* **71**, 15.

Hull, R. N., Peck, F. B., Jr., Ward, T. G., and Nash, J. C. (1962). *Am. J. Hyg.* **76**, 239.

Jackson, E. B., Ley, A. C., Binn, L. N., and Smadel, J. E. (1956). *J. Immunol.* **77**, 332.

Jenner, E. (1798). Available in Pamphlet Vol. 4232, Army Medical Library, Washington, D.C. Cassell, London.

Jensen, K. E., Peeler, B. E., and Dulworth, W. G. (1962). *J. Immunol.* **89**, 216.

Johnson, H. N. (1963). *Am. J. Trop. Med. Hyg.* **12**, 604.

Kaplan, C., and Micklem, L. R. (1961). *J. Hyg.* **59**, 171.

Kasel, J. A., Alford, R. H., Lehrich, J. R., Banks, P. A., Huber, M., and Knight, V. (1966). *Am. Rev. Respirat. Diseases* **94**, 168.

Katz, S. L., and Enders, J. F. (1965). *In* "Viral and Rickettsial Infections of Man" (Horsfall F. L., and Tamm, I, eds.), p. 796. Lippincott, Philadelphia.

Katz, S. L., Milovanovic, M. V., and Enders, J. F. (1958). *Proc. Soc. Exptl. Biol. Med.* **97**, 23.

Kempe, C. H. (guest ed.) "International Conference on Measles Immunization," Bethesda, Maryland, Nov. 7–9, 1961" (1963). *Am. J. Diseases Children* **103**.

Kessel, J. F., and Pait, C. F. (1949). *Proc. Soc. Exptl. Biol. Med.* **70**, 315.

Kim, H. W., Canchola, J. G., Vargosko, A. J., Arrobio, J. O., DeMeio, J. L., and Parrott, R. H. (1966). *J. Am. Med. Assoc.* **196**, 819.

Kissling, R. E., and Reese, D. R. (1963). *J. Immunol.* **91**, 362.

Koprowski, H. (1961). *J. Am. Med. Assoc.* **178**, 1151.

Koprowski, H., and Cox, H. R. (1948). *J. Immunol.* **60**, 533.

Koprowski, H., Jervis, G. A., and Norton, T. W. (1952). *Am. J. Hyg.* **55**, 108.

Koprowski, H., Black, J., and Nelson, D. J. (1954). *J. Immunol.* **72**, 94.

Koprowski, H., Norton, T. W., Jervis, G. A., Nelson, T. L., Chadwick, D. L., Nelson, D. J., and Meyer, K. F. (1956). *J. Am. Med. Assoc.* **160**, 954.

Koprowski, H., Ponten, J. A., Jensen, F., Ravdin, R., Moorhead, P., and Saksela, E. (1962). *J. Cellular Comp. Physiol.* **59**, 281.

Lloyd, W., Theiler, M., and Ricci, N. I. (1936). *Trans. Roy. Soc. Trop. Med. Hyg.* **29**, 481.

LoGrippo, G. A. (1958). *J. Immunol.* **88**, 198.

LoGrippo, G. A., and Hartman, F. W. (1955). *J. Immunol.* **75**, 123.

Luzyanina, T. Ya., Smorodintsev, A. A., and Mikutskaya, B. A. (1963). *Acta Virol. (Prague)* **7**, 562.

McClelland, L., and Hare, R. (1941). *Can. J. Public Health* **32**, 530.

McLean, I. Wm., Jr. (1961). *Am. Rev. Respirat. Diseases* **83**, 157.

Magill, T. P. (1940). *Proc. Soc. Exptl. Biol. Med.* **45**, 162.

Mascoli, C. C., Leagus, M. B., Weibel, R. E., Stokes, J., Jr., Reinhart, H., and Hilleman, M. R. (1966). *Proc. Soc. Exptl. Biol. Med.* **121**, 1264.

Matsuda, S. (1962). *Bull. Inst. Public Health, Tokyo* **11**, 173.

Meyer, H. M., Jr., Hostetler, D. D., Bernheim, B. C., Rogers, N. G., Lambin, P., Chassary, A., Labusquiere, R., and Smadel, J. E. (1964). *Bull. World Health Organ.* **30**, 783.

Meyer, H. M., Jr., Parkman, P. D., and Panos, T. C. (1966). *New Engl. J. Med.* **275,** 575.

Milovanovic, M. V., Enders, J. F., and Mitus, A. (1957). *Proc. Soc. Exptl. Biol. Med.* **95,** 120.

Nathanson, N., and Langmuir, A. D. (1963). *Am. J. Hyg.* **78,** 16.

Neurath, A. R. (1966). *Nature* **212,** 875.

Oppenheimer, F., Benesi, E., and Taylor, A. R. (1959). *Am. J. Public Health* **49,** 903.

Ormsbee, R. A. (1962). *J. Immunol.* **88,** 100.

Ormsbee, R. A., Bell, E. J., Lackman, D. B., and Tallent, G. (1964). *J. Immunol.* **92,** 404.

Parkman, P. D., Buescher, E. L., and Artenstein, M. S. (1962). *Proc. Soc. Exptl. Biol. Med.* **111,** 225.

Parkman, P. D., Meyer, H. M., Kirschstein, R. L., and Hopps, H. E. (1966). *New Engl. J. Med.* **275,** 569.

Pasteur, L. (1885). *Compt. Rend.* **101,** 765.

Pasteur, L., Chamberland, Roux, and Thuillier (1881). *Compt. Rend.* **92,** 1259.

Pasteur, L., Chamberland, and Roux (1884). *Compt. Rend.* **98,** 457.

Paul, J. R. (1961). *New Engl. J. Med.* **264,** 651.

Peck, F. B., Jr., Powell, H. M., and Culbertson, C. G. (1955). *J. Lab. Clin. Med.* **45,** 679.

Peck, F. B., Jr., Powell, H. M., and Culbertson, C. G. (1956). *J. Am. Med. Assoc.* **162,** 1373.

Perkins, F. T., and Hayflick, L. (1967). *Science* **155,** 723.

Pollard, E. C. (consulting ed.) "Inactivation of Viruses" (1960). *Ann. N.Y. Acad. Sci.* **83,** 4.

Polley, J. R., and Guerin, M. M. (1957). *Can. J. Microbiol.* **3,** 863.

Potash, L., Tytell, A. A., Sweet, B. H., Machlowitz, R. A., Stokes, J., Jr., Weibel, R. E., Woodhour, A. F., and Hilleman, M. R. (1966). *Am. Rev. Respirat. Diseases* **93,** 536.

Randall, R., Binn, L. N., and Harrison, V. R. (1963). *Am. J. Trop. Med. Hyg.* **12,** 611.

Regamey, R. H., Hennessen, H., Ikic, D., Ungar, J. (eds.). "Symposia Series in Immunobiological Standardization," Vol. I (1966). Karger, Basel (Switzerland).

Robbins, F. C., Enders, J. F., and Weller, T. H. (1950). *Proc. Soc. Exptl. Biol. Med.* **75,** 370.

Robinson, D., Berman, S., Lowenthal, J., and Hetrick, F. (1966). *Appl. Microbiol.* **14,** 1011.

Rowe, W. P., and Baum, S. G. (1964). *Proc. Natl. Acad. Sci. U.S.* **52,** 1340.

Ruegsegger, J. M., and Sharpless, G. R. (1962). *Arch. Internal Med.* **110,** 754.

Ruegsegger, J. M., Black, J., and Sharpless, G. R. (1961). *Am. J. Public Health* **51,** 706.

Sabin, A. B. (1955). *Ann. N.Y. Acad. Sci.* **61,** 924.

Sabin, A. B. (1957). *Special Pub. N.Y. Acad. Sci.* **5,** 113.

Sabin, A. B. (1959). *Brit. Med. J.* **1,** 663.

Sabin, A. B., and Tigertt, W. D. (1956). *Am. J. Hyg.* **63,** 217.

Sabin, A. B., Duffy, C. E., Warren, J., Ward, R., Peck, J. L., Jr., and Ruchman, I. (1943). *J. Am. Med. Assoc.* **122,** 477.

Salk, J. E. (1953). *Am. J. Public Health* **43,** 1384.

Salk, J. E., Bailey, M. L., and Laurent, A. M. (1952). *Am. J. Hyg.* **55**, 439.

Scherp, H. W., Bryan, W. R., Dawe, C. J., Earle, W. R., Habel, K., Huebner, R. J., Reinhard, K., and Smadel, J. E. (1963). *Science* **139**, 15.

Schwab, M. P., Fox, J. P., Conwell, D. P., and Robinson, T. A. (1954). *Bull. World Health Organ.* **10**, 823.

"Seminar on the Epidemiology and Prevention of Measles and Rubella" (1965). *Arch. Ges. Virusforsch.* **16**.

"Seminar on Japanese Encephalitis and Other Arbovirus Infections, Tokyo" (1962). WHO Regional Office, Manilla, Philippines.

Semple, D. (1919). *Brit. Med. J.* **2**, 333.

Sharpless, G. R., Black, J., Cox, H. R., and Ruegsegger, J. M. (1957). *Bull. World Health Organ.* **17**, 905.

Shein, H. M., and Enders, J. F. (1962). *Proc. Natl. Acad. Sci. U.S.* **48**, 1164.

Sherwood, R. W., Buescher, E. L., Nitz, R. E., and Couch, J. W. (1961). *J. Am. Med. Assoc.* **178**, 1125.

Smadel, J. E. (1960). In "Symposium on the Spotted Fever Group." Med. Sci. Publ. No. 7, WRAIR, pp. 55. U.S. Govt. Printing Office, Washington, D.C.

Smith, C. B., Purcell, R. H., Bellanti, J. A., and Chanock, R. M. (1966). *New Engl. J. Med.* **275**, 1145.

Smith, W., Andrewes, C. H., and Laidlaw, P. P. (1933). *Lancet* **2**, 66.

Smorodintsev, A. A. (1944). *Am. Rev. Soviet Med.* **1**, 400.

Smorodintsev, A. A. (1958). *Progr. Med. Virol.* **1**, 210.

Smorodintsev, A. A. (1961). *Progr. Med. Virol.* **3**, 245.

Smorodintsev, A. A., and Chalkina, O. M. (1955). In "Problems of Pathogenesis and Immunology of Virus Infections" (A. A. Smorodintsev, ed.), p. 329. Leningrad, Medgiz (in Russian).

Smorodintsev, A. A., and Klyachko, N. S. (1958). *Acta Virol. (Prague)* **2**, 137.

Smorodintsev, A. A., and Zhdanov, V. M. (1957). *Probl. Virol.* **2**, 65.

Smorodintsev, A. A., Boichuk, L. M., Shikina, E. S., Batanova, T. B., Bystryakova, L. V., and Peradze, T. V. (1960). *Acta Virol. (Prague)* **4**, 201.

Smorodintsev, A. A., Chalkina, O. M., Burov, S. A., and Ilyin, N. A. (1961). *J. Hyg. Epidemiol. Microbiol. Immunol. (Prague)* **5**, 60.

Smorodintsev, A. A., Luzyanina, T. Ya., and Mikutskaya, B. A. (1965). *Acta Virol. (Prague)* **9**, 240.

Stallones, R. A., Hilleman, M. R., Gauld, R. L., Warfield, M. S., and Anderson, S. A. (1957). *J. Am. Med. Assoc.* **163**, 9.

Stanley, W. M. (1944). *J. Exptl. Med.* **79**, 255.

Stanley, W. M. (1945). *J. Exptl. Med.* **81**, 193.

Stokes, J., Jr., Weibel, R. E., Buynak, E. B., and Hilleman, M. R. (1967). *Pediatrics* **39**, 363.

Svet-Moldavsky, G. Ja., Andjaparidze, O. G., Unanov, S. S., Karakajumcan, M. K., Svet-Moldavskaja, I. A., Mucnik, L. S., Hieninson, M. A., Ravkina, L. I., Mtvarelidze, A. A., Volkova, O. F., Kriegshaber, M. R., Kalinkina, A. G., Salita, T. V., Klimovickaja, V. I., Bondaletova, I. N., Rojhel, V. M., Kiseleva, I. S., Levcenko, E. N., Marennikova, S. S., and Leonidova, S. L. (1965). *Bull. World Health Organ.* **32**, 47.

Sweet, B. H., and Hilleman, M. R. (1960a). In "Second International Conference on Live Poliovirus Vaccines." Pan American Sanitary Bureau, Scientific Pub. No. 50, pp. 79. Washington, D.C.

Sweet, B. H., and Hilleman, M. R. (1960b). *Proc Soc. Exptl. Biol. Med.* **105,** 420.

Sweet, B. H., Tytell, A. A., Potash, L., Weibel, R. E., Stokes, J., Jr., Drake, M. E., Woodhour, A. F., and Hilleman, M. R. (1966). *Am. Rev. Respirat. Diseases* **94,** 340.

"Symposium on the Characterization and Uses of Human Diploid Cell Strains" (1963). Institute of Immunology, Zagreb, Yugoslavia.

Taylor, A. R., Kay, W. W., Timm, E. A., Hook, A. E., and McLean, I. Wm., Jr. (1957). *J. Immunol.* **79,** 265.

Theiler, M. (1951). *In* "Yellow Fever" (G. K. Strode, ed.), p. 39. McGraw-Hill Book Company, New York.

Theiler, M., and Smith, H. H. (1937a). *J. Exptl. Med.* **65,** 767.

Theiler, M., and Smith, H. H. (1937b). *J. Exptl. Med.* **65,** 787.

Timm, E. A., Rope, E. Z., and McLean, I. Wm., Jr. (1958). *J. Immunol.* **80,** 407.

Towle, L. R. (1960). *Public Health Rept.* **75,** 471.

Trlifajova, J., and Strizova, V. (1966). *J. Hyg. Epidemiol. Microbiol. Immunol. (Prague)* **10,** 510.

U.S. Dept. Health, Education and Welfare, Public Health Service, Biological Products Public Health Service Regulations, Title 42, Part 73, Revised Oct. 1, 1965. Washington, D.C.

van der Veen, J. (1963). *Am. Rev. Respirat. Diseases* **88,** 167.

Van Frank, R. M., Havens, M. L., MacFarlane, J. O., Board, A. V., Kirk, B. E., and Hosley, R. J. (1965). *J. Immunol.* **94,** 475.

Van Hoosier, G. L., Jr., Kirschstein, R. L., Abinanti, F. R., Hottle, G. A., and Baron, S. (1961). *Am. J. Hyg.* **74,** 209.

Weibel, R. E., Stokes, J., Jr., Buynak, E. B., Whitman, J. E., Jr., and Hilleman, M. R. (1967). *New Engl. J. Med.* **276,** 245.

Weller, T. H., and Neva, F. A. (1962). *Proc. Soc. Exptl. Biol. Med.* **111,** 215.

Wesslen, T. (1955). *Arch. Ges. Virusforsch.* **6,** 430.

Wiktor, T. J., and Koprowski, H. (1965). *Proc. Soc. Exptl. Biol. Med.* **118,** 1069.

Wiktor, T. J., Fernandes, M. V., and Koprowski, H. (1964). *J. Immunol.* **93,** 353.

Wisseman, C. L., Sweet, B. H., Rosenzweig, E. C., and Eylar, O. R. (1963). *Am. J. Trop. Med. Hyg.* **12,** 620.

Woodhour, A. F., Metzgar, D. P., Stim, T. B., Tytell, A. A., and Hilleman, M. R. (1964). *Proc. Soc. Exptl. Biol. Med.* **116,** 516.

Woodhour, A. F., Sweet, B. H., Tytell, A. A., Potash, L., Stokes, J., Jr., Weibel, R. E., Metzgar, D. P., and Hilleman, M. R. (1966). *Am. Rev. Respirat. Diseases* **94,** 350.

World Health Organ. Tech. Rept. Ser. **179** (1959). Annex 1, 11.

World Health Organ. Tech. Rept. Ser. **200** (1960).

World Health Organ. Tech. Rept. Ser. **263** (1963).

World Health Organ. Tech. Rept. Ser. **321** (1966).

World Health Organ. Tech. Rept. Ser. **323** (1966a). Annex 1, 11.

World Health Organ. Tech. Rept. Ser. **323** (1966b). Annex 2, 23.

World Health Organ. Tech. Rept. Ser. **323** (1966c). Annex 3, 37.

World Health Organ. Tech. Rept. Ser. **323** (1966d). Annex 4, 56.

World Health Organ. Tech. Rept. Ser. **325** (1966).

World Health Organ. Tech. Rept. Ser. **329** (1966).

Zdrodovskii, P. F., and Genig, V. A. (1962). *Vop. Virusol.* **7,** 355 (in Russian).

Zhdanov, V. M. (1961). *Ann. Rev. Microbiol.* **15,** 297.

10

Methods for Containment of Animal Pathogens at the Plum Island Animal Disease Laboratory

Jerry J. Callis and George E. Cottral

I. Introduction 465
II. General Features of a Microbiological Safety Program ... 466
   A. Rationale of Microbiological Safety 466
   B. Microbiological Safety Regulations 468
   C. Instructions 471
   D. Microbiological Safety Violations 472
III. Laboratory Location, Design, and Operation 472
   A. Location 472
   B. Design 473
   C. Traffic Control 473
   D. Operational Procedures 474
   E. Sewage and Air Control 475
IV. Animal Facilities 476
   A. Animal Supply 476
   B. Entry and Exit—Animal Rooms 477
   C. Techniques for Animal and Necropsy Rooms 477
V. Laboratory Techniques 478
   A. General Rules 478
   B. Laboratory Safety Precautions 479

I. Introduction

The Plum Island Animal Disease Laboratory (PIADL) was established to provide a facility in the United States for research on foreign diseases of animals. The need for this facility existed for many years but became increasingly apparent when foot-and-mouth disease (FMD) occurred in Mexico in 1946 and in Canada in 1952. The laboratory was authorized by Congress in 1948, but funds were not appropriated until 1952. The enabling legislation required that the research facility be located on a coastal island, separated from the mainland by deep, navigable waters. The Secretary of Agriculture was directed to provide facilities for research on FMD and other foreign, contagious

465

diseases of animals that, in his opinion, constituted a threat to the livestock industry of the United States.

Foot-and-mouth disease is one of the world's costliest livestock infections; most livestock sanitation authorities consider it the number one enemy of profitable animal husbandry. Every practical means for excluding FMD and other foreign diseases of animals is used daily at our various ports and border stations, and regulations regarding importation of animals, animal products, and animal disease agents for study are very strict. By these controls and good fortune, this country has been kept free from FMD since 1929. Therefore, special provisions were made for containment of viruses in PIADL facilities in contrast with the more lenient measures used in countries where FMD or other contagious diseases of livestock occur frequently.

II. General Features of a Microbiological Safety Program

A. RATIONALE OF MICROBIOLOGICAL SAFETY

The goal of any microbiological safety program should be to establish as complete control as necessary over the disease agents being investigated, to prevent where applicable (1) infection of the human, animal, or plant populations of the neighboring or contact areas, (2) infection of personnel handling disease agents and, (3) cross-infections in experimental subjects that would nullify results of investigation. When the host range or contagious nature of a disease agent is not known, the precautions should be stringent until definitive evidence on these factors has been obtained; it is less difficult to downgrade a safety program than to upgrade it.

A microbiological safety program may be likened to a wheel supported by five types of safety measures, and the hub word is "communicate." If the hub or any of these major safety measures is disregarded or fails, the safety program wheel becomes unbalanced or inadequate and may fail entirely. All microbiological safety measures may be classified under one or more of the five categories: avoid, protect, confine, dilute, and decontaminate (Fig. 1). To be effectively implemented, these measures must be communicated, and each employee must actively participate in the program.

1. Avoid

Unnecessary exposure to disease agents is avoided by restricting and controlling the movement of personnel and equipment into potentially contaminated areas.

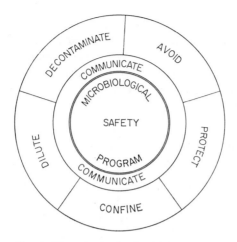

FIG. 1. The wheel of microbiological safety.

2. Protect

Individuals may be protected from infection with disease agents by vaccination or by use of protective clothing, masks, etc. Experimental animals may be protected from cross-contamination by confinement in isolation cages or rooms. The proper design of buildings and control of air, water, and sewage flow are also protective measures.

3. Confine

When disease agents are handled only within enclosed areas and sealable devices are used, they may be confined so that spread of contamination is controlled.

4. Dilute

The danger from disease agents may be reduced by dilution. The washing of animal rooms dilutes the contamination so that disinfectants may do a better job. Air filtration may be a form of dilution, depending upon efficiency of media.

5. Decontaminate

Contaminated surfaces and materials may be decontaminated by a variety of physical and chemical means. These may include methods from steam-pressure sterilization or pH changes to ethylene oxide, γ-radiation, or even sunlight exposure.

6. *Communicate*

When all applicable safety measures are outlined and communicated to all personnel involved so that they clearly understand what they may and may not do and what to do when accidents occur, a workable microbiological safety program will result and the wheel will revolve in a smooth manner.

B. Microbiological Safety Regulations

Before a microbiological safety program is put into effect, regulations should be promulgated to define the requirements and point out the acts of employees that are to be strictly controlled. As examples, the following regulations form the working basis of the microbiological safety program of the PIADL (the term "agent safety" as used herein is synonomous with "microbiological safety"):

1. *Admittance*

No person will be admitted to Plum Island, into animal quarantine units, into specified restricted areas, into the laboratory compound, or into the laboratories without having in his or her possession a specific approved pass or permit authorized by the director to enter such areas. Furthermore, the pass must be presented at the request of any guard or other safety representative who has been instructed to examine such passes.

2. *Visitors*

All official visitors must be sponsored by authorized employees of the PIADL staff and must be accompanied by a responsible employee at all times during their visit to Plum Island.

3. *Animal Contact*

a. All Plum Island employees and official visitors, as a condition of employment and admittance to Plum Island, must agree to avoid contact with susceptible animals off Plum Island and the actual areas where such animals are held for a period of 72 hours, dated from the time of last exit from Plum Island.

b. As a condition of employment and entry, all Plum Island employees and official visitors who enter the laboratories, the laboratory compounds, or any animal quarantine units must agree to avoid all contact with susceptible animals off Plum Island and the actual areas where such animals are held for 7 days, dated from last exit from the areas specified.

c. The susceptible animals referred to in (a) and (b) will vary in accordance with the disease or diseases being studied at a given time. All employees will be notified when any changes are made.

4. Vehicles

Only authorized vehicles may be brought to the Plum Island dock area from Long Island. These vehicles will not be permitted to proceed beyond the fenced Plum Island dock areas, and no other vehicle may be substituted for the authorized vehicles.

5. Introduced Items

All items introduced into the laboratories and laboratory compounds require advance approval of the safety officer or individuals designated by him except normal consumable operating supplies such as animals, eggs, feed, food, Dry Ice, chemicals, and glassware.

6. Personal Articles

No personal equipment may be brought to Plum Island or taken into the laboratories without specific agent safety authorization. The general rule for employees and official visitors is that they will enter and leave Plum Island with only personal items such as clothing, corrective appliances, jewelry, money, and cosmetics, worn or carried on the person. All other materials, equipment, and packages that are to be removed from Plum Island or from a laboratory by any individuals must be specifically approved for removal by the safety officer, who will also determine the need and method of disinfection for the various items.

7. Emergency

In the event of an agent safety emergency, the PIADL reserves the right to bar the admittance of any person or to detain temporarily any or all individuals on Plum Island, to require the individuals to take a decontaminating shower, and temporarily to substitute noncontaminated clothing for personal clothing before leaving Plum Island.

8. Removal of Materials from Laboratory

Authorized employees and official visitors may leave the exterior clean locker rooms and the laboratory compounds with only personal items, such as clothing, corrective appliances, jewelry, and money, worn or carried on the person. Nothing else may be removed from the laboratory buildings or the laboratory compounds without approval of the safety officer, who will prescribe the method of disinfection.

9. *Laboratory Entrance*

Persons entering the laboratories may do so only through approved entrances, and they must remove all clothing, corrective appliances, and jewelry before proceeding beyond the exterior clean locker rooms.

10. *Laboratory Exit*

Persons leaving the laboratories must do so via approved exits, and they must remove all laboratory clothing in the interior locker rooms and follow all applicable agent safety instructions pertaining to personal decontamination, including a decontaminating shower, before proceeding beyond the laboratory shower stalls.

11. *Decontamination*

All decontaminating procedures for personnel, equipment, and facilities and operation of all decontaminating equipment must be accomplished according to specific agent safety instructions.

12. *Wastes*

All trash, garbage, manure, and other waste materials must be disposed of on Plum Island in accordance with agent safety instructions.

13. *Insect and Vermin Control*

All reasonable precautions must be taken to prevent the introduction of parasites, insects, and vermin into the laboratories, the animal quarantine units, or onto Plum Island.

14. *Utilities*

Utilities and related equipment affecting agent safety of the Plum Island installation may not be altered without specific agent safety authorization.

15. *Storage or Disposal of Infectious Materials*

All biological materials, animals, animal tissues, fluids, and excreta must be handled and disposed of according to applicable agent safety instructions.

16. *Use of Instruments*

Laboratory equipment and instruments must be properly used according to specific operating instructions and with due regard to the prevention of unnecessary dissemination of infectious materials into or onto personnel, laboratory equipment, rooms, or corridors.

17. *Control of Laboratory Openings*

Emergency or sealed doors may not be opened nor may new openings be made through the exterior walls, roof, or doors of the laboratory buildings without specific agent safety authorization. (Emergencies threatening serious injury or death are excepted.)

18. *Safety Personnel*

All guards or other safety personnel engaged in agent safety enforcement procedures must carry out their special instructions and may not deviate therefrom without specific agent safety authorization.

19. *Encouraging Violations*

Employees may not aid, encourage, or direct any individual to violate a safety regulation or deviate from agent safety instructions.

20. *Reporting Violations*

Personnel shall report promptly to the director, through the safety officer, any agent safety violation that occurs or that is observed in the acts of others.

21. *Employee Participation*

All personnel shall cooperate at all times with the guards, other safety representatives, or other personnel to accomplish agent safety procedures in an orderly and expeditious manner.

22. *Director's Responsibility*

The director of the PIADL shall develop and issue or cause to be issued such additional instructions as are necessary to implement these agent safety regulations.

C. INSTRUCTIONS

Employees should be indoctrinated regarding the accepted methods for complying with all microbiological safety regulations by means of lectures, demonstration, and written safety instructions. The objective should be to help employees perform correctly rather than to catch them in booby traps. There are written safety instructions covering all important procedures.

D. MICROBIOLOGICAL SAFETY VIOLATIONS

The microbiological safety program should be backed up with provisions for enforcement and penalties for willful violations of the regulations and instructions. A microbiological safety review board is a helpful means for investigating alleged violations and making recommendations regarding seriousness and willfulness of the act involved. Final judgment should be left with administrative and personnel officials. Microbiological safety violations are divided into first- and second-degree violations, depending on the potential danger involved in the act, and the penalties may range from a verbal or written reprimand to loss of pay or dismissal.

An example of a first-degree microbiological safety violation is the unauthorized removal of virus materials from the laboratory. If such an act were willfully committed, the penalty would be dismissal.

III. Laboratory Location, Design, and Operation

The location, built-in safety features, convenience of floor plan, and efficiency of mechanical equipment for handling wastes and air all contribute to a successful laboratory microbiological safety program. Design deficiencies can greatly magnify safety problems and are costly to correct.

A. LOCATION

Plum Island contains about 800 acres situated about 1.5 miles off the eastern end of Long Island and over 10 miles from Connecticut and Rhode Island. The southerly prevailing winds of the warmer months and the northerly winds of winter, in addition to the large bodies of water surrounding the island, afford a great measure of dilution for any air- or water-borne disease agents that might escape laboratory air filtration or sewage heat inactivation. Furthermore, the closest land areas on eastern Long Island are practically devoid of livestock susceptible to the diseases under investigation.

B. DESIGN

A safety-designed laboratory building should be constructed in such a manner that it is virtually fireproof and so that each floor and room can be considered relatively waterproof, airtight, and insect- and verminproof. Thus, only the controlled entrances and intakes and exits and exhausts would need continual surveillance for trouble on the outside or between floors. All windows should be sealed shut and all expansion joints and pipe sleeves should be filled with a pliable material that continually effects a seal. It is disturbing to discover fluid dripping down from the floor above, or to find a colony of ants moving through joints attempting to relocate their disrupted ancestral homesite.

The interior walls, floors, and ceilings should be made of materials that are smooth and easily cleaned. They also should withstand disinfection, including use of either alkaline or acid solutions.

Electrical conduits, piping, and duct work should be confined to machinery areas and enclosed spaces to eliminate extra cleaning. However, if hollow spaces between walls exist, they should be sealed between rooms and floors and should not be violated by insertion of unsealed electrical conduits and boxes, piping, or duct work. If conventional construction were allowed, air movement between walls or through electrical conduits could carry pathogens from one infected area to another or to clean areas; this is particularly important in animal rooms and all contaminated areas.

Other built-in safety features include: double-door autoclaves, pass-through disinfectant traps, break-tanks for water supply system, conveniently located steam and water supply stations for wash down and cleaning, air locks, showers, storage facilities for sterilized rubber clothing, and safety equipment and filters on vent pipes.

C. TRAFFIC CONTROL

The laboratory floor plan should be carefully designed with due regard for definite flow patterns of movement into buildings and between laboratory areas for personnel, animals, feed, supplies, and equipment. The admittance of personnel into laboratories and the introduction or removal of materials should be accomplished only by trained personnel familiar with all safety precautions for the entire operation. The safety force at PIADL has this responsibility for the island as a whole and for each laboratory building.

Personnel entrances and exits are kept to a minimum—one for each sex to each major work area. In outer locker rooms, all clothing, jewelry, and appliances (including eyeglasses) are removed. In inner locker rooms, laboratory clothing is provided, as well as prescription eyeglasses. Upon leaving laboratory areas, all personnel are required to disrobe, scrub hands, clean fingernails, and take a soap bath shower in an intermediate area before entering the outer locker rooms to don personal attire. Laboratory clothing and towels are sterilized and then sent to the laboratory laundry for washing and redistribution.

Animals, equipment, and supplies are delivered to previously disinfected air locks, with mechanically interlocked doors to prevent opposite-end doors being opened simultaneously. After removal of contents, air locks are completely disinfected and sealed before reuse. Feed for large animals is either delivered by means of air locks or is elevated to a feed area where it is placed in closed feed chutes for controlled discharge into each animal room manger.

Autoclaves with interlocked doors at both ends also are used for pass-through of small pieces of equipment. The steam-sterilized chamber is superior to the chemically disinfected air lock for certainty of safety control.

D. OPERATIONAL PROCEDURES

All animal carcasses and burnable trash are incinerated. The material is moved through air locks or chutes to the incinerator area, which is attached to the laboratory building. The air locks, chutes, and corridors are disinfected after each use. The incinerators are charged only after they are operating at a temperature of 820°C or higher.

Nonburnable materials are removed from the laboratory after autoclave sterilization. The material is then buried in specific disposal areas. Biological materials, special equipment, and instruments are moved between laboratory buildings by enclosing them in safety containers, which then can be subjected to exterior-surface chemical decontamination in air locks. If instruments (e.g., microscopes, telephones, cameras, etc.) must be decontaminated prior to closure of safety containers, this is accomplished in gas sterilizers, using ethylene oxide or other gas sterilants. Gas sterilization also may be used for books and photographic film. Another technique for developed photographic film decontamination is immersion in a 2.0% solution of formalin at the point of exit. This may be used for both color and black and white emulsions. Developed black and white film also may be decontaminated in a bath of 2.0% acetic acid unless the pathogen is acid resistant. Movement of loaded film holders and cassettes between areas within laboratories is accomplished by wiping exterior surfaces with a disinfectant solution prior to placement in a sealable carrying case.

Materials with a residual amount of radioactivity from tracer studies are removed from the laboratory in sealed containers (disinfected) and buried in an isolated, marked area. Disposal equipment for liquids and burnable wastes from radioactive tracer studies, as well as the actual work areas, are monitored frequently to determine safety from a radiological standpoint.

E. SEWAGE AND AIR CONTROL

Liquid and sewage wastes from all laboratory buildings, including manure and blood from animal and necropsy rooms, are pumped through sealed piping to disposal plants, where the material is heated to destroy the pathogens before the material is released into the adjacent bodies of water. This may be done either by the batch-tank or by the continuous-flow retention tube methods. The minimum treatment consists of holding the material at a temperature of 93°C for 20 minutes.

Air pressure in laboratory buildings is controlled so that air flows from clean to buffer and thence to contaminated areas. Within potentially contaminated areas, air movement is from corridors into laboratories or animal rooms. The incoming air is filtered to remove dust and is heat tempered or air conditioned as seasonably necessary to control temperature and humidity.

Exhaust air is passed through electrostatic dust collectors or prefilters (throw-away type) and then through microbiological spun-glass filter beds. Safety cabinets are provided with their own filter chambers, which then are connected to room exhaust system. Special decontamination procedures are followed when the filter medium is removed and replaced. The used filter media are incinerated, leaving only a minimum residue of molten glass. In one laboratory building, zone air filtration is used for a series of rooms, while in another building each room or corridor has its own filters in ducts above the ceiling or within the room. Either system is workable, and the filter media used are about 99% efficient. The entire filter system must be monitored carefully so that clogged filters do not upset the control of air movement. The efficiency of the filter system also depends upon careful replacement of media and seal of supporting frames within duct work or filter chambers. All air exhaust ports or stacks should be located as far as possible from air intake ports.

IV. Animal Facilities

A. ANIMAL SUPPLY

Mice and guinea pigs are raised in isolated facilities on Plum Island. Most of the other species of animals are purchased from commercial breeders. Occasionally, swine, sheep, rabbits, and chickens are raised in small numbers for special purposes (e.g., specific pathogen- and colostrum-free pigs delivered by Caesarean section).

Cattle are brought from the breeder's ranch by a vendor's truck to a receiving station about 40 miles from the eastern end of Long Island. After unloading, the truck is disinfected and taken away. Then a federally owned truck is used to transport the cattle to the dock area of Plum Island via PIADL water transportation. The cattle are unloaded on a transfer platform and the truck is disinfected and removed from the island. The cattle then are loaded on a Plum Island-confined truck and taken to an animal holding facility. After a 14-day quarantine period, they may then be loaded on the Plum Island truck and taken to a transfer platform at the entrance to the walled compound of either laboratory. This truck is then disinfected before reuse. At one laboratory, the cattle are reloaded on a laboratory compound truck for delivery to the building air lock. At the other laboratory, the cattle are driven through fenced lanes and up a ramp to a second floor air lock. From these air locks, the animals are moved through corridors and animal wing air locks and then placed in their respectively assigned isolated and decontaminated rooms.

The objective of the various procedures is to break the chain of contact in as many places as necessary to prevent escape of pathogens from the laboratory and to protect the vendor's and other farms from any possible laboratory source of infection. Similar procedures are followed for delivery of other animals, except that small animals are placed in boxes or crates for the various transfers.

Animal feeds and other supplies are delivered to a laboratory receiving station at Orient Point, Long Island, by vendors' trucks and unloaded and reloaded on federally owned vehicles for shipment to Plum Island warehouses. From here the materials are passed through transfer facilities similar to those described above for eventual delivery to laboratory building air locks, where practical, making use of materials handling equipment and moving belts.

B. Entry and Exit—Animal Rooms

After removal of laboratory clothing, personnel may enter and leave animal rooms by three methods.

1. Rubber-Apparel Decontamination

Personnel don sterilized rubber garments (pants, boots, jacket, hat, and gloves), which may or may not be disinfected upon entry, but which must be disinfected and rinsed in the vestibule or air lock of the animal room prior to exit. After leaving the room, rubber clothing is removed and resterilized in an autoclave before reuse. Before redressing in laboratory clothing, personnel are required to wash the face and the part of the neck not covered by rubber clothing. A modification used in one laboratory is that rubber garments are left hanging in the air lock of the animal room for reuse in the same room for the duration of the experiment; they are then resterilized before use in another experiment.

2. Personnel Decontamination

Personnel enter wearing no clothing, but don sterilized coveralls, boots, and gloves in the animal room vestibule or air lock and leave clothing in this area upon exit. With this system, personnel must take a decontaminating shower before leaving the vestibule or shower stall and redressing in laboratory clothing.

3. Common Corridor Approach

Making use of a common corridor between animal rooms, personnel may don rubber garments or coveralls and proceed from room to room without decontamination between rooms, provided the rooms are entered in order of least-expected to most-expected infection (e.g., as in a titration) or if all animals are already known to be similarly infected or when all animals involved are to be destroyed and given necropsy examination. With this method, decontamination procedures would be followed before exit from the common corridor and entry into other laboratory areas.

C. Techniques for Animal and Necropsy Rooms

1. Exposure of Animals

Infectious materials and equipment necessary for animal inoculation are taken into the animal rooms in closed metal carrying cases. The animal room is considered potentially contaminated from a microbiological safety standpoint and thus is subject to restrictions at the moment when vials or containers of infectious material are opened or pierced with a hypodermic needle. Thus, from this point, all equipment or containers of biological material must be disinfected in the room vestibule or air locks prior to removal. Carrying cases containing infectious material are opened in safety cabinets to retrieve biological materials and then are sterilized in an autoclave before removing the used equipment.

2. *Necropsy Facilities*

Necropsy rooms should be adjacent to animal wing corridors and also should have a convenient means of access to the incinerator area for disposal of carcasses. The corridors should have tight-fitting doors so that animals from any room may be taken to necropsy without disturbing the isolated integrity of any other room or contaminating other laboratory areas. The necropsy room should have only the bare necessities, since everything in the room and adjacent corridors involved in moving animals from their room to necropsy must be washed and decontaminated before reuse or opening to other laboratory areas.

3. *Decontamination of Rooms*

The decontamination procedure for rooms consists of:

a. Removing and disposal of prefilters and other objects that are to be discarded.

b. Washing with running water to remove any excreta, feed debris, and dust.

c. Scrubbing the entire room and its contents with a detergent solution.

d. Rinsing to remove the detergent.

e. Spraying the room with 2.0% sodium hydroxide solution and flooding the floor with the same solution.

f. Rinsing the room after a waiting period of 20 minutes and draining the floor disinfectant.

g. Replacing a prefilter.

h. Respraying the rooms with disinfectant and applying the final rinsing immediately before reuse of the room.

V. Laboratory Techniques

A. GENERAL RULES

So-called common sense rules should be followed in handling infectious materials in the laboratory. Before beginning any of the many procedures common to microbiological laboratories, the investigator and his technicians should review their operations from a safety standpoint to determine what safeguards are needed. Their safety objectives should be to provide containment and decontamination procedures to avoid danger from aerosols, drop spilling of infectious materials, contamination of objects by contact with used equipment, and aspiration or movement of infectious materials through equipment beyond control points. If safety techniques are not used, the laboratory room, personnel, and equipment all may become grossly contaminated, and the disease agent may be spread throughout the laboratory building.

B. LABORATORY SAFETY PRECAUTIONS

Laboratory safety precautions may be applied in various degrees from the open-bench aseptic techniques used by general bacteriologists to the entirely closed system employed for extremely hazardous human pathogens. The PIADL safety precautions fall between these two methods. The goal has been to handle the infectious materials as follows:

1. Perform the techniques of general virus preparation, dilution, harvest, removal of supernatant fluids, etc., within safety cabinets that have controlled air flow, exhaust air filtration, and provision for cabinet interior decontamination.

2. Wear rubber gloves and protective clothing when handling infectious materials and decontaminate exposed parts after completion of the operation.

3. Avoid the mouth pipeting technique.

4. Introduce and remove infectious materials in closed vials, bottles, or containers whose exterior surfaces may be disinfected at the moment of their removal from the safety cabinet.

5. Use autoclave sterilization or otherwise decontaminate all equipment removed from the safety cabinet and decontaminate the cabinet interior after completion of procedures. For weighing, centrifugation, and other operations, virus materials in small, closed containers may be disinfected, removed, and replaced in the safety cabinet several times before the completion of a procedure.

6. Use sealable centrifuge cups to avoid aerosol if tubes break, or have a centrifuge attached to the safety cabinet.

7. Load delivery equipment (such as syringes, bulb pipets, gravity flow devices, and electron microscope specimen holders) with infectious material within the safety cabinet and then transport in a closed con-

tainer to the site of use with large apparatus. Use aseptic precautions and disinfectant pans or pads to catch any drops of material spilled when filling apparatus (e.g., electrophoresis).

8. Retrieve preparations from large apparatus by again using precautions as in item 7.

9. Label clearly all preparations of infectious material and store in containers capable of withstanding the thermal shock of freezing and thawing. Freezer chests are difficult to decontaminate.

10. Carry infectious materials to and from various instruments in closed metal containers, and any equipment used to handle the material should be considered contaminated.

11. Have assistant hand hold (wearing gloves) tissue culture tubes or bottles within the entrance port of the safety cabinet for seeding with infectious materials. Flame the neck of the containers upon removal and resealing. This technique is considered less hazardous than operation on an open bench. A safer procedure would be to have an incubator for tissue cultures or embryonating eggs attached to the safety cabinet so that the entire operation may be accomplished within the enclosed environment.

12. Provide isolation rooms with exit decontamination facilities for personnel and equipment for large-volume repetitive techniques (tissue cultures, eggs) or for use of apparatus too large or complex to be placed within safety cabinets (e.g., electrophoresis or chromatography). In some cases, an entire laboratory suite may be considered a contaminated and isolated area. The difficulty with this procedure becomes apparent when a change is made in the disease agents being studied and the formidable task of decontamination is contemplated. Gas sterilization may be used to decontaminate large areas in lieu of decontamination of each object within a room by disinfectant solutions

11 Methods of Storage and Preservation of Animal Viruses

Thomas G. Ward

I. Introduction 481
II. Principles 482
III. Glycerol Storage and Shipping 484
    A. Preparation of Glycerol Solutions 484
    B. Swabs 484
    C. Temperature 485
    D. Length of Storage 485
IV. Refrigeration 485
    A. Diluents 485
    B. Time of Storage 485
    C. Uses 486
V. Freezing 486
    A. Diluents 486
    B. Apparatus 486
    C. Techniques 487
VI. Lyophilization and Freeze-Drying 488
    A. Introduction 488
    B. Techniques 488
    References 489

I. Introduction

The maintenance of animal viruses over long periods of time in a state in which infectiousness remains essentially unchanged has been of inestimable value in the study of viruses. In this chapter some of the principles involved in the various techniques employed are examined along with the laboratory methods for carrying out the procedures.

Edward Jenner, in the latter half of the eighteenth century, preserved vaccinia virus by the simple process of air-drying the scabs. Although he was concerned with maintaining a supply of material with which to inoculate individuals, he also demonstrated the capacity of the virus to survive for long periods of time by this rather crude method of preparation.

Leslie (1811, 1818) used sulfuric acid in a broad pan under a container of water. When the chamber was exhausted, the water froze through vaporization, with the loss of latent heat. Sublimation of the water vapor to the sulfuric acid diminished the ice to the point of exhaustion. This information rested for almost a century without its application to the preservation of microbiol life.

Shockell (1909) recorded the first observation for preserving serum, rabies virus, and meat-preserving bacteria by drying, a process used by some workers today.

The advent of liquid nitrogen together with modern evacuation equipment led to the development of current techniques, the detailed description of which is beyond the scope of this chapter.

Flosdorf and Mudd (1935) were the first to freeze-dry clinical materials. Their observations led to the use of dried plama during World War II.

II. Principles

All animal viruses are living material and thus are not simple structures but vary considerably in their complexity and in their reaction to changes in the physical and chemical state.

A prime consideration in the preservation of animal viruses by freeze-drying, freezing, refrigeration, lyophilization, or glycerol storage is to maintain maximum infectivity with little or no change in antigenicity. The latter will usually not be affected unless the protein moiety is changed. The methods employed must always recognize that protein preservation is essential, and the techniques need to be valid for the preservation of protoplasm in its complicated state.

The nonalteration of the virus surface is considered equally important from the viewpoint of antigenicity and is required if one expects to lose less than 90% (1 log) of the infectivity.

The thermal half-life of the virus in question is an important consideration with respect to the temperature at which the material is prepared, since the various procedures must be accurately controlled.

In general, one should keep the temperature at the cracked ice (0°C) level throughout the procedure until the virus solution can be dried, frozen, or stored in whatever system one is using. Denaturation by organic solvents must be avoided, since viruses are particularly sensitive to the action of these agents. The glassware should be clean and sterile and should be rinsed well with distilled water to remove all traces of the chemical cleaning fluid, soap, or detergents used to clean it.

To retard the action of enzymes which may be present in the virus solution (allantoic fluid from embryonated eggs, peritoneal exudates, tissue suspensions, tissue culture cells and media, etc.), it is necessary to maintain 0°C by use of the cracked ice bath.

If one cannot process the material at once it should be protected from the growth of adventitious bacteria, preferably by storage at 0°C. Bacteriostatic agents, such as merthiolate, should not be added, particularly if one is going to dry the material, since the extraction of water will concentrate the bacteriostatic material, which may cause harm to the virus.

It is preferable to shield the material from UV rays, since these cause deterioration of the virus.

The pH of the suspending medium is critical, since many animal viruses are quite sensitive to changes in the hydrogen ion concentration below pH 6.0. Most of the viruses to be preserved should be maintained at neutral or slightly alkaline pH values—up to 7.8–8.0.

The molarity and the isoelectric point are also points to consider, but since most workers do not use concentrated salt solutions they pose no real danger.

One should avoid shaking the material excessively or causing a foam to form; the use of reducing agents may be indicated in some instances, but usually these materials are not needed. Unfavorable ionic environments should be avoided.

Bryan *et al.* (1950, 1951) indicated the stability of Rous sarcoma virus in a variety of buffers, thus demonstrating the need for selection of the correct buffer pH to maintain the virus. Boesche and Drees (1957), working with encephalomyocarditis virus, was able to demonstrate similar importance of pH to this agent.

In the use of sublimation a low temperature, well below freezing, of the virus solution is essential to prevent chemical change of the labile components.

Among the advantages of freeze-drying are: (1) No foaming occurs because the virus solution is frozen solid. (2) Permanent dispersion is avoided, since the solution is shell frozen to the ampule prior to the application of the vacuum. (3) There is low volatility, despite the vacuum process; the low temperature prevents the escape of these substances, and even toward the end of the drying cycle, when the temperature rises, there is not enough moisture left to volatilize components. (4) Coagulation remains minimal; since the solute molecules and the virus particles are colloidally dispersed, the virus is locked into position. (5) Case hardening does not occur, since as the evaporating frozen ice layer recedes it leaves more and more surface exposed. The lower moisture content renders the product more stable. (6) Oxidation is held to a minimum, since the high vacuum makes the availability of oxygen scant or essentially absent. (7) Sterility of the final product is observed, since the ampule is sealed under vacuum.

III. Glycerol Storage and Shipping

This method is one of the oldest procedures for the preservation of viruses for short periods of time until the material can be placed in refrigeration. It is used in the field, and as the specimens thus preserved are usually clinical material (throat swabs, nasal secretions, anal swabs, etc.) or specimens secured from animal tissues when one is investigating an epizootic, glycerol is used primarily to protect infectiousness of the virus particle for subsequent isolation.

A. PREPARATION OF GLYCEROL SOLUTIONS

The diluent is selected on the basis of the indicator system one expects to inoculate on return of the specimen to the laboratory. For example, if one wishes to use tissue culture cells, he would select Hank's balanced salt solution with 5% calf serum, or if embryonated eggs or mice are the animals to be inoculated, buffered (ph 7.2–7.4) saline would be quite sufficient. To the sterile substrates is added 15% by volume of sterile, buffered (pH 7.2–7.4) glycerol which has been prepared previously. The resulting mixture is distributed in a sterile manner into screw-capped test tubes, usually in 1.0-ml amounts.

B. SWABS

Sterile cotton swabs on applicator sticks are used to collect throat and anal swabs. The specimen is collected and placed in the screw-capped vial, and the end of the applicator stick is broken, burned, and kept in the vial. The cap is replaced, secured with sealing tape, and the tube placed in a mailing tube or a secure rack for transport to the laboratory.

C. TEMPERATURE

If possible, it is preferable to keep the material in cracked ice until it reaches the laboratory. Glycerol is used, however, when no refrigeration is available. The material should be kept out of sunlight, in as cool a place as possible.

D. LENGTH OF STORAGE

Glycerol-stored specimens should be processed as rapidly as possible, since viruses lose their infectiousness with considerable rapidity under room temperature conditions in glycerol-fortified materials.

IV. Refrigeration

This type of preservation of animal virus materials is the most widely used, and all virologists have had experience with its techniques and pitfalls.

A. DILUENTS

One need not be too concerned about the menstruum in which the animal virus is suspended as long as the pH is about 7.0, the osmatic pressure is near that for normal saline, and the vessel containing the suspension is clean, covered, and relatively safe. Ordinarily, buffered saline, most tissue culture media, saline with added serum, or 10% tissue suspension are all excellent diluents. A screw-capped test tube, a vial of almost any size, or various plastic bottles serve as satisfactory containers.

B. TIME OF STORAGE

In this parameter one is dealing with short periods of time for most viruses. On the other hand, influenza virus harvested from allantoic fluid of the embryonated egg stored in screw-capped glass vials in an ordinary refrigerator will maintain infectiousness for at least a year. There will be a 1 or 2 log fall in the titer, but this is immaterial if one is dealing with an infectious dose of 8 or 9 logs.

C. USES

An ice box or ordinary refrigerator that maintains a temperature below 4°C may be used for storage of most animal viruses while one is doing short-term experiments. The antigenicity of most animal viruses will remain essentially constant for several weeks if sterile. The laboratory refrigerator is an essential part of the equipment of a virus laboratory, and one will have constant use for temperatures of 1°–4°C.

V. Freezing

A. DILUENTS

In this method of preservation one is dealing with an entirely different order of shock to the virus particle than is encountered in refrigerator storage. Rightsel and Greiff (1967) classified the problems into three basic stages: "(1) The preparation of the material, including the addition of protective substances, (2) the temperature and rates of freezing, the temperature of storage, the temperature of drying by sublimation of water *in vacuo,* and (3) the thawing of frozen suspensions, or the rehydration of the dried product, and the measurement of residual activities."

The diluent employed must contain at least 1%, and preferably 50%, of protein material (serum, tissue suspensions, etc.) or a substitute (egg albumin, bovine serum albumin, etc.) in order to protect the protein coat of the virus particle covering the essentially infective component of nucleic acid, which is suspended in an aqueous solute with rays of water extending to the lipoprotein segments.

Allantoic fluid of the egg should be fortified with 1% rabbit serum or 5% bovine serum albumin. Fluids harvested from tissue culture cells that contain serum as an additive for the maintenance of the cells needs no further treatment.

B. APPARATUS

The three main methods for freezing animal virus materials are the electric, Dry Ice, and liquid nitrogen techniques. The electric deep freezes vary from −20 to −100°C with two-stage condensors. They have been on the market long enough that the reliability is high, but one should always have Dry Ice available in case of a power failure.

Dry Ice at a temperature of about −76°C is used extensively but requires constant maintenance and care. One of the serious drawbacks to the use of Dry Ice is the CO_2 adsorption to the product stored followed by a lowering of the pH. This can occur overnight and may destroy the virus specimen. To alleviate this difficulty, one must use glass-sealed ampules of Pyrex or equivalent glass. Another drawback has to do with the temperature differential of the box in question; for example, at the bottom of the Dry Ice chest the temperature will be close to −76°C, but near the top it may be only −30°C.

There are several electric deep freezes that are in the temperature range of −20 to −100°C. These boxes have a varying capacity, from a few cubic feet to several dozen cubic feet. Those that keep the temperature below −50°C are 6–20 cubic feet and are designed with the lid on top. In this fashion the cold air does not "roll out." Those that maintain temperature above −50°C may be purchased with doors that swing open. These often have compartmentalized inner doors so that the cold does not escape from all compartments. There are a variety of inserts, metal, plastic, and paper, that one may use for cataloging purposes. If one consults the catalog of a good laboratory supply house he will find a suitable instrument.

During the past decade the use of liquid nitrogen has advanced rapidly. Instruments of considerable capacity (45,000 1-ml ampules) are available at reasonable prices. Liquid nitrogen is in good supply in all centers. One may use screw-capped vials of good quality glass, since the vapor phase of N does not change the pH. Various sizes with a revolving shelf or shelves, compartmentalized with metal inserts, constitute adequate instruments that are easily cataloged. The low temperature (−257°C) makes long-term storage of more specimens possible for anyone.

C. Techniques

1. The volume of virus suspensions is placed in an ampule twice the size of the volume to be frozen. This will allow for expansion in thawing.

2. If storage is to be in the Dry Ice chest, an ampule that may be sealed should be used. The glass must be Pyrex or its equivalent.

3. A screw-capped vial may be used for storage in the electric deep freeze or in liquid nitrogen, since the pH will not be affected.

4. The ampule is quick frozen in Dry Ice and alcohol and is shaken gently to facilitate rapid freezing.

5. To thaw, the ampule is removed from the deep freeze and placed in a water bath at 37°C. This rapid thawing will prevent some of the ice crystallization, which destroys most of the virus.

VI. Lyophilization and Freeze-Drying

A. INTRODUCTION

Since these methods constitute the most important techniques.currently in use, a somewhat more complete examination appears justified (see Lennette and Schmidt, 1964). Most of the lyophilization and freeze-drying is now carried out by shell-freezing the material in an ampule that is then subjected to a very high vacuum (10 μ of mercury or less). This is accomplished by the use of three-stage oil-diffusion pumps, high-vacuum stopcocks, and a condensor surrounded by Dry Ice and alcohol or liquid nitrogen, which is placed between the pump and the ampule. Any moisture that sublimates from the frozen surface of the virus suspension makes its way toward the vacuum pump and is instantly removed from the gaseous state by being frozen to the inside of the condensor. This assists further in lowering the vacuum and prevents the moisture from reaching the oil-diffusion pump.

The diluent employed is vital in these procedures, as demonstrated by Rightsel and Greiff (1967), Greiff et al. (1964; Greiff and Rightsel, 1966, 1967), and by Melnick and Wallis (1963; Melnick, 1965). One should remember to protect the virus from physicochemical stresses by the use of protein, serum, or chemical additives (Pollard, 1953; Parkes and Smith, 1960).

B. TECHNIQUES

1. An ampule should be used that is at least three times as large as the volume to be processed. This will allow for shell-freezing and give greater surface exposure when the vacuum is applied.

To a 3-ml ampule is added 1 ml, to a 15-ml ampoule is added 5 ml, etc. The contents are shell-frozen by swirling in a Dry Ice–alcohol bath, and the ampoule is left submerged until all ampules have been prepared.

2. Each ampule is rapidly transferred to the exhaustion manifold. Time is crucial in order to prevent the shell-frozen material from melting.

3. The vacuum pump is started immediately.

4. The condensor and all connections should be checked prior to filling the ampules. One should check for leaks, check the capacity of the pump by the vacuum gage, and have all connectors greased with silicon and ready for use.

5. Evacuation should be allowed to proceed until all material is dry. There will remain on the outside of the ampule no moisture of condensation.

6. For best results the ampule is sealed under vacuum, and in general the material may then be stored at 4°C or in many instances at room temperature.

7. In reconstituting, one should add back the volume of sterile distilled water equivalent to the original starting material. The substance is shaken, pipeted, and transferred to suitable laboratory glassware.

REFERENCES

Boesche, P., and Drees, O. (1957). *Naturwissenschaften* **44,** 544.

Bryan, W. R., Mauer, M. E., Maloney, J. B., Mood, M. T., and White, C. L. (1950). *J. Natl. Cancer Inst.* **11,** 929.

Bryan, W. R., Mauer, M. E., Maloney, J. B., Calman, D., White, C. L., and Mood, M. T. (1951). *J. Natl. Cancer Inst.* **11,** 929.

Flosdorf, E. W., and Mudd, S. (1935). *J. Immunol.* **29,** 289.

Greiff, D., and Rightsel. W. (1966). *In "Cryobiology"* (H. T. Meryman, ed.), Chap. 15, pp. 698–725. Academic Press, New York.

Greiff, D., and Rightsel, W. (1967). *Cryobiology* **3,** 432.

Greiff, D., Rightsel, W., and Schuler, E. E. (1964). *Nature* **202,** 624.

Lennette, E. H., and Schmidt, N. S., eds. (1964). "Diagnostic Procedures for Viral and Rickettsial Diseases," 3rd ed. Am. Public Health Assoc., New York.

Leslie, J. (1811). *Ann. Chim. (Phys.)* **78,** 177.

Leslie, J. (1818). *Phil. Mag.* [2] **51,** 411.

Melnick, J. L., (1965). *Federation Proc.* **24,** 5.

Melnick, J. L., and Wallis, C. (1963). *Proc. Soc. Exptl. Biol. Med.* **112,** 894.

Parkes, A. S., and Smith, A. V. (1960). "Recent Research in Freezing and Drying." Blackwell, Oxford.

Pollard, E. C. (1953). "The Physics of Viruses." Academic Press, New York.

Rightsel, W. A., and Greiff, D. (1967). *Cryobiology* **3,** 423.

Shockell, L. F. (1909). *Am. J. Physiol.* **24,** 325.

12 Methods of Preservation and Storage of Plant Viruses

Harold H. McKinney and Gustave Silber

I. Introduction 491
II. Laboratory Methods of Preservation 492
    A. Direct Freezing 492
    B. Freeze-Drying (Lyophilization) 492
    C. Chemical Dehydration *in Situ* at Atmospheric Pressure 494
    D. Acetone Powder 499
    E. Glycerine 500
    References 501

I. Introduction

Plant viruses represent a group of organisms whose maintenance for long periods presents problems from the viewpoint of stability and economics. Those viruses that are transmitted by manual methods lend themselves to certain preservation techniques that circumvent the necessity of keeping the virus in living hosts. Preservation techniques applicable to plant viruses can be grouped into the following broad classes: (1) freezing, (2) dehydration, and (3) freeze-drying. The choice of method for preserving viruses is in part dependent on the nature of the specific virus.

Stable viruses, as exemplified by tobacco mosaic virus and most of its strains, can be successfully preserved for many years in extracted plant juice or tissue that is merely air dried and stored at room temperature. Other less stable viruses can be preserved for a limited storage period by freezing the juice or tissue.

II. Laboratory Methods of Preservation

A. DIRECT FREEZING

Freezing temperatures have long been used for storage of plant viruses in tissues and in purified preparations, but no extensive long-term comparative studies have been made to determine the optimum storage temperatures for different viruses. Though temperatures near —20°C are satisfactory for the storage of some labile viruses for several months or a year, better preservation can sometimes be obtained by lower temperatures.

Best and Gallus (1953) successfully preserved tomato spotted wilt virus for 36 days by quickly freezing infected tissue. Best (1961) lengthened the storage period of this same virus to 6 years by freezing and storing the infected tissue at —69°C. Harvested leaves were immediately taken to a cold room (2°C), cut into small pieces, and placed in glass bottles which were either corked or closed with screw caps. The final seal was a special wax composed of an equal mixture of paraffin and petroleum jelly. This wax melted near 50°C and remained firm without cracking at —69°C. Containers of infected tissue were dipped into the melted wax to seal their tops and transferred immediately to a Dry Ice storage box. This method, to date, surpasses all others for preserving tomato spotted wilt virus.

Liquid nitrogen offers promise as a means of preserving many plant viruses. Barley stripe mosaic virus (type strain), cucumber mosaic virus (yellowing strain), lily-fleck corn virus, sugarcane mosaic virus (strain B), tobacco ringspot virus, and tobacco streak virus survived to some degree after 2–3 weeks storage at —196°C (McKinney et al., 1961). In these preliminary tests fresh and/or chemically dehydrated leaf tissue was loaded into small test tubes containing air or 30% glycerine. Loaded tubes were either flame sealed or closed with corks held in place with zinc oxide tape. Further studies are required to determine the best methods for processing the preparations. Since all chemical denaturation processes appear to stop near —100°C (Merryman, 1956), it is possible that virus activity may be preserved at a high level for an extremely long period when stored in liquid nitrogen.

B. FREEZE-DRYING

Rapid freeze-drying in vacuum has been known and utilized for many years to preserve biological materials. The technique received its greatest impetus from demands of World War II, but it still has not been widely used for the preservation of plant viruses. Dykstra and Du Buy (1942) found potato vein-banding mosaic virus and potato Canada streak virus highly active for at least 4 months when the plant juices were extracted in an atmosphere of carbon dioxide, lyophilized, and stored in sealed glass tubes held at room temperatures. Attempts within the past 15 years to preserve labile plant viruses by freeze-drying in vacuum have become more prevalent; their success in some instances lends support to the usefulness and promise of the technique. Hidaka and Tomaru (1960) reported good retention of activity of cucumber mosaic virus in lyophilized infected tobacco tissue. Leaf tissue was cut into small pieces, frozen in an acetone Dry Ice bath, and vacuum dried at a pressure of 10^{-4} mm Hg. Infectivity of tissue stored in ampoules sealed at a pressure of 10^{-1} mm Hg and stored at $0°$–$5°$C was higher than that of tissue removed from open ampules stored over calcium chloride at the same temperature. Activity of the virus was good after 14 months' storage. Best (1961) preserved tomato spotted wilt virus in freeze-dried samples of infected tissue at $-20°$C for more than 32 months. The greater fraction of the tissue's original infectivity was lost during the drying process.

Timian and Klosterman (1962) reported the storage of barley stripe mosaic virus at $-15°$C in lyophilized whole plants and expressed sap without loss of infectivity for 12 months. Material was prefrozen with Dry Ice, and ampules were evacuated for 6 hours at room temperature at a pressure of 0.02–0.05 mm Hg. Tubes were sealed under vacuum and stored at $-15°$C.

Toler and Hebert (1964) reported that lyophilized extracts of oat mosaic virus stored at $-20°$C were active after 234 days. In contrast, the virus was infectious for 204 days in frozen crude juice stored at $-20°$C in polyethylene bags and for 135 but not 198 days when preserved in leaves desiccated over calcium chloride.

If one attempts to freeze-dry extracts of plant viruses by the evaporative technique, the troublesome problem of frothing is encountered. Various methods have been devised to degas the extracts before freezing occurs in order to prevent bubble formation. The centrifugal evaporative freezing technique under vacuum, as described by Greaves (1944), eliminates the need for degassing extracts to be frozen and also has the advantage of distributing the liquid in the tubes so that it offers a better shape for freezing.

Hollings and Lelliott (1960) used the centrifugal freeze-drying method to preserve 46 isolates of 39 virus species. All cultures except that of potato virus A were active after 4–11 months' storage. We learned recently that cucumber mosaic virus, alfalfa mosaic virus, tobacco necrosis virus, and tobacco etch virus cultures were still infectious after 5 years' storage (M. Hollings, personal communication).

Hollings and Lelliott chose a method of freeze-drying the virus preparations that gave good results with bacteria. Seven percent each of peptone (Oxoid) and alpha glucose (w/v) was added to expressed plant juice. About 0.25 ml of this mixture was placed in 0.5-ml ampules (Edwards) and allowed to remain overnight at 0°C. The open ampules were then processed by the centrifugal vacuum method of Greaves (1944, 1954). Hollings and Lelliott used a slightly modified Edwards Model L.5 freeze-drier, which used P_2O_5 as a desiccant.* The Vitis centrifugal Bio-drier, which utilizes a reusable desiccant, would seem to serve as well.

The drying process consisted basically of centrifuging (under vacuum) open ampules or tubes placed in a rotor in a nearly vertical position. Five to 10 minutes' centrifugation sufficed to remove 15–20% of the water and prevented frothing of the preparation as it froze. The centrifuge was then stopped, and further drying by sublimation while under vacuum was continued for 6–24 hours. Ampules were then constricted, dried to completion on a vacuum manifold for 6–24 hours at 0.009–0.02 mm Hg, and flame sealed at this pressure. Storage of sealed ampules was at room temperature.

C. Chemical Dehydration *in Situ* at Atmospheric Pressure

A simple but effective means of preserving many plant viruses is to dehydrate infected tissue chemically near 1°C (McKinney, 1953; McKinney et al., 1965). Tissue is dehydrated in aluminum baking pans 1.5 inches deep, 11 inches long, and 7 inches wide. A piece of cotton gauze is supported by wire screen whose ends are bent downward 0.5 inch to elevate the gauze from the calcium chloride on the bottom of the pan. A piece of window glass serves as a cover.

Prime infected leaf tissue from young actively growing plants is superior to older tissue as a source material. The tissue is cut with shears into small pieces approximately 0.5 inch square or less. No more than 50 gm of tissue should be put into a pan. Large midribs in leaves from tobacco and corn plants are removed and discarded from the

---

* Trade names are given solely for the purpose of providing specific information. Mention of a trade name does not constitute a guarantee or warranty of the product by the U.S. Department of Agriculture or an endorsement by the Department over other products not mentioned.

main mass of tissue. The weight of fresh granular calcium chloride in the bottom of the pan should be at least double the weight of the water in the tissue. The glass cover is sealed tightly to the pan with fresh, high-grade zinc oxide surgical tape 1 inch wide after the clipped tissue is spread evenly over the gauze. The pan is then placed in a refrigerator controlled for 1°C. Pans can be stacked on each other. The dehydrated tissue is ready to be placed in storage bottles after 5–10 days.

Two-ounce bottles with 24-mm openings are preferred for storage. These bottles take a No. 5 rubber stopper, which is made of soft rubber that will not harden at temperatures near freezing. This stopper makes a tight seal, whereas many screw caps allow water vapor to enter the bottle. About 0.8 gm of reagent-grade anhydrous magnesium perchlorate (Anhydrone), which may be covered with a small amount of cotton or a piece of gauze, is placed in the bottom of each bottle. Another 0.8 gm of this dehydrant is placed on a small piece of porous paper whose corners are brought together, wired tightly with a soft copper or iron wire, and placed on the top of the dried tissue within the bottle. The bottles are tightly stoppered for storage.

At the end of the initial dehydration period, the pans are transferred to the laboratory and allowed to reach the laboratory temperature before they are opened. All operations should be carried out as rapidly as is possible in the laboratory. After removing the wad of Anhydrone from one bottle by means of tweezers, the bottle is ready to receive the dehydrated tissue from an aluminum funnel with a shortened tip that is about 22 mm in diameter. The gauze and tissue are carefully lifted from the desiccating pan and spread around the inside of the funnel cone. The tissue is scraped from the gauze with a spatula and pushed into the bottle with an aluminum rod. The wad of Anhydrone is replaced on top of the tissue and the bottle is tightly stoppered and then stored at 1°C. The results from longevity tests on virus species and strains preserved by chemical dehydration of tissue are shown in Table I. These results are based on the use of prime leaf tissue (McKinney et al., 1965).

The data from longevity tests on alfalfa, bean, and pea viruses (Table II), contributed by W. J. Zaumeyer, Crops Research Division, Agricultural Research Service, U.S. Department of Agriculture, are based on tissues processed and stored in the manner described for the viruses listed in Table I.

The results shown in Table III, contributed by J. S. Boyle, Pennsylvania State University, are based on the following modification of

TABLE I

Longevity of Viruses in Clipped Leaf Tissue Dehydrated over Calcium Chloride and Stored in Rubber-Stoppered Bottles with Magnesium Perchlorate (Anhydrone) Near 1°C

Virus	Strain	Reservoir host[a]	Assay plant[a]	Age of culture (years)	Infection (%)
Alfalfa mosaic	Beltsville, Md. cult.	8-A	8-A, B	16½	100.0
Barley stripe mosaic	Latent	13-B	5-A	7¼	70.0
Barley stripe mosaic	Very mild (Glacier 2)	5-C	5-B	5⅔	90.0
Barley stripe mosaic	Mild	5-B	5-B	5⅔	100.0
Barley stripe mosaic	Oklahoma moderat	5-C	5-A	16 1/12	95.0
Barley stripe mosaic	Type	13-B	5-A	14 1/12	100.0
Barley stripe mosaic	Moderate LIT	5-A	5-A	5 1/12	34.7
Barley stripe mosaic	Moderate LSP	5-B	5-A	6	25.0
Barley stripe mosaic	Moderate NSP	13-B	5-A	5½	45.0
Barley stripe mosaic	Yellow-leaf	13-B	5-A	5½	100.0
Barley stripe mosaic	White-leaf	5-B	5-A	2⅔	80.0
Barley stripe mosaic	Coarse-blotch	5-D	5-A	6 5/12	52.0
Barley stripe mosaic	Fleck-blotch	5-B	5-A	6⅔	100.0
Barley stripe mosaic	California mild oat	13-B	1-C	3¾	92.0
Barley stripe mosaic	Spindle-stripe oat	5-D	5-B	2½	66.6
Barley stripe mosaic	Moderate oat	13-B	5-B	9	75.0
Barley stripe mosaic	California moderate oat	1-C	1-C	3¾	97.5
Barley stripe mosaic	Oklahoma moderate oat	1-C	1-C	3¾	50.0
Brome mosaic	Type	2	5-A	16	100.0
Brome mosaic	Type	13-B	5-A	15	100.0

Cucumber mosaic	Type (S. P. Doolittle cult.)	8-A	3, 8-A, B	15¼	100.0
Cucumber mosaic	Celery (S. P. Doolittle cult.)	8-A	8-A, B	17⅓	100.0
Cucumber mosaic	From squash, Beltsville, Md.	8-A	8-A, B	19	20.0
Lily fleck	Corn (F. P. McWhorter cult.)	8-A	15	8⅙	11.7
Nothoscordum mosaic	Teneriffe cult.	9	9	6¼	55.0
Oat mosaic (soil-borne)	Apical	1-B	1-C	2⅔	7.9
Oat mosaic (soil-borne)	Eyespot	1-B	1-C	1¾	6.9
Oat mosaic (soil-borne)	Field cult. (North Carolina)	1-A	1-C	5	13.1
Potato X	Common (E. S. Schultz cult.)	8-A	8-A, B	15	85.0
Potato Y	E. S. Schultz cult.	8-A	8-A, B	15⅙	7.5
Sugarcane mosaic	"B" (E. F. Todd cult.)	15	15	3⅔	17.0
Tobacco etch	Very mild (Pa. cult.)	8-A	8-A, B	15	25.0
Tobacco etch	Severe (Allen farm cult.)	8-A	8-A, B	13¼	10.0
Tobacco ringspot	W. C. Price cult.	8-A	8-A, B	17½	50.0[b]
Tobacco ringspot	Soybean bud blight	8-A	8-A, B	17 7/12	40.0
Tobacco streak	R. W. Fulton cult.	8-A	8-A, B	7¾	100
Wheat mosaic (soil-borne)	Rosette	13-A	13-B	4½	90.0
Wheat mosaic (soil-borne)	Yellow (Clemson cult.)	13-B	13-B	11⅚	16.0
Wheat streak mosaic	Very mild (Kansas No. 42)	13-B	13-B	7½	10
Wheat streak mosaic	Green	13-B	13-B	16	70
Wheat streak mosaic	Yellow	13-B	13-B	16½	80

[a] Numbers and letters refer to species and varieties of plants, respectively, as listed in Table IV.
[b] Twenty percent of the plants developed systemic symptoms; 30% had only single local lesions and no systemic virus.

TABLE II

LONGEVITY OF SOME LEGUME VIRUSES IN CLIPPED LEAF TISSUE DEHYDRATED OVER CALCIUM CHLORIDE AND STORED IN RUBBER-STOPPERED BOTTLES WITH MAGNESIUM PERCHLORATE (ANHYDRONE) NEAR 1°C[a]

Virus	Strain	Reservoir host[b]	Assay plant[b]	Age of culture (years)	Activity
Alfalfa mosaic	Yellow	10-C	10-C	7	High
Alfalfa mosaic	Yellow patch	12	10-B	6⅔	Low
Alfalfa mosaic	Vein necrosis	10-C	10-C	3⅓	Low
Alfalfa mosaic	Idaho	10-D	10-C	1 5/12	High
Alfalfa mosaic	Yellow spot mosaic	10-C	10-C	3 1/12	High
Bean (southern) mosaic	Type	10-A	10-C	8½	High
Bean pod mottle	Type	10-E	10-C	3 5/6	High
Bean yellow mosaic	Type (New Jersey)	14	10-C	2 7/12	Medium
Pea streak	Type	11	11	2¾	Medium
Tobacco streak	Red node	10-C	10-C	7	Low

[a] Data contributed by W. J. Zaumeyer.
[b] Numbers and letters refer to species and varieties of plants, respectively, as listed in Table IV.

TABLE III

LONGEVITY OF VIRUSES IN CLIPPED LEAF TISSUE DEHYDRATED AND STORED OVER
CALCIUM CHLORIDE IN CONTAINERS SEALED WITH GRAFTING TAPE
AND MAINTAINED NEAR 2°C[a]

Virus	Strain	Reservoir host[b]	Assay plant[b]	Age of culture (years)	Activity
Cherry (sour) necrotic ringspot	—	3	6	$9\frac{11}{12}$	Very low
Cucumber green mottle mosaic	Common	3	3	10	Very low
Potato X	—	7	4, 7	$9\frac{2}{3}$	Very low
Tomato ringspot	—	8-A	3, 8-A	$9\frac{3}{4}$	Very low

[a] Data contributed by J. S. Boyle.
[b] Numbers and letters refer to species and varieties of plants, respectively, as listed in Table IV.

the method already described. The clipped virus-infected leaf tissues were dehydrated and stored over calcium chloride in round tin ointment containers 3 inches in diameter and 1 inch high. Two filter papers separated the clipped tissue from the desiccant. The container was sealed with grafting tape, and storage was at temperatures near 2°C. The original calcium chloride usually remained in the containers throughout the entire period of storage. Table IV identifies the species and varieties listed in Tables I–III.

Many viruses have very short survival times when tissue for preservation is taken from old or stunted plants. Survival time is also greatly reduced when water vapor enters a storage bottle that is not properly stoppered, or when the bottle is opened frequently to remove samples of tissue. These factors doubtlessly operated in some of the early cultures of the oat mosaic virus and in the cultures of several other very labile viruses that failed to survive storage for short periods. The authors have found that zinc oxide tape seals are not sufficiently moisture proof for permanent storage containers and that it is best to discard the calcium chloride at the end of the preliminary drying period.

D. ACETONE POWDER

Toler and Hebert (1964) used the acetone powder method to preserve the oat mosaic (soil-borne) virus in their studies. Diseased leaves were collected from oat plants 2–3 weeks after the young seedlings had

TABLE IV

NUMBERS AND LETTERS DESIGNATED SPECIES AND VARIETIES, RESPECTIVELY, OF RESERVOIR AND ASSAY PLANTS AS THEY APPEAR IN TABLES I, II, AND III

1. *Avena sativa* L.: (A) Cherokee, (B) Letoria, (C) Statesville
2. *Bromus inermis* Leyss
3. *Cucumis sativus* L.
4. *Gomphrena globosum* L.
5. *Hordeum vulgare* L.: (A) Atlas, (B) Atsel, (C) Chevron, (D) Moore
6. *Momordica balsamina* L.
7. *Nicotiana glutinosa* L.
8. *N. tabacum* L.: (A) Samsun (B) Holmes' Samsun-NN
9. *Nothoscordum fragrans* Kuth
10. *Phaseolus vulgaris* L.: (A) Black Valentine, (B) Bountiful, (C) Pinto U.I. 111, (D) Stringless Green Refugee, (E) Tendergreen
11. *Pisum sativum* L. Perfected Wales
12. *Trifolium repens* L. *latum* (Ladino clover)
13. *Triticum aestivum* L. em. Thell.: (A) Harvest Queen (rosette susceptible), (B) Michigan Amber
14. *Vicia faba* L. *minor* (broad bean)
15. *Zea mays* L. Golden Giant Sugar

been inoculated. All processing was done in a cold room (2°C) and with equipment cooled to that temperature. The acetone was cooled to —15°C before use. The cooled leaves were chopped into pieces about 0.5 inch long and placed in a Waring Blendor with 10 parts by weight of the cold acetone. The material was filtered through filter paper in a Büchner funnel after blending. The material on the filter paper was washed twice by resuspension in the cold acetone (one-third the volume used for blending) and by refiltering. The washed precipitate was placed in a vacuum-type desiccator over concentrated sulfuric acid and dried overnight. The dried powder was placed in test tubes over calcium chloride, closed with rubber stoppers, and stored at —20°C.

Bioassays of material dried and stored in this manner demonstrated that the virus was active after 6.5 months, but inactive after 12 months. The value of this method should not be judged at this time on the basis of the soil-borne oat mosaic virus, since this has been a difficult virus to preserve for long periods (Table I).

E. GLYCERINE

Glycerine in solutions ranging from 40 to 60% has been tested to a limited extent for preserving a few plant viruses *in situ* (Bercks, 1950).

Limited comparisons, however, have indicated that the decline of activity was greater in tissue stored in glycerine than in control tissue dehydrated over calcium chloride at atmospheric pressure when storage temperatures were slightly above the freezing point (McKinney, 1953).

REFERENCES

Bercks, R. (1950). *Phytopathol. Z.* **16**, 508–510.
Best, R. J. (1961). *Virology* **14**, 440–443.
Best, R. J., and Gallus, H. P. C. (1953). *Nature* **172**, 315.
Dykstra, T. P., and Du Buy, H. G. (1942). *Science* **96**, 189–190.
Greaves, R. I. N. (1944). *Nature* **153**, 485–487.
Greaves, R. I. N. (1954). *In* "Biological Applications of Freezing and Drying" (R. J. C. Harris, ed.), pp. 87–127. Academic Press, New York.
Hidaka, Z., and Tomaru, K. (1960). *Virology* **12**, 8–13.
Hollings, M., and Lelliott, R. A. (1960). *Plant Pathol.* **9**, 63–66.
McKinney, H. H. (1953). *Ann. N.Y. Acad. Sci.* **56**, 615–620.
McKinney, H. H., Greeley, L. W., and Clark, W. A. (1961). *Plant Disease Reptr.* **45**, 755.
McKinney, H. H., Silber, G., and Greeley, L. W. (1965). *Phytopathology* **55**, 1043–1044.
Meryman, H. T. (1956). *Science* **124**, 515–521.
Timian, R. G., and Klosterman, H. J. (1962). *Phytopathology* **52**, 554–556.
Toler, R. W., and Hebert, T. T. (1964). *Phytopathology* **54**, 428–433.

13 *The Optical Diffractometer*

Roy Markham

I. The Apparatus 504
II. The Alignment of the Optical System 507
III. Experimental Procedure 510
IV. The Use of the Optical Diffractometer 511
V. Other Methods for Examining Diffraction Patterns 527
References 529

Viruses are usually made from simple structural units arranged in regular arrays, and therefore electron micrographs of viruses also have similar regularities, though these may be somewhat imperfect because of the harsh treatment to which the particles are subjected during their examination. Such regularities as survive may be detected in a number of ways, one of which is by using the electron micrographs as diffraction gratings for visible light. Diffraction methods have, of course, been used for very many years in light microscopy for the elucidation of structures near the limits of visibility, and optical diffraction was used on viruses as early as 1950, when Wilkins *et al.* showed that the crystalline inclusions of tobacco mosaic virus were sufficiently perfect gratings to separate the lines of the mercury arc spectrum. The application of optical diffraction methods to electron micrographs of viruses, however, had to await the development of modern negative staining techniques, and was first described by Klug and Berger in 1964.

Optical diffraction methods have the advantage of being particularly sensitive to small regularities and are capable of providing a fair amount of discrimination against random "noise," though the extent of such discrimination is poor compared with that achieved by x-ray diffraction methods. Nevertheless, the technique is a powerful weapon in the armory of the electron microscopist.

It should, perhaps, be remarked here that the discrimination referred to above is not obtained without penalty. Diffraction methods are by virtue of their nature ambiguous, and this is the penalty that has to

503

be paid for the extraction of the additional information. It might be noted here that those results obtained so far by diffraction methods unaccompanied by complementary techniques do not suggest that these problems have been entirely overcome. One has only to refer to x-ray diffraction experiments, in which case the diffraction pattern or "transform" has to be accepted without any other choice, to see how frequently the reciprocal structure has been deduced from the data available. In x-ray diffraction, ambiguities have to be resolved by careful and tedious experimentation. In the case of visible light diffraction, this has to be achieved by careful examination of the original electron micrographs by one or another of several independent methods.

The apparatus first used by Klug and Berger was originally designed (Taylor and Lipson, 1964) for the examination of diffraction spectra produced by macroscopic patterns of circular holes punched in an opaque base. These patterns represented the projections of atoms in crystal lattices on planes, and the objective was to compare their transforms with those produced by the actual atoms in analogous x-ray diffraction experiments, a kind of empirical approach to frequency changing from the x-ray spectrum to the visible one. Needless to say this kind of apparatus was not ideally suited to the examination of electron micrographs which have a much smaller size and also very much smaller spacings, these being of the order of 0.1–0.5 mm in electron micrographs taken at the more usual electron-optical magnifications (50–100 thousand times).

The availability of low-power helium-neon lasers removes most of the problems connected with diffractometer design, because not only do these lasers provide a source of coherent light at more than adequate intensity, but they can also be used for the accurate and rapid alignment of the optical system, a procedure which has hitherto been both difficult and time consuming. Moreover, the light intensity available is such that a final stage of magnification can be incorporated in the diffractometer, permitting a usable size transform to be recorded directly in a few seconds on a 5 inch × 4 inch Polaroid P/N film. A diffractometer incorporating these features may be assembled from commercially available parts with a minimal amount of modification.

I. The Apparatus

The basic apparatus is mounted on a triangular section optical bench (Fig. 1). The laser, a, which produces light at 6328 dnm,* is

* 1 dnm $= 10^{-10}$m $= 1$ Å.

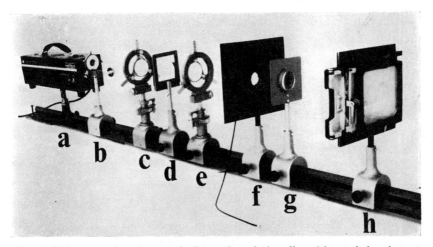

FIG. 1. This composite photograph shows the relative dispositions of the elements comprising the diffractometer. The elements are considerably closer than they are in use. Details of the actual distances are given in the text. The elements are: *a*, laser on special saddle mount; *b*, beam spreading lens in centering mount; *c*, first collimating lens; *d*, screen holder; *e*, second collimating lens; *f*, metal screen with shutter; *g*, projection lens; *h*, camera back and Polaroid back.

model 130 B (Spectra Physics, Mountain View California, U.S.), and is operated with a hemispherical resonator. It is mounted on a modified optical bench saddle cut down to 30 mm above the bench level (Fig. 2). On the saddle is fitted a cranked vertical pin for horizontal adjustment which carries a Lablox adjustable angle adapter (Gallenkamp, London, England, No. SM-528), the solid end of which has a ½-inch screw, 12 threads/inch, cut on it to fit the laser base plate, which is locked in position by a flat locknut. The height of the laser beam is about 18.6 cm above the level of the optical bench.

The other components (Fig. 1) are: *b*, a microscope objective holder with centering (No. 2055) adapted to hold a 5-cm focal length biconcave lens; *c*, an adjustable and traversing lens holder (No. 2035) modified as in Fig. 3, and mounted on a saddle with vertical adjustment (No. 2017); *d*, a glass screen holder (No. 2056) for carrying the electron micrographs being examined; *e*, as *c*; *f*, a 20-cm square metal plate holding a 1⅛-inch aperture photographic shutter; *g*, a 10-cm focal-length projection lens (No. 2044); and *h*, a standard 5 inch × 4 inch camera back mounted on an optical bench pin, and carrying a Polaroid 5 inch × 4 inch film back. Items *b, d, f, g,* and *h* are mounted on saddles (No. 2008), and the saddle for *a* may be No. 2012 (but that in the figures is not). The four-figure serial numbers are those of

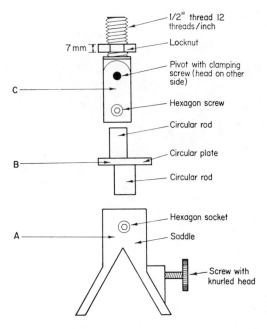

FIG. 2. Details of the adjustable mount for the laser are given. A, short saddle; B, cranked pin with central flat plate; C, adjustable angle adapter with thread cut to fit laser base. B permits the lateral adjustment of the laser beam with respect to the optical bench, while C allows the beam to be tilted up or down.

the Precision Tool and Instrument Co. Ltd., 353, Bensham Lane, Thornton Heath, Surrey, England.

The lenses in c and e are 2 inches in diameter, first-quality, plano-convex lenses of 1-m focal length, hard surface-bloomed, and were obtained from C. J. Whilems, Forest Road, Barkingside, Essex, England. The actual maximum lens aperture used is rarely more than 10 mm so that there is nothing to be gained by using more complex lens systems.

The approximate distances from the saddle of a to that of the rest of the components, when the final projection magnification is about 3.5 times are: b, 19 cm; c, 111.5 cm; d, 121.5 cm; e, 131.5 cm; f, 234.5 cm; g, 247 cm; h, 289 cm. Components a to e may be mounted on a 2-m optical bench (No. 2004) and f, g, and h on a 1-m bench (No. 2002).

The optical bench is set up inside a darkened room, preferably painted matt black inside, when no camera bellows will be needed. If space is at a premium the apparatus may be "folded." Plane mirrors suitable for doing this are also available (No. 2069). If the use of bellows is intended, note that it is important that the source (the laser beam and its negative lens) be very well shielded, because the final transform is a series of images of the "point" light source and its surroundings.

II. The Alignment of the Optical System

The main optical bench (No. 2004) is preferably permanently fixed on a substantial base and in our laboratory is mounted floating on short vertical tubes resting on heavy wall brackets, and leveled with a clinometer. However, leveling feet (No. 2006) are available which enable the apparatus to be set up on normal laboratory benching.

First, the laser (a, Fig. 1) is fixed at one end of the bench and aligned approximately by eye. A card is put on a screen holder (No. 2056) (d, Fig. 1), and the center of the laser beam is marked on it when it is as near to the exit window as possible. The holder is then removed to the other end of the bench, and the laser beam adjusted to

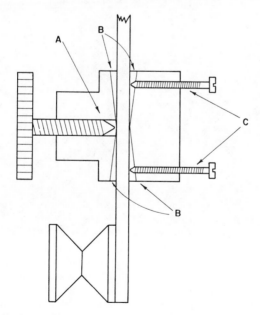

FIG. 3. Modifications made to the top arm clamp of the collimating lens holders are: at A removal of the pressure pad and pointing of the clamping screw, and at B relieving of the metal on both sides to permit a small amount of rocking movement, which is controlled by the two fine screws added at C.

fall on the mark. The beam is then parallel to the bench, but not necessarily vertically above it. The saddle mount of the screen holder is rotated 180°, when the lateral deviation of the beam can be seen directly. The lateral adjustment provided (Fig. 2) on the pin of the saddle carrying the laser is used to correct this lateral deviation.

After the beam is aligned in this way the same card in its holder may be used to set up any further optical benches in line with the main bench.

The next procedure is to set up the first collimating lens (c, Fig. 1) approximately 95 cm from the laser exit mirror, with its plane face toward the latter. The lens holder is rotated slightly on its vertical axis around the saddle pin so that the beams, reflected from the two lens surfaces, fall to one side of the laser exit mirror (a, Fig. 4).

It will be noted that two main beams are reflected back, and may be seen as two spots of light. One spot (b, Fig. 4) is small, and comes from

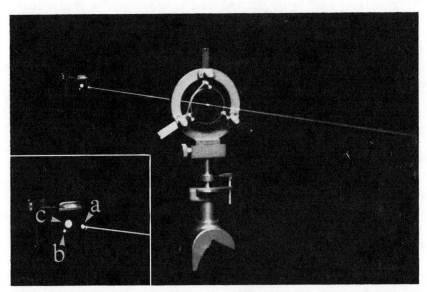

Fig. 4. Photograph shows the laser beam hitting the first collimating lens, and also shows the position of the spots from the reflected beams (magnified in the insert). The collimating lens has been rotated slightly around its vertical axis so as to make the two main reflected beams fall to the left of the laser exit mirror a. The beam b, from the plane surface of the lens, can be seen to fall below the level of a, indicating that the lens is tilted backward slightly about its horizontal axis. The beam c, from the convex surface of the lens is broader, and falls above and to the right of b, indicating that the center of the lens is too high and to the right of its correct position. When the adjustment is complete both b and c will fall on a.

the plane surface of the lens. Its position in a vertical plane is solely a matter of the verticality of the lens itself, and may be adjusted by the two fine screws on the top arm clamp (Fig. 3). The position of the other spot (c, Fig. 4) relative to spot b is indicative of the displacement of the optical axis of the lens from the laser beam, which may be corrected by employing the vertical and horizontal movements provided on the lens mount. When spots b and c fall on each other and level with a (Fig. 4), the lens holder is rotated about its vertical axis to make the spots fall exactly on a. This makes the optical axis of the lens fall along the laser beam.

The second collimating lens (e, Fig. 1) is then placed in position with its convex side toward the laser. It too is rotated to one side, and two more spots will be seen to the side of the laser exit mirror. These are adjusted in a similar way, i.e., the two spots are made to fall on top of each other at the same level as the laser mirror, and the lens is rotated on its vertical axis to direct the reflected beams into the latter.

Lens g (Fig. 1) is then placed in position and adjusted by hand in its holder in a similar way, though this adjustment is not particularly critical. Tilt may be applied, if required, by bending the metal frame by hand. If required this lens may be mounted on a carrier equipped with vertical and lateral adjustments (No. 2018).

Then the negative lens (b, Fig. 1) is put in position and adjusted by means of its centering screws so as to illuminate the collimating lenses centrally. After this has been accomplished, a card is put to one side of the laser and a distance (5 cm) behind the negative lens, b, equal to the (negative) focal length of the latter. A flat mirror is placed between the collimating lenses in such a position that the reflected beam falls on the card. The collimating lens (c) is then adjusted so as to focus the beam to a point. This completes the main adjustment of the critical lenses. Note that the focal length of the diverging lens is such that the beam is expanded about 20 times and does not quite fill the collimating lenses. If a larger area is needed, which is not likely, the focal length of the negative lens should be reduced. A positive lens of similar focal length would be equally suitable for expanding the beam, but would increase the length of the apparatus by about 10 cm, and in addition would tend to give rather more trouble from lens surface reflexions. Neither type of lens is free from this latter defect, which may be eliminated by the use of a convex or concave mirror system. This latter arrangement requires much additional apparatus, and is unnecessary unless image recombination experiments should be contemplated.

Finally, the projection lens (g) is placed so as to focus the beam to a point on the ground-glass screen of the plate holder (h). The relative positions of g and h may be varied widely, so as to provide any degree of magnification of the diffraction pattern. The final focusing is extremely easy to accomplish.

III. Experimental Procedure

The object to be examined, which is usually a photographic negative, and which is placed at d, (Fig. 1), must be masked to exclude as much of the background as possible. This can be done by applying black plastic masking tape, preferably to the back of the photographic plate. In order to record periodic detail it is not, in general, necessary to include many repeats, or even more than one repeat, in the structure, but the size of the spots recorded will be inversely proportional to the width of the area sampled, and will, of course, record the overall size and shape of the mask. Contrast in the object will be by virtue of both amplitude and phase variations in the emulsion, but in our experience it is not necessary nor even desirable to enclose the plates in optical flats to eliminate the latter. It should, however, be mentioned here that phase gratings do not necessarily obey Friedel's law (Taylor and Lipson, 1964, pp. 31 and 71), which implies that the transforms have, of necessity, a twofold axis of symmetry. This effect is, of course, well known to users of spectroscopic gratings, many gratings being made purposely to throw light preferentially into one of the two spectra in any one order. It is always advisable to focus the final diffraction pattern on the ground-glass screen of the plate holder before taking a photograph, but the magnification will change if focusing has to be done.

Since the primary diffraction image is magnified in the apparatus, the precise magnification has to be recorded if quantitative measurements are to be made. This can be done by making a transform from a ruled scale, or other object, placed anywhere between the collimating lenses, and, of course, if such a scale should be recorded simultaneously with the transform, a built-in calibration is achieved. The magnification factor may also be determined from the optical constants of the apparatus, but the method described above has the positive advantage that distances on the photograph may be directly related to the (reciprocal) distances on the electron micrograph plate.

The photographic exposure required has to be determined empirically, and several exposures may be needed to cover the range of intensities encountered. Naturally Polaroid P/N film is used for convenience. Other material having a much higher contrast may be required for certain objects.

IV. The Use of the Optical Diffractometer

The optical diffractometer is an extremely powerful tool because of its facility for picking out regularities in photographs which may be obscured. A characteristic which makes it of even more interest to electron microscopists is that the smaller the detail present, the easier it is to detect and measure. Interpretation of the results is rather more of a problem than the actual making of the transforms. A very comprehensive illustrated account of the patterns produced by regular arrays of circular holes is given by Taylor and Lipson (1964), but, with a few exceptions, their examples are grossly unlike anything one obtains from electron micrographs. Also it is only too easy to fall into the trap of thinking that the transform obtained is that of the object which was put into the electron microscope. It is not. In fact it is the transform of that part of the electron micrograph which is examined. This is essentially a record of the stain distribution on the object, local distortion in the image, random noise both from the stained object and from the plate, and, most importantly, all electron microscopic artifacts, such as image shift and astigmatism. In these regards the optical transform differs very much from the superficially similar x-ray diffraction pattern, which tends not to record details from the irregular parts of the object at all, does not require special staining techniques, and is insensitive to object shift, which may be all important in electron microscopy, even when it is of the order of a few dnm. This effectively limits the possibilities of applying Fourier analysis methods to the analysis of transforms of electron micrographs.

Another factor applying to transforms from electron micrographs is that the structures studied are at, or near, the limits of resolution of the electron microscopes, so that only a few orders at most of the spectra are produced, even by what is effectively a perfect line grating such as is presented by the rows of overlapping platinum atoms in platinum phthalocyanine crystals (Fig. 5). This object should have a pattern with orders at approximately 12,6,4,3, etc., reciprocal dnm, but usually only the first-order pattern is recorded by the electron microscope itself, so that the image only contains zero and first-order information, and as a consequence is effectively a sinusoidally modulated grating (Fig. 6) and so the transform itself usually shows only

FIG. 5. In this electron micrograph of (unstained) platinum phthalocyanine crystal, the flat phthalocyanine molecules have a central Pt atom and are seen edge on. The Pt atoms are 12 dnm apart in one direction, 2 dnm in the other.

zero and first-order spectra, though with care the second order can occasionally be resolved.

This reciprocity between the resolution of the electron micrograph and the spectra produced in the diffractometer is useful, because it serves to give a direct estimate of the quality of the electron micrographs (Fig. 7). Naturally, nonlinear distortion in the transfer char-

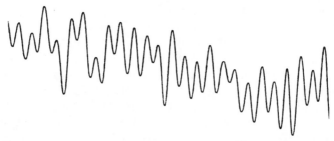

FIG. 6. This microdensitometer trace across the rows of platinum atoms in platinum phthalocyanine shows that although the crystal should behave as a line grating the electron microscope resolution is such that only the first-order spectrum is recorded, so the tracing is a sine wave with a modulation of larger wavelength superimposed, but lacking finer details (see also Fig. 16E).

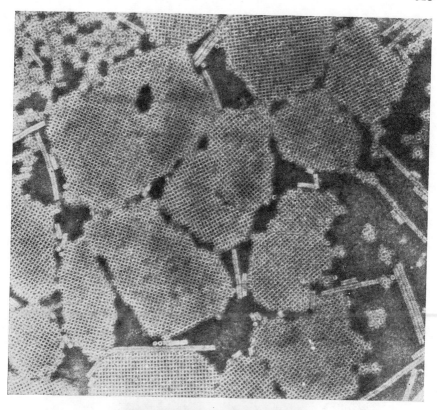

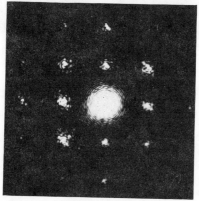

FIG. 7. Top: Crystalline array is of tobacco mosaic virus A protein (MacLeod *et al.*, 1963) showing the body-centered (pseudo) tetragonal structure. The shortest center-to-center distance is about 100 dnm. Below is the optical transform of part of this electron micrograph, which shows that regular periodic detail of less than about 50 dnm is missing.

acteristic of the electron micrographs will tend to produce spurious higher orders, probably odd orders, but these do not seem to present much of a problem, presumably because they are very weak.

A further point of interest is that astigmatism of the electron optics is accompanied by an astigmatic transform pattern of the "noise" distribution (Hills, 1967).

The interpretation of the spectra obtained is relatively straightforward if one bears in mind both the inherent ambiguities of the method and the unpredictability of the negative staining procedure. The electron micrograph may be regarded as a two-dimensional diffraction grating, the distances between the various pairs of spots being related to the reciprocal of the grating spacings producing them, and the orientation of the latter being at right angles to the lines connecting the pairs of spots (Figs. 8 and 9). These relationships need not necessarily hold absolutely in the case of arrays of particles. The angular diffraction is so small that no correction need be made for sine effects,

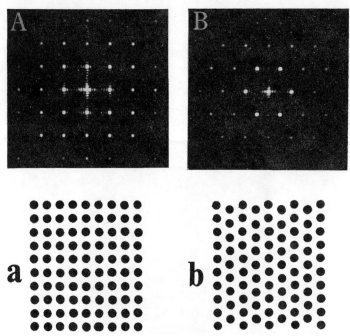

Fig. 8. A is a transform of a square lattice of spots (a). B is a transform of a similar array (b) which has alternate rows displaced by half a period. Note that in B the spots seen in A are still present though some are very weak, and that a new series of spots corresponding to twice the period in a horizontal direction predominates.

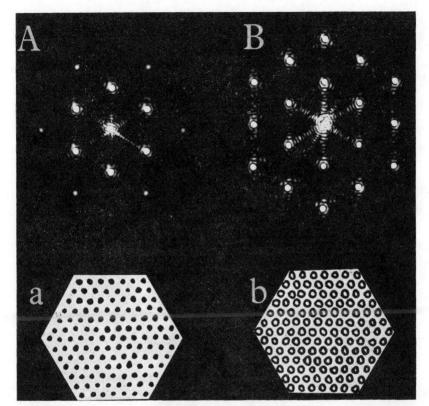

Fig. 9. A is transform of a hexagonal lattice of spots (a); and B is transform of a similar lattice (b) made up from rings instead of spots. Note that the transform hexagon is rotated by 90° (30°) relative to that in the lattice of spots, and that the ring shape causes the accentuation of the higher order spots.

the distance to any spot from the center spot being proportional to the corresponding angular deviation. The size of the grating spaces may be calculated from the optical constants of the apparatus, but it is easier and more convenient to refer distances to the various orders of a 1-mm period grating, or alternatively to the 12-dnm spacing of platinum phthalocyanine crystals, which will correct simultaneously for the electron microscope magnification as well.

Electron micrographs from viruses tend to be somewhat complicated because they are usually stained on both surfaces as a consequence of rotational Brownian movement during drying, and not only is one surface, that near the substrate, more intensely stained, but the stain on the other side tends to have its center of mass nearer the particle

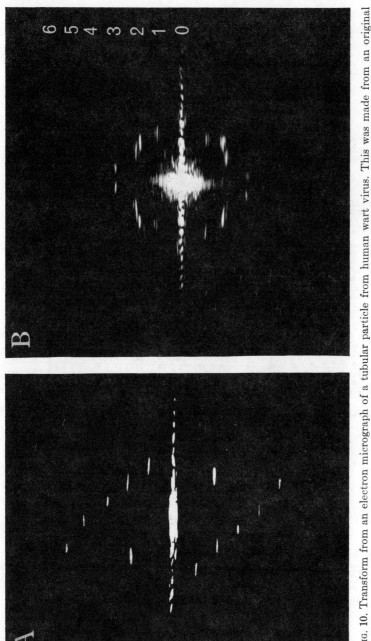

FIG. 10. Transform from an electron micrograph of a tubular particle from human wart virus. This was made from an original photograph kindly supplied by Dr. Noyes (Noyes, 1964, Fig. 5), and shows that the particle is helical, and that both front and back are visible. A shows the main details extracted from one side only, whereas B is the untouched transform. Compare with Fig. 14, and note that six spots are missing, or very weak, near the center. This is probably because the rod is made up from rings of subunits. In B, the layer lines are visible up to the sixth, and the near-meridional spots on the third layer line indicate that the structure repeats every three turns. Note, however, that the location of spots on layer lines 1 and 2 is not precise and that spots on line 3 are not at equal angles to the vertical axis. This means that stain has penetrated deeper on one side than the other. The basic structure is a two-start helix made from protein hexamers, each helix probably having 28 rings in every three turns (Bancroft et al., 1967).

center, so that the spectra from the opposite sides are not simple mirror images (Fig. 10). Shrinkage on the opposite sides of particles may also not be constant. Further complications arise when small image shifts are also present. For example, the simple hexagonal array which is so commonly found in viral structures gives rise to 3 main pairs of first-order spots (Fig. 11). Since all three pairs of spots come from the same diffracting objects, their intensities should be comparable, but they rarely are, and image shift may cause one pair or two pairs to disappear altogether (Fig. 12).

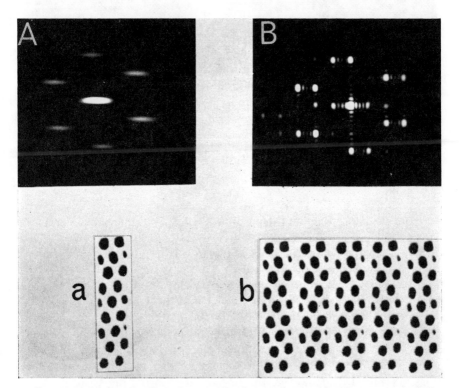

FIG. 11. A is the transform from a drawing *a* of one side of a two-start helix, having a repeat in every three turns, with twenty-eight structures in each repeat. B is the transform from a "crystal" of five identical parallel objects *b* showing that the transform of the side-to-side packing distance is recorded on top of the transform A, the maxima corresponding to the places where the two transforms coincide. The very small spots are a result of the finite size of the "crystal" and would not be seen in an infinite crystal. The number of orders is limited in these examples by having the spots in the drawings unsharp.

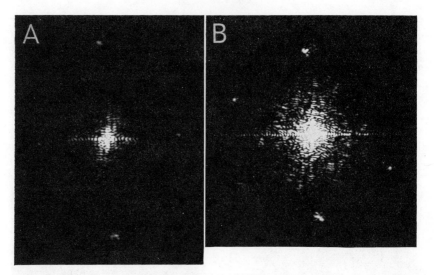

FIG. 12. Transforms are obtained from published (Anon, 1967) electron micrographs of crystalline arrays of T2 bacteriophage head protein. In A, the image movement has almost obliterated regular detail, though the electron micrograph itself showed distinct striations. In B, the same spots can be seen, as well as the other faint ones indicating that the lattice is hexagonal. The magnification is slightly different in A and B, and A is dimensionally distorted presumably by lens astigmatism.

Frequently, too, the stain deposition is such that the first-order pattern is reduced or eliminated. This is particularly characteristic of structures composed of rings, as are many virus particles, and sometimes it may be possible to identify what are obviously second- and third-order spectra by their spacings, when the first is completely absent. More frequently the first orders may be very weak (Fig. 13).

A series of objects of particular interest to virologists is the helixes. They may be recognized by several features, the most important of which is the tendency of a prominent spot, originating from the primary or shallowest pitch, to fall slightly to one side of the meridian (Figs. 14 and 15). However, this is not necessarily the case, because negative staining artifacts may cause one helix to be replaced by a two-start helix of opposite sense. When this happens, the clue is the presence of a regular pattern (usually hexagonal) tilted to the long axis of the particle (Fig. 16).

Another characteristic of helixes that may be of use in their identification is that they exhibit a series of secondary spots at the same level as the primary one, corresponding in location to the maxima of various

FIG. 13. Transform of a single layer of protein subunits from turnip yellow mosaic virus (Hitchborn and Hills, 1967b), negatively stained with uranyl acetate showing suppressed first-order spots, indicated by arrow heads, at 78 dnm spacing. Compare with Fig. 9.

Bessel functions (Fig. 14). This property is of use in x-ray diffraction, but helical viruses when stained and dried are no longer projections of helixes because the particles flatten to some extent, and the staining process effectively curtails the profile of the cylinder so that only the central region contains what information is still present. An extreme case of this is found in relation to the cylindrical tubes formed as a consequence of certain virus infections (Hitchborn and Hills, 1967a) (Fig. 17). In these cases the tubes flatten completely and, therefore, behave effectively as two thin sheets superimposed on each other at an angle. The only indication of the original helical and tubular nature of these

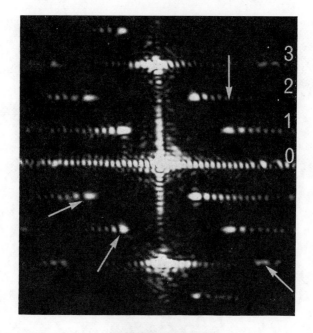

Fig. 14. Top: transform of the mirror image of a drawing of a helical structure (below) formed of oval subunits having a width of three times that of their height, and repeating in every three turns. Note the layer lines numbered 1–3, and also the arrows, which point along directions in which the diffraction spots lie in parallel rows. Compare with Fig. 10A.

bodies is that the transforms suggest that two identical structures are present having regularities oriented at equal and opposite angles to the long axis of the plates (Fig. 17). In this particular example, both sides of the helix are about equally intense, but, more usually, one side predominates.

It is sometimes possible to apply the concept of "layer lines" and "row lines" for the interpretation of optical transforms from virus particles (Figs. 10, 14, and 15). But, unlike x-ray diffraction patterns, optical transforms may contain hundreds of sharp spots, and it is often

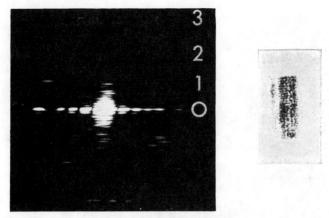

FIG. 15. This figure is of a rattle virus rod and its transform. Note that the first three layer lines can be recognized, and that both sides of the particle are present, though one is faint.

difficult to decide where the individual layer lines actually are, and since it appears that even the apparent pitch on the two sides of the particles may be slightly different, the complications are obvious, and each case must be treated according to its own merits.

A very remarkable application of diffractometry has recently been made by Hitchborn and Hills (1967b) to decide the "handedness" of their collapsed tubular inclusions. Shadowed carbon replicas of the tubes were made and while these (Fig. 18A) do not appear to have any recognizable fine structure, their optical transforms show that a simple hexagonal array is present (Fig. 18B), and this must represent the structure of the upper surfaces of the tubes, and so may be related in space to the axes of the latter.

An interesting possibility of optical diffraction is that one can examine published electron micrographs simply by copying them on lantern plate material. For this not even a camera is required, a photographic enlarger sufficing. The figure should be reduced in size to about the original electron-optical magnification. The halftone screen, if resolved, will confirm that the resulting plate has not lost detail, and will provide an array of spots on the transform, each of which will contain the whole pattern from the original object (Fig. 19). The subsidiary patterns often appear to be better than the main one, but this is probably merely a subjective effect. Examination of published electron micrographs is often very revealing, particularly of technical deficiencies.

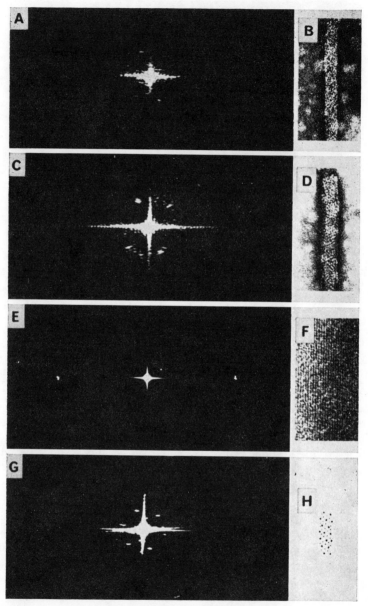

FIG. 16. A is a transform from B, a "narrow tube" of cowpea chlorotic mottle virus protein. C is a transform from D, a "wide tube" of cowpea chlorotic mottle virus protein. E is a transform of F, a crystal of platinum phthalocyanine. G is a transform of H, a model drawing of D (Bancroft et al., 1967).

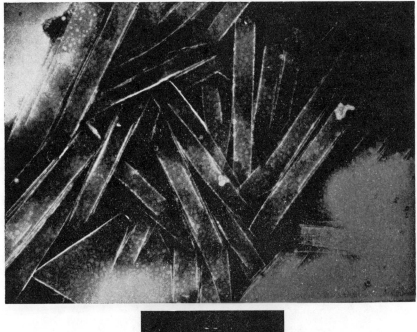

FIG. 17. Above are tubular inclusions of turnip yellow mosaic virus protein (A.R.C. Virus Unit Christmas Card, 1966), and below a transform from such a tube, showing that the true helical structure has been destroyed on drying, and is replaced by two layers of hexagonal mesh each tilted slightly and equally to either side of the long axis of the flattened tube. The spots are at a spacing of 45 dnm. Compare with Figs. 13 and 18.

Arrays, for example, parallel arrays of rods, or two-dimensional crystalline arrays of particles, present a further feature, and that is the presence of a series of maximums at spacings equal to the center-to-center spacings of the particles (Figs. 11 and 20). These are of use in measuring the distances involved in these spacings, but do not contribute to the elucidation of the substructure of the individual particles

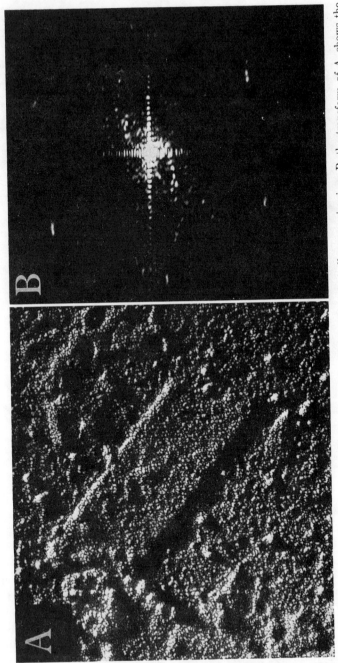

FIG. 18. A is a carbon replica of a shadowed tubular inclusion of turnip yellow mosaic virus. B, the transform of A, shows the structure is hexagonal, and that the hexagons are skewed to the long axis of the inclusion, which in B is vertical with respect to the figure.

Fig. 19. This transform of a tubular particle of polyoma virus (Mattern *et al.*, 1967, Fig. 8,L) illustrates the various spectra obtained from a halftone illustration. The central transform is the most intense, but with increased exposure, all the other spots will also contain the full transform of the particle though lens (lens *f* in Fig. 1) aberrations may be limiting. The tube is evidently seen from both surfaces and is helical.

and, indeed, may well obscure it. Certainly, so far as rods are concerned it is preferable to study them individually.

A particular case of using optical transforms for the further analysis of electron micrographs was presented by Hitchborn and Hills (1967a), who used them to obtain the approximate orientation and spacing of structures in order to carry out "linear integration" (Markham *et al.*, 1964).

When a structure has been decided on, it is possible to check it by making a model drawing having the same features. This is recorded on a plate or film for examination in the diffractometer. In doing this it is neither desirable nor necessary in most instances to include fine details (Figs. 8, 9, 11, 14, and 16). The areas covered by opaque and trans-

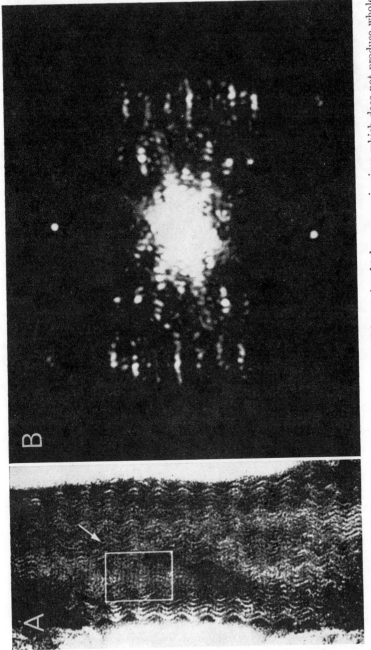

FIG. 20. This crystalline array of protein helixes is of the PM 2 strain of tobacco mosaic virus, which does not produce whole virus particles (Siegel *et al.*, 1966), and B its transform. Note particularly that the transform is modulated along its horizontal axis by the center-to-center spacing of the helixes. The meridional spot, which is on the sixth layer line, corresponds to a distance along the particle axis of 47 dnm, which is presumably the axial displacement of the individual "subunits" along the long axis of the helixes.

parent detail should not differ much from 3 to 1 at the outside, so that the lower order spectra are favored. In addition, sharp edges between light and dark areas should be avoided. This can be arranged in the drawing, or the picture may be made out of focus deliberately (Fig. 11). When a satisfactory model has been made, one then has to decide whether this is proof of the selected structure or of its dual, i.e., whether the opaque and transparent regions are as drawn or whether they should be reversed.

An obvious extension of diffractometry is the selective filtering of the diffraction spectra and subsequent recombination of the image by optical methods. This procedure is outlined by Taylor and Lipson (1964, p. 142), and has been employed by Bancroft, et al. (1967) (Fig. 21), and Klug and de Rosier (1966) for the extraction of further information from electron micrographs. At present, the procedure is in a developmental state, and the main problems would appear to lie in evading the production of spurious structures. The chief difficulty in such work at present would seem to be that the simple subtraction of certain spectra is not quite what is required for true image reconstruction, the procedure required being more in the nature of a demodulation than a subtraction. This is well borne out by Taylor and Lipson (1964, Plate 4b). However, the results obtained so far are quite encouraging, and probably refinements in methodology will eventually permit the production of much improved images of virus particles by such techniques.

It is interesting to note that what is an essentially identical system has been used in ordinary photographic work to reduce the effects of incorrect focus and of astigmatism (Cox, 1964). In this procedure the amplitudes of various zones of the diffraction patterns are modified by masks.

V. Other Methods for Examining Diffraction Patterns

Naturally, since most optical instruments produce diffraction spectra of one sort or another, many such instruments may be pressed into service in an emergency. In fact, our first diffractometer employed the interference optics of a Spinco Model E ultracentrifuge, and was quite suitable for examining such things as electron micrographs of platinum phthalocyanine crystals.

The plate was put in place at the level of the cell and the diffraction image was recorded on a plate placed above the top mirror mount (Spinco Part No. 325760), which was removed and replaced by a

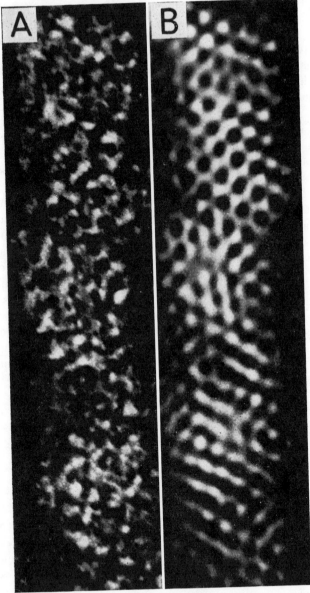

FIG. 21. This tubular particle is of the cowpea chlorotic mottle virus protein, A, (Fig. 16D) and its image reconstructed on the diffractometer, B. In this case (Bancroft *et al.*, 1967), only six rays were used in conjunction with the central carrier ray.

collapsible tube for focusing (Markham and Hills, 1963). In this work the interference slit was used, because the objects studied were linear arrays, but the slit could be replaced by a pinhole of 50–100 μm diameter for general objects with a consequent loss of light intensity.

Gall (1966) has described the use of a microscope as a diffractometer. In this case, he placed a 100-μm pinhole in the diaphragm aperture of the condenser and focused the objective on its image. The photograph to be examined was reduced and placed behind the objective lens, and the diffractometer pattern was viewed through the eyepiece. As with the other method described above, this is at best a makeshift, and the light intensities are of necessity very small.

REFERENCES

Anon (1967). *Virology.*

Bancroft, J. B., Hills, G. J., and Markham, R. (1967). *Virology* **31,** 354.

Cox, A. (1964). "Photographic Optics," 13th Ed. Focal Press, London and New York, p. 425.

Finch, J. T., and Holmes, K. C. (1967). *In* "Methods in Virology" (K. Maramorosch and H. Koprowski, eds.), Vol. III, p. 351, Academic Press, New York.

Gall, J. G. (1964). *J. Cell. Biol.* **31,** 130A.

Hills, G. J. (1967). Unpublished.

Hitchborn, J. H., and Hills, G. J. (1967a). *Science* **157,** 705.

Hitchborn, J. H., and Hills, G. J. (1967b). Unpublished.

Klug, A., and Berger, J. E. (1964). *J. Mol. Biol.* **10,** 565.

Klug, A., and de Rosier, D. J. (1966). *Nature* **212,** 29.

MacLeod, R., Hills, G. J., and Markham R. (1963). *Nature* **200,** 932.

Markham, R., and Hills, G. J. (1963). Unpublished.

Markham, R., Hitchborn, J. H., Hills, G. J., and Frey, S. (1964). *Virology* **22,** 342.

Mattern, C. F. T., Takemoto, K. K., and De Leva, A. M. (1967). *Virology* **32,** 378.

Noyes, W. F. (1964). *Virology* **23,** 65 (Fig. 5).

Siegel, A., Hills, G. J., and Markham, R. (1966). *J. Mol. Biol.* **19,** 140.

Taylor, C. A., and Lipson, H. (1964). "Optical Transforms." G. Bell and Sons, Ltd., London.

Wilkins, M. H. F., Stokes, A. R., Seeds, W. E., and Oster, G. (1950). *Nature* **166,** 127.

14

Contamination of Cell Cultures by Mycoplasma (PPLO)

Arthur Brown and Julius E. Officer

I. Introduction 531
II. Properties of Mycoplasma 532
III. Sources of Mycoplasma Contamination 533
IV. Procedures for Detection, Elimination, and Prevention
    and Control of Mycoplasma Contamination 535
    A. Detection 535
    B. Elimination of Mycoplasma 552
    C. Prevention and Control 559
V. Summary 561
    Acknowledgments 561
    References 561

I. Introduction

Since the initial discovery that cell cultures and viral seeds can be contaminated with Mycoplasma (PPLO)*, and in spite of repeated confirmation and warnings on this subject, many laboratories are still plagued with the problem (Robinson et al., 1956; Collier, 1957; Hearn et al., 1959; Rothblat and Morton, 1959; Pollock et al., 1960; Hayflick and Stinebring, 1960; Carski and Shepard, 1961; Coriell, 1962; Barile et al., 1962; Herderscheê et al., 1963; Hayflick, 1965). The purposes of this chapter are to present the problems associated with Mycoplasma contamination in cell cultures and in virology and to discuss in detail some of the methods that have been used successfully to detect, eliminate, and prevent and control such contamination. Although Mycoplasma contamination presents some special problems because of its frequently insidious nature (inapparent infection), it should be pointed

---

* These microorganisms, commonly called pleuropneumonia-like organisms after the first recognized species (Nocard and Roux, 1898), are now classified as *Mycoplama* spp. (Breed *et al.,* 1957).

out that there are other kinds of contamination of cell cultures that require equally important corrective measures (see especially, Coriell, 1962; Barile and Schimke, 1963).

II. Properties of Mycoplasma

The Mycoplasma are a heterogeneous group of microorganisms composed of saprophytic and parasitic species (Freundt, 1958; Kleineberger-Nobel, 1962), nonfermentative, heterofermentative, and homofermentative species (Smith, 1964), widely diverse serological groups (Clyde, 1964; Lemcke, 1964; Hayflick and Chanock, 1965), and species whose DNA compositions differ significantly (Neimark and Pene, 1965; Neimark, 1967; McGee et al., 1967). Furthermore, Mycoplasma apparently vary widely in a number of other characteristics, including what may be several modes of replication ("Biology of the PPLO," 1960; Kleineberger-Nobel, 1962; Eaton, 1965; "Biology of the Mycoplasmas," Second Conference, 1967), production of cell lysins or toxins (Sabin, 1941; Kraemer, 1964), hemolysins (Somerson et al., 1963), and cytopathic effects [(cpe) e.g., Girardi et al., 1965]. They share the following properties: they are the smallest known microorganisms capable of extracellular growth in cell free media. Their smallest "elementary bodies" are the same size as many viruses (their diameters range from 125 to 250 mμ). They possess a three-layered "unit membrane" similar to mammalian cells, but lack a cell wall and are therefore pleomorphic and resistant to certain antibiotics, e.g., penicillin and cycloserine, but are frequently sensitive to others, particularly the tetracyclines. Most Mycoplasma exhibit characteristic colonial morphology on agar medium such that the center is embedded into the agar, often giving a "fried egg" appearance. The growth of Mycoplasma is inhibited on artificial media by specific antiserum. The parasitic Mycoplasma have a requirement for cholesterol for growth.

Many properties of Mycoplasma are shared by stable L forms of bacteria. The relationship of Mycoplasma to bacteria and to stable L forms has been of interest ("Biology of the PPLO," 1960; reviews by Eaton, 1965; Morton, 1965; Hayflick, 1965; "Biology of the Mycoplasmas," Second Conference, 1967) and will be discussed further in relation to sources of cell-culture contamination.

The problems associated with contamination of cell cultures and other materials by Mycoplasma are of direct interest to virologists because they share many properties with viruses. Hayflick (1965) has listed these as size, filterability, morphology by electron microscopy, sensitivity to ether, ability to hemagglutinate and cause hemadsorption, resistance to certain antibiotics, inhibition of growth by homologous antiserum, and the production of a cpe. It has been found, for example, that virus pools made in cell culture may contain Mycoplasma in high concentrations (Carski and Shepard, 1961; Hayflick, 1965). It is known that Mycoplasma affect virus plaque formation, the production of a cpe, or the replication of viruses (Brownstein and Graham, 1961; Rouse *et al.*, 1963; O'Connell *et al.*, 1964; Butler and Leach, 1964; Somerson and Cook, 1965). There are other examples of the direct effects of Mycoplasma, varying from subtle to extreme, that may affect or be confused with virus infections (Hayflick, 1965; Eaton, 1965; Girardi *et al.*, 1965). It is especially pertinent to point out that Mycoplasma have been confused with viruses when the causative agents have been sought for various leukemic, neoplastic, and other diseases (see, for example, reviews by I. Macpherson, 1966; Barile, 1967; Hayflick and Stanbridge, 1967; Murphy *et al.*, 1967). Mycoplasma contamination of cell cultures have misled investigators through their effects on cell growth (Kenny and Pollock, 1963); cell morphology (Pollock *et al.*, 1963; Fogh *et al.*, 1965); chromosome patterns or cell transformations (Fogh and Fogh, 1965; Paton *et al.*, 1965; I. A. Macpherson and Russell, 1966); cell nutrition, metabolism, and nucleic acids (Powelson, 1961; Hakala *et al.*, 1963; Kenny and Pollock, 1963; Schimke and Barile, 1963; Nardone *et al.*, 1965; Randall *et al.*, 1965); and cell antigens (Coriell, 1962; Barile, 1967).

The effects described above have been reviewed in detail by several investigators (e.g., I. Macpherson, 1966). The dangers of ignoring the effects of Mycoplasma, which may cause serious, complete misinterpretations of experimental results obtained in cell culture, are clear. However, it is important to recognize that irrespective of the myriad of effects owing to Mycoplasma contamination, one cannot be justified in completely ignoring all previous studies made with contaminated cultures, since many of the basic effects described occurred despite the presence of Mycoplasma.

III. Sources of Mycoplasma Contamination

Cell cultures are contaminated with Mycoplasma from two major sources in the laboratory: (1) other contaminated cell cultures or material in the same laboratory; and (2) the investigator handling the culture who is a carrier. In the case of the former, it has been shown that (one) Mycoplasma may infect a cell culture, and that, like other microorganisms, may spread from such contaminated cultures via aerosols and/or via apparatus used in the cell culture laboratory (O'Connell *et al.*, 1964). It is of interest that Coriell (1962) has shown that even cell culture cross-contamination by other mammalian cells can occur via aerosol droplets. Many individuals are known to harbor Mycoplasma in their upper respiratory tract and genitalia, from which they can contaminate cultures via the aerosol route or with their hands. Several studies have confirmed the human carrier as a source because most of the Mycoplasma isolated from cell cultures were human strains. However, there has recently been an increasing number of reports that have identified nonhuman strains of Mycoplasma as contaminants of cell cultures and specimens (Bailey *et al.*, 1961; Girardi *et al.*, 1965; Tully, 1966; Barile, 1967; Hayflick and Stanbridge, 1967; Murphy *et al.*, 1967).

Mycoplasma contamination of tissues for primary cell culture or of the serum used in cell culture media is rare (e.g., Barile *et al.*, 1962; Eaton, 1965; Hayflick, 1965) and apparently is not an important source for contamination of cell strains or cell lines, especially considering the total number of isolations. However, the role of carriers and aerosols in the initial contamination of primary cultures has been pointed out by Girardi *et al.* (1965), I. Macpherson (1966), and Barile, (1967). A third controversial source of Mycoplasma contamination has been suggested but not proved. Some investigators believe that many "Mycoplasma" isolated from cell cultures are in reality stable L forms of contaminating bacteria that were produced, selected, and maintained by penicillin and other antibiotics used commonly in cell-culture media (Smith et al., 1957; Holmgren and Campbell, 1960; I. A. Macpherson and Allner, 1960; Pease and Laughton, 1962; Carter and Greig, 1963). L forms could also be produced by the action of normal or immune serum on bacteria present in cell cultures that is known to produce protoplasts or unstable L forms *in vitro* (Dienes *et al.*, 1950; Muschel *et al.*, 1959) and in cell cultures (Hatten and Sulkin, 1966). There appears to be a correlation between Mycoplasma contamination of cell cultures and the use of antibiotics in the cultures (Barile *et al.*, 1962). However, this does not necessarily mean that antibiotics are inducing stable L forms. Instead, it is probable that those laboratories using antibiotics are more likely to practice poor aseptic technique; thus, the antibiotics (particularly penicillin and streptomycin) increase the chances of survival and persistence of contaminating Mycoplasma by eliminating accompanying antibiotic-sensitive microorganisms. In the absence of antibiotics, contaminating microorganisms would probably be unmasked. It is important to recall that Mycoplasma are all naturally resistant to penicillin, and most are resistant to streptomycin, but, in addition, Mycoplasma strains resistant to a number of other antibiotics have been found (Balduzzi and Charbonneau, 1964; Eaton, 1965; Friend et al., 1966; Hayflick and Stanbridge, 1967).

Positive proof for accepting the thesis that Mycoplasma are in reality stable L forms would first require agreement on whether known stable L forms are indeed distinguishable from Mycoplasma. It is recognized that there is a great deal of heterogeneity in both groups, although it is apparently greater among L forms. Second, evidence claiming a relationship should be obtained that is based on hybridization techniques and/or the guanine and cytosine content of their DNA and other good markers (e.g., antigens) or, preferably, combinations of markers in the organism examined before and after conversion and reconversion. A beginning has been made in this direction. The negative correlation obtained thus far in studies using DNA composition and hybridization techniques is suggestive but not yet conclusive because the studies have been limited in number, the bacteria chosen for comparison may not have been selected properly, and because some Mycoplasma themselves show wide variation in relatedness (Rogul et al., 1965; Reich et al., 1966a,b; Niemark, 1967; McGee et al., 1967). On the other hand, the sharing of a common antigen by a bacterium and a Mycoplasma by itself does not necessarily prove a direct relationship; for example, the suspected relationship between Streptococcus MG and Mycoplasma pneumoniae, based largely on the fact that they share a common antigen, has recently been shown to be only a fortuitous one (Eaton, 1965; McGee et al., 1965), like that of Proteus X19 to Rickettsia prowazeki.

It seems to the present authors that the relationship of Mycoplasma to stable L forms of bacteria is still an open question, but that the burden of proof is on those who claim a relationship.

IV. Procedures for Detection, Elimination, and Prevention and Control of Mycoplasma Contamination

A. DETECTION

1. Introduction

There are several media available that are satisfactory for the majority of Mycoplasma (e.g., Lemcke, 1965). However, a survey of the literature, a consideration of the heterogeneity of the group, and experience with different kinds of Mycoplasma suggest that even the best of the methods and/or media in use are not sufficient to detect all

Mycoplasma (Barber and Fabricant, 1962; Barile and Schimke, 1963; Carski, 1963). There are no data at the present time for estimating precisely the percentage of negative cell cultures that may, in fact, contain Mycoplasma. One can guess from data of laboratories where the best proved techniques and many mammalian cell cultures from many different laboratories have been tested that relatively few have been undetected; an upper limit might be 15%. [It is more difficult, however, to estimate those that may have been undetected from materials other than the usual cell cultures (Barile, 1967; Hayflick and Stanbridge, 1967; Murphy et al., 1967).] It is entirely possible that a class of potential isolates exists that cannot be cultivated and subcultured on presently constituted media, presumably because of nutrient insufficiency (Hayflick and Stanbridge, 1967; Murphy et al., 1967). It has been the experience of several investigators that structures resembling Mycoplasma have been observed in electron micrographs of cell cultures or, in fact, in normal and leukemic human and animal tissues in situ from which the Mycoplasma could not be cultivated. Whether these structures are actually Mycoplasma, viruses, other microorganisms, or even artifacts, is often difficult to determine (see the excellent photographs of Anderson, 1965; Hummeler et al., 1965a,b; Figs. 1–4). This question can be answered with certainty only when the suspected microorganisms are identified by more satisfactory criteria than morphology alone, e.g., cultural, immunological, etc. It is for these and other reasons to be stated later that at least two different media are recommended for primary isolation of Mycoplasma.

Some Mycoplasma produce a cpe in cell cultures, often by depleting certain media of essential nutrients such as arginine, which many Mycoplasma use as a source of energy (Pollock et al., 1963; Barile and Schimke, 1963; Rouse et al., 1963; Butler and Leach, 1964; Hummeler et al., 1965a). The majority, however, even in heavily contaminated cultures (10^7 colony-forming organisms/ml or more), produce no overt cpe and no visible turbidity in the media, although subtle effects can frequently be detected by experienced workers (I. Macpherson, 1966). The best means of detecting these microorganisms, therefore, as with most other bacteria, depends on cultivating and demonstrating them on agar culture media.

Certain methods of detection that are useful for rapid screening and that have been found to correlate well with culture methods using agar media are (1) the fluorescent-antibody (fa) method (Barile et al., 1962), (2) the demonstration of a relatively specific arginine deiminase present in many Mycoplasma and some other bacteria (Barile and

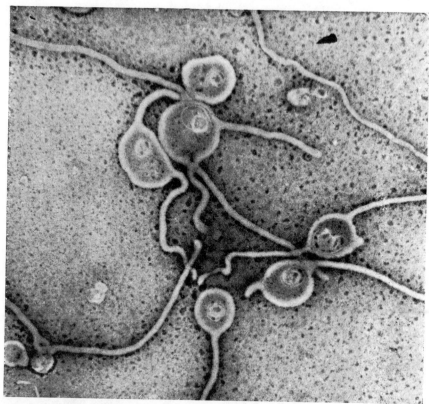

FIG. 1. Negatively stained Mycoplasma demonstrating the filaments. × 20,000. From Anderson and Barile (1966).

Schimke, 1963), and (3) a simple microscopic staining method (Fogh and Fogh, 1964). Because of nonspecificity in their identification of Mycoplasma (except for the fa method, which requires many antisera), low sensitivity, or other uncertainties, these methods are considered to be less desirable than the direct and most widely accepted method, which depends on the eventual cultivation and demonstration of Mycoplasma colonies on agar media.

If the presence of Mycoplasma is indicated by the rapid methods, yet the organisms fail to grow out on the agar media, further attempts at isolation should be made using additional media and/or other incubation conditions.

Several useful agar media have been described that are composed of a variety of complex organic constituents (e.g., Barile et al., 1958;

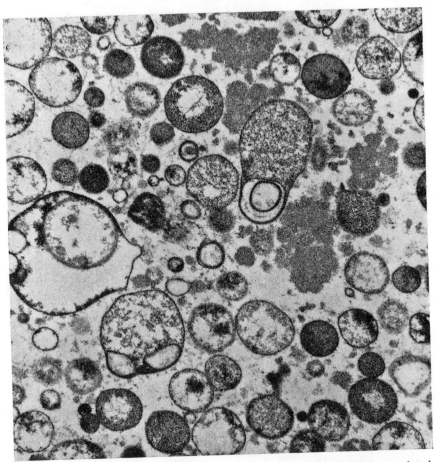

Fig. 2. Various forms of Mycoplasma, including "elementary bodies," vacuolated forms, forms that appear to contain a nuclear area, cytoplasm, and ribosomelike granules. × 40,000. From Anderson and Barile (1965).

Kleineberger-Nobel, 1962; Hayflick, 1965; Lemcke, 1965). Such media are also able to detect low-grade infections by other bacteria that are sometimes not detectable in thioglycollate broth or standard blood media (Coriell, 1962; Barile and Schimke, 1963). The most widely used medium is that described by Hayflick (1965). However, several comparative studies have shown that the use of more than one medium yielded a larger number of isolations than the use of any single medium, or one medium may permit better growth of certain strains than a second medium, and vice versa (Barber and Fabricant, 1962; Barile and

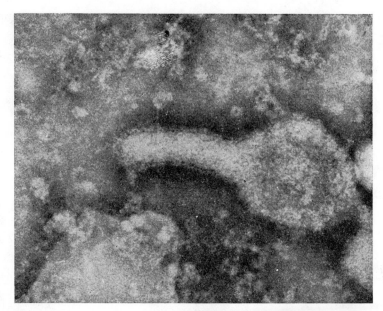

FIG. 3. Tailed elementary body, negative contrast. × 200,000. From Hummeler *et al.* (1965b).

Schimke, 1963; Carski, 1963). The optimal growth of Mycoplasma requires an enriched medium composed of serum, a meat infusion and/or a protein digest, yeast extracts* different pH values (e.g., 6.0 and 7.8), and incubation under both aerobic and anaerobic (95% N_2–5% CO_2) conditions. The yeast extract provides principally vitamins, purines, pyrimidines, and presumably other unknown nutrients that are required or that are stimulatory for growth of Mycoplasma. The serum is known to provide sterol, fatty acids, amino acids, and native protein as requirements or as growth stimulators, and presumably other unknown nutrients and "detoxifiers" (Smith, 1964). The peptone presumably provides a source of amino acids and peptides. The source of serum is critical and depends not only on the species but also on the individual animal.

* The fresh extract in Mycoplasma agar medium prepared according to Hayflick's directions (1965) was instrumental in permitting the isolation of *M. pneumoniae* when the same or similar media containing other yeast extracts failed. Recently, an apparently gentler heating procedure has been used for extraction that is carried out at pH 4.5 instead of 8.0 (Hers, cf., Lemcke, 1965). Hayflick's yeast extract permits the appearance of *M. pneumoniae* colonies showing only granular centers, but the Hers yeast extract permitted the appearance of typical "fried eggs" and also gave "excellent growth of other Mycoplasmas." Further evaluation of this product is indicated.

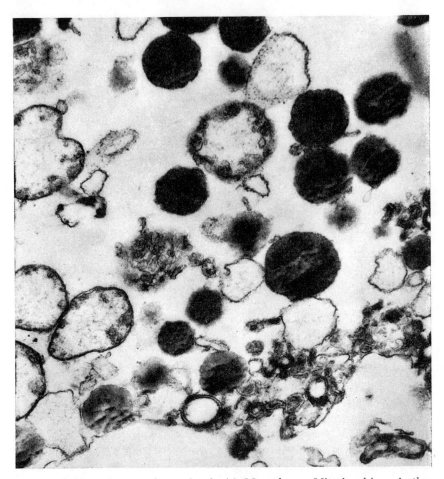

Fɪɢ. 4. Artifacts that may be confused with Mycoplasma. Mitochondria and other particles released from a necrotic tissue-culture cell. × 45,000. From Anderson (1965). See photographs of other artifacts and viruses that may be confused with Mycoplasma in Anderson (1965) and Hummeler *et al.* (1965b).

The serum should be noninhibitory and fresh or from frozen stock, since its ability to support the growth of Mycoplasma decreases with storage time. The safest procedure is to pretest commercial sera or collect it from animals whose sera have previously proved satisfactory, preferably on a number of different, known, unadapted isolates. Pretesting applies as well to agar, certain batches of which have been found to inhibit the growth of Mycoplasma (Lynn and Morton, 1956), to different batches of peptone or extracts of other natural materials used in cultivating fastidious microorganisms (Gieskin *et al.*, 1957), and to the complete medium.

2. *Cultivation*

To detect Mycoplasma, cell cultures without antibiotics may be tested directly, but otherwise they should be washed once with a balanced salt solution or antibiotic-free medium and maintained in media free of antibiotics through at least one transfer. Samples should be taken preferably during two different growth phases (logarithmic and stationary phases) and from cultures whose pH value is above 7.0. A drop of supernatant medium and cells, both untreated and lightly sonicated, are scraped from monolayers or removed from suspension cultures and placed directly on two Mycoplasma agar plates and streaked with a bacteriological loop or spread by a glass spreader. At the same time, 0.2 ml should be passaged at least twice in Mycoplasma broth (e.g., 4 ml in a Wasserman tube to give sufficient depth for microaerophilic enrichment) and simultaneously in a Mycoplasma-free cell line (A. Brown and Officer, 1960; Kraemer *et al.*, 1963; Girardi *et al.*, 1965; Armstrong *et al.*, 1965, Murphy *et al.*, 1967) or in primary cultures* †. The passages in liquid media should be made at 3- or 4-day intervals at 1 : 10 dilutions and subcultured on agar during each passage. One set of cultures is incubated aerobically at 35°–37°C in a humidified incubator and a second set for the first 3–4 days in an anaerobic jar that contains a humidified atmosphere of 95% nitrogen and 5% carbon dioxide. It is important to emphasize that the latter may be critical for primary isolation (Barile and Schimke, 1963). It is uncertain, however, whether anaerobic conditions per se or the presence of 5% CO_2 is important. Carski (1967) recently found that incu-

---

* These must be shown to be free of Mycoplasma by an independent enrichment technique if results are positive; other controls are also necessary. The danger of using cell cultures for enrichment are: (1) any contaminants in the laboratory may also be enriched, and (2) the samples tested may contain substances (e.g., nucleic acids) that may stimulate a latent infection to become obvious, thus giving a false positive with respect to the sample tested.

† We have found two out of four different Mycoplasma strains that assay 10–100 times higher by the cell-culture enrichment technique than by direct colony counts on Mycoplasma agar if decimal dilutions of the sample are first inoculated into the Mycoplasma-free cell cultures, and, after 3 days of incubation, a drop from each culture is spread on agar. Control inoculations into spent or fresh cell-culture medium without cells or into Mycoplasma broth before the subsequent inoculation onto Mycoplasma agar gave approximately the same results as direct colony counts on Mycoplasma agar. This demonstrates in a somewhat different way that cell cultures can sometimes be more useful than some available Mycoplasma media.

bation in air in the presence of 5–10% CO_2 can substitute for the 95% N_2–5% CO_2 atmosphere for human strains that could not form colonies in normal air incubators. Cultures may be examined daily and should be held for 2 weeks before discarding them as negative for Mycoplasma.

Another medium used successfully in comparative tests for isolating Mycoplasma from cell cultures is the opaque blood medium of Barile et al. (1966). The latter permits unusually luxuriant growth of many Mycoplasma, but it does not support the growth of *M. pneumoniae,* which is not, however, a cell-culture contaminant. Individual colonies appear in a stereoscopic microscope to be sharp; they appear white against the red background ("fried eggs" can be seen). This medium is also useful for detecting hemolytic strains. It is presently being used with supplements (Barile et al., 1966), as indicated for the Hayflick Mycoplasma agar medium given in detail later.

It has been reported that larger colonies and an increased number of isolations of Mycoplasma were obtained from clinical materials when the medium was adjusted to an acid pH (6.0 or 6.8) rather than an alkaline pH (7.4–8.0) (Shepard and Lunceford, 1965; Hayflick and Stanbridge, 1967; Shepard, 1967). The pH adjustment is made with 1 N HCl added to the medium, including the precalculated amount necessary to acidify the serum that is added later, so that precipitates are avoided (Shepard and Lunceford, 1965).

3. Identification

Most Mycoplasma form minute colonies on semisolid media about 0.05–0.2 mm in diameter that can be first observed microscopically at about 2 days (3–4 days macroscopically with oblique incident light); they are usually well developed by 6–7 days (approximately 0.5–1.0 mm). Colonies may be examined by incident light with a dissecting microscope or by transmitted light with an ordinary microscope at a magnification of 100 ✕. Focus on the surface of the agar is aided by finding the lines of streaking. Colonies often appear homogeneously granular, with or without a dense center, and a spreading, thin periphery typical of a "fried egg" owing to the embedding of their centers in the agar. Many, however, do not show the "fried egg" morphology and may appear only vacuolated or may remain small (e.g., Shepard, 1956; Hearn et al., 1959). Several typical types of Mycoplasma colonies (unstained) may be seen in Figs. 5–8 (Hearn et al., 1959). A section of a Mycoplasma colony embedded in the agar may be seen in Fig. 9 (Barile et al., 1958). Because the embedded portions

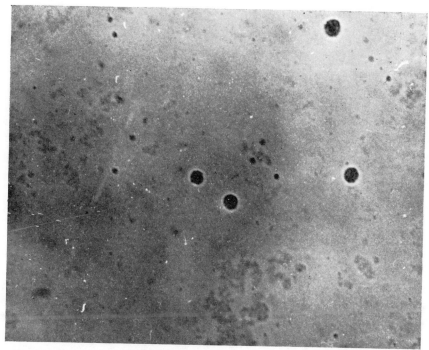

FIG. 5. Mycoplasma colonies isolated from L cell cultures 48 hours after inoculation. × 100. From Hearn *et al.* (1959).

are difficult to transfer by normal brushing with a bacteriological loop, this fact may be used as an aid in their identification as Mycoplasma and not bacterial colonies. The Dienes stain (Hayflick, 1965) can be used as an additional aid for observing Mycoplasma colonies and for differentiating them from typical bacterial colonies. A few drops of a 1 : 100 dilution of the Dienes stain is placed on the agar or gently brushed on the agar near the colonies with a cotton applicator that was dipped in undiluted stain. Most Mycoplasma colonies stand out distinctly with dense, blue-staining centers and light blue peripheries; bacterial-colonies, although first stained, are decolorized in 15–30 minutes, whereas the Mycoplasma are not. Individual Mycoplasma cannot be identified by light microscopy with certainty by the novice from either liquid or agar cultures, although granules, filaments, large bodies, and other pleomorphic shapes have been described (Dienes, 1963) (see Figs. 1–4). An agar block containing the colonies is cut out and inverted on a slide to make an "impression smear." The entire slide containing the block is then immersed in Bouin's fixative for several hours,

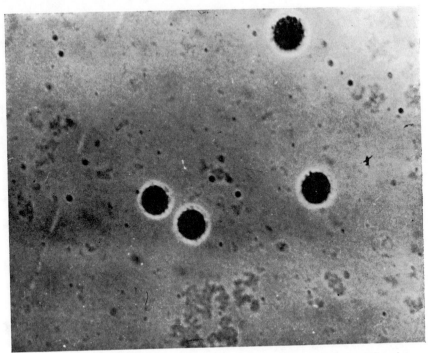

Fig. 6. Mycoplasma colonies isolated from L cell cultures 96 hours after inoculation. × 100. From Hearn *et al.* (1959).

and, after the removal of the block, it is washed and then stained with Giemsa. The stained impression of the colony has a characteristic vacuolated appearance and shows "large bodies" about 0.3–1.0 μ in diameter when viewed under the oil immersion lens. A more rapid technique, similar to the one above, which depends on hot water fixation and demonstrates Mycoplasma free of agar and fixative reagents, has been described by Clark *et al.* (1961). Identification of serotypes can be made by a variety of methods, which are summarized by I. Macpherson (1966). However, a recently developed technique (Del Guidice *et al.*, 1967) suggests that individual types, and mixtures of types found naturally in specimens or cell culture, can be identified directly on agar by a fa method.

Recently developed light microscopic methods that depend solely on morphological criteria of individual Mycoplasma without intervening agar cultivation (Fogh and Fogh, 1964; Clark, 1965) show some promise of being useful, but certain identification is still made only with the aid of cultivation techniques.

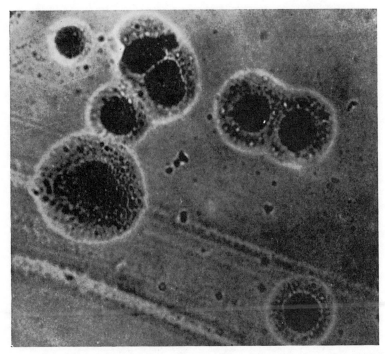

FIG. 7. "Fried egg" type of Mycoplasma colony isolated from an L cell culture. × 450. From Hearn *et al.* (1959).

4. Subculture from Agar

Since Mycoplasma are usually embedded in the agar, one must use a scalpel or a stiff bacteriological loop to cut out agar blocks for transfer to broth or agar. Vigorous mechanical rubbing of the inverted agar block on the surface of a new sterile agar plate or into a broth tube will provide the best chances for a successful transfer. Not all subcultures are successful (Hayflick and Stanbridge, 1967; Murphy *et al.*, 1967), presumably because of nutrient insufficiency.

5. Media Constituents and Reagents

a. Mycoplasma Agar. The medium developed by Hayflick (1965) is widely used to detect many tissue-culture Mycoplasma, *M. pneumoniae* and others. Prepare Difco PPLO agar or BBL Mycoplasma agar base according to directions on the bottle. To 7 parts of agar melted and cooled to 45°C, add aseptically 2 parts of untreated horse serum and 1 part of 25% yeast extract (see below). The pH should be adjusted

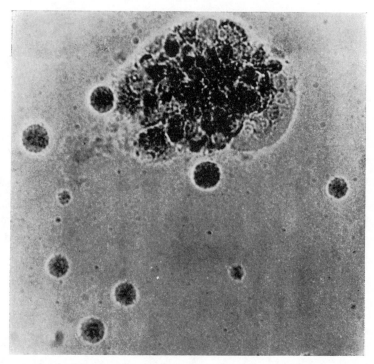

Fig. 8. A clump of L cells surrounded by Mycoplasma colonies. Unstained. From Hearn *et al.* (1959).

Fig. 9. Sagittal section of a colony of Mycoplasma. The colony is submerged in the agar and the central button is more deeply embedded than the peripheral growth. Dienes methylene blue azure stains. × 175. From Barile *et al.* (1958).

to 7.6–7.8, if necessary. Difco blood agar base or the BBL trypticase soy agar can substitute for the Difco PPLO agar preparations mentioned earlier. Barile *et al.* (1966) recently supplemented this medium and the opaque blood medium (Barile *et al.,* 1958) with 10 μM

arginine and glutamine, 0.5% glucose, and the vitamins as in Eagle's cell-culture medium (1959). The latter are choline, folic acid, nicotin-amide, pantothenate, pyridoxal, and thiamine at 1 mg/liter; inositol at 2 mg/liter; and riboflavin at 0.1 mg/liter. These vitamins can be obtained in a mixture commercially as a 100 × stock solution.

b. *Mycoplasma Broth*. Difco PPLO broth, or beef heart infusion broth or BBL trypticase soy broth is supplemented with 10% yeast extract stock solution and 20% horse serum and adjusted to pH 7.6–7.8.

c. *Yeast Extract*. The medium developed by Hayflick uses fresh yeast extract prepared as follows: add 250 gm of active dry Baker's yeast (Fleischmann's type 2040) to 1 liter of distilled water and heat until boiling. Filter through two sheets of Whatman 12 filter paper and add sufficient NaOH to raise the pH to 8.0. Dispense in 10-ml aliquots, autoclave, and store at −20°C. This material is stable for about 2 months.

d. *Horse Serum*. If commercial horse serum is used, it should be pretested, as suggested earlier. However, some commercial establish-ments maintain pretested horses for use in cell-culture media and Mycoplasma identification.

e. *Dienes Stain*. Dissolve 2.5 gm of methylene blue, 1.25 gm of azure II, 10.0 gm of maltose, and 0.25 gm of sodium carbonate in 100 ml of distilled water.

6. *Artifacts and Controls*

Nonliving artifacts have been a problem for investigators attempting to isolate and identify PPLO (Laidlaw, 1925; T. M. Brown *et al.*, 1940) because they are transferable in series and "grow" like colonies. Such pseudocolonies are composed of calcium and magnesium soaps that form slowly, and by their crystalline growth mimic Mycoplasma colonies in time of appearance and in size. The "stegasma" described by Zwil-lenberg and Bonifas (1964) may be of a similar nature. Photographs of artifacts may be seen in Figs. 10–19. Careful microscopic observa-tions, however, show that these and other artifacts do not have the round granular "fried egg" or even vacuolated morphology of Myco-plasma colonies; nor are they stained as genuine Mycoplasma with the Dienes stain. In addition to the above, one can further identify artifacts such as these as follows:

Broth or liquid samples of suspected Mycoplasma may be irradiated with UV light of germicidal wavelengths (GE lamp, 15 W) for 15 min-utes at a distance of about 24 inches, or heated at 60°C for 10 minutes. Mycoplasma colonies should appear before and not after such treat-

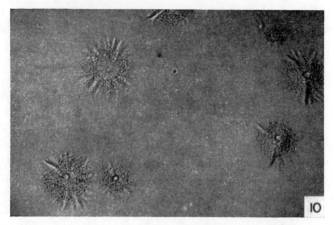

Fig. 10. Pseudocolonies incubated 14 days on 30% horse serum agar. Pure "growth" is shown on the 10th subculture. Flat illumination was used. The central "amber bodies" are very marked. × 115. From Brown *et al.* (1940).

ments. Broth known to be sterile and a known positive Mycoplasma broth culture should be used as controls in this test. Artifacts will generally not be affected by the treatment.

The pseudocolonies, as opposed to the Mycoplasma colonies, can be disrupted easily by brushing them lightly with a bacteriological loop. Hayflick (1965) points out that the soap artifacts will dissolve in weak

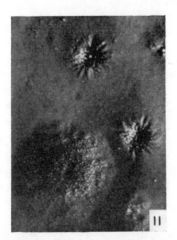

Fig. 11. Pseudocolonies incubated 7 days on 30% horse serum. Inoculation was with minced pneumonic mouse lung. Oblique illumination was used. Two small crater-like pseudocolonies and one larger colony of pleuropneumonia-like microorganisms of type A Sabin are apparent. × 115. From Brown *et al.* (1940).

Fig. 12. Pseudocolonies incubated 12 days on heavily inoculated 30% horse serum agar. Crowded pseudocolonies with numerous "amber bodies" are apparent and little peripheral "growth." × 115. From Brown *et al.* (1940).

acid and that Formalin or merthiolate will prevent Mycoplasma colony formation, but will not prevent the appearance of the artifacts. Commercially available Mycoplasma medium containing "agamma" horse serum [globulins removed] are supposed to help eliminate artifacts (Hayflick and Stanbridge, 1967). We have not had sufficient experience with this medium to attest to its merits or deficiencies with respect to artifacts and/or growth of Mycoplasma.

Mycoplasma colonies can be confused with plated cells. The latter can be differentiated from Mycoplasma colonies by observing whether the colony enlarges and by brushing the colonies with a loop. The cells

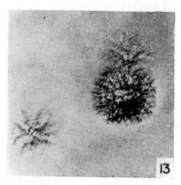

Fig. 13. Pseudocolonies incubated 2 weeks on 30% rabbit serum agar. × 115. From Brown *et al.* (1940).

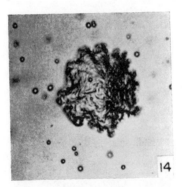

FIG. 14. Pseudocolonies incubated 6 weeks on 30% rabbit serum agar. Pseudo-colonies have a marked chiseled appearance. × 115. From Brown *et al.* (1940).

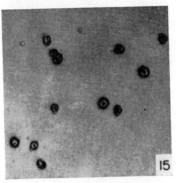

FIG. 15. Pseudocolonies incubated 2 weeks on 30% ascitic fluid agar. Pseudo-colonies appear as small discs with a central depression. × 115. From Brown *et al.* (1940).

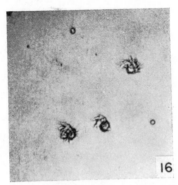

FIG. 16. Pseudocolonies incubated 1 week on 30% beef serum agar. A small central concave disc is apparent with curved pereipheral areas forming cockscomb pseudocolonies. × 115. From Brown *et al.* (1940).

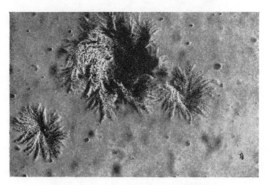

FIG. 17. A galaxylike colony 6 weeks old. × 150. From Bonifas (1963).

will separate (and may be individually recognized), while Mycoplasma will not. In addition, nuclei can be observed microscopically in mammalian cells. The cells are eliminated from samples by centrifugation or after liquid broth-to-broth enrichment. Figure 8 (Hearn *et al.,* 1959) shows Mycoplasma colonies adjacent to cells.

If possible, it is worth including a known Mycoplasma-free and a known Mycoplasma-contaminated culture (or Mycoplasma added to cells) in the isolation and identification procedures cited above. One

FIG. 18. A radial colony 6 weeks old. × 350. From Bonifas (1963).

FIG. 19. A unilayered colony. × 65. From Bonifas (1963).

must be careful, of course, that the known positive Mycoplasma do not provide the source of future contamination in the laboratory.

B. ELIMINATION OF MYCOPLASMA

1. Introduction

The permanent elimination of Mycoplasma from contaminated cultures is sometimes time consuming and difficult to achieve. It is recommended, therefore, that if possible one should replace them with the commonly used cell lines that are certified free of Mycoplasma and that can be obtained by the American Type Culture Collection, Rockville, Maryland. Stocks of such lines can be kept in frozen storage (e.g., Wallace, 1964) for future use. Frequently, however, new lines or unusual mutants may be established that become contaminated and that are important to save. These may require treatment.

Various methods for eliminating Mycoplasma from contaminated cultures have been proposed. They include the use of heat (Hayflick, 1960), antibiotics (e.g., Hearn et al., 1959; Pollock et al., 1960; Fogh and Hacker, 1960; Balduzzi and Charbonneau, 1964; Gori and Lee, 1964; Friend et al., 1966), and Mycoplasma antisera (Pollock and Kenny, 1963; Herderscheê et al., 1963). Permanent cures have been obtained most consistently with antibiotics and with antisera. These methods will be described in detail below. It is important to emphasize here, however, that (1) there is no single, universal cure, (2) results with each of the treatments have been somewhat variable, and (3) the

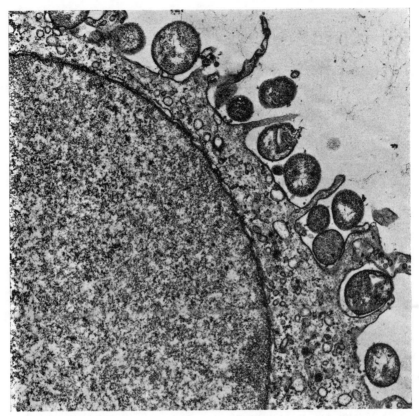

FIG. 20. Mycoplasma closely associated with the surface of a HeLa cell culture. × 31,000. From Barile (1965).

conclusion that permanent elimination has been achieved after removal of the antibiotic is valid only if the test for Mycoplasma is highly sensitive. Methods depending only on the presence of high concentrations of microorganisms should not be used.

Apparently, contamination may recur in treated cultures even when optimum procedures are used to eliminate, detect, and prevent recontamination. It is believed by some that this is an indication that Mycoplasma that cannot be eliminated are inaccessible to the therapeutic agent, either because they are capable of intracellular residence or growth or because they are effectively shut off from surface contact by being enclosed in crypts or vacuoles near the cell surface. While the vast majority of studies show a preponderance of Mycoplasma on or adjacent to the outside of the cell surface, there are several papers that

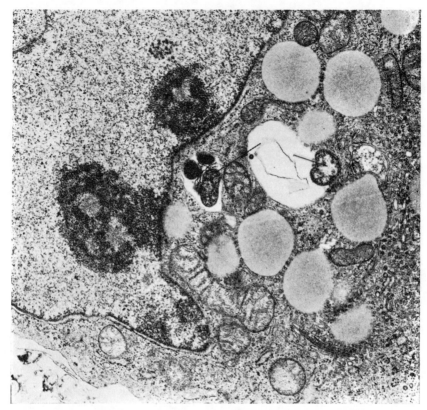

FIG. 21. Mycoplasma within membrane-lined vacuoles in the cytoplasm of a HeLa cell. × 31,000. From Anderson and Manaker (1966).

appear to show them intracellularly as well, or in locations that seem to preclude outer surface contact (Edwards and Fogh, 1960; Carmichael et al., 1964; Hummeler et al., 1965a; Anderson and Manaker, 1966). Figures 20–22 show electron micrographs of Mycoplasma that illustrate the usual case and also cases where the Mycoplasma may be unavailable to therapeutic agents. Although observations under the light microscope of cells stained by fa or the usual histological stains may be somewhat more difficult to interpret with respect to their intracellular location than electron micrographs, careful observation of cells in focus stained by histological stains show forms that may very well be intracellular (Hayflick and Stinebring, 1960); the same may be true of a few cells that showed perinuclear staining by fluorescent antibody,

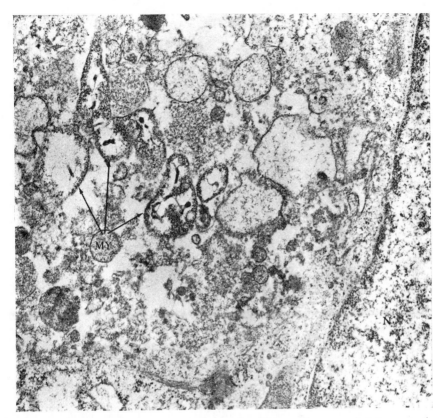

FIG. 22. Mycoplasma free in cytoplasm of a HeLa cell surrounded by necrotic area. × 50,000. From Hummeler *et al.* (1965a).

even though the majority of cells showed specific extracellular antigen (Carski and Shepard, 1961). Perinuclear staining is usually accepted as one indication of the intracellular residence of bacteria.

In view of the above, it has been suggested that toxic concentrations of antibiotics might be successful in curing cell cultures of Mycoplasma when nontoxic concentrations fail (e.g., Hearn *et al.*, 1959; Gori and Lee, 1964). The danger of selecting genetic variants of the mammalian cells by such treatment is real, but not inevitable. If the cell line must be saved free of Mycoplasma, one may be forced to use toxic concentrations of drugs. The present authors have found that selection of cell variants did not occur after such treatment of Chang's human liver cells. The cell line retained the characteristics of clonal morphology and the same degree of susceptibility to the psittacosis agent before and after treatment with toxic concentrations of aureomycin (Officer and Brown, 1961).

2. Antibiotic Treatment

a. *Selection of Antibiotic.* It is useful to determine the susceptibility of the isolated Mycoplasma to various antibiotics. This is most simply done by seeding a concentrated number of Mycoplasma (approximately 10^7–10^8) on a Mycoplasma agar plate onto which are placed commercially available antibiotic sensitivity discs of different concentrations.

The diameter of the zone of inhibition is taken as a measure of antibiotic activity. Penicillin, streptomycin, and sulfa compounds may be omitted, since most Mycoplasma are resistant to these drugs; in certain cases with streptomycin, the microorganism may be sensitive, but some animal cells may be partly impermeable to the drug, thus preventing effective streptomycin inhibition. Kanamycin, chloramphenicol, the tetracyclines, novobiocin, tylosin, and others are usually included in the sensitivity tests (see Table I).

Among the common antibiotics in use, kanamycin is one of the least toxic for animal cells in culture and should be the one of choice if the Mycoplasma are sensitive to it. Pollock *et al.* (1960) recommended high but nontoxic concentration levels of antibiotic to prevent the emergence of resistant strains during treatment. However, kanamycin has been found in some cases to lower growth rates of animal cells and reduce cloning efficiency in concentrations that produce no obvious cpe. If the Mycoplasma are kanamycin resistant, other antibiotics (e.g., aureomycin or tylosin) may be selected, and a concentration then chosen just below the toxic level for the cells. The latter may be estimated roughly by determining the lowest concentration that will cause a cpe within 72 hours. Combinations of structurally unrelated antibiotics may be chosen for treatment to prevent the emergence of resistant strains (Balduzzi and Charbonneau, 1964). As a guide to the selection of useful antibiotics, I. Macpherson (1966) lists a table taken from a presentation by Perlman and Brindle (1965) which shows the stability, cytotoxicity, and recommended therapeutic levels of various antibiotics that have been used against Mycoplasma in cell culture (Table I). The concentrations recommended may inhibit the growth of the contaminating Mycoplasma, but may not cure the cultures.

b. *Treatment with Nontoxic Doses.* The following procedure was taken largely from Pollock *et al.* (1960). Three replicate cultures are established by incubation for 3 days. Medium is replaced completely

TABLE I
ANTIBIOTICS USEFUL IN CONTROLLING MYCOPLASMA CONTAMINATION
IN TISSUE CULTURES[a]

Antibiotic	Stability[b] in tissue-culture media	Concentration showing marked cytotoxicity (μg/ml)	Minimum concentration inhibiting Mycoplasma in artificial medium (μg/ml)	Concentration[c] recommended for controlling Mycoplasma in tissue cultures (μg/ml)
Chloramphenicol	High	30	15	30
7-Chlortetracycline	Very low	80	40	100
6-Dimethyl-7-chlor-tetracycline	High	15	5	10
Erythromycin	Moderate	300	15	50
Fusidic acid	High	40	20	20
Gentamicin	High	3000	1	200
5-Hydroxytetra-cycline	Moderate	35	5	10
Hygromycin B	Moderate	300	15	50
Kanamycin	Very high	10000	25	200
Neomycin B	Very high	3000	15	50
Novobiocin	Low	200	10	50
Paromomycin	High	5000	20	50
Spiramycin	Moderate	1000	1	50
Tetracycline	Moderate	35	2	10
Tylosin	Moderate	300	1	10

[a] From Perlman and Brindle (1965; cf. I. Macpherson, 1966).

[b] Stability scale: half-life of 2 days, very low; 4 days, low to moderate; 8 days, very high.

[c] Recommended on the basis of a 3-day incubation period between changes of medium

with fresh growth medium: the tube cultures receive 100 μg/ml kanamycin in the replacement medium, which is made to contact all surfaces of the container in order to contact all Mycoplasma. Twice during the subsequent treatment period the cultures are redispersed with trypsin and used for propagation of three new cultures each after using a light cell inoculum that will, however, allow good cell multiplication. Three days after the second such passage, treatment is discontinued; the total period of treatment is 3 weeks. Cells should be tested periodically: the first 2 weeks after cessation of treatment and monthly thereafter under both aerobic and anaerobic conditions, since mixed infections are known to occur and one may have eliminated only the aerobe. Disrupted cells (e.g., light sonic treatment) added to the sample of intact cells should be tested after antibiotic treatment to unmask possible latent, intracellular infections. As a positive control on the media used for detection, recent unadapted isolates or fastidious Mycoplasma should be tested, if possible. Such cultures can be obtained from the American Type Culture Collection, Rockville, Maryland.

c. *Treatment with Toxic Doses.* The treatment using concentrations of drug toxic for the cells (Hearn et al., 1959) has failed only once in our hands. The tests were carried out on (1) many different contaminated lines in our laboratories among different groups separated on two floors of a building, and (2) on a number of different lines sent to us for cure from other investigators in the United States who failed to cure their lines with nontoxic levels of antibiotics. The exception to the treatment was our failure to cure a line maintained in a serum-free medium. We have not yet tested whether serum or a serum substitute is necessary to effect a cure, since the line was lost before a test could be made. [Does serum promote pinocytosis or otherwise promote drug entry or effectiveness? (see, for example, Shepard, 1958).]

The following procedure makes use of aureomycin, but it should also be adaptable to other drugs. Use a concentration above the minimum toxic level for the cells by at least 2-fold (200 μg/ml). Maintain the drug in the medium each time a medium change or cell transfer is made; this usually requires a drug addition every 2–3 days. Extreme necrotic effects should be avoided, and untreated control cultures should be frozen or carried (in a separate room) in the event the culture is lost. When the toxic effect is moderate (50–70% of cells show a cpe), lower the concentration to below the toxic level (in our hands 10–50 μg/ml). Repeat the treatment with a cycle of toxic and then nontoxic concentrations of drugs if necessary; in most cases, it is not necessary. Cultures at the time of transfer should not be seeded too heavily; i.e., avoid treating the cells only in their stationary phase of growth. Cures are usually effected after 1 or at most 2 weeks of treatment. After medium changes and at least one transfer in the presence of the nontoxic level of drug, maintain the cultures in medium free of antibiotic and test periodically, as described earlier for kanamycin.

3. Antiserum Treatment

One advantage of antiserum for treatment is that it can be used simultaneously as a nutrient for the cells and decontaminant against the Mycoplasma. Disadvantages are that a specific antiserum is required for each antigenic type isolated, and the procedure for making antiserum is time consuming. There is, however, one commercially available polyvalent antiserum known to the authors (BBL) that is made against several common cell-culture contaminants and that has been used for treatment. The procedure for the preparation of antigen, antisera, and treatment of cultures may be found in the papers by Pollock and Kenny (1963) and Herderscheê et al. (1963). Only the procedure for treatment (Pollock and Kenny, 1963) is given below.

Treatment. Suspensions of the cell line to be treated are allowed to become established in growth medium with an inoculum small enough to allow logarithmic growth at the beginning of treatment. The growth medium should contain 5% of the specific antiserum and should be placed in contact with all surfaces of the vessel. [The antiserum used by Pollock and Kenny (1963) had an agglutinin titer of $\frac{1}{320}$.] Five days after establishment, the cultures are fed with the same medium, and 6 days later with control medium for a total treatment period of 11 days. If this procedure is insufficient, it may be modified by employing two successive cycles of transfer and maintenance in the presence of antiserum, before normal serum is used. Tests for permanent elimination of the Mycoplasma are conducted according to the same procedure given earlier for the kanamycin treatment.

C. PREVENTION AND CONTROL

A consideration of the possible sources of Mycoplasma contamination discussed in Section III and evidence obtained from certain studies (Coriell, 1962) lead one to the inevitable conclusion that the best prevention of Mycoplasma contamination of cell cultures is stringent aseptic technique. The incorporation of antibiotics apparently causes the relaxation of aseptic techniques, which is responsible not only for Mycoplasma contamination but for contamination by other microorganisms and, at least in part, for mammalian cell cross-contamination.

A return to stringent aseptic technique without antibiotics should permit early recognition of contamination and prevent the possible emergence of L forms that may be inducible by antibiotics, if, indeed this is a source of Mycoplasma contamination. At the same time, the absence of antibiotics from culture media allows the best chance for antibiotic treatment when it might later become necessary, since there are no antibiotics present to select potential antibiotic-resistant variants. Certainly on a small scale, and for maintaining stock cultures, there should be no problem in making meticulous aseptic technique a routine. It has been a common observation, however, that it is uncommon practice to maintain cultures without antibiotics even on a small scale, since "it is too inconvenient and the antibiotics work." Furthermore, many investigators who remove antibiotics do so only with stock cultures that are kept in frozen storage; the "working" cultures are then usually carried in antibiotics, the rationale being that this procedure is safe, since one can always go back to the stock culture if contamination appears. Unfortunately, however, the antibiotic-containing cultures are not usually tested until some overt incident occurs. It seems that whenever antibiotics are used in cell culture, instead of a safety factor one creates a hazard that is often magnified by carelessness.

A few large-scale producers of cell cultures have indicated that it is unrealistic and not economical to attempt production of cells in large quantity without antibiotics. It is said that a break in aseptic technique must occur no matter how stringent the protocol. One wonders whether such a conclusion is defensible, especially if cell-culture production is carried out in batches in a properly designed environment and by properly trained personnel. Nevertheless, it is common practice for large-scale producers of cells (frequently because it is difficult to obtain and keep properly trained personnel) to employ low concentrations of antibiotics to which Mycoplasma are sensitive, as well as penicillin and streptomycin. High but nontoxic concentrations of aureomycin or tylosin (50 μg/ml), which prevent the emergence of resistant strains, have been used successfully for Mycoplasma prophylaxis by a few investigators (e.g., Hayflick and Stanbridge, 1967). It is emphasized here, however, that this may not eliminate Mycoplasma contamination, but only mask it or invite the danger of other kinds of contamination (see Coriell, 1962).

Coriell (1962) presented in some detail a set of technical methods, certain features of design, and the procedures used in his cell-culture laboratory to minimize contamination of any kind. Other publications dealing with laboratory design to minimize infection and contamination are available (Wedum et al., 1956; Fox, 1964), including a recently adopted design based on the principle of laminar air flow (e.g., Agnew, 1963). Special cell-culture rooms equipped with UV light, air filters, positive air pressure, etc., are all excellent physical aids, but properly trained personnel with the right attitude are probably more important than all the rest.

In brief, constant vigilance, routine monitoring, and strict aseptic technique using antibiotic-free media are recommended for preventing contamination of cell cultures by Mycoplasma.

V. Summary

The properties of Mycoplasma were considered in relation to the problems of contamination they pose for investigators who use cell cultures. Satisfactory methods available for the detection, elimination, and prevention and control of Mycoplasma contamination of cell cultures were discussed, and a selected few were recommended for routine use.

In order to provide the largest number of isolations and the best growth of Mycoplasma, at least two media were recommended for concurrent use in cultivating Mycoplasma under a variety of properly controlled conditions. If the contaminated cultures could not be easily replaced with Mycoplasma-free lines, then elimination of the Mycoplasma must be attempted. Three detailed methods for eliminating Mycoplasma from cell cultures were presented, two of which depend on the use of antibiotics and one on antiserum. Two chief (but not the only) sources of Mycoplasma contamination of cell cultures were considered to be human carriers and material in the laboratory (e.g., other cell cultures) that may be contaminated with Mycoplasma. A third possible source was discussed, namely, that some Mycoplasma found in cell cultures are, in fact, stable L forms of contaminating bacteria that were produced and selected by the antibiotics commonly used in cell-culture media. This possibility is still under consideration, but the evidence for it was judged to be, as yet, unproved. It was recommended that whatever the source of Mycoplasma contamination, routine testing of cultures should be done and strict aseptic technique be used without antibiotics in suitable physical facilities by properly trained personnel.

ACKNOWLEDGMENTS

We wish to thank the scientists who supplied unpublished information and photographs and who reviewed the manuscript. We are especially grateful to Drs. M. F. Barile, T. R. Carski, L. Hayflick, A. N. Gorelick, and R. D. Costlow for their critical reviews and suggestions.

REFERENCES

Agnew, B. (1963). "Laminar Flow Clean Room Handbook," Agnew-Higgens Inc., Garden Grove, California.
Anderson, D. R. (1965). *Wistar Inst. Symp. Monograph* **4**, 113.
Anderson, D. R., and Barile, M. F. (1965). *J. Bacteriol.* **90**, 180.
Anderson, D. R., and Barile, M. F. (1966). *J. Natl. Cancer Inst.* **36**, 161.

Anderson, D. R., and Manaker, R. A. (1966). *J. Natl. Cancer Inst.* **36,** 139.

Armstrong, D., Henle, G., Somerson, N. L., and Hayflick, L. (1965). *J. Bacteriol.* **90,** 418.

Bailey, J. S., Clark, H. W., Feltz, W. R., Fowler, R. C., and Brown, T. M. (1961). *J. Bacteriol.* **82,** 542.

Balduzzi, P., and Charbonneau, R. J. (1964). *Experientia* **20,** 651.

Barber, T. L., and Fabricant, J. (1962). *J. Bacteriol.* **83,** 1268.

Barile, M. F. (1965). *Wistar Inst. Symp. Monograph* **4,** 171.

Barile, M. (1967). *Ann. N.Y. Acad. Sci.* **143,** 557.

Barile, M. F., and Schimke, R. T. (1963). *Proc. Soc. Exptl. Biol. Med.* **114,** 676.

Barile, M. F., Yaguchi, R., and Eveland, W. C. (1958). *Am. J. Clin. Pathol.* **30,** 171.

Barile, M. F., Malizia, W. F., and Riggs, D. B. (1962). *J. Bacteriol.* **84,** 130.

Barile, M. F., Bodey, G. P., Snyder, J., Riggs, D. B., and Grabowsky, M. W., (1966). *J. Natl. Cancer Inst.* **36,** 155.

Biology of the Pleuropneumonia-like Organisms. (1960). *Ann. N.Y. Acad. Sci.* **79,** 309.

Biology of the Mycoplasma. (1967). *Ann. N.Y. Acad. Sci.* **143,** 1.

Bonifas, V. H. (1963). *Pathol. Microbiol.* **26,** 696.

Breed, R. S., Murray, E. G. D., and Smith, N. R. (1957). *In* "Bergey's Manual of Determinative Bacteriology," 7th ed., p. 914. Williams & Wilkins, Baltimore, Maryland.

Brown, A., and Officer, J. E. (1960). Unpublished observations.

Brown, T. M., Swift, H. F., and Watson, R. F. (1940). *J. Bacteriol.* **40,** 857.

Brownstein, B., and Graham, A. F. (1961). *Virology* **14,** 303.

Butler, M., and Leach, R. H. (1964). *J. Gen. Microbiol.* **34,** 285.

Carmichael, L. E., Fabricant, J., and Squire, R. A. (1964). *Proc. Soc. Exptl. Biol. Med.* **117,** 826.

Carski, T. R. (1963). Personal communications.

Carski, T. R. (1967). Personal communication.

Carski, T. R., and Shepard, M. C. (1961). *J. Bacteriol.* **81,** 626.

Carter, G. R., and Greig, A. S. (1963). *Can. J. Microbiol.* **9,** 317.

Clark, H. W. (1965). *J. Bacteriol.* **90,** 137?.

Clark, H. W., Fowler, R. C., and Brown, T. M. (1961). *J. Bacteriol.* **81,** 500.

Clyde, W. A., Jr. (1964). *J. Immunol.* **92,** 958.

Collier, L. H. (1957). *Nature* **180,** 757.

Coriell, L. L. (1962). *Natl. Cancer Inst. Monograph* **7,** 33.

Del Guidice, R. A., Robillard, N. F., and Carski, T. R. (1967). *J. Bacteriol.* **93,** 1205.

Dienes, L. (1963). *Ann. N.Y. Acad. Sci.* **108,** 375.

Dienes, L., Weinberger, H. J., and Madoff, S. (1950). *J. Bacteriol.* **59,** 755.

Eagle, H. (1959). *Science* **130,** 432.

Eaton, M. D. (1965). *Ann. Rev. Microbiol.* **19,** 379.

Edwards, G. A., and Fogh, J. (1960). *J. Bacteriol.* **79,** 267.

Fogh, J., and Fogh, H. (1964). *Proc. Soc. Exptl. Biol. Med.* **117,** 889.

Fogh, J., and Fogh, H. (1965). *Proc. Soc. Exptl. Biol. Med.* **119,** 233.

Fogh, J., and Hacker, C. (1960). *Exptl. Cell Res.* **21,** 242.

Fogh, J., Hahn, E., and Fogh, H. (1965). *Exptl. Cell Res.* **39,** 554.

Fox, G. (1964). *U.S., Public Health Bibliog. Ser.* **54.**

Friend, C., Patuleia, M. C., and Nelson, J. B. (1966). *Proc. Soc. Exptl. Biol. Med.* **121,** 1009.

Freundt, E. A. (1958). "The Mycoplasmataceae (The Pleuropneumonia Group of Organisms)." Munksgaard, Copenhagen.

Gieskin, R. F., Guss, M. C., and Eigelsbach, H. T. (1957). *Bacteriol. Proc. (Soc. Am. Bacteriologists)* 57, 59.

Girardi, A. J., Larson, V. M., and Hilleman, M. R. (1965). *Proc. Soc. Exptl. Biol. Med.* 118, 173.

Gori, G. B., and Lee, D. Y. (1964). *Proc. Soc. Exptl. Biol. Med.* 117, 918.

Hakala, M. T., Holland, J. F., and Horoszewicz, J. S. (1963). *Biochem. Biophys. Res. Commun.* 11, 466.

Hatten, B. A., and Sulkin, S. E. (1966). *J. Bacteriol.* 91, 285.

Hayflick, L. (1960). *Nature* 185, 783.

Hayflick, L. (1965). *Texas Rept. Biol. Med.* 23, 285.

Hayflick, L., and Stanbridge, E. (1967). *Ann. N.Y. Acad. Sci.* 143, 608.

Hayflick, L., and Chanock, R. M. (1965). *Bacteriol. Rev.* 29, 186.

Hayflick, L., and Stinebring, W. R. (1960). *Ann. N.Y. Acad. Sci.* 79, 433.

Hearn, H. J., Jr., Officer, J. E., Elsner, V., and Brown, A. (1959). *J. Bacteriol.* 78, 575.

Herderscheê, D., Ruys, A. C., and van Rhijn, G. R. (1963). *Antonie van Leeuwenhoek, J. Microbiol. Serol.* 29, 368.

Holmgren, N. B., and Campbell, W. E., Jr. (1960). *J. Bacteriol.* 79, 869.

Hummeler, K., Armstrong, D., and Tomassani, N. (1965a). *J. Bacteriol.* 90, 511.

Hummeler, K., Tomassani, N., and Hayflick, L. (1965b). *J. Bacteriol.* 90, 517.

Kenny, G. E., and Pollock, M. E. (1963). *J. Infect. Diseases* 112, 7.

Kleineberger-Nobel, E. (1962). "Pleuropneumonia-like Organisms (PPLO) Mycoplasmataceae." Academic Press, New York.

Kraemer, P. M. (1964). *Proc. Soc. Exptl. Biol. Med.* 115, 206.

Kraemer, P. M., Defendi, V., Hayflick, L., and Manson, L. A. (1963). *Proc. Soc. Exptl. Biol. Med.* 112, 381.

Laidlaw, P. P. (1925). *Brit. J. Exptl. Pathol.* 6, 36.

Lemcke, R. M. (1964). *J. Hyg.* 62, 199.

Lemcke, R. M. (1965). *Lab. Pract.* 14, 712.

Lynn, R. J., and Morton, H. (1956). *Appl. Microbiol.* 4, 339.

McGee, Z. A., Rogul, M., Falkow, S., and Wittler, R. G. (1965). *Proc. Natl. Acad. Sci. U.S.* 54, 457.

McGee, Z. A., Rogul, M., and Wittler, R. G. (1967). *Ann. N.Y. Acad. Sci.* 143, 21.

Macpherson, I. (1966). *J. Cell Sci.* 1, 145.

Macpherson, I. A., and Allner, K. (1960). *Nature* 186, 992.

Macpherson, I. A., and Russell, W (1966). *Nature* 210, 1343.

Morton, H. (1965). *In* "Bacterial and Mycotic Infections of Man" (R. Dubos and J. G. Hirsch, eds.), 4th ed., p. 786. Lippincott, Philadelphia, Pennsylvania.

Murphy, W. H., Bullis, C., Ertel, I. J., and Zarafonetis, C. J. D. (1967). *Ann. N.Y. Acad. Sci.* 143, 544.

Muschel, L. H., Carey, W. B., and Baron, L. S. (1959). *J. Immunol.* 82, 38.

Nardone, R. M., Todd, J., Gonzales, P., and Gaffney, E. V. (1965). *Science* 149, 1100.

Neimark, H. C. (1967). *Ann. N.Y. Acad. Sci.* 143, 31.

Neimark, H. C., and Pene, J. J. (1965). *Proc. Soc. Exptl. Biol. Med.* 118, 517.

Nocard, E., and Roux, E. R. (1898). *Ann. Inst. Pasteur* 12, 240.

O'Connell, R. C., Wittler, R. G., and Faber, J. E. (1964). *Appl. Microbiol.* 12, 337.

Officer, J. E., and Brown, A. (1961). *Virology* 14, 88.

Paton, G. R., Jacobs, J. P., and Perkins, F. T. (1965). *Nature* **207**, 43.

Pease, P. E., and Laughton, N. (1962). *J. Gen. Microbiol.* **27**, 383.

Perlman, D., and Brindle, S. A. (1965). *Ann. Meeting Am. Soc. Microbiol.* [Summary in *Bacteriol. Proc. (Soc. Am. Bacteriologists)* **65**, 120 (1965)].

Pollock, M. E., and Kenny, G. E. (1963). *Proc. Soc. Exptl. Biol. Med.* **112**, 176.

Pollock, M. E., Kenny, G. E., and Syverton, J. T. (1960). *Proc. Soc. Exptl. Biol. Med.* **105**, 10.

Pollock, M. E., Treadwell, P. E., and Kenny, G. E. (1963). *Exptl. Cell Res.* **31**, 321.

Powelson, D. M. (1961). *J. Bacteriol.* **82**, 288.

Randall, C. C., Gafford, L. G., Gentry, G. A., and Lawson, L. A. (1965). *Science* **149**, 1098.

Reich, P. R., Somerson, N. L., Hybner, C. J., Chanock, R. M., and Weissman, S. M. (1966a). *J. Bacteriol,* **92**, 302.

Reich, P. R., Somerson, N. L., Rose, J. A., and Weissman, S. M. (1966b) *J. Bacteriol.* **91**, 153.

Robinson, L. B., Wichelhausen, R. H., and Roizman, B. (1956). *Science* **124**, 1147.

Rogul, M., McGee, Z. A., Wittler, R. G., and Falkow, S. (1965). *J. Bacteriol.* **90**, 1200.

Rothblat, G. H., and Morton, H. E. (1959). *Proc. Soc. Exptl. Biol. Med.* **100**, 87.

Rouse, H. C., Bonifas, V. H., and Schlesinger, R. W. (1963). *Virology* **20**, 357.

Sabin, A. B. (1941). *Bacteriol. Rev.* **5**, 1.

Schimke, R. T., and Barile, M. F. (1963). *Exptl. Cell Res.* **30**, 593.

Shepard, M. C. (1956). *J. Bacteriol.* **71**, 362.

Shepard, M. C. (1958). *J. Exptl. Med.* **107**, 237.

Shepard, M. C. (1967). *Ann. N.Y. Acad. Sci.* **143**, 505.

Shepard, M. C., and Lunceford, C. D. (1965). *J. Bacteriol.* **89**, 265.

Smith, P. F. (1964). *Bacteriol. Rev.* **28**, 97.

Smith, P. F., Peoples, D. M., and Morton, H. E. (1957). *Proc. Soc. Exptl. Biol. Med.* **96**, 550.

Somerson, N. L., and Cook, M. K. (1965). *J. Bacteriol.* **90**, 534.

Somerson, N. L., Taylor-Robinson, D., and Chanock, R. M. (1963). *Am. J. Hyg.* **77**, 122.

Tully, J. G. (1966). *Proc. Soc. Exptl. Biol. Med.* **122**, 565.

Wallace, R. E. (1964). *Proc. Soc. Exptl. Biol. Med.* **116**, 990.

Wedum, A. G., Hanel, E., Phillips, G. B., and Miller, O. T. (1956). *Am. J. Public Health* **46**, 1102.

Zwillenberg, L. D., and Bonifas, V. H. (1964). *Pathol. Microbiol.* **27**, 95.

15 Methods for the Study of Colicine and Colicinogeny

Haruo Ozeki

I. Introduction 565
II. Detection of Colicinogenic Strains 567
   A. Demonstration of Colicine Production on Agar Plates 567
   B. Isolation of Bacterial Strains Resistant to Colicines .. 569
   C. Identification of Colicine Types 570
   D. Detection and Isolation of Colicinogenic Bacteria from
      Noncolicinogenic Cells in a Mixed Population 572
III. Genetic Transfer of Colicinogenic Properties 574
   A. By Cell-to-Cell Conjugation 575
   B. By Phage-Mediated Transduction 578
   C. Elimination of Colicinogenic Factors 580
IV. Production of Colicine 581
   A. Lacunae Assay, Counting the Number of Colicine-
      Producing Cells 582
   B. Titration of Colicine 585
   C. Induction of Colicine Production 587
   D. Colicine Preparation 587
V. Mode of Action 588
   References 591

I. Introduction

Colicines are bactericidal antibiotics, protein in nature, produced by some strains of Enterobacteriaceae and active only on some strains of this family. Similar types of antibiotics have also been found in other groups of bacteria, such as megacines in *Bacillus megaterium,* pyocines in *Pseudomonas pyocyanea,* etc., and for these the more general term "bacteriocines" has been proposed. The first report of a colicine was made by Gratia in 1925. The development of the study of colicines was reviewed by Fredericq (1957), who has made many important contributions to our current knowledge of the subject. Readers are also referred to some other reviews for detailed references to the literature (Iváno-vics, 1962; Fredericq, 1963; Reeves, 1965).

Although many different colicines are known, they appear to form a natural class of antibiotics, since they share several fundamental characteristics. Colicines are quite different from ordinary antibiotics; in fact, they exhibit certain similarities to virulent bacteriophage in their killing action. They act on sensitive bacteria by adsorption to specific receptors, which may also act as receptors for a phage, and remain on the cell surface while they are acting. Their action is expressed almost immediately after their adsorption. Kinetic studies show that adsorption of a single colicine molecule is sufficient to kill a sensitive bacteria. Colicines, however, unlike phages, contain no nucleic acid and do not multiply in the cells they kill.

Strains that produce colicine are called "colicinogenic." Colicinogenic strains are quite common in nature—as common as lysogenic strains. They are sometimes utilized for bacterial typing in epidemiological studies (Vieu, 1964). Colicinogenic bacteria are usually resistant, or immune, to the action of the colicine they produce.

The ability of a bacterial strain to produce a particular colicine is in general a stable genetic character and is attributed to the possession of a corresponding genetic determinant termed a "colicinogenic factor" (or *col* factor). Colicines have been classified into groups A, B, C, etc., and colicinogenic factors responsible for the production of these colicines are, respectively, designated as *col* A, *col* B, *col* C, etc. *Col* factors are dispensable genetic structures for bacteira, and have been classified as "episomes" or "plasmids." A strain may produce two or more colicines, and such a strain must carry the two or more different *col* factors corresponding to them. Although every cell in a colicinogenic strain, as a rule, maintains the *col* factor, only a small fraction of the population actually produces colicine at any one time, and these cells are in consequence nonviable. The condition resembles phage production in a lysogenic culture. Moreover, colicine production in certain colicinogenic strains is inducible by various agents that are known to induce prophage development. Unlike phage, however, colicine can be released without lysis of the cells.

Colicinogenic factors do not form independent infectious particles, but can be transmitted through cell conjugation, from one strain to another, independent of the host chromosome. The transmission or infection in this manner is sometimes very efficient, and epidemic spread of the *col* factor takes place in noncolicinogenic bacterial population to which a small number of colicinogenic bacteria have been introduced.

These features are quite similar to those of the sex factor F in *E. coli*. In fact, certain *col* factors act as a sex factor, facilitating the transmission of bacterial chromosome, although the frequency is very low. Where studied, the chemical nature of *col* factors seems to be DNA, and their size appears to be comparable to that of other episomes, such as temperate phages or F factors.

Thus *col* factors resemble temperate phages on one hand and sex factors on the other; and colicines can be compared with virulent phages, especially with the protein coat or tail-end proteins of them (see Fredericq, 1958a; Jacob and Wollman, 1961). These remarkable similarities explain why this chapter has been included in this book. One may consider that the study of *col* factors is related to the study of latent defective virus that do not produce infectious virus particles, but are potentially lethal agents upon induction. Their existence is mainly recognized by the production of a distinct class of antibiotics that are as efficient as they are unique in their mode of action. The study of colicine action has also led to the interesting problem of how a colicine molecule can act so efficiently from the cell surface. The problem seems to be of fundamental importance in biology. Recently, Nomura (1963, 1964) studied detailed modes of action of colicines and proposed a general model that will be mentioned later.

II. Detection of Colicinogenic Strains

A. DEMONSTRATION OF COLICINE PRODUCTION ON AGAR PLATES

The production of colicine by a given strain may be revealed by covering the colonies developed on agar plates with sensitive indicator bacteria. The colonies grown from either single bacteria or from stab inocula may be sterilized by chloroform vapor; i.e., a small amount of chloroform is put in the lid of the plate, which is kept upside down to expose the colonies to the vapor. This method is not applicable to plastic dishes, since chloroform melts them; a watch glass may be used instead of a lid, on which a few drops of chloroform is placed at the center. After 5–10 minutes of exposure, the plate is left open at room temperature for 10 minutes or so to allow the chloroform to evaporate. The plate is then covered with a layer of soft agar seeded with about 2×10^8 bacteria of a suitable indicator strain. After overnight incubation, colonies of colicinogenic bacteria are surrounded by a clear inhibition zone in the confluent growth of the indicator bacteria (Fig. 1). The colonies on agar plates occasionally are moved or crumbled when the soft agar layer of indicator is poured over the plate. If this

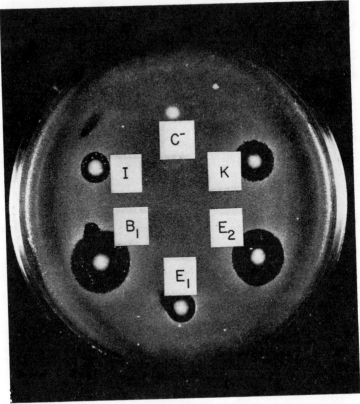

Fig. 1. Inhibition zones produced by strains of *S. typhimurium* LT2 made colicinogenic for various colicines. The colicinogenic factor *col* K was transferred from *E. coli* K-49 to *S. typhimurium* LT2; *col* E2 and *col* I from *Sh. sonnei* P9 to LT2; *col* B from *E. coli* K-77; and *col* E1 from *E. coli* K-12–30. The colonies originating from stab inocula of these colicinogenic strains of LT2 as well as the parental noncolicinogenic LT2 (*col⁻*) on a broth agar (24 hours at 37°C) were treated with chloroform vapor and then covered with soft agar layer of general indicator, *E. coli* ∅. The photograph was taken after overnight incubation at 37°C.

disturbs the test, a better result may be obtained by dripping soft agar onto each colony instead of pouring it, or by plating the colicinogenic bacteria in a soft agar layer that will be covered with the second indicator layer after chloroform treatment.

In order to confirm that the zones owe to colicines rather than bacteriophages, the following tests may be used. The plate showing the inhibition zones are sterilized again by chloroform vapor, and a part of the zone is transferred by a needle to a fresh plate of indicator bacteria.

No plaque formation is a favorable sign for colicines. Colicines are sensitive to proteolytic enzymes, while phages are generally not, and thus the addition of trypsin (e.g., 200 µg/ml) to the soft agar together with indicator bacteria usually markedly reduces the size of colicine zones.

As in the case of phage, colicinogenic properties cannot be demonstrated unless a suitable indicator strain is available. Accordingly, a systematic search for colicinogenic strains involves the initial steps of collecting a wide variety of strains and testing them against each other in all possible combinations. In practice, however, the classical strain of Gratia, *E. coli* strain ϕ, is known to be sensitive to almost all types of colicines and thus can be used as a general indicator to test whether a given strain is colicinogenic or not. Strains of *E. coli* K-12 or Row may also be used as a general indicator. The colicinogenic strains thus detected will be classified according to the type of colicine they produce. This will be described later.

Cross-streaking of a colicine-sensitive strain against a colicinogenic one on the surface of an agar plate, without using soft agar technique, may also reveal the colicinogenic property of the latter by the growth inhibition of the former at the intersecting area. In this case, however, simultaneous inoculation of both strains is usually not satisfactory. Cross-streaking in two steps is recommended; i.e., the colicinogenic strain is streaked first, incubated for a day or two, killed by chloroform vapor, and then the indicator culture is cross-streaked against it. The essential point is that the time necessary for the production of a sufficient amount of colicine as well as its diffusion in the agar must be allowed before applying the indicator bacteria. In certain colicinogenic strains, the majority of colicines synthesized are released from the cells upon chloroform treatment, and therefore the above method of delayed cross-streaking is essential to visualize the colicine production of such a strain.

The production of colicine by a given strain may also be detected by spotting the culture medium on the surface of a plate seeded with indicator bacteria. These methods are described in Section IV.

B. Isolation of Bacterial Strains Resistant to Colicines

When the plates showing clear zones surrounding colicinogenic colonies are incubated further, small colonies of indicator bacteria may be developed within the zones (see Fig. 1). The number of such colonies per zone varies, depending upon the type of colicine involved as well as the indicator strain applied. These colonies are mostly the colicine-resistant mutants derived from the indicator strain, and may be purified by successive streaking. Resistant mutants usually lack the specific receptor sites for colicine adsorption (though other classes of resistant mutants are also possible; see below). A mutant that is resistant to a particular type of colicine still retains the sensitivity for other colicines to which it was susceptible. By repetition of the above procedure, doubly or triply resistant indicators can be obtained. Fredericq (1957) reported an instance in which an indicator strain was made resistant to eight different colicines by eight successive steps.

Several examples are known in which the receptor site for a certain colicine is common to a certain phage, such as between colicine K and phage T6, or colicine E and phage BF23. Accordingly, a colicine-resistant strain could be obtained by selecting against the corresponding phage.

Indicator strains resistant to known type(s) of colicines are utilized for the identification of a colicine type of a given strain.

C. Identification of Colicine Types

Colicines produced by various strains differ in numerous characteristics, such as specificity of receptor sites, modes of action, diffusibility in agar, thermostability, electrophoretic mobility, antigenic property, etc. Colicines have been conventionally classified into groups according to the specificity of their receptors (Fredericq, 1965a). The standard colicinogenic strains originated from Fredericq's collection, and these have been used in many laboratories as the type strains (see Table I).

In order to identify the colicines produced by unknown strains, their activity has to be tested against a set of mutants resistant to known colicines to see which type of mutant is resistant to the unknown colicine. Conversely, a mutant resistant to the unknown colicine may be derived and tested against the standard set of strains to see against which it is resistant. To test whether two given colicinogenic strains produce the same type of colicine, the above reciprocal check may be done without using the standard type strains.

Colicinogenic strains isolated from nature are often doubly or triply colicinogenic. The identification of colicine types of these strains is more complicated, since they remain active against every single resistant mutant and must be tested against doubly or triply resistant mutants for all possible combinations. Since, however, different colicines often produce different sized zones of inhibition, it may be worthwhile to apply a mixture of indicator bacteria, as, for instance, a general indicator

TABLE I

STANDARD COLICINOGENIC STRAINS[a]

Strain	Colicines produced[b]
E. coli CA7	V and M
E. coli CA18	B
E. coli CA23	D
E. freundii CA31	A
E. coli CA38	E3 (E) and I
E. coli CA42	E2 (F)
E. coli CA46	G
E. coli CA53	I
Paracoli CA57	C
E. coli CA58	H
Paracoli CA62	E1 (J) and I
E. coli K-235	K and X[c]
Sh. boydii P1	S1
Sh. sonnei P9	E2 (S3) and I
Sh. dispar P14	E1 (S5)
Sh. dispar P15	S4

[a] From Fredericq (1965a).

[b] The former names of the colicines are given in parentheses.

[c] The name X was given by Miyama et al. (1961); cf. colicine X in Papavassiliou (1961).

strain mixed with a few percent of various single resistant mutant, and to see which resistant mutant gives a turbid outer zone with a clear central region. In this way the most diffusible colicine may be identified, making it easy to detect the others. Similarly, resistant colonies will not appear in the central part, where two colicines are present, but may be picked from the outer zone and used to identify the most diffusible colicine. Then, by using the resistant mutant obtained as the indicator, the resistant mutant for the second type of colicine may be obtained.

It must be emphasized that the classification of colicines into groups is based upon the specificity of their receptors, and a group may contain colicines that differ in their mode of action or chemical constitution. For instance, colicines of group E could be subdivided according to the specific immunity of a strain conferred by transfer of colicinogenic factors E; i.e., a strain made colicinogenic for a colicine of subgroup E1 is resistant to colicine E1, but still sensitive to colicines of E2 and E3 and to phage BF23. On the other hand, the same strain made colicinogenic for a colicine of subgroup E2 is resistant to colicines of E2, but still sensitive to E1 and E3 and to phage BF23 (Fredericq, 1956). The mode of action of these colicines is also very different; i.e., E1 inhibits all macromolecular synthesis of sensitive bacteria, while E3 stops only protein synthesis, and E2 causes degradation of DNA in cells (Nomura, 1963).

Furthermore, even colicines belonging to the same subgroup are sometimes serologically distinguishable from each other, e.g., colicine E2 corresponding to the *col* E2 factor originally carried by *Shigella sonnei* P9 is different from that of *E. coli* K-317, although both colicines are produced by *Salmonella typhimurium* LT2 to which those colicinogenic factors have been transferred (Lewis and Stocker, 1965).

Under these circumstances, it is recommended that colicines and *col* factors be described by the type designation followed by the name of the original strain from which it was isolated, such as E1–K30, E2–P9, E2–K317, K–K49, etc. In the following text, however, these detailed nomenclatures are often avoided for the sake of convenience, since the main purpose here is to illustrate the methods. Colicinogenic strains are indicated by adding the names of *col* factors in parentheses; e.g., *E. coli* K-12 (*col* E1–K30), *S. typhimurium* LT2 (*col* I–P9) (*col* E2–P9), or simply *S. typhimurium* LT2 (*col* I), and so on. Noncolicinogenic strains are indicated, if necessary, by adding *col⁻* in parentheses. Colicine-resistant strains are designated by giving the name of the colicine(s) immediately following a diagonal line; e.g., *E. coli* K-12/E, *E. coli* Row/I, *E. coli* φ/I,E, etc.

D. Detection and Isolation of Colicinogenic Bacteria from Noncolicinogenic Cells in a Mixed Population

In order to detect and isolate colicinogenic clones from a mixed population of colicinogenic and noncolicinogenic bacteria, the following procedures may be used, with variations according to the proportion of *col⁺* to *col⁻* bacteria.

1. When the proportion of *col⁺* is very high (> 10%), the mixture is streaked or plated for single-colony isolation, and individual colonies are randomly picked and tested for their colicinogeny.

2. When the proportion is not so high (10^{-1}–10^{-4}), either (a) replica plates made by the aid of velvet are tested for the presence of colicinogenic clones; colonies corresponding to them are then picked from the master plates, or (b) a suitable number of bacteria from the mixed culture are plated with soft agar and after incubation a further layer containing indicator bacteria is added without chloroform treatment; after further incubation, colonies underlying the centers of inhibition zones are picked; a second uninoculated soft agar layer (3–5 ml) may be

added on the first layer before incubation to avoid having colonies on the surface of the plates, which otherwise would obscure the appearance of inhibition zones if they are crumbled by and grown in the indicator layer (Sandwich plate technique) (Fig. 2).

3. When the proportion is very low ($< 10^{-5}$) and therefore a vast number of bacteria must be plated, the above sandwich plate technique may still be applicable, but the detection of the colicinogenic colonies is not very easy. If the bacteria are exacting for certain nutritional factors, such as an amino acid, a clearer result may be obtained by plating the bacteria on a minimal agar (that may be enriched with a small amount of broth) on which the bacteria grow very poorly. In this case, the bacteria may be spread on the agar surface without soft agar. After incubation for 2 days, the bacteria (not chloroformed) are overlaid

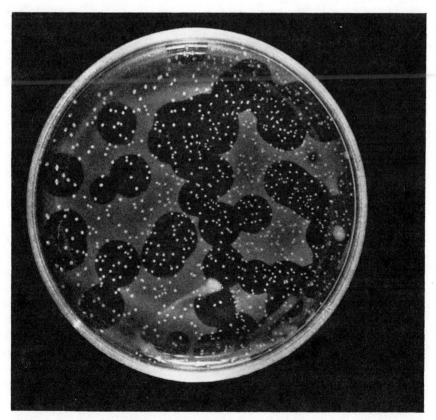

FIG. 2. Detection of colicinogenic colonies among noncolicinogenic colonies by the sandwich plate technique.

with a layer of soft minimal agar containing indicator bacteria that can grow on this medium. After overnight incubation, the indicator bacteria (but not the bacteria plated) will grow, and tiny zones of inhibition may be observed. A small piece of agar containing a zone is cut out, and from this (or by repeating the same procedure, if necessary) the colicinogenic clone can be isolated.

III. Genetic Transfer of Colicinogenic Properties

Certain colicinogenic strains when grown in broth together with non-colicinogenic strains transmit their colicinogenic property to some of the noncolicinogenic cells. Colicinogeny cannot be transmitted by a bacterium-free culture filtrate or a culture killed with chloroform. It is inferred that the colicinogenic character is transmitted from one bacterium to another by the transfer of *col* factors through cell conjugation. Transfer of *col* factors takes place not only between *E. coli* strains but also between strains of *E. coli, Shigella, Salmonella, Klebsiella, Providencia, Serratia,* or *Proteus.* The *col* factors that are not transmissible by themselves may be transmitted with the aid of other episomes that facilitate cell conjugation. Certain *col* factors, furthermore, can be transferred from one strain to another by phage-mediated transduction.

This process of transmission of *col* factors is not only an interesting biological phenomenon, but it also provides a useful method for studying colicines and colicinogeny. By transferring *col* factors from naturally occurring colinogenic strains to a well-analyzed laboratory strain, one can study colicines and colicinogeny in a "defined" genetic background. Moreover, the transfer of *col* factors has been successfully applied to the study of the physicochemical nature of *col* factors. Since *col* factors, differing from phages, do not exist separate from their host bacteria, experiments along this line have been restricted to utilizing the transmission of *col* factors, which is, fortunately, in most cases independent of that of the host chromosome. For instance, the bacteria in which only the *col* factors are labeled with ^{32}P can be obtained by the transfer of *col* factors from a ^{32}P-labeled donor bacteria to an unlabeled recipient bacteria. By following the inactivation of *col* factors from ^{32}P decay occurring in the recipients, one may estimate the sizes of the factors (Lavallé and Jacob, 1961; Ozeki, 1965a). Similarly, a quantitative correlation between the transfer to nonradioactive recipients of *col* factor(s) and of specific labels (^{14}C-thymidine) incorporated by the donor bacteria led to the evidence for DNA transfer accompanying the transmission of *col* factors, as well as an estimate of the sizes of *col* factors involved (Silver and Ozeki, 1962). Taking those results together, the *col* factors studied (*col* I–P9, *col* E2–P9, and *col* E1–K30) contain roughly in the order of 10^5 phosphorus atoms/factor (1.1, 0.8, and 1.3×10^5 P atoms, respectively) (Ozeki, 1965a). It is also possible to characterize *col* factors by transferring them to organisms whose DNA might differ markedly from *col* DNA in buoyant density and examining DNA of such a colicinogenic strain in a CsCl density gradient. Recently, DeWitt and Helinsky (1965) were successful in using *Proteus mirabilis* ($\rho = 1.700$) as the host to which *col* E1 was transferred from *E. coli* K-30 ($\rho = 1.710$); they could detect an additional DNA that is not detected in the original *Proteus* strain and that accompanies the appearance of *col* factor (0.3% of the total DNA, having $\rho = 1.710$). The genetic transmission of *col* factors may also be applied to various other problems, but, in this section, only the basic methods concerning this phenomenon will be described.

A. By Cell-to-Cell Conjugation

1. *Growing Colicinogenic and Noncolicinogenic Strains Together*

To test for the transmission of *col* factor(s) from a colicinogenic donor strain to a noncolicinogenic recipient strain, a volume of broth (e.g., 5 ml) is inoculated with approximately equal volumes (e.g., 0.1 ml, or a loopful) of broth cultures of both strains and incubated overnight either standing or with gentle agitation. The recipient bacteria must be distinguishable (and preferably selectable) from the donor bacteria by drug resistance, nutritional requirements, colony morphology, etc. The mixed culture is then plated for detection and isolation of colicinogenic recipient clones, according to the methods described in Section II,D, depending upon the proportion of the recipient cells that acquired colicinogeny.

If the recipient strain is sensitive to the colicine produced by the donor strain, some precautions may be taken to prevent the death of recipient bacteria occurring in mixed culture, such as adding trypsin (100–200 µg/ml) to the culture or using a colicine-resistant derivative of the recipient strain. In some cases if such precautions are not taken, the mixed culture may end up with a high proportion of the surviving recipient cells acquiring *col* factor. Since the recipient cells soon become insensitive, or immune, to the colicine upon receiving the corresponding *col* factor, they are selected under these conditions.

The transmission of certain *col* factors is very efficient. For instance, when *Sh. sonnei* P9 (*col* I)(*col* E2) and *S. typhimurium* LT2 (noncolicinogenic and naturally resistant to nearly all colicines) were grown together in broth inoculated with about 10^5 cells/ml of each strain, 50% or more of the latter population became colicinogenic during overnight incubation; about 50% of *Salmonella* cells had acquired *col* I, and about 5% *col* I and *col* E2 together (Ozeki *et al.*, 1962). Similarly, when *S. typhymurium* LT2 (*col* I) thus obtained was grown overnight with a genetically marked strain of LT2, e.g., streptomycin-resistant mutant LT2 Sm^r, again more than 50% of the latter became colicinogenic for colicine I. Thus the *col* I originally carried by *Sh. sonnei* P9 is a readily transmissible factor, and it was later confirmed that the *col* I itself can confer mating ability on the host bacteria. These extensive transmissions can be achieved even by starting the mixed culture with an excess of recipient bacteria (e.g., donor/recipient = $\frac{1}{100}$). This has been explained as the results of serial transmission, or "epidemic spread," of the *col* factor among the recipient bacteria. A further explanation of this phenomenon will be given in the next section.

Certain *col* factors are transmissible but less efficiently, and certain others are not transmissible at all. The transmissibility of a *col* factor is determined by the genetic character of the factor itself, but the host bacteria may effect transmission as well. Nontransmissible factors might be transferred in the presence of other transmissible factors or by phage-mediated transduction (see below).

2. High-Frequency Colicinogeny Transfer (HFC)

In the above section, the transmission occurring during prolonged incubation of a mixed culture was described. In certain colicinogenic strains, the efficiency of transmission was as high as 50% or more after overnight incubation. When, however, the transfer experiment is performed for a short time with the same combination of donor and recipient strains, the proportion of recipient cells acquiring *col* factor is usually very low. For instance, when broth cultures (2×10^8 cells/ml) of *S. typhimurium* LT2 (*col* I) and of LT2 Sm^r (*col*$^-$) were mixed in equal parts and incubated for 1 hour at 37°C, the proportion of recipient cells acquiring *col* I was only about 0.01%, while on prolonged incubation of the same culture the proportion reached about 50%. This phenomenon was studied in detail, and it has been revealed that: (1) in a broth culture of LT2 (*col* I), only about 1 bacterium in 5000 is a competent donor, able to pair with and transmit *col* I factor to an acceptor bacterium not carrying *col* I; (2) in contrast, every bacterium that has just acquired *col* I becomes a competent donor; (3) the bacterium infected with *col* I becomes a competent donor within less than a generation's time and produces two daughter cells, both of which are also competent donors. This competence is retained for several generations in the progeny (Ozeki *et al.*, 1962; Stocker *et al.*, 1963; Ozeki, 1965; see also Monk and Clowes, 1964). Thus the epidemic spread of *col* I, mentioned above, has been explained as the results of serial transmission of *col* I among recipient bacteria, initiated by the few recipient cells that originally received it.

Based upon these observations, a high-frequency colicinogeny transferring (HFC) donor preparation, that is, a culture containing a high proportion of bacteria newly infected with *col* I, may be obtained by growing *col* I+ and *col*⁻ bacteria together at an appropriate ratio (Stocker *et al.*, 1963; Monk and Clowes, 1964). An example of such a procedure is as follows. Five milliliters of broth is inoculated with a donor strain carrying *col* I and an intermediate strain not carrying *col* I in the ratio of 1 : 20 (total cell count, about 10^6/ml; *col* I+ cells, 5%). After overnight incubation at 37°C (*col* I+ cells have increased to about 50%), the mixed culture is diluted 10- to 20-fold with fresh broth and incubated for 2 hours (*col* I+ cells now are about 90%). About 40% of the cells acquired *col* I during the last 2 hours of incubation, and therefore on mixing with other *col*⁻ recipients they transmit *col* I at high frequency. If the first overnight culture gives a very high proportion of *col* I+ cells (e.g., 80%), about equal portions of pure intermediate culture (*col*⁻) may be added for the second 2 hours' culture in order to supply enough noncolicinogenic intermediate cells. The details of this procedure, such as the initial ratio of the donor and intermediate, inoculum size, duration of the second incubation, etc., may be modified in each case. The principle, however, seems to be applicable to other *col* factors or episomes in which the gene functions responsible for the mating ability are usually repressed, because they may be expressed for a while when the episome is transmitted into bacteria not carrying the same episome (cf. the zygotic induction of a prophage). Indeed, this idea has been successfully applied to certain multiple-drug-resistant factors, R, to obtain a high-frequency transmission (Watanabe, 1963).

In general, the process of cell conjugation seems to be sensitive to mechanical force, and therefore the handling of mating mixture, or even of donor preparation, must be done carefully; sucking and blowing out of mating mixtures with a narrow-mouth pipet may break up the mating pairs. Incidentally, it was revealed by separating the mating pairs with a blender that a *col* factor can be transmitted within a few minutes after the onset of pairing (Smith *et al.*, 1963).

3. *Transfer of Col Factors by the Aid of Other Col or Sex Factors*

Certain *col* factors are not transmissible at all, or are but at a very low frequency. Some of these *col* factors, however, become transmissible when certain other *col* factors or a sex factor that is able to confer mating ability to the host bacteria is also present in the same cell. For instance, strains carrying *col* E2 (from *Sh. sonnei* P9) do not transmit this factor to any detectable extent, but the strains carrying *col* E2 and *col* I do transmit both factors. Moreover, when the bacteria carrying *col* E2 alone are newly infected with *col* I, they transmit both *col* factors at high frequency and not merely the newly gained *col* I. Such an HFC donor culture may be prepared in the same way as described above, by using an intermediate strain carrying *col* E2 instead of a noncolicinogenic one. Similarly a strain carrying both *col* E1 and *col* E2 can act as intermediate donor, transmitting *col* I, *col* E1, and *col* E2 together at high frequency (Smith *et al.*, 1963). In these cases, if the intermediate strains already carry *col* I, they do not become competent donors. Thus the *col* I originating from *Sh. sonnei* P9 is not only transmissible by itself but also facilitates the transfer of other *col* factors in the same cell which are otherwise nontransmissible; moreover, *col* I also makes it possible to transfer the bacterial chromosome, although the frequency is very low (Ozeki and Howarth, 1961; Clowes, 1961).

The well-known fertility factor, F, or even the R factor, is also able to facilitate the transmission of certain *col* factors (see Fredericq, 1965b). In the bacteria carrying F factor, either F^+ or Hfr, the mating ability is constitutively expressed, differing from the *col* I, and therefore a high frequency of transmission of *col* factors from such strains is achieved easily, without the necessity of making an HFC donor preparation. *Col* factors are usually transmitted as units independent of both the F factor and the bacterial chromosome. In certain cases, however, *col* factors are combined with the F factor and are transmitted jointly or integrated into the bacterial chromosome (Fredericq, 1965b).

B. BY PHAGE-MEDIATED TRANSDUCTION

Besides cell conjugation, certain *col* factors can be transmitted from one strain to another by phage-mediated transduction. The instances of transduction of *col* factors has so far been reported only in the generalized transduction systems; e.g., *col* E2 in *S. typhimurium* LT2 by phage P22, or *col* E1, *col* B, or *col* V in *E. coli* K-12 by phage P1; *col* I and *col* K gave negative results in both systems (Ozeki and Stocker, 1958; Fredericq, 1958b, 1959, 1965b).

Transduction experiments of *col* factors generally follow the same procedures as are used for any other genetic elements. In generalized transduction systems, the frequency of transduction of a given gene is usually very low (one transduction per 10^5–10^7 phage particles), and this is also the case for *col* factors. Accordingly, the bottleneck of the experiments will be how to detect or isolate colicinogenic transductants from a vast number of noncolicinogenic recipient bacteria. Negative results evidently cannot be regarded as the evidence for the absence of transduction of *col* factors.

The lysates of colicinogenic donor bacteria usually contain colicines that often disturb the experiments. It is advisable to treat the lysate with trypsin, after removal of cells or debris by spinning, to destroy free colicine; the residual trypsin activity may be neutralized by a trypsin inhibitor (e.g., soy bean trypsin inhibitor, Worthington Biochemical Corporation).

Transduction of *col* factors can be detected either by the formation of colicinogenic clones or by the colicine production of the phage-infected bacteria themselves: (1) Transductants resulting in the formation of stable colicinogenic clones are detected and isolated by plating the recipient cells immediately after phage adsorption following the methods described in Section II,D. If an auxotrophic mutant is used as a recipient strain, and if the colicinogenic donor strain carries the prototrophic allele of the auxotrophic marker, the transduction of that marker can also be detected on the plates used for scoring *col* factor by plating the transducing mixture on minimal medium (see Section II,D,3), giving rise to large colonies; this gives a direct measure of the relative frequency of transduction between *col* factor and an ordinary gene. (2) Another simple method of detecting the transduction may be achieved by the application of the "lacunae" technique (a lacuna is a tiny but visible clearing formed in the soft agar layer of indicator bacteria by the colicine released from a single bacterium; see Section IV,A for details). An example of this technique is as follows. The recipient bacteria of *S. typhimurium* LT2 (Sm^s) were infected with phage P22 grown on LT2 (*col* E2) and incubated in broth for about 2 hours after phage adsorption to allow the synthesis of colicine by the *col* factors introduced into recipient bacteria (*col* E2 is not transmissible by cell mating). An appropriate amount of this culture was then inoculated into soft agar containing streptomycin and streptomycin-resistant indicator bacteria and poured on the top of a streptomycin agar plate (so killing the recipient bacteria). The lacunae become visible after 6–8 hours of incubation (one lacuna per approximately 10^7 active phage applied), and these must have resulted from the transduction of *col* E2 factor, since no lacunae were formed with either recipient culture alone or phage alone, and also no lacunae were seen if the indicator strain used was resistant to colicine E2. In this instance, since the production of this colicine has been known to be inducible, UV irradiation of the bacteria after infection of transducing phage markedly increased the number of lacunae ($\times$ 10). Moreover, when the recipient cells were irradiated before phage infection, the number of lacunae observed was as high as that obtained by irradiating the bacteria after phage infection; this phenomenon is called "preinduction." The number of lacunae, in this instance, was usually 5–10 times greater than the number of stable colicinogenic clones. This is presumably because the necessity for the steps involved in establishment of stable colicinogeny is circumvented in the lacunae method.

Recently, Fredericq (1965b) reported an interesting case of joint transduction of *col* factor and bacterial genes, or two *col* factors together (*col* B and *col* V), by phage P1 from *E. coli* carrying an F' episome that contains the *try cys* B region of the bacterial chromosome, *col* B and *col* V. The transduction of these *col* factors was detected as stable colicinogenic clones, and the number of such transductants was strikingly increased if the recipient strain was already carrying the F agent, such as F'*lac*, F'*gal* or even a partially deleted F agent (Fd). The *col* factors were probably transmitted to the same extent into either F' or F⁻ recipients, but the presence of the F agent in some way facilitated the establishment of stable colicinogeny by presumably joining with the *col* factor.

C. Elimination of Colicinogenic Factors

In general, the colicinogenic property of naturally occurring strains is a fairly stable hereditary characteristic that is only rarely lost. Laboratory strains made colicinogenic by the various ways just described show more variability in their stability. For instance, among the derivatives of *S. typhimurium* LT2, strains colicinogenic for *col* I, *col* E2, or *col* E1, were stable after prolonged storage at room temperature on Dorset's egg slopes, while a strain carrying *col* B (from *E. coli* K-77) was less stable (only 10–15% were colicinogenic when the strain was streaked after storage for a year), and one carrying *col* K (from *E. coli* K-49) was much less stable (about 0.2% was colicinogenic under the same condition) (Ozeki *et al.*, 1962). Similarly, *col* factors transmitted into *Serratia marsecense* were generally less stable (Amati and Ozeki, 1962).

It would be convenient if one could eliminate, or cure, *col* factors experimentally from a given colicinogenic strain. Unfortunately, however, no general method for this purpose has been worked out. Treatment with acridine dyes, which, it is well known, very efficiently cures the F factor from F^+ strains of *E. coli* K-12 does not appear to work on *col* factors. Clowes (1965) recently reported that certain *col* factors can be eliminated with high efficiency from thymineless strains under conditions of partial deprivation of thymine: under these conditions R factors and F factors from F^+ cells (but not from Hfr cells) were also cured. After the treatment of colicinogenic bacteria with a mutagen, N-methyl-N'-nitro-N-nitrosoguanidine, a considerable fraction of cells was found to have lost the ability to produce colicine. Whether they are cured or still carrying defective *col* factors has not been studied yet (Ogawa and Ozeki, 1964). Among the streptomycin-resistant mutants isolated from *E. coli* K-235 (*col* K) (*col* X), clones that have lost the ability to produce colicine X are often found (Miyama *et al.*, 1961). Moreover, in the same double colicinogenic strain, the transfer of the R factor induces loss of the *col* K or *col* X from this strain (Kato and Hanaoka, 1962).

IV. Production of Colicine

As mentioned earlier, the production of colicine by a colicinogenic strain resembles in several respects the production of phage particles in a lysogenic bacteria. All the colicine produced by a colicinogenic culture, either spontaneously or after induction, is synthesized and released by a fraction of the bacterial population that consequently becomes nonviable. In certain colicinogenic strains, the colicine production is inducible, while in others it is not. When it is inducible, the inducing agents are often the same as those that are effective in prophage induction. Unlike phage, however, colicine synthesized in bacteria can be released without lysis of the cells. In certain strains, the amount of colicine produced by a single bacteria is enough to form a small clear spot in a colicine-sensitive indicator layer. These clear spots, which look like phage plaques, have been called "lacuna(e)" to distinguish them from phage plaques (Ozeki *et al.*, 1959). The production of lacunae provides a simple method of counting the number of bacteria synthesizing colicine either spontaneously or after induction.

Colicine released in the culture medium may be detected by spotting the clear supernatant of the culture on an indicator lawn. The titration of colicine may be achieved by spotting drops of a serial dilution of the preparation to determine the highest dilution of the preparation that still gives a clear inhibition zone. Although the sensitivity of this end-point dilution method varies according to the type of colicine concerned, one may compare the titers of different preparations of a given type of colicine under standardized conditions.

A more precise method of titration of colicine activity is to measure the number of active colicine particles per milliliter of preparation. This can be done biologically, since a single particle or molecule of colicine is able to kill a bacterium (single-hit killing process). Thus the term "multiplicity," expressing the average number of killing particles applied to a cell, may be used in a way analogous to that which has been widely used in phage work.

A. LACUNAE ASSAY (COUNTING THE NUMBER OF COLICINE-PRODUCING CELLS)

The technique used for lacunae counts is essentially the same as that for counting the phage-producing cells in phage experiments. Three milliliters of soft agar seeded with about 2×10^8 cells of an indicator strain and an appropriate number of colicinogenic bacteria are poured on an agar plate and incubated; lacunae may be visible after about 6 hours at 37°C (Fig. 3). The number of lacunae is directly proportional to the number of colicinogenic bacteria incorporated into the soft agar layer. The presence of colicinogenic cells and indicator bacteria together within the same soft agar layer is technically essential for the formation of lacunae. If the former are first spread on a plate and then an indicator layer is poured on the top, or if the indicator layer is poured first and then a suspension of colicinogenic cells is spotted on it, generally lacunae will hardly be visible. Colicine kills the indicator bacteria but does not lyze them. Accordingly, once the indicator bacteria has grown to the extent of being visible, the clearings are no longer produced, even if the cells are killed later by colicine.

In order to confirm that the tiny clearings observed are caused by colicine synthesized and released by single bacteria, the following points may be checked. If the clear spots are the result of colicine, no spots will be produced with an indicator strain particularly resistant to that colicine; or trypsin (200 μg/ml of soft agar) in the soft agar will prevent the appearance of the spots. Although the spots look like phage

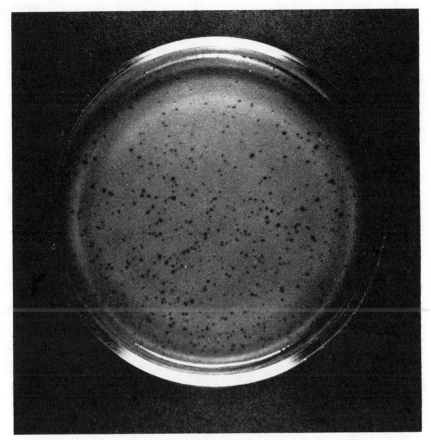

Fig. 3. Lacunae formed by *S. typhimurium* LT2 (*col* E2) in an indicator lawn of *E. coli* ∅. The photograph was taken after 7 hours' incubation at 37°C.

plaques, no lytic activity will be found when they are cut out and tested on a fresh plate of the indicator bacteria. In order to break up any cell clumps, the colicinogenic culture may be treated in a blender just before its inoculation into the soft agar. To prevent the growth of colicinogenic bacteria in the soft agar layer, streptomycin or chloramphenicol may be added to the soft agar with the drug-resistant indicator strain. When the use of drugs is not possible, the colicinogenic cells may be killed by treatment with chloroform for 5–10 minutes just before the inoculation. Under these conditions, lacunae are still produced, which must be caused by cells which at the time of plating already contained enough colicine to form clearings by releasing it. The number of lacunae without these treatments is usually higher than that with them, and therefore the lacunae are also formed by bacteria that synthesize colicine on the plate. This is more evident after colicine induction. If a colicinogenic culture is plated immediately after the induction with and without killing the bacteria, a striking difference in the numbers of lacunae will be observed; however, if the culture is plated after about 100 minutes, incubation in broth, allowing the synthesis of colicine, no difference in lacunae counts will be seen. In this way, the kinetics of colicine synthesis after induction may be followed (Fig. 4).

The production of colicine by single bacteria, as well as the death of such bacteria, has also been demonstrated by isolating each bacteria by micromanipulation. The results of the micromanipulation correlated well with the lacunae counts of the same induced culture (Ozeki *et al.*, 1959).

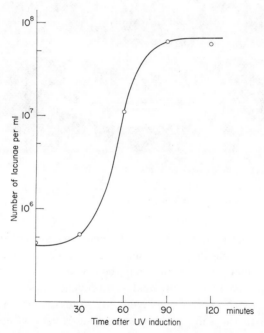

FIG. 4. Lacuna production induced by UV irradiation. UV-irradiated bacteria of *S. typhimurium* LT2 Sm^s (*col* E2) were suspended in broth (10^8 cells/ml) and incubated at 37°C. At intervals, aliquots were inoculated into streptomycin soft agar containing streptomycin-resistant indicator bacteria and poured on streptomycin agar plates to determine the number of lacunae. The total cell count did not increase significantly in the 2-hour incubation period.

B. Titration of Colicine

1. Spot Test (End-Point Dilution Method)

The titer of a colicine preparation may be arbitrarily defined as the maximum dilution of the preparation that still gives a clear zone of inhibition by spotting it on an indicator lawn under standardized conditions. A uniform indicator lawn may be prepared in the following way: 3–5 ml of a 1 : 10 dilution (in saline) of overnight culture of suitable indicator strain is poured on an agar plate; the plate is kept for 5–10 minutes at room temperature and the excess liquid then removed; the plate is incubated about 30 minutes at 37°C, by which time the surface should be dry. A soft agar indicator layer may also be used, but it must be made uniform in thickness. This may be done by keeping the surface of the basal agar smooth and horizontal. These plates may be dried for about 30 minutes at 37°C before use; otherwise it takes a long time to adsorb all the spotted liquid. The colicine preparation is serially diluted (e.g., 2-fold), and a drop of each dilution is spotted on the indicator lawn. The results may be scored after 6–8 hours of incubation, and the maximum dilution giving a clear (or almost clear) inhibition zone will be taken as the colicine titer of the culture.

2. Punch-Hole Assay

Assay of colicine titer by the punch-hole test are made on plates containing a bottom layer of nutrient agar and a top layer with indicator bacteria. The holes are punched out with a cork borer giving a constant diameter (e.g., 1 cm). The holes are filled with a constant volume of the appropriate colicine sample, and the plates are immediately put in a refrigerator (at 4°C) and allowed to diffuse colicine (e.g., for 40 hours). The plates are then transferred to an incubator (they may be opened for 2–3 hours to insure a dry surface) and incubated overnight. The diameters of the zone of inhibition are measured, and from those the titers of colicine may be determined by referring to a standard curve. A standard assay curve for a given type of colicine may be made by plotting the logarithm of the concentration of colicine against the diameter of the inhibition zone (see Mayr-Harting, 1964).

3. Determination of the Number of Killing Particles

It has been shown that the killing action of most colicines is a single-hit process (Jacob et al., 1952; Nomura, 1963). Thus the number of killing particles in a colicine preparation can be determined by measuring the survivors of bacteria treated with various dilutions of the preparation. For example, colicine-sensitive bacteria $(2 \times 10^8/\text{ml})$ are mixed with various concentrations of a colicine preparation and incubated for 10 minutes at 37°C for colicine adsorption; chloramphenicol (40 μg/ml) may be added to prevent the growth of bacteria during this incubation period. The adsorption of colicine is usually irreversible, and it is practically complete within a few minutes under these conditions. The cultures are then diluted and plated for viable counts. Figure 5 shows a

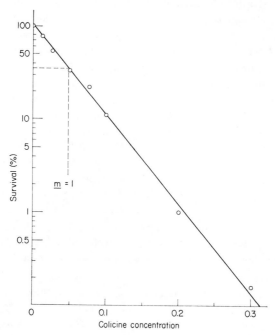

FIG. 5. A single-hit killing curve and the titration of killing particles (see text).

typical result obtained from such an experiment performed with *E. coli* K-12 and colicine E2. From the single-hit killing curve obtained, the number of killing particles per milliliter of original preparation may be estimated by applying the Poisson distribution (e.g., the concentration that gives 36% survivors contained killing particles equal to the number of bacteria treated, or a multiplicity of 1). The number of killing particles thus measured may not be equal to the actual number of active colicine molecules in the medium, as will be described later.

C. Induction of Colicine Production

The procedures used for inducing phage production in lysogenic strains are generally applicable to the induction of colicine production in an inducible colicinogenic strain. UV irradiation with a sublethal dose is most commonly used for this purpose. Colicine synthesis may also be induced efficiently by adding a low concentration of mitomycin C to a colicinogenic culture (0.2–1 μg/ml), or by treating the cells for 5–10 minutes at 10–20 μg/ml. Instances of thymineless induction (Luzzati and Chevallier, 1964) or of induction occurring at high temperature (Kohiyama and Nomura, 1965) have also been reported. The phenomenon of preinduction of colicine production was described in Section III,B.

The inducibility of colicine synthesis appears to depend not only upon the col factor itself but also upon the host bacteria carrying colicine. For instance, col I from Sh. sonnei P9 is not inducible by UV irradiation in S. typhimurium LT2, but it is inducible in certain derivatives of E. coli K-12 (Amati, 1963). Recently, a mutant of col I was isolated in our laboratory whose colicine production is induced in S. typhimurium LT2 at 43°C (Ohoki, 1966). On the other hand, in certain cases the mutations of host bacteria are known to cause the high-temperature induction of certain col factors (Kohiyama and Nomura, 1965).

The induction of a colicinogenic culture may be visualized either as the increase in the number of lacunae (see Fig. 4) or in the amount of colicine produced after a certain time of incubation. Where these two measures are possible, their kinetic curves are usually parallel after the induction. The induction increases the number of cells producing colicine in the culture and not the amount of colicine produced per cell.

Phagelike multiplication of col factors occurring after the induction has been suggested by Amati (1964) and Luzzati and Chevallier (1964), although this may not be the essential process of colicine production (Kohiyama and Nomura, 1965).

D. Colicine Preparation

In general, colicine preparations are handled like those of proteins. Since colicines are usually not particularly thermosensitive, the handling is relatively easy.

A crude colicine preparation may be obtained from a liquid culture of colicinogenic strain in the following way. The culture is sterilized by shaking with a small amount of chloroform (or pasteurized by heating at 60°C for 40 minutes) and stored for several hours or overnight in the cold to allow the release of colicine from cells to the medium; the cells are then removed by centrifugation. Preparations made with colicines released from bacteria are obviously much cleaner than those obtained by opening up the cells, though the latter method gives a somewhat higher titer of colicine.

High titers of a colicine preparation may be achieved more easily with an inducible strain. When it is desired to induce a large volume of culture, mitomycin c (0.2–1 μg/ml) may be added instead of using UV irradiation, and the culture is incubated for several hours before chloroform treatment. Since colicinogenic bacteria may still adsorb colicine in the medium, a colicinogenic strain that is also resistant (lacking the receptor site) to its own colicine type may give a higher-titer preparation. Colicines can be partially purified and also concentrated by fractional precipitations with $(NH_4)_2SO_4$ and/or ethanol. Colicine preparations thus obtained are dialyzed against water and may be lyophilized for storage. These preparations are usually good enough for many kinds of experiments, but if necessary colicine may be further purified by applying various standard techniques available for the purification of proteins (see Goebel and Barry, 1958; Barry et al., 1965).

The molecular weight of a colicine may be estimated by sucrose-gradient centrifugation technique (Martin and Ames, 1961) by assaying the colicine activity of each fraction obtained. Proteins whose molecular weight are known, such as cytochrome c or hemoglobin, may serve as the reference in the same centrifuge tube. The molecular weight of colicine E2–P9 estimated in this way was roughly 60,000, in agreement with the value obtained by Helinsky (in Maeda and Nomura, 1966), and that of colicine I–P9 was about 13,000 (Ohoki, 1966). The molecular weight of colicine A–CA31 estimated from a purified preparation was about 50,000 (Barry et al., 1965).

Several colicines have been purified, namely, colicines K, V, and A. These colicines appear to be a complex of protein, carbohydrate, and lipid (lipocarbohydrate protein). The colicine activity is associated with the protein moiety, and the O somatic antigen of the producer strain may be associated with it (see Hinsdill and Goebel, 1964; cf. Reeves, 1963).

V. Mode of Action

Colicines are bactericidal, but not bacteriolytic, agents. Various colicines exhibit their antibiotic activity in a variety of ways. Some of them arrest all macromolecular synthesis in sensitive bacteria (e.g., colicine K or E1), while some others inhibit only protein synthesis (e.g., colicine E3); still others (e.g., colicine E2) cause degradation of bacterial DNA, or even prophage induction in a lysogenic strain (Nomura, 1963).

Despite the variety of effects with regard to their mode of action, all colicines have certain features in common:

1. Colicines act on sensitive bacteria by being fixed to specific receptor sites.

2. Colicines remain at the bacterial surface while they are acting.

3. The fixation of a single particle of colicine is able to bring about the death of a bacterium.

4. Colicines do not act on the bacteria that carry the corresponding *col* factors, although they retain receptors and can adsorb the colicines.

This section will be concerned with those general points and not with the individual mode of action of each colicine, since the methods involved for study of specific colicine actions, such as measuring the metabolic activity of bacteria, the stability of nucleic acids, etc., are general techniques that are beyond the scope of this chapter.

Specificity of receptor sites for each type of colicine has been described already (or, more precisely, colicine types are so defined). Upon mixing a colicine preparation with sensitive bacteria, colicine adsorption to the receptor site usually takes place very quickly. If the bacteria are in excess and their population density is high enough, the adsorption of colicine is practically complete within a few minutes at 37°C, although it is much slower at 0°C. The fixation of colicine to the bacterial surface is irreversible, as can be shown by the failure of colicines to be removed by dilution or washing. Dead cells or even extracts of sensitive bacteria also specifically neutralize colicines, probably by fixing them, while those prepared from resistant bacteria have no action. Antiserum prepared against a sensitive strain can block the receptors, protecting the bacteria from the colicine activity, while the serum shows no direct anticolicine activity.

By measuring the activity of colicine left in the solution after adsorption, one may estimate the number of killing units that can be adsorbed onto the surface of one bacterium. Such an estimate made by Mayr-Harting (1964) was 11 lethal units of colicine E2 per *E. coli* cell, while the value obtained with the same colicine by Maeda and Nomura (1966) was 20–30 per bacterium. When, however, the amount of colicine adsorbed to a cell was measured by using purified radioactive colicine E2 (thus eliminating the final measurement of killing activity), the value was as high as 2000–3000 colicine molecules per cell; i.e., one killing unit of colicine E2 corresponds to about 100 molecules (Maeda and Nomura, 1966). Although this calculation was dependent upon the purity of colicine preparations as well as the estimate of the molecular weight of colicine protein, it seems most likely that one killing unit of colicine corresponds to many colicine molecules. A similar situation exists in the case of megacine; i.e., in purified megacine c preparation, one killing hit corresponds to the adsorption of about 100 molecules per bacterium (Holland, 1962). Since the killing action is a single-hit process (see Fig. 5) not requiring the cooperative functions of several particles, one may consider that a single colicine particle causes, with certain probability, the death of a sensitive cell, although another explanation that a colicine preparation contains many inactive particles is still possible.

Maeda and Nomura (1966) also showed from the competition experiments performed with their radioactive colicine preparations that the receptor sites of colicine E2 are indeed common with colicine E3, as it has been predicted biologically, and yet these two colicines exhibit entirely different antibiotic activity (see above). Thus the receptor does not specify the apparent mode of colicine action.

Since the fixation of colicines to the receptors of sensitive cells is irreversible, the action of colicine is therefore usually bactericidal. These "colicine-killed bacteria," however, may recover their metabolic activity or viability when they are treated with a proteolytic enzyme, presumably by destroying the colicines that therefore must have remained on the bacterial surface during their action (Nomura and Nakamura, 1962; Reynolds and Reeves, 1963). The extent of reversibility of the killing action is dependent upon the type of colicine. If certain irreversible damage, such as DNA degradation caused by colicine E2, has already proceeded in the cells, they obviously can no longer recover viability. Even in such a case, however, trypsin removes colicine, as was demonstrated by using radioactive colicine E2 (Maeda and Nomura, 1966). They also showed that the receptors, which had been occupied with colicine molecules, become vacant after trypsin treatment, by demonstrating the reavailability of sites for colicine adsorption. In certain strains of E. coli K-12, a brief treatment of colicine E2, i.e., the bacteria are treated with colicine E2 first and then with trypsin within several minutes after the adsorption, bring about the elongation or snake formation of the bacteria after prolonged incubation: all the metabolic activity is apparently normal except the cell division (Ozeki, 1965b).

Recently, Nomura (1964) proposed an interesting model for the action of colicine, which is as follows. Some kind of reversible change, occurring at the receptor site caused by colicine adsorption, is transmitted along the cell membrane to the killing or biochemical target by some specific transmission mechanism and causes eventual death or observable biochemical change. The biochemical target is different, depending on the kind of colicine, but all biochemical targets have the common property that each is affected by a specific stimulus sent through a transmission mechanism. Immunity in colicinogenic cells owes to an alteration in the mechanism responsible for the initiation and/or transmission of such specific stimuli. A detailed description of this proposed model has been given by Nomura and Maeda (1965). The observation that spheroplasts made by lysozyme treatment can adsorb colicine but that they are much more resistant to the colicine than the intact cells favors the presence of a transmission mechanism along the cell membrane. A special class of colicine-resistant mutants that still can adsorb colicine has been isolated (mutationally immune; Clowes, 1965). In these mutants, according to Nomura's hypothesis, either the transmission mechanism or the biochemical target may have been altered.

Thus the study of colicine and colicinogeny may not only be related to that of phages and episomes but also to the study of membrane function, one of the most fascinating problems of cellular organization, as has been pointed out by Luria (1964) and others.

REFERENCES

Amati, P. (1963). *Biochim. Biophys. Acta* **74,** 783.
Amati, P. (1964). *J. Mol. Biol.* **8,** 239.
Amati, P., and Ozeki, H. (1962). Unpublished data.
Barry, G. T., Everhart, D. L., Abbott, V., and Graham, M. G. (1965). *Zentr. Bakteriol. Parasitenk., Abt. I. Orig.* **196,** 248.
Clowes, R. C. (1961). *Nature* **190,** 988.
Clowes, R. C. (1965). *Zentr. Bakteriol., Parasitenk., Abt. I. Orig.* **196,** 152.
DeWitt, W., and Helinsky, D. R. (1965). *J. Mol. Biol.* **13,** 692.
Fredericq, P. (1956). *Compt. Rend. Soc. Biol.* **150,** 1514.
Fredericq, P. (1957). *Ann. Rev. Microbiol.* **11,** 7.
Fredericq, P. (1958a). *Symp. Soc. Exptl. Biol.* **12,** 104.
Fredericq, P. (1958b). *Carnegie Inst. Wash. Year Book* **57,** 396.
Fredericq, P. (1959). *Comp. Rend. Soc. Biol.* **153,** 357.
Fredericq, P. (1963). *J. Theoret. Biol.* **4,** 159.
Fredericq, P. (1965a). *Zentr. Bakteriol., Parasitenk., Abt. I. Orig.* **196,** 140.
Fredericq, P. (1965b). *Zentr. Bakteriol., Parasitenk., Abt. I. Orig.* **196,** 142.
Goebel, W. F., and Barry, G. T. (1958). *J. Exptl. Med.* **107,** 185.

Gratia, A. (1925). *Compt. Rend. Soc. Biol.* **93**, 1040.

Hinsdill, R. D., and Goebel, W. F. (1964). *Ann. Inst. Pasteur* **107**, Suppl. 5, 54.

Holland, I. B. (1962). *J. Gen. Microbiol.* **29**, 603.

Ivánovics, G. (1962). *Bacteriol. Rev.* **26**, 108.

Jacob, F., and Wollman, E. L. (1961). "Sexuality and the Genetics of Bacteria." Academic Press, New York.

Jacob, F., Siminovitch, L., and Wollman, E. L. (1952). *Ann. Inst. Pasteur* **83**, 295.

Kato, Y., and Hanaoka, M. (1962). *Biken's J.* **5**, 77.

Kohiyama, M., and Nomura, M. (1965). *Zentr. Bakteriol., Parasitenk., Abt. I Orig.* **196**, 211.

Lavallé, R., and Jacob, F. (1961). *Compt. Rend.* **252**, 1678.

Lewis, M. J., and Stocker, B. A. D. (1965). *Zentr. Bakteriol., Parasitenk., Abt. I Orig.* **196**, 173.

Luria, S. E. (1964). *Ann. Inst. Pasteur* **107**, Suppl. 5, 67.

Luzzati, D., and Chevallier, M. R. (1964). *Ann. Inst. Pasteur* **107**, Suppl. 5, 152

Maeda, A., and Nomura, M. (1966). *J. Bacteriol.* **91**, 685.

Martin, R. G., and Ames, B. N. (1961). *J. Biol. Chem.* **236**, 1372.

Mayr-Harting, A. (1964). *J. Pathol. Bacteriol.* **87**, 255.

Miyama, A., Ozaki, M., and Amano, T. (1961). *Biken's J.* **4**, 1.

Monk, M., and Clowes, R. C. (1964). *J. Gen. Microbiol.* **36**, 365.

Nomura, M. (1963). *Cold Spring Harbor Symp. Quant. Biol.* **28**, 315.

Nomura, M. (1964). *Proc. Natl. Acad. Sci. U.S.* **52**, 1514.

Nomura, M., and Maeda, A. (1965). *Zentr. Bakteriol., Parasitenk., Abt. I. Orig.* **196**, 216.

Nomura, M., and Nakamura, M. (1962). *Biochem. Biophys. Res. Commun.* **7**, 306

Ogawa, H., and Ozeki, H. (1964). Unpublished data.

Ohoki, M. (1966). Unpublished data.

Ozeki, H. (1965a). *Zentr. Bakteriol., Parasitenk., Abt. I. Orig.* **196**, 160.

Ozeki, H. (1965b). Unpublished results.

Ozeki, H., and Howarth, S. (1961). *Nature* **190**, 986.

Ozeki, H., and Stocker, B. A. D. (1958). *Heredity* **12**, 525.

Ozeki, H., Stocker, B. A. D., and DeMargerie, H. (1959). *Nature* **184**, 337.

Ozeki, H., Stocker, B. A. D., and Smith, S. M. (1962). *J. Gen. Microbiol.* **28**, 671

Papavassiliou, J. (1961). *Nature* **190**, 110.

Reeves, P. R. (1963). *Australian J. Exptl. Biol. Med. Sci.* **41**, 163.

Reeves, P. R. (1965). *Bacteriol. Rev.* **29**, 24.

Reynolds, B. L., and Reeves, P. R. (1963). *Biochem. Biophys. Res. Commun.* **11**, 140.

Silver, S., and Ozeki, H. (1962). *Nature* **195**, 873.

Smith, S. M., Ozeki, H., and Stocker, B. A. D. (1963). *J. Gen. Microbiol.* **33**, 231.

Stocker, B. A. D., Smith, S. M., and Ozeki, H. (1963). *J. Gen. Microbiol.* **30**, 201.

Vieu, J. F. (1964). *Ann. Inst. Pasteur* **107**, Suppl. 5, 93.

Watanabe, T. (1963). *J. Bacteriol.* **85**, 788.

16 Methods of Virus Classification

C. H. Andrewes

I. Introduction 593
II. Fundamental Characters Useful for Defining Major Groups 595
    A. Chemical Composition 595
    B. Morphology 596
    C. Genetic Characters 599
III. Characters Used for Defining Groups at Lower Levels 599
    A. Antigenic Structure 599
    B. Site of Growth—Nuclear or Cytoplasmic 600
    C. Stability to Heat, pH, Trypsin, and Other Agents 601
    D. Formation of Inclusion Bodies 601
    E. Biological Behavior 602
    F. Tropisms, Pathology, and Symptomatology 603
IV. Characters of the Main Groups of Viruses 603
    A. Groups of Viruses of Vertebrates 604
    B. Groups of Viruses Pathogenic for Arthropods 609
    C. Groups of Viruses Pathogenic for Plants 609
    D. Groups of Bacteriophages 610
V. Discussion 610
    References 612

I. Introduction

This chapter does not describe methods in detail, as do the other chapters, but rather attempts to show how available techniques can be applied to the difficult problem of virus classification. It is unfortunately even more true in this area than in the classification of animals and plants that the obvious and easily determined characters are not the ones most useful for classification. The useful characters often require the more complex techniques available only to the specialist. Simpler methods for making a provisional judgment with respect to the group to which an unknown virus belongs will be referred to later (Section V).

In early attempts to classify viruses, for instance, Holmes' (1948) proposals, too much emphasis was placed on what species and what tissues were attacked and on the consequent pathological changes and symptoms in the host. Much of the work directed toward producing a more rational system of classification has been oriented by discussions at successive international microbiological congresses. At the Congress held at Rio de Janeiro in 1950, there was formed a Virus Subcommittee of the International Commission on Bacteriological Nomenclature (1951). This subcommittee formulated eight criteria that were thought to be useful for the classification of viruses:

1. Morphology and methods of reproduction
2. Chemical composition and physical properties
3. Immunological properties
4. Susceptibility to physical and chemical agents
5. Natural methods of transmission
6. Host, tissue, and cell tropisms
7. Pathology, including inclusion body formation
8. Symptomatology (purposely placed last, since this criterion is of minor importance)

Certain groups thought suitable were proposed for immediate study: the psittacosis–lymphogranuloma group, insect pathogenic viruses, the pox group, the influenza group, and the arthropod-borne encephalitides.

This was a useful first step, but ideas have moved forward rapidly since 1950. The first two of the Rio criteria, morphology and chemical composition, are now given far more emphasis than the other six, which are valuable not so much for defining the major groups as for subdividing these into smaller categories. The major virus groups can be satisfactorily classified in terms of a few fundamental characters (Andrewes *et al.*, 1961). These characters, termed "essential integrants" by Lwoff *et al.* (1962), concern the complete mature form of the virus particle, the virion. Properties of the vegetative phase of a virus are less readily defined.

The reason for emphasizing morphology and chemical composition is simple: these characters are stable, while practically all the others are labile, readily changing either naturally or as a result of manipulation in the laboratory. An alternative method of classifying viruses would be to adopt Sneath's (1957) application of Adansonian principles: as many characters as possible would be compared, equal weight would be given to each, and classification would be based on degrees of similarity. A computer is usually desirable for evaluating the results. A preliminary attempt to apply this system to viruses was made by Andrewes and

Sneath (1958), but the results were not very revealing. A difficulty arises from the fact that there are comparatively few stable characters available; to overwhelm these few with a much larger number of labile characters is hardly likely to lead to a useful result.

The "system" of Lwoff *et al.* (1962) proposes that when chemical and structural characters are used for the first steps in classification, it is logical to integrate all viruses into one hierarchical system, whether the viruses are parasites of vertebrates, arthropods, plants, or bacteria. The results of such an attempt will be considered later.

II. Fundamental Characters Useful for Defining Major Groups

A. CHEMICAL COMPOSITION

There is general agreement that the true viruses contain either DNA or RNA, but not both. This excludes from the viruses the *Chlamydozoáceae* (see Section V). The type of nucleic acid is most certainly discovered by obtaining an infectious nucleic acid from those viruses where this is possible and identifying it by determining its susceptibility or nonsusceptibility to RNase or DNase or by other means. More commonly the nature of the nucleic acid is deduced according to whether virus multiplication is inhibited by halogenated deoxyribosides such as 5-iodo-2'-deoxyuridine (IUDR). This compound inhibits multiplication of DNA but not RNA viruses in tissue culture, though it may not influence the cytopathic effect. The corresponding bromine compound (BUDR) can also be used; so can FUDR, but this has a different mode of action and may be less helpful. The results of tests with such substances must be interpreted with caution. Adenoviruses are less readily suppressed than are poxviruses, and, with lower doses of the inhibitor, inhibition may be only temporary (Seto *et al.*, 1964). Another confusing fact is that the fowl sarcoma virus, generally thought to contain RNA, is dependent for its growth on cellular functions with which DNA is concerned, and these can be suppressed by IUDR or by actinomycin D (Temin, 1964; Force and Stewart, 1964; Bader, 1965). Similar observations have been reported with regard to influenza A virus (Barry *et al.*, 1962), of which the multiplication is depressed by actinomycin D.

Another method of determining the nature of viral nucleic acids is by staining with acridine orange (Armstrong, 1956). By fluorescence microscopy masses of RNA-containing viruses in cells stain orange–red, whereas the DNA-containing viruses appear yellowish-green. It seems, however, that viruses such as reoviruses containing double-stranded

RNA stain as do the DNA viruses, and a phage with single-stranded DNA stains red (Mayor, 1964) like a ribovirus. The DNA viruses have been referred to as deoxyviruses, and those containing RNA as riboviruses (Cooper, 1961).

Other chemical information may prove useful as further knowledge is gained, for instance, on the ratios of the various nucleotides in the nucleic acids and on the presence and nature of any incorporated enzymes (Wildy, 1962). In some virus groups information is becoming available concerning the molecular weights of the virion or of the viral nucleic acid; the facts disclosed are likely to prove useful for classification.

B. MORPHOLOGY

1. *Symmetry*

This has been determined by use of the techniques of electron microscopy, including negative-staining methods, and of x-ray diffraction. As far as is known, all viruses are composed of one or another kind of nucleic acid within a package made up of large numbers of similar protein subunits. The whole package of nucleic acid and protein is called a nucleocapsid. If naked, it constitutes the whole virion; but there may be an outer envelope in addition. The protein subunits or capsomeres are symmetrically arranged in one or more of three ways: (1) There may be a cage or box—known as a capsid—with subunits or capsomeres regularly arranged in a symmetrical "surface crystal"; this crystal most commonly has 235 icosahedral symmetry, but other forms of symmetry occur. The capsomeres themselves are composed of still smaller "structural units" and these may be shared by adjacent capsomeres. (2) Symmetry may be helical, with structure units arranged symmetrically in a spiral around the nucleic acid. As far as is known, all viruses with helical symmetry with the exception of some that are pathogenic for insects contain RNA. The viruses with this structure may exist, as do many plant viruses, as fairly rigid rods or as long sinuous threads; or the nucleocapsid may be curled up and contained within an outer shell, as in myxoviruses. It has been suggested that, since there are no capsids to be counted, the helical viruses may be conveniently subdivided according to the diameter of the internal helix. This is 9–10 mμ for the true influenza viruses and 17–18 mμ for the rather different virus group containing mumps, Newcastle disease, and the parainfluenza viruses. Other diameters are described in the plant virus world. (3) Symmetry may be complex. Very many bacteriophages have heads and tails, the latter having very elaborate structure. Lwoff *et al.* (1962) refer to their symmetry as "binal." The heads of at least some, including the RNA phages, have icosahedral symmetry, while the tails of at least some have helical symmetry. The relative arrangements of nucleic acid and protein in the poxviruses have not been determined with certainty. There are tubular threads and other structures not seen in smaller viruses, with the threads apparently lying superfically in the virion.

2. *Number of Diameter of Capsomeres*

The number of capsomeres is important in classification. For icosahedral capsids, where n is the number of capsomeres along each side of a triangular face on the surface, the number of capsomeres is shown by the formula $10^{(n-1)} + 2$, though other arrangements are known. Viruses are known having 12 capsomeres (phage X174), 42 (papovaviruses—possibly), 92 (reoviruses and RNA phages), 162 (herpesviruses), 252 (adenoviruses), and 812 (Tipula irridescent virus). The capsomeres may be hollow prisms or may have a simpler structure. Klug and Finch (1965) maintain that papovaviruses have icosahedral symmetry with 72 structure units and that the arrangement is skew, symmetry being right-handed for some and left-handed for others.

3. *Other Aspects of Shape*

Many plant viruses and a few phages exist as rods or threads. Differences in the mean length of rods and threads of plant viruses have been used as a basis of classification by Brandes and Wetter (1959), though others consider this an unreliable character. Some RNA viruses, those of vesicular stomatitis and others related to it, have a bullet shape, rounded at one end and truncated at the other; the center is partly hollow (Reczko, 1961). Most viruses with icosahedral symmetry are roughly spherical, an icosahedral form of the whole virion being more apparent in some viruses than in others. Many poxviruses are brick-shaped or oval, one axis being a little longer than the other. The naked viruses have a fairly uniform shape; the envelopes that other viruses possess are in general readily deformable, so that the virions appear pleomorphic in electron micrographs. Many normally spherical viruses may occasionally grow as filamentous forms; the influenza viruses do this, and so among the DNA viruses does polyoma. In both instances, though in different ways, it seems that the cause is abnormal assembly, so that the surface ingredients form a cylinder instead of a sphere. The tails seen in mouse leukemia and some other viruses are quite different in nature from the organized tails of phages; there is dispute whether they are or are not artifacts. It is reported (de Harven and

Friend, 1964) that they appear or do not appear according to the treatment of preparations for electron microscopy.

4. *Presence of Envelopes*

There is in general very good correlation between presence of an envelope outside the nucleocapsid and susceptibility of a virus to fat solvents, for such envelopes seem as a rule to contain lipid, and this must usually remain intact if infectivity is to be preserved. The most commonly used test is to treat a virus suspension with 20% ethyl ether at 4°C for 18–24 hours. In the original description of the test (Andrewes and Horstmann, 1949), suspensions to be tested were made up in broth containing 10% horse serum. After treatment overnight, ether was allowed to evaporate at room temperature, and parallel titrations were done out of treated and control preparations. Almost all viruses proved to be either highly resistant or highly sensitive. The test is of value for classification except for the poxviruses, since viruses in this group behave variously. Vaccinia and its relatives are highly resistant; rabbit myxoma is sensitive; other viruses, such as orf, have intermediate susceptibility.

Recently the use of chloroform has been advocated as giving more reliable results. The virus suspension is shaken with 2% chloroform, then allowed to stand at 4°C overnight; centrifugation is used to remove all but traces of chloroform (Wittman and Matheka, 1958). Feldman and Wang (1961) used 5% chloroform and tested immediately after 10 minutes' shaking. Vaccinia and fowlpox were shown to be susceptible, and it is probable that all poxviruses behave alike.

Deoxycholic acid was shown by W. Smith (1939) to inactivate some viruses and not others. Theiler (1957) used it diluted 1 : 1000, particularly to differentiate arboviruses from other viruses. The substance was allowed to act for 1 hour at 32°C. Results corerspond closely to those obtained with ether and chloroform.

For some viruses, e.g., myxoviruses and fowl tumor viruses, it has been shown that the surface membrane is partly composed of host constituents that apparently become incorporated in it as the virus is extruded from the cell. This is seen with some viruses that are liberated, either from the cell surface or into vesicles in the cytoplasm, in a gradual manner, perhaps a few at a time and with no destruction of the cell as an inevitable or immediate result. There is a striking contrast between this method of virus release and the sudden bursting of an infected bacterial cell with resulting liberation of hundreds of particles of a virulent phage.

5. Presence of Projections and Hemagglutinins

The envelopes of a number of viruses, e.g., myxoviruses, are covered with surface projections having the appearance of spikes directed outward. These projections are very numerous when present and may be arranged regularly or irregularly, but do not form surface crystals as do capsomeres. The membrane itself is, of course, a readily deformable structure, unlike a rigid capsid. In many but not all instances the surface projections carry the virus hemagglutinin. Pieces of membrane may be separated when virus is broken up and may curl up into rosettes 35–65 mμ across. Some viruses agglutinate erythrocytes by other mechanisms. In any case, presence of hemagglutinin is not a fundamental taxonomic character, since different strains of one virus may or may not hemagglutinate, and the character may be lost after serial passage in the laboratory.

6. Size

Size in itself is unsafe to use as a taxonomic character. It does, however, turn out that members of virus groups defined on the basis of other criteria do fall within a limited size range. The arboviruses form an apparent exception, for here the range in size is considerable, from 25 to 100 mμ in diameter. It is, however, almost certain that the viruses currently covered by the term "arbovirus" do not constitute a homogeneous assembly. The methods used in determining virus sizes have been discussed elsewhere in this treatise.

C. GENETIC CHARACTERS

Genetic characters may prove to be important, but they have not yet been sufficiently studied to permit us to make a judgment. Possibility of genetic recombination or even of phenotypic mixing of characters generally indicates close relationships. One has not, however, been able to rely implicitly upon this criterion since the demonstration that an SV 40 antigen can be incorporated into an adenovirus.

III. Characters Used for Defining Groups at Lower Levels

A. ANTIGENIC STRUCTURE

As far as is known, there are no instances of overlap in antigenic characters between members of different major groups. Within these groups, however, there are often shared antigens, particularly nucleoprotein antigens revealed by the complement-fixation and gel diffusion tests. Members of one group, however, may be so related or they may not; if they are, the fact is very helpful. Let us consider a few examples. Members of the picornavirus group may show cross-reactions in the complement-fixation test, but the neutralization test gives far more specific results and is used to separate individual viruses within the group. As in other groups, individual members of say, the ECHO viruses are regarded on this basis as separate serotypes and are given serial numbers. Not all members of one serotype are antigenically identical, and it may be difficult to decide whether a virus should be classified as a "new" type or not. Particularly confusing is the fact that some cross-reactions are "one way"; i.e., a virus is neutralized by a heterologous antiserum but the converse relationship is not evident.

Almost all the adenoviruses so far examined share a common antigen; only the avian strains do not do so. Adenoviruses are thus antigenically more homogeneous than are most of the other families. There are other antigens that are specific for the numbered serotypes, and still others that are shared by a few closely related strains. These antigens can be beautifully sorted out by the help of the agar gel diffusion test (Pereira, 1960); they are associated with different structural elements on the virus surface (Valentine and Pereira, 1965).

The antigenic relations within the arbovirus group are particularly complex. Some stand quite alone and others fall into quite obvious groups that seem to be natural ones, since there are other, correlated characters. The A, B, C, and Bunyamwera groups are the chief of these. There exist, however, all degrees of closeness of relationship, so that it becomes a matter of rather arbitrary personal judgment when an isolate should be regarded as an entity and when it should be viewed as a variant of an existing virus.

Apart from viruses that are biologically similar but antigenically distinct, there are viruses showing the opposite character: the viruses of variola, vaccinia, cowpox, and ectromelia behave very differently in their host range and pathogenicity, yet by crude serological tests they are alike, and they can be separated only by more refined techniques. From all this it is clear that antigenic relationships are of varying degrees of usefulness in sorting out different groups, and their application requires much intelligent discrimination. They may prove more useful in classifying plant than animal viruses.

B. Site of Growth—Nuclear or Cytoplasmic

A classification of viruses of vertebrates as nuclear or cytoplasmic is not quite simple, for some viruses begin their cycle of development within the nucleus, and here their nucleoprotein may be synthesized. They may then pass out into the cytoplasm, acquiring further components, visible in electron micrographs of thin sections as one or more outer membranes. This is the case with the herpesviruses. The adenoviruses and papovaviruses, on the other hand, are apparently formed wholly in the nucleus. Most of the other viruses seem to multiply within the cytoplasm, though there may be associated changes in the nucleolus, and some virus may be detected in the nucleus at a later stage. We cannot place too much reliance on site of growth as a taxonomic character. Among the myxoviruses, the true influenza viruses seem to start their development in the nucleus and complete it in the cytoplasm, though development of most of the other viruses in this family takes place in the cytoplasm. In the picornavirus group, also, development is in general cytoplasmic, but for the encephalomyocarditis virus it may begin in the nucleus; this, however, is a matter of dispute. Growth in nucleus or cytoplasm does, however, seem to be a useful character for subdividing the insect-pathogenic viruses.

C. STABILITY TO HEAT, pH, TRYPSIN, AND OTHER AGENTS

These characters are of value in individual instances, but none is of general applicability. Their sensitivity to a rather acid pH, around 5.3, conveniently separates the rhinoviruses from most of the other picornaviruses. Other characters useful in classifying picornaviruses are the sensitivity or lack of it to HBB [2(α-hydroxybenzyl) benzimidazole] and guanidine (Eggers and Tamm, 1961; Tamm and Eggers, 1962) and stabilization to heat inactivation at 50°C by 1 M MgCl$_2$ (Wallis and Melnick, 1962). Hamparian and his colleagues (1963) make considerable use of acid and heat stability in their proposals for classifying animal viruses. Sensitivity to trypsin provides a character confirming the separation of the A and B arboviruses, which was arrived at on a serological basis. The remarkable resistance of the virus of scrapie to boiling and to treatment by 8% Formalin is a reason for regarding this as an altogether unusual virus.

D. FORMATION OF INCLUSION BODIES

The term "inclusion body" includes a number of intracellular bodies of different nature. Some are matrices within which masses of virions are contained; others are made of proteins that are probably byproducts or surplus ingredients of virus synthesis; still others, particularly the intranuclear inclusions of Cowdry's (1934) A type, are "gravestones," evidence of the damage done to the nucleus by the virus infection. Inclusions may be in the nucleus or the cytoplasm, or in both. The nuclear inclusions found in the herpesviruses, those of Cowdry's A type, are sufficiently characteristic to have guided workers, quite correctly, to placing unknown viruses in that group—and this in spite of the fact that they are really fixation artifacts. In conventionally fixed and stained preparations the nuclear inclusions show up as eosinophilic masses separated by a halo from marginated basophilic chromatin. They must be distinguished from enlarged nuceoli, and it is necessary (Pereira, 1961) to know the whole cycle of development before deciding on their nature. Nuclear inclusions seen in Rift Valley fever, measles, and some viruses of other groups resemble them rather closely.

Many of the insect-pathogenic viruses are rodlike virions enclosed in bundles in a crystalline polyhedral protein inclusion within the nucleus, and these are included in the nuclear polyhedroses. Others are spherical virions contained in polyhedra within the cytoplasm; still others consist of single rods in smaller crystalline granules—the granuloses. Thus within this virus group the inclusions have formed an important basis for classification.

E. Biological Behavior

The chief character to be considered under this heading is whether or not a virus undergoes a developmental cycle in both vertebrate or arthropod or in both plant or arthropod. The nature of the arthropod concerned may also be important. Some viruses, for instance, fowlpox and myxomatosis and some plant viruses, may be mechanically carried by insects, and this is a matter quite irrelevant to classification. The great majority of viruses now classified as arboviruses multiply in vertebrates as well as in arthropods, usually mosquitoes or ticks and sometimes *Phlebotomus*. There are, however, a few viruses that have the general properties of the B group of arboviruses, including antigenic structure, and for which no arthropod vector is known. These are viruses infecting bats. It may be that the vector remains to be discovered, or perhaps some other means of transmission has been acquired in the course of evolution. Other instances are known in which arboviruses are, for a while, transmitted without benefit of arthropod. Route of transmission may thus be a guide to classification, but it must not be too implicitly relied upon, since it is not an invariably stable character. All viruses transmitted to vertebrates by arthropods do not necessarily belong to the same family: the virus of vesicular stomatitis is morphologically very distinct from the majority of such viruses. African horse sickness and blue tongue viruses are probably distinct also, and they may possibly prove to be reoviruses, since the former at least has 92 capsomeres (Polson and Deeks, 1963).

F. TROPISMS, PATHOLOGY, AND SYMPTOMATOLOGY

These characters, formerly the main basis for virus classification, are now relegated to a position of much less importance. Moreover, their determination hardly involves the methods discussed in this book. Their existence often serves to conceal rather than to reveal relationships; it was only when serological and other methods were applied that the viruses of measles, rinderpest, and dog distemper were found to be related to each other. Similar unexpected relationships are now coming to light all the time.

There has been a tendency to talk of tumor viruses as a distinct group. It is true that most of the known virus tumors in animals are caused by viruses belonging to particular groups, for example, those of the fowl tumor–leukosis complex, the rodent leukemias, and the papovaviruses. All the viruses in the last group, with the exception of the K virus and the rabbit kidney vacuolating virus (Hartley and Rowe, 1964), cause either cancers or papillomas, but it must be remembered that polyomavirus, for instance, is normally present as a latent transmissible infection of mice and does not cause tumors at all. Similarly, with the agents associated with fowl tumors and leukosis, malignancy is only an occasional manifestation of infection with a normally harmless agent. Some adenoviruses are potentially oncogenic. Oncogenesis is thus a poor basis for classification.

IV. Characters of the Main Groups of Viruses

A provisional committee for nomenclature of viruses, appointed by the International Association of Microbiological Societies, met in Paris in June, 1965, and made recommendations concerning virus nomenclature. These were published (1965) in the expectation that comments would be received and could be considered before the proposals were embodied in a formal code at the international congress in Moscow in July, 1966. When an international committee for nomenclature of viruses was elected at that congress, it accepted many of the proposals of the provisional committee, but did not agree to the erection and naming of higher Taxa, at least for the present.

All viruses are considered together in the outline classification shown in Tables I and II. It is, however, convenient now to deal separately with viruses affecting vertebrates, insects, plants, and bacteria.

A. Groups of Vertebrates

1. *RNA Viruses*

The name "picornavirus" means "very small ('pico') + RNA." The cubical symmetry may be icosahedral, but if, as has been suggested, there are 60 capsomeres, the $10^{(n-1)^2} + 2$ formula clearly does not apply. The viruses may be rhombic triacontahedra with 32 capsomeres (Mayor, 1964).

Most picornaviruses multiply in the cytoplasm, and some can be seen there lying in crystalline aggregates. Most of them have their normal habitat in the alimentary canal or respiratory tract; a few inhabit both. A number have the power to invade and damage the central nervous system. Some, but not all, bear hemagglutinins. Their antigenic relations were considered in Section II,A.

Reoviruses are larger, with an unusual double-stranded RNA; this is seen also in the wound tumor virus of sweet clover, which is otherwise similar morphologically. An antigenic relation between these viruses infecting animals and plants, respectively, was reported by Streissle and Maramorosch (1963), but others have failed to confirm this finding. The reoviruses and one or more of the similar plant viruses seem to multiply particularly in cell spindles. The three known serotypes of reovirus each seems capable of infecting vertebrates of many orders. They have been recovered from primates, rodents, ungulates, and marsupials, but infection is usually inapparent. Hemagglutinins are reported.

Arboviruses have been hitherto defined as viruses having a biological cycle in both vertebrates and arthropods. This is not a fundamental character, but it should soon become evident that most of the viruses now classed as arboviruses form a natural group. They seem to have surface spikes, as have myxoviruses. The symmetry of their nucleocapsids is, however, not finally settled. Most of them agglutinate erythrocytes, especially goose cells. They are not known to cause any disease in the arthropods in which they multiply and are probably equally harmless to their normal vertebrate hosts, causing disease only when they reach an unusual host.

Myxoviruses were originally defined partly on the basis of their affinity for mucins. In the case of those on the surface of erythrocytes,

TABLE I

OUTLINE OF CLASSIFICATION OF DNA-CONTAINING VIRUSES

"Strandedness"	Two stranded							One stranded	
Symmetry of nucleocapsid	Cubical					Helical	Binary	Cubical	
Presence of envelope (+ or 0)	+	0				?	0	0	
No. of capsomeres	162	812	252	72 or 42	12	?		32	?
Viruses in group	Herpes-viruses	Irridescent insect viruses	Adeno-vi-ruses	Papova-viruses	Bacteriophage X174, possibly adeno-associated viruses	?Nuclear polyhedro-sis group of insect pathogens	Tailed bac-teriophage	Latent rat virus, minute mouse virus	A few bac-terio-phages

TABLE II

OUTLINE OF CLASSIFICATION OF RNA-CONTAINING VIRUSES

"Strandedness"	Two stranded	One stranded				
Symmetry of nucleocapsid	Cubical	Helical				Cubical
Presence of envelope (+ or 0)	0	0	+			0
No. of capsomeres or diameter of nucleocapsid in mμ	92	10–20 mμ	9 mμ	18 mμ	15–18 mμ bullet-shaped	30 or 60
Viruses in groups	Reoviruses, some plant viruses (e.g., wound tumor)	Elongated plant viruses	Myxoviruses	Paramyxoviruses	Rabies, vesicular stomatitis, sigma virus of *Drosophila*, some plant viruses	Picornaviruses, spherical plant viruses, a few insect pathogens

this character was related to their capacity for hemagglutination. The affinity for mucins also gave the group its name. Other characters are now seen to be more important, for example, the helical symmetry of their nucleocapsids and the presence of an envelope with radiating spikes. Some "paramyxoviruses" are in fact seen now to belong naturally to the group, although no hemagglutinating powers have yet been demonstrated.

The myxoviruses are conveniently divided into two subgroups (Waterson, 1962). The true influenza viruses are a little smaller, their nucleocapsids have a diameter of 9–10 mμ, their nucleoprotein antigen is formed in the nucleus, filamentous forms are common, and there are other differences. The parainfluenza, mumps, and Newcastle disease viruses differ in these characters, the nucleocapsids being 17–18 mμ across and the virus developing apparently wholly in the cytoplasm. A division into myxoviruses and paramyxoviruses on these lines has been suggested. The three serologically related viruses, measles, dog distemper, and rinderpest, resemble the latter group morphologically. Another virus of similar structure is the respiratory syncytial virus.

Other Probably Helical RNA Viruses. The precise boundaries of the myxovirus and paramyxovirus groups remain very uncertain. Bovine diarrhea and the serologically related swine fever are said to be similar, as is the virus of infectious bronchitis of chickens. The surface spikes of the latter virus seem to carry knobs. The viruses of vesicular stomatitis and rabies might come to be classified here were it not for their unusual bullet shape (Reczko, 1961). We have also the groups of fowl leukosis–fowl tumor viruses and the viruses causing leukemia and mammary cancer in rodents. Some of those mentioned have envelopes with surface spikes while some have not. For some a helical core is likely; for others it is yet to be demonstrated. We have here in fact a large collection of viruses whose morphology and mutual relations have not yet been fully worked out.

2. DNA Viruses

The papovaviruses include those causing papillomas in various mammals, polyoma, and the vacuolating virus, SV 40. They have no membranes and have apparently 42, or perhaps 72, hollow capsomeres. A diameter of 52–54 mμ is likely for the true wart viruses and one of 43–45 mμ for the others (Crawford and Crawford, 1963). They multiply within nuclei, where they may be seen regularly packed together. Tubular structures may form, apparently when something goes wrong with virus synthesis. Most members cause at times cell proliferation (warts and cancers). The provisional committee preferred the name "papillomavirus" to "papovavirus," but the latter has now been officially reinstated.

The adenoviruses are rather larger, 70–90 mμ across, with 252 capsomeres. The structure of these capsomeres is still uncertain. There are no outer membranes. As with papovaviruses, multiplication occurs in cell nuclei, and these viruses occur in crystalline arrangement. All but avian adenoviruses share a common antigen.

The herpesviruses are again rather larger, but since they have an outer membrane, it is more difficult to define their diameter precisely; it is approximately 100–150 mμ. The 162 capsomeres have the form of hollow prisms. Development begins in the nucleus and is completed as the virus passes outward; release from cells is probably gradual. A characteristic feature of the family is the production of type A intranuclear inclusions (Section III,D).

The poxviruses are larger and more complex. External diameters are about 200–300 mμ. Some appear brick-shaped, others oval, with none wholly spherical. There are external membranes, but some poxviruses are ether sensitive and others are not. Possibly all are inactivated by chloroform. They certainly do not have cubical symmetry, but how the nucleoprotein is arranged is uncertain. We do not know whether the tubules made visible by electron microscopy and sometimes arranged in a spiral manner are composed of protein or of nucleoprotein. Development is wholly in the cytoplasm, and this may contain inclusion bodies of two kinds, one consisting of virions, perhaps embedded in a matrix and the other consisting of protein but free from virions. All the poxviruses share a common nucleoprotein antigen. Members of the group characteristically give rise to skin lesions, often called pocks, or to proliferative tumorlike growths of limited duration.

Small DNA viruses have recently been described. Their diameter is 22–30 mμ and one report says that they have cubical symmetry with 12 capsomeres (Payne et al., 1964). Their DNA is apparently single stranded. The group contains the latent rat virus of Kilham and Olivier (1959), and this is related to other viruses isolated by Toolan (1960). The viruses have been described as osteolytic (Dalldorf, 1960) because of changes produced particularly in the skulls of suckling hamsters. "Satellite" viruses associated with adenoviruses contain DNA and are of similar size, but their DNA is said to be double stranded, so they may fall into a different group. The name Parvovirus, proposed by the provisional committee (1965), is likely to be officially confirmed.

B. GROUPS OF VIRUSES PATHOGENIC FOR ARTHROPODS

K. M. Smith (1962) has recently reviewed the present state of ideas concerning the classification of viruses of this group; these are at present not in step with those proposed for viruses of vertebrates. A primary division has been into those arthropod viruses giving or failing to give rise to inclusions. The inclusion-producing viruses have then been divided into those yielding relatively large polyhedra (polyhedroses) and those giving smaller bodies (granuloses). The polyhedroses are divided again into nuclear and cytoplasmic, according to where the inclusions develop. When we come to consider the chemical composition and morphology of these viruses, we find that there is only partial correlation with the proposed tentative classification. The viruses of the very numerous nuclear polyhedroses group are deoxyviruses, probably with a protein shell around a helically arranged nucleoprotein core; these probably form a natural group. With respect to the others, interpretation is much less certain. There seem to be both deoxyviruses and riboviruses among the viruses growing in the cytoplasm. It would seem logical to break away from the tentative scheme described above and to rearrange the viruses on the lines employed for vertebrate pathogens.

C. GROUPS OF VIRUSES PATHOGENIC FOR PLANTS

All viruses in this category are RNA viruses. Moreover, none have envelopes, and we cannot, therefore, make subdivisions based on these characters. We have, however, some viruses with cubical and others with helical symmetry. The former can be subdivided according to their number of capsomeres.

A number of plant viruses with helical symmetry have been placed by Brandes into six groups, as shown in Table III.

TABLE III
PROPOSED SUBDIVISIONS OF SOME PLANT VIRUSES

Shape	Normal length (mμ)	Number that can be placed in the group
Rigid rods	130–210	4
Rigid rods	300	5
Flexible threads	480–580	7
Rods, rigid to slightly flexible	620–500	13
Flexible threads	730–760	16
Very flexible threads	1250	1

D. Groups of Bacteriophages

No logical attempts at naming phages have been made, and little has been suggested concerning their classification. A recent writer (Bradley, 1965) has, however, tried to impose some order on to the group. He classifies phages, first, into those with double-stranded DNA in their composition—and this is by far the largest group—second, those with single-stranded DNA, and third, those with RNA. The next criteria are those of morphology and host range, and Bradley provides two dendrograms, one giving second place, after nucleic acid composition, to morphology, the other promoting host range to that position. He favors the second alternative, holding that phages may have had a different evolutionary history from that of other viruses and that in consequence host range is relatively more important. In one case in which fundamentally similar phages attack bacteria of different families, Bradley suggests that it may be the bacterial taxonomists who are in error!

Morphologically, all phages examined by electron microscopy have fallen into one or another of six groups: A, with contractile tails; B, with long noncontractile tails; C, with short noncontractile tails; D, tailless, with large capsomeres; E, tailless, with small capsomeres; and F, filamentous phages. There are many variations in morphology, permitting subdivisions at lower levels. It is interesting that RNA-containing coliphages are icosahedra with 92 capsomeres, thus being very similar to reoviruses and some plant viruses.

Serology is another useful character at a lower level. Phages placed in any of the six morphological groups do not cross-react with those in any other group. On the other hand, it is not surprising that not all morphologically similar phages behave alike in these tests.

V. *Discussion*

It is now generally recognized that viruses form a class in their own right and that they can no longer be regarded as a subdivision of bacteria. Thus virus nomenclature is to be considered henceforth by an international committee independent of that which deals with the nomenclature of bacteria. The Rickettsiae and the Chlamydozoaceae (psittacosis group) are now regarded as bacteria. Organisms related to psittacosis have been excluded from the viruses and should no longer be called viruses. They contain both RNA and DNA, they have cell walls containing muramic acid, they probably divide by binary fission at some stage in their cycle, and they are susceptible to many chemotherapeutic agents that affect bacteria but not viruses.

Only recently has serious attention been given to the possibility of classifying all viruses in one system, whether they attack plants or animals. As already indicated, there are cogent reasons for doing this even though there may be little support for the idea of a monophyletic origin. Some viruses multiply in both plants and insects; others multiply in both vertebrates and insects. Some plant and animal viruses are indistinguishable from each other morphologically. On the other hand, it can be argued that there are a limited number of ways in which replicating biological entities can be assembled, and that the similarities between certain plant and animal viruses are coincidental. To bring all viruses into one system brings about an artificial result. All classifications are, however, artificial, and the criticism is valid only if the end result is merely to emphasize morphological similarities and differences and to help in no other way. Useful classifications are those that are helpful in many ways.

Most workers until recently felt that a binominal nomenclature of the Linnean type was not suitable for immediate application to viruses. The provisional virus nomenclature committee (1965) proposed, however, that the time had come to construct a binominal nomenclature based on the Linnean system, but with modifications. It was recognized that animal virologists would mostly continue to use the names to which they were accustomed. Something better than the present system of naming was, however, badly needed in the world of plant viruses and bacteriophages. Since the subject is such a new one, it is feasible to construct a nomenclature that will not be hampered by the laws of priority, which in other fields have proved such an obstacle to stability of names. To this end it is likely that a code of nomenclature for viruses will be officially put forward in the near future. It will be relatively easy to validate existing names or construct new ones for groups of viruses. To do so for individual viruses is a far more difficult task, for among viruses what correspond to species are commonly even less sharply demarcated than among larger beings. Moreover, characters that would on the face of things be useful are often extremely labile. These difficulties probably stem from the fact that viruses, because of their tremendous rate of multiplication, can evolve more rapidly than can plants and animals.

Virologists may seek guidance in this chapter how they may classify an apparently new virus which they may have encountered. It will be evident that reliance on symptomatology will only too often lead to mistaken conclusions. It is also evident that the methods of isolating and identifying the nucleic acid and enumerating capsomeres are laborious and difficult. Of the tests discussed here, the following will be useful for obtaining first indications of how to place a virus in the right group. (1) Filtration through accurately graded, preferably gradocol, membranes will give an idea of size, provided the worker avoids the pitfalls described elsewhere in this volume. (2) Determination of sensitivity to ether or chloroform will distinguish the viruses with membranes from those lacking membranes—except perhaps among the poxviruses. (3) If the virus can be cultivated, determination of its sensitivity to inhibition by IUDR or a related compound will usually enable one to determine the type of nucleic acid contained. If these tests aid in determining where to place the unknown virus, the worker can then plan to make comparisons with selected other viruses on a serological basis and to proceed, if necessary, to further tests.

Tables I and II outline possible classifications of DNA- and RNA-containing viruses. Information is insufficient to include in the tables the poxviruses, arboviruses, many other RNA-containing viruses, and insect pathogens.

REFERENCES

Andrewes, C. H., and Horstmann, D. M., (1949). *J. Gen. Microbiol.* **3,** 290.
Andrewes, C. H., and Sneath, P. H. A. (1958). *Nature* **182,** 12.
Andrewes, C. H., Burnet, F. M., Enders, J. F., Gard, S., Hirst., G. K., Kaplan, M. M., and Zhdanov, V. M. (1961). *Virology* **15,** 52.
Armstrong, J. A. (1956). *Exptl. Cell Res.* **11,** 640.
Bader, J. P. (1965). *Virology* **26,** 253.
Barry, R. D., Ives, D. R., and Cruickshank, J. G. (1962). *Nature* **194,** 1139.
Bradley, D. E. (1965). *J. Roy. Microscop. Soc* [3] **84,** 257.
Brandes, J., and Wetter, C. (1959) *Virology* **8,** 99.
Cooper, P. D. (1961). *Nature* **190,** 302.
Cowdry, E. V. (1934). *Arch. Pathol.* **18,** 527.
Crawford, L. V., and Crawford, E. M. (1963). *Virology* **21,** 258.
Dalldorf, G. (1960). *Bull. N.Y. Acad. Med.* [2] **36,** 795.
de Harven, E., and Friend, C. (1964). *Virology* **23,** 119.
Eggers, H. J., and Tamm, I. (1961). *Virology* **13,** 545.
Feldman, H. A., and Wang, S. S. (1961). *Proc. Soc. Exptl. Biol. Med.* **106,** 736.
Force, E. E., and Stewart, R. C. (1964). *Proc. Soc. Exptl. Biol. Med.* **116,** 803.
Hamparian, V. V., Hilleman, M. R., and Ketler, A. (1963). *Proc. Soc. Exptl. Biol. Med.* **112,** 1040.
Hartley, J. W., and Rowe, W. P. (1964). *Science* **143,** 258.
Holmes, F. O. (1948). *In* "Bergey's Manual of Determinative Bacteriology," p. 1127. Williams & Wilkins, Baltimore, Maryland.
Kilham, L., and Olivier, L. J. (1959). *Virology* **7,** 428.
Klug, A., and Finch, J. T. (1965). *J. Mol. Biol.* **11,** 403.
Lwoff, A., Horne, R., and Tournier, P. (1962). *Cold Spring Harbor Symp. Quant. Biol.* **27,** 51.

Mayor, H. D. (1964). *Virology* **22,** 156.

Mayor, H. D., and Hill, N. O. (1961). *Virology* **14,** 264.

Payne, F. E., Beals, T. F. and Preston, R. E. (1964). *Virology* **23,** 109.

Pereira, H. G. (1960). *Nature* **186,** 571.

Pereira, H. G. (1961). *Advan. Virus Res.* **8,** 245.

Polson, A., and Deeks, D. (1963). *J. Hyg.* **61,** 149.

Provisional Committee for Nomenclature of Viruses. (1965). *Ann. Inst Pasteur* **109,** 626.

Reczko, E. (1961). *Arch. Ges. Virusforsch.* **10,** 588.

Seto, Y., Toyoshima, S., and Ueda, T. (1964). *Nature* **201,** 219.

Smith, K. M. (1962). *Advan. Virus Res.* **9,** 195.

Smith, W. (1939). *J. Pathol. Bacteriol.* **48,** 557.

Sneath, P. H. A. (1957). *J. Gen. Microbiol.* **17,** 184 and 201.

Streissle, G., and Maramorosch, K. (1963). *Science* **140,** 996.

Tamm, I., and Eggers, H. J. (1962). *Virology* **18,** 439.

Temin, H. M. (1964). *Virology* **23,** 486.

Theiler, M. (1957). *Proc. Soc. Exptl. Biol. Med.* **96,** 380.

Toolan, H. W. (1960). *Science* **131,** 1446.

Valentine, R. C., and Pereira, H. G. (1965). *J. Mol. Biol.* **13,** 13.

Virus Subcommittee of the International Commission on Bacterial Nomenclature. (1951). *Intern. Bull. Bacterial Nomenclature Taxonomy* **1,** 1.

Wallis, C., and Melnick, J. L. (1962). *J. Bacteriol.* **84,** 389.

Waterson, A. P. (1962). *Nature* **193,** 1163.

Wildy, P. (1962). *Symp. Soc. Gen. Microbiol.* **12,** 145.

Wittman, G., and Matheka, H. D. (1958). *Monatsh. Tierheilk.* **10,** 161.

17 Experimental Design and Statistical Methods of Assay

A. Kleczkowski

The Summation Symbol 616
I. Introduction 617
    Practical Ways of Computing Sums of Squares of
    Deviations from the Mean 624
II. Experimental Design 625
    A. Randomization 626
    B. Elimination of Sources of Variation 627
    C. Quantities Computed from Data Provided by
       Experimental Results 634
    D. Factorial Experiments 635
III. Probability 638
IV. Frequency Distributions 642
    A. Contingency Tables 642
    B. The Binomial Distribution 644
    C. The Poisson Distribution 650
    D. The Normal Distribution 656
    E. Bivariate and Multivariate Distributions
       Regression and Correlation 661
V. Tests of Significance 667
    A. A Test by Assumption of Random Selection 668
    B. The χ^2 Test 671
    C. Tests of Significance of Means and Differences
       of Means of Large Samples 677
    D. The t Test 679
    E. The Variance Ratio Test (R Test) 687
    F. Analysis of Variance 690
    G. Transformation of the Variate 696
    H. Significance of a Single Number from a Population
       Whose Distribution Is Binomial of Poissonian 703
VI. Estimation of Virus Concentration 705
    A. Estimation by the Dilution Method 705
    B. Estimation by Plaque Count 713
    C. Estimation by the Local Lesion Method 716
    Appendix
       Simple Derivations of Some Properties of the Mean
       and of the Variance 724
    References 730

The Summation Symbol

The summation symbol must be explained at the start because the reader must understand its meaning if he is to follow this chapter. If some other symbols are not understood, particular points of argument may be missed, but one should still be able to understand the conclusions and to follow the text.

Particular values of a variable quantity x are symbolized by adding subscripts to x. Thus x_1, x_2, and so on, are the first, the second, and so on value of x. Generally, x_i means the ith value of x.

The summation symbol $\sum_{i=1}^{n}$ (or $\sum_i$) means the sum of n values of a quantity that follows the symbol, the subscript i taking all the values from 1 to n. Thus

$$\sum_{i=1}^{n} (x_i) = x_1 + x_2 + x_3 \cdots + x_n$$

If $f(x)$ is any function of x, the summation symbol means that

$$\sum_{i=1}^{n} f(x_i) = f(x_1) + f(x_2) + f(x_3) \cdots + f(x_n)$$

If the quantity following the symbol has no subscript i, the quantity is simply added n times. Thus $\sum_{i=1}^{n}(a) = na$ and $\sum_{i=1}^{n}(x_j) = nx_j$, whatever the value of x_j happens to be. It should be realized that $\sum_{i=1}^{n}(x_i)$ and $\sum_{j=1}^{n}(x_j)$ are two different ways of writing the same thing.

To take an example, let $f(x)$ be $(x + c)^2$. Then

$$\sum_{i=1}^{n} (x_i + c)^2 = (x_1 + c)^2 + (x_2 + c)^2 + (x_3 + c)^2 \cdots + (x_n + c)^2$$

We can also write

$$\sum_{i=1}^{n} (x_i + c)^2 = \sum_{i=1}^{n} (x_i^2 + 2cx_i + c^2) = \sum_{i=1}^{n} (x_i^2) + 2c\sum_{i=1}^{n} (x_i) + nc^2$$

Since we can write $f(x_i) = y_i$, obviously no separate explanations are needed of application of the summation symbol to a variable quantity and to a function of the quantity.

When there are several groups of values of x, the symbol x_{ij} means the ith value of the jth group. When there are n values of x in each group and there are k groups, $\sum_{i=1}^{n}(x_{ij})$ means the sum of n values of the jth group, i.e.,

$$x_{1j} + x_{2j} + x_{3j} \cdots + x_{nj}$$

and

$$\sum_{j=1}^{k}\left[\sum_{i=1}^{n}(x_{ij})\right] \quad \text{or} \quad \sum_{j=1}^{k}\sum_{i=1}^{n}(x_{ij})$$

means the sum of all the values of x in all the groups, i.e.,

$$(x_{11} + x_{21} + x_{31} + \cdots + x_{n1}) + (x_{12} + x_{22} + x_{32} \cdots + x_{n2})$$
$$+ \cdots + (x_{1k} + x_{2k} + x_{3k} \cdots + x_{nk})$$

When there are two different variables, x and y, the difference between $\sum_{i=1}^{n}(x_i y_i)$ and $\sum_{i=1}^{n}(x_i y_j)$ must be noted. $\sum_{i=1}^{n}(x_i y_i)$ implies that there are n corresponding pairs of values of x and y and means the sum of their products, i.e., $x_1 y_1 + x_2 y_2 + x_3 y_3 \cdots + x_n y_n$. $\sum_{i=1}^{n}(x_i y_j)$ means the sum of products of n different values of x and one particular value of y, i.e., $x_1 y_j + x_2 y_j + x_3 y_j \cdots + x_n y_j$. Therefore,

$$\sum_{i=1}^{n}(x_i y_j) = y_j \sum_{i=1}^{n}(x_i)$$

Finally,

$$\sum_{j=1}^{k}\left[\sum_{i=1}^{k}(x_i y_j)\right] \quad \text{or} \quad \sum_{j=1}^{k}\sum_{i=1}^{n}(x_i y_j)$$

means the sum of products of all n values of x with all k values of y, i.e.,

$$(x_1 y_1 + x_2 y_1 + x_3 y_1 \cdots + x_n y_1) + (x_1 y_2 + x_2 y_2 + x_3 y_2$$
$$\cdots + x_n y_2) \cdots (x_1 y_k + x_2 y_k + x_3 y_k \cdots + x_n y_k)$$

Similarly, if $f(x,y)$ is a function of two variables, x and y,

$$\sum_{i=1}^{n} f(x_i,y_i) = f(x_1,y_1) + f(x_2,y_2) + f(x_3,y_3) \cdots f(x_n,y_n)$$

$$\sum_{i=1}^{n} f(x_i,y_j) = f(x_1,y_j) + f(x_2,y_j) + f(x_3,y_j) \cdots + f(x_n,y_j)$$

and

$$\sum_{j=1}^{k}\left[\sum_{i=1}^{n} f(x_i,y_j)\right] = \sum_{j=1}^{k}\sum_{i=1}^{n} f(x_i,y_j) = [f(x_1,y_1) + f(x_2,y_1) + f(x_3,y_1) \cdots$$
$$+ f(x_n,y_1)] + [f(x_1,y_2) + f(x_2,y_2) + f(x_3,y_2) \cdots$$
$$+ f(x_n,y_2)] + [f(x_1,y_3) + f(x_2,y_3) + f(x_3,y_3) \cdots$$
$$+ f(x_n,y_3)] \cdots + [f(x_1,y_k) + f(x_2,y_k) + f(x_3,y_k) \cdots + f(x_n,y_k)]$$

I. Introduction

The science of statistics is a branch of applied mathematics that deals with variable fluctuating numbers obtained as a result of experiment or observation, provided the numbers belong to populations of measurements or counts that correspond to well-defined populations of objects or events. Populations of numbers that are obtained in work on viruses are not unique or exceptional in any way, and many textbooks on statistics and on experimental design deal adequately with most types of statistical problems encountered in virus research. No useful purpose would, therefore, be served by a systematic treatment here of statistical methods that have become classical and that can be found in textbooks. This chapter is intended for virologists who are not familiar with statistical methods; its purpose is to indicate some possibilities, to discuss some general principles and a few selected problems that are encountered in virus research especially frequently, and to provide enough information for the reader to solve simple statistical problems with the aid of statistical tables. A short list of statistical tables, textbooks, and of some relevant papers is appended. This chapter is not intended to give any information about virology itself, and the various examples from virus research are selected only to illustrate statistical problems and principles. Some of the examples are actual experimental results and some are fictitious.

Only methods of analyzing results of experiments arranged according to a few of the most simple kinds of design are considered here; complicated kinds of design would often give more precise results, but they would require methods of analysis that are beyond the scope of this chapter. The less precise results may be satisfactory provided the measure of precision is estimated correctly. When the maximum precision is required, a suitable textbook or a professional statistician should be consulted.

The purposes of statistical examinations are many and various, but they are usually either directly or indirectly concerned with assessing the significance of some fluctuating quantities by calculating the probability of their occurring by chance, or finding the limits within which they may fluctuate by chance with a specified probability. The science of statistics can, therefore, be considered as an application of the theory of probability to examine the significance of numerical results obtained by experiment or observation.

The fluctuating quantity that is obtained as a result of measurements or counts is called the "variable" or the "variate." A variate can be continuous, i.e., capable of taking any value within its range of variation (for example, results of weighings), or it can be discontinuous (or discrete), i.e., capable of taking only certain values, usually integers (for example, results of counts of numbers of times an event has occurred). Methods of dealing with the two kinds of variate usually differ, but when a discontinuous variate takes rather large values, i.e., when intervals between successive possible values are small by comparison with their magnitudes, the variate can often be treated as if it were continuous.

Populations of objects or events can be finite or infinite in the sense that they are so large that we can deal only with samples that are small fractions of the total numbers. Usually we deal with samples from infinite populations that actually exist ("actual populations") or that potentially exist ("hypothetical populations").

Whenever we have to examine a large actually existing population we have to take a sample from it. It is important that the sample should be taken at random, i.e., in such a way that any member of the population has the same chance of being taken as any other member. If this condition is not fulfilled, a biased selection may be made, and this would lead to wrong conclusions about the population. Any technique of random sampling must be objective and may present various difficulties that have to be overcome in ways suitable to particular circumstances. For example, if a feature, such as height or weight, of people of a country were to be examined, there would be a problem of taking for examination a random sample of the people.

When objects or events exist only as a result of application of some procedure, they can be considered as a sample from a hypothetical infinite population that would exist if the procedure were repeated indefinitely. Such a sample cannot be taken at random in the same way as from an actual population. However, provided the experimenter does not make any selection and uses all the sample of results that he has obtained, a subjective bias is excluded, and so in this sense the sample can be considered as taken at random from a population of results that could be obtained under a given set of circumstances.

Results obtained in virus research are often samples from hypothetical populations. For example, a group of people treated with a vaccine can be considered a sample from a population that would exist if a large number of people were similarly vaccinated. A population of numbers of some kind of artifacts, for example, numbers of local lesions produced by inoculating a virus preparation into a number of hosts, can be considered as a sample from an infinite population of numbers of lesions that would be produced if we repeated the procedure indefinitely. Numbers of plaques per plate formed by a bacteriophage can be considered as a sample from a population of numbers of plaques per plate that would be obtained if we went on with the procedure of obtaining the plaques.

Results of measurements of some objects may vary because dimensions of the objects vary. However, results of a measurement may also vary even when a measured object is constant. The variability then results solely from the imperfection of the procedure of measurement. We have then a sample of results from a hypothetical population that would be obtained if the procedure of measurement were repeated indefinitely.

In any population different values of a variate occur with different relative frequencies. The relationship between the magnitude of a variate and the frequency with which it occurs is called "frequency distribution." A frequency distribution can be shown by means of a graph, or it can be obtained as an equation that gives the relative frequency as a function of the magnitude of a variate. Most statistical examinations are based on frequency distributions given in the form of equations. A decision about the type of frequency distribution of a given variate is called a "specification."

In theory different classes of variates can be distributed in infinitely many ways, but in practice we are usually confronted with a few possibilities, and a specification can usually be made. This does not mean that a given variate is distributed exactly according to a given equation, but it may be distributed nearly enough to allow us to use the equation to compute probabilities of occurrence of different values of the variate at least approximately.

Having specified the distribution of a variate, the next step in a statistical examination usually is to estimate a specific (usually small) number of "parameters" that occur as constants in the equations that characterize the distributions. There are many different parameters, but the most important are the "mean" and the "variance." The mean is the arithmetic mean of the population of values of a variate and is usually designated by the symbol μ. Thus, if N values of a variate are $x_1, x_2, x_3 \cdots x_N$, the mean is

$$\mu = \frac{1}{N} \sum_{i=1}^{N} (x_i) \tag{1}$$

If the population is infinite, the number N is infinitely large. The variance is the arithmetic mean of squared deviations of values of the variate from the mean of the population and is usually designated by the symbol σ^2. Thus the variance is

$$\sigma^2 = \frac{1}{N} \sum_{i=1}^{N} (x_i - \mu)^2 \tag{2}$$

Here again, if the population is infinite, the number N is infinitely large. The "standard deviation," usually designated by the symbol σ, is the square root of the variance.

The mean of the population of values of a variate is the parameter which determines the "position" of the distribution of the values, and the variance (or standard deviation) gives a measure of "dispersion" of the values around their mean. If the variance is zero, there is no dispersion at all and all the values of a variate are equal. The use of the term "variate" is then not justified.

It must be remembered, however, that the value of the variance (and of the standard deviation) depends not only on dispersion but also on the unit of measurement, and, therefore, is not an absolute measure of dispersion. If it is to be compared with any other quantity, the comparison will have a meaning only if the other quantity is in the same units and of the same dimensions.

Unless predicted *a priori* from some theoretical considerations, the values of parameters of infinite populations remain unknown in principle, because they are based on infinitely large numbers (N) of values of variates. However, if we have a random sample of values whose number is finite but large, say several hundred or more, we can assume that true values of parameters can be obtained.

Equations (1) and (2) can, therefore, be assumed to give the values of μ and σ provided N is large and the values of a variate have been taken at random. We may, however, have only a small random sample of values, and then all we can do is to obtain a more or less inexact estimate of a parameter. Such an estimate is called a "statistic." It is a generally accepted convention that parameters are designated by Greek letters and the corresponding statistics by the corresponding Latin letters. Thus, the mean of a population is μ, whereas an estimate of the mean calculated from a small sample is m. Similarly, the variance of a population is σ^2, whereas its estimate, which is also called the "sampling variance," is s^2.

The value of a statistic computed from a sample of n values of a variate will vary from one such sample to another, and so there are populations of values of statistics, and their standard deviations are called "standard errors." A statistic must be computed so that the mean of a number of independently obtained values of the statistic tends to the value of the parameter as the number increases. In other words, the mean of a large population of values of a statistic must equal the corresponding parameter. A statistic that fulfills this condition is called "consistent." A statistic that does not fulfill the condition, and its mean tends to a "wrong" value, is called "inconsistent."

Thus, the arithmetic mean of a small random sample of values of a variate, i.e.,

$$m = \frac{1}{n}\sum_{i=1}^{n}(x_i) \tag{3}$$

(where n is a small number), is a consistent estimate of the mean of the population because its mean value does tend to μ given by Eq. (1) (see Appendix). By contrast, the mean of squared deviations of a small sample of values of a variate from the mean of the sample m, i.e.,

$$\frac{1}{n}\sum_{i=1}^{n}(x_i - m)^2$$

is not a consistent estimate of the variance of the population because its mean value does not tend to the value of σ^2 given by Eq. (2), but to $\sigma^2\,(n-1)/n$ (see Appendix). Therefore, a consistent estimate of the variance of the population is

$$s^2 = \frac{1}{n-1}\sum_{i=1}^{n}(x_i - m)^2 \qquad (4)$$

which is called the "sampling variance." The divisor is not the number of deviations of the values from their mean but the number of the deviations minus 1, which is the number of degrees of freedom. When n is large, it does not make much difference whether the divisor is n or $n-1$, but it does when n is small.

The number of degrees of freedom is an important concept in statistics, and it generally means the number of "independent" values of which s^2 is a function. The value of s^2 given by Eq. (4) is a function of deviations of n values of x from the value of m, but because the value of m is itself a function of the n values of x [see Eq. (3)], there are only $n-1$ independent deviations of x from m. This is obvious from the fact that

$$\sum_{i=1}^{n}(x_i) = nm$$

[see Eq. (3)], so that

$$\sum_{i=1}^{n}(x_i - m) = 0$$

and, therefore,

$$x_n - m = -\sum_{i=1}^{n-1}(x_i - m)$$

Thus, the deviations of $n-1$ values of x from m determine the deviation of the nth value of x, so that s^2 is in fact a function of $n-1$ independent variables. If the value of the mean were known a priori, deviations of all n values from it would be independent, and so the number of degrees of freedom would be n. Since, however, the value of the mean is estimated from the values of x, there is a "loss of a degree of freedom" for estimation of the mean.

We shall see later that in some circumstances deviations of different values of x must be taken not from the mean but from values that are different functions of several different quantities. If the quantities must be independently estimated from the values of x, there is a loss of a degree of freedom for estimation of each quantity.

The following facts (proved in the Appendix) concern means and variances of all populations, irrespective of the type of their frequency distributions.

1. If each value of a variate is increased or decreased by adding or subtracting a constant, the mean is similarly increased or decreased, whereas the variance remains unchanged. This is called a "change of origin."

2. If all values of a variate are multiplied by a constant, a, the mean and the standard deviation are also multiplied by a, and the variance is multiplied by a^2. This is called a "change of scale."

3. If the variance of a variate is σ^2, the variance of the mean of n values of the variate is σ^2/n, so that the standard error of the mean is $\sigma/n^{1/2}$.

4. The variance of the sum or difference of any two variable quantities that are independent of each other is the sum of their variances.

The precision of an estimation is defined as the reciprocal of the variance of the estimate. This, of course, is not an absolute measure because it depends on the scale of measurement. The precision is equivalent to what is called the "weight" of an estimate, or the "amount of information" contained in it. Since the variance of a mean of n values of a variate is inversely proportional to n, i.e., to the number of replications of the procedure that results in obtaining a value of the variate, the precision of estimation of the mean can be increased indefinitely by increasing the number of replications. The necessary number of replications will depend on the variability of the variate and on the degree of precision required in a particular problem. Considerations of cost and time may be involved, and increasing the precision more than necessary may be wasteful.

The important concept, to be used below, is that of the "weighted mean." If we have two independent estimates of the same unknown quantity, say a_1 and a_2, and if the variances of the estimates are, respectively, σ_1^2 and σ_2^2, taking the arithmetic mean of the two estimates will lead to what can be termed a loss of some of the information contained in the two estimates, because the weight (which is a measure of the amount of information) of the mean will be smaller than the sum of the weights of the two estimates. The procedure that results in retention of all the information is that of computing the so-called weighted mean, which is

$$m_w = \frac{a_1/\sigma_1{}^2 + a_2/\sigma_2{}^2}{1/\sigma_1{}^2 + 1/\sigma_2{}^2} \tag{5}$$

The variance of the weighted mean is

$$\text{var}(m_w) = \frac{1}{1/\sigma_1{}^2 + 1/\sigma_2{}^2} \tag{6}$$

(which can be deduced from the facts concerning means and variances, given above), so that the weight of m_w is $1/\sigma_1{}^2 + 1/\sigma_2{}^2$, which is the sum of the weights of the two estimates.

PRACTICAL WAYS OF COMPUTING SUMS OF SQUARES OF DEVIATIONS FROM THE MEAN

To compute the sampling variance, the sum of squares of deviations of n values of a sample from their mean, m, i.e., $\sum_{i=1}^{n} (x_i - m)^2$, must first be computed. To subtract m from all the values of x and then square the results is a laborious procedure. Labor can be saved by making use of the following identity

$$\sum_{i=1}^{n} (x_i - m)^2 = \sum_{i=1}^{n} (x_i{}^2) - nm^2$$

The squares of all the n values of x are obtained and added (which can be done rapidly if a calculating machine is available), and then the value of nm^2 is subtracted. Alternatively, one can subtract the value of T^2/n, where T is the sum of all n values of x (since $T^2/n = nm^2$).

If the values of x are inconveniently large to be squared, an alternative procedure is to decrease them by subtracting a value, say d (which is called the "working mean"), from all of them. Further procedure is based on the identity.

$$\sum_{i=1}^{n} (x_i - m)^2 = \sum_{i=1}^{n} [(x_i - d) - (m - d)]^2 = \sum_{i=1}^{n} (x_i - d)^2 - n(m - d)^2$$

Thus the values squares of $x - d$ are added, and then the value of $n(m - d)^2$ is subtracted. This procedure is especially convenient when all the values of x are integers and may be used in preference to the previous procedure even when the values of x are not large.

II. Experimental Design

The precision of experimental results and the ease with which they can be examined statistically greatly depend on the experimental design. A thoroughly bad experimental design may preclude any subsequent statistical examination. Here we can discuss only general principles of experimental design and a few simple designs. Two terms that will be used frequently are "experimental unit" and "treatment." An experimental unit is one of a number of similar objects, or sets of objects, that are used to test the effect of anything that is intended to be investigated. An object may be more or less complex, animate or inanimate, and may even be abstract in the sense of being an occasion or an opportunity. Thus, an object can be a whole animal, a part of an animal (such as an area of its skin), a plot of ground with plants growing on it, a single whole plant, a part of a plant (such as a single leaf or an area of a leaf), a test tube or a Petri dish with a bacterial culture, or it can be a particular occasion when an apparatus or machinery was used.

A treatment is what we do with an experimental unit in the course of an experiment. Treatments may be simple or complex, and they may differ from each other qualitatively or quantitatively. An experimental unit used as a control is also called a treatment even if nothing is done to it. Any unit should be able to receive any treatment, so that the assignment of treatments to different units should depend entirely on the experimenter's decision.

Experiments can be of many different kinds, but we shall be concerned here only with those that can be defined as subjecting each of a number of experimental units to any one of a number of different treatments and then collecting any qualitative or quantitative data (such as results of measurements or counts) that are relevant to the purpose of the experiment.

Experimental design, with which we are concerned here, means making a decision about the number of experimental units that will be required and allocating treatments to the units. All the technical aspects of the experiment, such as the way the treatments are applied or the way any measurements or counts are made, are assumed to be satisfactory. It should be emphasized that a statistical examination cannot function as a means of salvaging results of an experiment that is technically faulty.

The way an experiment should be designed may be determined by circumstances, such as the type of experimental units, and so there may be no choice. When a choice can be made, a design that gives the greatest possible ,precision is to be preferred. However, it must be taken into account that when results are to be analyzed statistically they must be analyzed by the method appropriate to the design, since otherwise their precision and significance will be falsely assessed. Analyses appropriate to some designs are rather complicated and may be beyond the competence of the experimenter. Aided by a statistical laboratory equipped with an electronic computer, complexity of the analysis may not be an obstacle, but experimenters doing the analyses themselves need to keep the design within the limits of their competence to make the subsequent analysis, which may exclude all but the simplest designs.

Only a few types of simple experimental design will be described now; methods of analyzing their results are described in Section V,F. Possibilities of increasing precision of results by using more complicated designs will be indicated.

A. Randomization

When experimental units do not fall naturally into groups which may differ in any way that might affect the magnitude of the variate with which we are going to deal, or when it is decided not to divide the units into such groups, the units are allocated to different treatments at random. Such a procedure is called "unrestricted" or "complete randomization" to distinguish it from "restricted randomization," discussed later. We may or may not allocate an equal number of units to each treatment, but the choice of units to be allocated to different treatments is random.

Random allocation is unnecessary only when units can be assumed to be identical. For example, containers, such as test tubes or Petri dishes containing equal volumes of the same bacterial culture, or sets of such test tubes, may be considered identical, and all we need to do is allocate certain numbers (equal or unequal) of the containers to different treatments, for example, inoculations with different preparations of a bacteriophage. However, if there is a possibility that the containers are affected differentially during subsequent incubation, for example, by being placed in parts of an incubator that differ in temperature or light intensity, positions in the incubator should be allocated to different containers at random.

When experimental units are not identical (when they are, for example, animals, plants, sets of animals or plants, plots of ground, and so on), random allocation to different treatments must be done properly, so that every experimental unit has an equal probability of being allocated to any particular treatment. Any procedure of allocation must be impersonal and objective, excluding any possibility of a subjective bias. This must be emphasized strongly. An objective allocation to treatments can be done by some "game of chance," such as giving identification numbers to the units, writing the numbers on cards, shuffling the cards, and then drawing them blindly and allocating the corresponding units to different treatments. Alternatively, tables of random numbers can be used. When an objective randomization procedure has been applied, the result should be accepted as it is and not "improved" by any adjustment.

A subjective allocation of experimental units to different treatments in a way that looks haphazard may not be properly random. For example, units that may differ from others in some recognizable way may be unwittingly allocated preferentially to some particular treatments. This may introduce a bias in favor of some treatments. Another possibility is that the experimenter may be trying, also perhaps unwittingly, not to favor any particular treatment by distributing units that may share some recognizable feature equally among different treatments. This may result in an increased precision of estimations, but it may ruin the possibility of a proper statistical examination, because randomization is then not unrestricted, as intended, but has gone some way toward being one of the types of restricted randomization to be described below. Consequently, such an experiment would not correspond properly to any particular type of design, and, therefore, cannot be subjected to any particular method of statistical analysis without leading to false results.

B. ELIMINATION OF SOURCES OF VARIATION

1. Randomized Blocks

Experimental units may differ from each other in such a way that the experimenter may know that some of them will give greater or smaller values of a variate than other units. It may then be possible to increase the precision of comparisons between results of treatments by making use of this knowledge. This can be done by dividing the units into groups, so that each group is composed of units that can be expected to behave similarly, and allocating units to treatments, so that every treatment occurs once in any particular group. Such groups of units are usually called "blocks." Allocation of treatments to units within each block is made at random, and the design is called "randomized blocks." The principle of this design is that randomization is restricted only by one factor, which is division of units into blocks.

With effective grouping into blocks units will vary less within blocks than between blocks. A result of the design is that the effects of all treatments are compared several times, using every time a group of units with relatively small variability. The variation between blocks may then be assumed to be eliminated from comparisons between mean values of results of different treatments, because every mean will be similarly affected by every block. For example, if a block of units produces exceptionally large values of any variate, means of results of all treatments will on average be increased by the same quantity. However, this can be so only when effects of blocks and of treatments are additive. If they are not additive, a transformation of the variate may be required, so that the effects on the transformed values are additive. For example, if the effect of belonging to a block is equivalent to multiplication of some value of the variate by a factor, and the effect of a treatment to multiplication by another factor, obviously a transformation of values of the variate into logarithms will make both effects additive. If the effects are definitely not additive, and if a suitable transformation cannot be found, the procedure of analysis of variance (described in Section V,F), which must be applied to allow for elimination of variation between blocks, is not valid.

Division of units into blocks may be quite obvious. For example, when experimental units are areas of the skin of a number of animals, several areas occurring on each animal, an obvious block would be areas of the skin of the same animal. When units are whole animals, those from the same litter can be treated as a block. When units are single leaves of plants, a natural block would be leaves of the same plant. When units are plots of ground, a block would be a group of plots that are close together and may be expected to be reasonably uniform in fertility. Experience of the experimenter and knowledge of the history of the experimental field may be called upon to judge the way blocks should be formed. When units are whole plants, the experimenter may know from experience that some features of the plants, such as age, size, color, and so on, may be correlated with susceptibility to treatments, for example, infection with preparations of a virus, and he can group plants into blocks according to such features.

Statistical analysis of results obtained in an experiment designed as randomized blocks is described in Section V,F.

Let us consider comparisons of infectivity of different preparations of a plant virus that forms local lesions on inoculated leaves of French bean plants, the number of lesions per leaf being a measure of infectivity. The plants are in the stage of two primary leaves that occupy the same position on the plant and are roughly similar. We have decided to use half leaves as experimental units, so that there are four units on each plant and two on each leaf.

When we have only two virus preparations to compare, we can choose half leaves on each leaf as blocks, because halves of the same leaf differ in susceptibility to the virus less than different leaves of the same plant, and much less than leaves of different plants. Therefore, we inoculate each virus preparation into one half of each leaf of several plants, thus eliminating variation between leaves from the comparison between the two virus preparations. There may be a systematic difference between left and right halves of leaves because one may be more conveniently inoculated than the other, but we may decide not to eliminate this source of variation and allocate left and right halves of the leaves to the two treatments at random. The resulting design will be that of randomized blocks, and the results should be analyzed accordingly.

If, however, we decide to increase the precision of the comparison by also eliminating any variation between right and left halves of the leaves by designing the experiment so that each treatment will occur not only once on each leaf but an equal number of times on the right and on the left halves, the design will cease to be that of randomized blocks, and the results will have to be analyzed differently. Randomization will be limited to allocation of leaves to any one of the treatments to be applied on the right and on the left, and also to the decision as to which treatment is to be number 1 or number 2. Whether or not this design will be an improvement on that of randomized blocks will depend on whether or not there is an appreciable systematic difference between results of inoculations of the right and of the left halves of leaves.

When four different preparations of the virus are to be compared, the natural group of units to form a block are four half leaves on the same plant. Therefore, we inoculate each preparation into one half leaf of each of a number of plants. If the design is to be that of randomized blocks, half leaves of each plant are allocated to treatments at random. A result of randomization, obtained by shuffling four cards, may, for example, look like that shown in Table I. We may, however, try to insure that all treatments are compared with each other approximately with the same precision by making each treatment occur an equal number of times on the same leaf with every other treatment, a procedure called "balancing." Table II shows how this can be done, and it also shows that the minimum number of plants needed to realize this requirement are three. Thus, the number of plants to be used in the experiment must be a multiple of three, the design shown in

Table II being repeated on each additional lot of three plants. A random allocation of units to treatments will be limited to a random assignment of any of the three arrangements marked "Plant No. 1, 2, and 3" in Table II to the plants that are to be used, by the fact that the choice of which leaf is to be No. 1 or No. 2 is quite arbitrary, and also by random allocation of treatments to the letters A, B, C, and D.

TAPLE I

RANDOMIZED BLOCKS: FOUR TREATMENTS IN BLOCKS OF FOUR UNITS

	Plant no.											
	1		2		3		4		5		6	
Leaf No. 1	C	D	B	D	A	C	D	A	C	A	D	B
Leaf No. 2	B	A	C	A	D	B	C	B	B	D	C	A

The resulting design is not that of randomized blocks. It has become what is called "balanced incomplete blocks" (a block is two half leaves on each leaf) which are grouped into replicates, each plant being a replicate. Whether or not this design will be an improvement on that of randomized blocks will depend on whether or not variation between leaves of the same plant is appreciably greater than the variation between half leaves of the same leaf. The method of analysis of the results is much more complicated than that of randomized blocks and is beyond the scope of this chapter.

TAPLE II

A MODIFICATION OF THE DESIGN SHOWN IN TABLE I

	Plant no.					
	1		2		3	
Leaf No. 1	A	B	A	C	D	A
Leaf No. 2	C	D	D	B	B	C

Incomplete blocks are used when the number of treatments exceeds that of units in a block, so that all treatments cannot occur in every block. Balanced incomplete blocks are arranged in such a way that each treatment occurs an equal number of times with any other treatment in the same block, the assignment of treatments to units within blocks being random. Table III gives an example of seven treatments in seven blocks with three units in every block. Table IV gives an example of five treatments in five blocks with four units in every block. The random assignment of treatments to units within blocks is not shown in the tables. The method of analyzing the results, which is beyond the scope of this article, is based on the assumption of effects of blocks and

TABLE III

BALANCED INCOMPLETE BLOCKS: SEVEN TREATMENTS IN SEVEN BLOCKS WITH THREE UNITS IN EACH BLOCK

Block			
I	A	B	D
II	B	C	E
III	C	D	F
IV	D	E	G
V	E	F	A
VI	F	G	B
VII	G	A	C

treatments being additive and involves adjustments in treatment means to allow for effects of all blocks. It is described, for example, in "Experimental Design" by Cochran and Cox (1950).

2. *Latin Squares*

Division of experimental units into blocks, as described above, is a division in one way only. We may, however, be able to group units in several different ways simultaneously. Grouping in more ways than two is beyond the scope of this chapter, but we shall consider a way of

TABLE IV

BALANCED INCOMPLETE BLOCKS: FIVE TREATMENTS IN FIVE BLOCKS WITH FOUR UNITS IN EACH

Block				
I	A	B	C	D
II	B	C	D	E
III	C	D	E	A
IV	D	E	A	B
V	E	A	B	C

grouping in two ways to obtain a design known as "Latin square." We shall consider this method with a few examples. First, let us assume that we are to test four different chemicals for their effect on the rate of multiplication of a virus that appears in the bloodstream of an animal. Animals are injected with a virus preparation together with each of the four chemicals and also without any of them (control), so that there are five different treatments. After a suitable interval, blood samples are taken and virus concentration in them is determined by a suitable method.

Let us assume that the animals available for the experiment belong to five different varieties and that five animals of each variety can be used. Susceptibility of animals to virus infection and to the chemicals may depend on the variety, and so animals of each variety could form a natural block. Let us also assume that the animals within each variety are of different ages and that the animals of all varieties can be divided into five age groups. It is also possible that susceptibility of the animals to the virus and to the chemicals depends on age, and so animals of each age group could also form a natural block. However, we can group the animals simultaneously according to variety and according to age. This can be done by giving all the animals some identification symbols and arranging the symbols (on paper) in rows according to variety and in columns according to age. If the treatments are then allocated so that each occurs once in every row (i.e., in each variety) and once in each column (i.e., in each age group), the design known as Latin square is obtained (see Tables Va and b, in which capital letters represent different treatments). Since there are five rows and five columns, the design is called a 5×5 Latin square.

It is obvious at a glance that an interchange of rows and of columns does not affect the principle of the design. Therefore, randomization can be obtained by starting from a systematic arrangement shown in Table Va and by assigning to each row, and then to each column, a new position at random. This may lead to an arrangement shown in Table Vb. Finally, we can also assign at random the symbols A–E to the different treatments.

The result of this design is that variation from differences between varieties (rows) and from differences in age (columns) is eliminated

TABLE V

5×5 LATIN SQUARE

a					b				
A	B	C	D	E	C	A	D	E	B
B	C	D	E	A	E	C	A	B	D
C	D	E	A	B	D	B	E	A	C
D	E	A	B	C	A	D	B	C	E
E	A	B	C	D	B	E	C	D	A

from differences between means of any two treatments, because every mean is similarly affected (increased or decreased) by every row and by every column. However, this can be so only when effects on rows, columns, and treatments are additive. When they are not, a transformation of the variate may be required, as explained in the preceding section.

As another example, let us consider a comparison of infectivities of five preparations of a virus by the local lesion method on plants that have several leaves on different positions on the stem, using whole leaves as experimental units. We assume that plants may differ in susceptibility to the virus and also that there is a gradient in susceptibility of leaves depending on their position on the stem. To eliminate both sources of variation from comparisons between virus preparations, we can use five plants with five leaves on each (unwanted leaves can be stripped off), and we can use the 5×5 Latin square design by arranging leaves that belong to the same plants as columns and leaves that occupy the same positions on the stem as rows.

In principle only a proper, i.e., completely randomized, Latin square design, like that shown in Table Vb, should be used. If a systematic arrangement, like that shown in Table Va, is used instead, randomization will be limited to a random assignment of plants to different columns and to a random assignment of the letters A–E to the different treatments. The positions of treatments relative to each other will then be fixed, and this will be an additional restriction of randomization, which is assumed not to occur in a Latin square design. Thus, a systematic design can be recommended only if it greatly helps to find quickly the particular leaves that are to be inoculated and to avoid mistakes and if the speed of inoculations is an important factor in the experiment.

As an example of another kind, let us consider a field experiment to compare effects of infection with four different viruses on the yield of a crop. We assume that there may be a variation in fertility of the soil, although we may not know the direction of its gradient. We may divide the field into 25 plots of approximately equal area, not necessarily square, so that the plots are arranged in five rows and five columns. We have five different treatments: infection with each of the four viruses and no infection (control). The treatments are applied to the plots according to the design of a 5×5 Latin square, as described above. This time the systematic design shown in Table Va is absolutely unacceptable because the treatments are arranged diagonally; therefore, if the gradient of fertility happens to be also directed diagonally, a bias would be introduced. It is, therefore, essential that a properly randomized arrangement such as that shown in Table Vb be used. Variation in fertility with the gradient directed along the rows or along the columns, or both, will be eliminated from the comparisons between results of treatments.

Analysis of results obtained in experiments designed as Latin squares is described in Section V,F.

C. Quantities Computed from Data Provided by Experimental Results

When results of each of several experiments are used to compute a certain quantity, each result of the computation can be treated as if it were a value of a variate, provided the same experimental design has been used throughout and there was no bias in favor of any treatment. A sample of such values can be examined statistically as if it were taken from an infinite population of values that would be obtained if the experiment were repeated indefinitely. Single experiments need not then be analyzed statistically at all. They simply provide the quantities that are used as different values of a variate. The procedure is convenient because complicated methods of analysis that are appropriate to some experimental designs may thus be avoided, and it can be recommended when many experiments can be made within a short time. Since results of single experiments do not have to be analyzed, the experiments can be planned according to a design that gives the greatest possible precision, even if the analysis would present great difficulties.

To consider an example, let us assume that we want to estimate the value of a constant of inactivation of a plant virus by UV radiation from a given source. To do this, samples of a virus preparation are irradiated with different doses of the radiation, and infectivities of the samples are then compared with that of the nonirradiated preparation. Let us assume that this means that infectivities of eight different preparations are to be compared, four of which are irradiated preparations and four of which are different concentrations of the nonirradiated virus preparation. Any suitable experimental design can be used, such as randomized blocks, balanced incomplete blocks, or the 8×8 Latin square.

When local lesions have been produced and counted, infectivities of the irradiated samples can be estimated by graphic interpolation. A graph is obtained by plotting the means of suitably transformed numbers of lesions (see Section V,G) produced by the four differently concentrated solutions of nonirradiated virus against logarithms of the concentrations, thus getting four points. A smooth line is then drawn following the course indicated by the points, so that the points may deviate from the line approximately equally in both directions. The line may have to be slightly curved. The mean of similarly transformed numbers of lesions produced by an irradiated sample will then correspond to a point on the line, and the abscissa of the point will correspond to the logarithm of the concentration of the nonirradiated virus whose infectivity is about equal to that of the irradiated sample.

Having in this way estimated the residual infectivities of the four irradiated samples, the value of the constant of inactivation is computed as described in Chapter 3 of this volume. Several such experiments will provide several estimates of the constant, thus giving a sample of estimates. The standard error of the mean of the sample can then be computed quite simply without bothering about the design of the experiments.

D. FACTORIAL EXPERIMENTS

When the effects of several factors on some material need to be examined it may be advantageous to examine effects of the factors, both separately and in various combinations, in the same experiment. Such experiments are called "factorial," and they stand in opposition to the older principle that factors should be examined one at a time. The factorial arrangement not only saves time and labor but it can also reveal interactions between the factors.

The principle of procedure will be explained on a simple example of three factors, each of which is either present or absent (no gradation of levels).

Let us assume that we want to know the effect of infection with two viruses, A and B, each causing only a mild disease, on the rate of growth of a young animal. We may also want to test the effect of a special feeding on the growth and whether the special feeding can counteract the effect of infection. Thus we have three factors: infection with A (factor A), infection with B (factor B), and the special feeding (factor C). The presence or absence of each factor occurs in combination with the presence or absence of each of the other two factors, so that we have $2 \times 2 \times 2 = 8$ treatments, and therefore the experiment is called "$2 \times 2 \times 2$ factorial." The 8 treatments are: ABC, AB, AC, BC, A, B, C, (0). The symbol (0) means the absence of any of the factors. There are several replications of each treatment, and the treatments are distributed among animals according to a suitable experimental design. The animals are weighed at the beginning and at the end of the experiment, and the increments in weight are recorded. The mean of the increment in a group of animals receiving the same treatment is designated below by the same symbol as that for the treatment.

Let us first consider the effect of factor A. This can be obtained from the four following comparisons:

A − (0)	No other factor present
AB − B	Factor B present
AC − C	Factor C present
ABC − BC	Factors B and C present

These comparisons show not only the effect of A in the absence and in the presence of the other factors but also the effects of the other factors on the effect of A (interactions). Analogous four comparisons can be obtained for the effects of each of the other two factors. It is obvious, therefore, that more conclusions can be drawn from a factorial experiment than from experiments that examine effects of the factors one at a time.

It may sometimes be convenient to present the results of the experiment in terms of the formal expressions for the "main effects" and "interactions." The mean value of the four comparisons giving the effects of A, namely,

$$\tfrac{1}{4}[ABC + AB + AC + A - BC - B - C - (0)]$$

is called the "main effect" of A. The main effects of other factors are obtained similarly. The meaning of the main effect is quite simple when effects of different factors are additive, i.e., when effects of different factors, when acting singly, are added when the factors are acting jointly. When this is so, all four comparisons for effects of a factor will be expected to have the same value, and the main effect is simply an estimate of this value. However, there is no reason why any particular set of data should obey the law of additivity, whose main reason for existence is its statistical convenience. Any appreciable deviation from the law makes the values of the four comparisons unequal, and the simple meaning of the main effect is then lost. How much a given set of data does actually deviate from the law is shown by the values of the expressions called "interactions."

The interaction between A and B is defined as the effect of B on the effect of A, which is measured by the difference between the effects of A in the presence and absence of B. When C is absent, the difference is

$$\tfrac{1}{2}\{ (AB - B) - [A - (0)] \} = \tfrac{1}{2}[AB - A - B + (0)]$$

and when C is present, it is

$$\tfrac{1}{2}[(ABC - BC) - (AC - C)] = \tfrac{1}{2}(ABC - AC - BC + C)$$

(The coefficient $\tfrac{1}{2}$ is introduced to conform to the expressions given above.) The fact that the letters A and B can be interchanged without altering the expressions means that the effect of B on the effect of A is identical to the effect of A on the effect of B. Interactions between C and each of the other factors are given by analogous expressions.

The total interaction between A and B is given by the mean value of the two expressions above, which is

$$\tfrac{1}{4}[ABC + AB - AC - BC - A - B + C + (0)]$$

The interaction among all three factors is defined as the effect of one on the interaction between the other two. Thus, the interaction among A, B, and C is measured by the difference between interactions between A and B in the presence and absence of C, which is

$$\tfrac{1}{4}[ABC + A + B + C - AB - AC - BC - (0)]$$

(Again the coefficient $\tfrac{1}{4}$ is introduced to conform to other expressions.) The fact that all the letters can be interchanged without altering the expression means that the effects of each of the three factors on the interaction between the other two are identical.

For convenience the expressions for the main effects of all three factors and for all the total interactions are listed below. The symbol $\times$ stands for interaction.

Main effect of A:	$\tfrac{1}{4}[ABC + AB + AC + A - BC - B - C - (0)]$
Main effect of B:	$\tfrac{1}{4}[ABC + AB + BC + B - AC - A - C - (0)]$
Main effect of C:	$\tfrac{1}{4}[ABC + AC + BC + C - AB - A - B - (0)]$
Interaction A $\times$ B:	$\tfrac{1}{4}[ABC + AB + C + (0) - AC - BC - A - B]$
Interaction A $\times$ C:	$\tfrac{1}{4}[ABC + AC + B + (0) - AB - BC - A - C]$
Interaction B $\times$ C:	$\tfrac{1}{4}[ABC + BC + A + (0) - AB - AC - B - C]$
Interaction A $\times$ B $\times$ C:	$\tfrac{1}{4}[ABC + A + B + C - AB - AC - BC - (0)]$

The interactions between two factors are called those of "first order," and between three factors of "second order."

A glance at any of the expressions for interaction will show that their values will be expected to be zero if the law of additivity of effects of the factors is obeyed. Therefore, the extent to which any of these expressions deviates from zero will give the measure of deviation from the law of additivity.

When the data do not conform to the law of additivity they can sometimes be made to conform by a suitable transformation. Let us assume, for example, that the effects of factors, when applied separately, are equivalent to the multiplication of a quantity by corresponding coefficients, and that joint effects of the factors are equivalent to multiplication by the products of their corresponding coefficients. The data will then show interactions that may differ greatly from zero. The transformation of the data into logarithms will result in all interactions being zero (i.e., not differing significantly from zero).

There is not space here to discuss more complicated factorial experiments. The general principle is always the same, and interactions give a measure of departure from additivity of effects of different factors, but details of the procedure may be quite different from those shown above, especially when factors are used at several different levels.

III. Probability

Since the science of statistics is largely based on the theory of probability, a few aspects of the theory must be briefly considered. The term "probability" has different meanings, but the one in which it is used here can be defined as follows: when a system contains n alternative possibilities, all of which are equally likely, and m of the possibilities entail the occurrence of an event, the probability of the event is

$$p = m/n \qquad (7)$$

The term "possibility" means any kind of circumstance or trial that may, but need not, result in occurrence of the event. The number of possibilities may be finite or infinite. The stipulation that all n possibilities are "equally likely" means that it is impossible to predict which of them will be realized on a given occasion rather than on any other, and that when the number of occasions is large enough all the possibilities will have occurred an equal number of times. This may imply an infinite number of occasions.

An event whose probability is given by Eq. (7) may be any kind of phenomenon that can be described qualitatively or quantitatively. A quantitative event may mean that a variable quantity, or variate, takes a certain value or a value within certain limits.

The value of probability can often be obtained, or postulated, *a priori*. This may be so when frequencies of occurrence of some phenomena can be shown theoretically, or be assumed, to belong to some particular types of distribution (see Section IV), or because some properties of an object are known. For example, when a die is thrown we postulate that the probability of a particular face turning up is $1/6$, which means we think that when the die is thrown many times a particular face will be turned up on one sixth of the total number of occasions. We assume that the die is symmetrical and that it is thrown in such a way that everyone of its six faces is equally likely to be turned up. Whether we are right or not can be tested experimentally by actually throwing the die many times and noting the results.

When the value of p is not known *a priori*, it can be obtained empirically by counting the number of times an event has occurred (m), and also the number of possibilities when it could have occurred but did not $(\overline{m})$, and substituting m and n $(= m + \overline{m})$ into Eq. (7). When the number of possibilities can be assumed infinite, n possibilities obtained empirically (by observation or experiment) represent only a sample, and, therefore, Eq. (7) will give us only an estimate of p. The greater the sample, the more certainly the estimate will approach the "real" value of p. Usually we can also obtain the standard error of our estimate of p, and thus have some idea with respect to the limits within which the "real" value of p should be. (see Section V).

A reverse operation is often performed, namely the estimation of the "expected" number of occurrences of an event when the probability of the event is known theoretically or has previously been estimated empirically. If the probability is p and the number of trials to obtain the event is N, the expected number of successes is

$$M = pN \tag{8}$$

When N is small, the actually obtained number of successes may differ considerably from M.

When a variate x is discontinuous (i.e., takes only discrete values as, for example, when all its values are integers) the symbol $\phi(x)$ can be used to denote the probability of the variate taking a particular value. Thus the probability of x taking the value of x_i is

$$p_i = \phi(x_i) \tag{9}$$

Comparing this with Eq. (7), we see that $\phi(x_i) = m_i/n$, where m_i is the number of possibilities when $x = x_i$ and n the total number of possibilities. In Eq. (9) $\phi(x)$ is treated as a function of x and is called the "probability function" irrespective of whether it is derived theoretically or obtained empirically.

When a variate x is continuous, the probability of its value being within an infinitesimal interval dx (i.e., between $x_i + \frac{1}{2}dx$ and $x_i - \frac{1}{2}dx$) will, obviously, be also infinitesimal. We shall designate it by dp and call it the "probability differential." The probability differential will be proportional to the length of the interval dx, and we can use the symbol $\theta(x)$ for the ratio dp/dx at any particular value of x. Thus, when $x = x_i$, $dp/dx = \theta(x_i)$, so that the probability differential is

$$dp = \theta(x_i)dx \tag{10}$$

Therefore, the probability of x taking any value between x_1 and s_2 is

$$p = \int_{x_1}^{x_2} \theta(x)dx \qquad (11)$$

Comparing this with Eq. (7) we see that

$$\int_{x_1}^{x_2} \theta(x)dx = m/n$$

where m is the number of possibilities when x is between x_2 and x_1, and n the total number of possibilities. The values of m and n should be assumed to tend to infinity. Here $\theta(x)$ is also treated as a function of x irrespective of whether it is derived theoretically or obtained empirically. When the variate is continuous, $\theta(x)$ is called the "probability function" or the "probability density."

The fact, which will be used later in the chapter, is that the sum of probabilities for all possible values of a variate equals 1. This is obviously so because the number of possibilities that the variate will take any possible value is the total number of possibilities. Thus $\Sigma_i\, m_i = n$, so that

$$\sum p_i = \sum_i m_i/n = n/n = 1$$

Thus, when a variate is discontinuous

$$\sum_i p_i = \sum_i \phi(x_i) = 1 \qquad (12)$$

and when a variate is continuous

$$\int dp = \int_a^b \theta(x)dx = 1 \qquad (13)$$

where a and b are the limits within which the value of the variate can vary. Plotting the values of $\phi(x)$ or of $\theta(x)$ of Eqs. (12) and (13) against the values of x will give a "probability histogram" or a "probability curve" (see Section IV).

An event complementary to an event e is the nonoccurrence of e, which will be designated by $\bar{e}$. If the probability of e is p, the probability of $\bar{e}$ is $q = 1 - p$. This is so because $p = m/n$, where m is the number of possibilities when e occurs and n the total number of possibilities. Therefore, the number of possibilities when e does not occur is $n - m$, and so the probability of $\bar{e}$ is $q = (n - m)/n = 1 - m/n = 1 - p$.

There are two operations on probabilities that will be used later, namely, addition and multiplication. If a and b are two "mutually exclusive" events with probabilities p_a and p_b, the probability of occurrence of either a or b is $p_a + p_b$. For example, the probability of a die falling with either 5 or 6 up is $1/6 + 1/6 = 1/3$. This is so because if m_a is the number of possibilities when a occurs, m_b the number of possibilities when b occurs, and n the total number of possibilities, $p_a = m_a/n$ and $p_b = m_b/n$. The number of possibilities when either a or b occurs is $m_a + m_b$, so that the probability of this is

$$p = (m_a + m_b)/n = m_a/n + m_b/n = p_a + p_b.$$

This reasoning can be easily extended to several mutually exclusive events with probabilities p_a, p_b, p_c, ... The probability of any one of them occurring, irrespective of which, is $p = p_a + p_b + p_c \cdots$.

If a and b are two events with probabilities p_a and p_b, and if the two events are independent of each other (i.e., the occurrence of one does not affect the probability of occurrence of the other), the probability of both events occurring together is $p_{ab} = p_a p_b$. For example, when a coin is tossed and a die is thrown, the probability that the coin will fall head up and the die with 6 up is $1/2 \times 1/6 = 1/12$. Or when a die is thrown twice, the probability that it will fall with 5 up the first time and 6 up the second time is $1/6 \times 1/6 = 1/36$.

This can be proved as follows. Let $p_a = m_a/n_a$ and $p_b = m_b/n_b$, so that there are two independent systems: system A containing n_a alternative possibilities, m_a of which entail the occurrence of a, and system B containing n_b alternative possibilities, m_b of which entail the occurrence of b. To consider the probability of both a and b occurring together, we have to imagine a third system of alternative possibilities, say system AB, each possibility in AB being a coincidence of one from A and one from B. If the systems A and B are independent, any one of n_a possibilities in A can coincide with any one of n_b possibilities in B, so that the total number of possibilities in AB is $n_{ab} = n_a n_b$. Similarly, any one of m_a possibilities in A when the event a occurs can coincide with any one of m_b possibilities in B when the event b occurs, so that the number of possibilities in AB when both a and b occur together is $m_{ab} = m_a m_b$. Therefore, the probability of a and b occurring together is

$$p_{ab} = m_{ab}/n_{ab} = m_a m_b/n_a n_b = (m_a/n_a)(m_b/n_b) = p_a p_b.$$

The reasoning can be easily extended to any number of independent events occurring together. If the probabilities of several independent events a, b, c, d, . . . are, respectively, p_a, p_b, p_c, p_d, . . . , the probability of their occurring together is $p_a p_b p_c p_d \cdots$. Occurrence of the same event r times in succession in r independent trials is equivalent to the occurrence of r independent events together. Thus, if the probability of the event occurring in any single trial is p, the probability of its occurring every time in r independent trials is p^r.

IV. Frequency Distributions

Frequency distribution means the numbers in which members of a population or of a sample occur in different classes when classified according to a qualitative or a quantitative feature. The classes can be natural or arbitrary, and the number of classes can be finite or infinite. When the feature according to which classification is made is a continuously variable quantity, intervals between limits for different classes can be chosen arbitrarily and they can be finite or infinitesimal.

The simplest kind of distribution occurs when there are only two classes, for example, when there are two different kinds of particles of a virus. The distribution is then specified by stating the proportions in which they occur. When members of a population can be divided into several classes, the distribution can be shown by a table in which classes are specified in one column and their frequencies in another parallel column. When the feature according to which classification is made is a variable quantity, the distribution can be shown by a histogram, which is made by dividing the horizontal axis into segments corresponding to class intervals and placing on each segment a rectangle whose area is proportional to the corresponding class frequency (see Fig. 2A–C). When the variable is continuous, class intervals can be as small as we please, provided the values are numerous enough to be distributed among all of them with reasonable frequencies. As the number of values increases, class intervals can be made so small that the upper ends of the rectangles will tend to form a continuous curve, called the "frequency curve." It will become a probability curve if class frequencies are expressed as proportions of the total number of values. The area under the curve will then equal unity. When a variate is continuous and the number of its values is infinite, a probability curve is the only graphic way of presenting frequency distribution (see Fig 1, which is an example of such a curve). The whole area under the curve equals 1, and the probability of the variate taking a value within certain limits equals the segment of the area between the limits (for example, the shaded areas in Fig. 1).

A. CONTINGENCY TABLES

An example of the way frequency distributions can be presented are so-called "contingency tables." Such tables can be used when members of a sample can be divided into classes in two different ways according to two different kinds of features, and when we want to know whether there is an association between the two kinds of features.

Let us assume, for example, that animals that belong to the same species but to four different varieties have been exposed to a source of infection with a virus, after which some animals remained healthy, some succumbed to the disease, and of the latter some survived and some died. We can, therefore, divide the animals into four groups according to the variety, and each of the groups can be further divided into three classes according to the result of exposure to infection. We have, therefore, $4 \times 3 = 12$ different classes, or "cells." (The term "cell" is convenient when the term "class" has already been reserved to mean something else.)

Arranging the class frequencies in rows according to variety and in columns according to the response to infection gives a contingency table (see Table VI). Such an arrangement helps us to see whether there is an association between the varieties and the responses to infection, or, in other words, whether or not animals of the different varieties differ in susceptibility to the infection. In general, a contingency table is given a symbol $m \times n$ when there are m columns and n rows.

The totals at the bottom of the table show how all the animals used in the experiment are divided into three groups according to the results of exposure to infection. If the varieties did not differ at all with respect to the results of exposure to the infection, animals of each

TABLE VI

A CONTINGENCY TABLE[a]

Variety	Succumbed to the disease		Did not succumb to the disease	Totals
	Died	Survived		
I	10	45	65	120
	(17.25)	(42.0)	(60.75)	
II	3	17	30	50
	(7.2)	(17.5)	(25.3)	
III	13	24	33	70
	(10.1)	(24.5)	(35.4)	
IV	20	26	34	80
	(11.5)	(28.0)	(40.5)	
Totals	46	112	162	320

[a] Numbers without parentheses are actually observed, and numbers in parentheses are those that would be expected on the assumption that a response to infection does not depend on the variety.

variety would be expected to be similarly distributed among the corresponding classes. If the animals of each variety (i.e., marginal totals on the right-hand side of the table) are distributed in proportion to the totals at the bottom of the table (or the other way round, which will give the same results), class frequencies will be obtained (shown in Table VI by the numbers in the parentheses) that would be expected if the responses of the animals to the infection did not depend on the variety. Whether there is a dependence can then be judged from the magnitude of the differences between the observed and the expected frequencies. Whether the differences are too large to have occurred simply by chance can be tested by the χ^2 test (see Section V,B,1).

It may seem strange that expected class frequencies can be fractions (as they are in Table VI), because we cannot expect a fractional number of animals to occur in a class. However, the expected class frequencies are extimates of mean values of the numbers of animals that would occur in the corresponding classes if the experiment were repeated exactly many times and if responses of the animals to the infection did not depend on the variety.

It will be shown in Section V,B that applying the χ^2 test to the results in Table VI leads to the conclusion that the differences between the expected and the observed class frequencies are probably too great to have occurred simply by chance. We shall thus conclude that the response of the animals to the infection does depend on the variety.

Table VI shows that the greatest differences between the observed and expected class frequencies occur in the classes containing animals that died as a result of infection. The conclusion is that mortality rates definitely differ between animals of the different varieties. However, it remains possible that the proportion of animals that succumb to the disease, irrespective of whether they die or survive, does not depend on the variety. To test this, we can lump together the classes of animals that succumbed to the disease (i.e., those that died and those that survived) and thus obtain another contingency table (see Table VIa). It will be shown in Section V,B that the result of the χ^2 test leads to the conclusion that the differences between the expected and the observed class frequencies in Table VIa are not too large to have occurred simply by chance. We can, therefore, conclude that the proportions of animals that succumbed to the disease do not depend on the variety.

B. The Binomial Distribution

Solutions of most statistical problems are usually based on the use of various theoretical frequency distributions. There are many such dis-

TABLE VIa
TABLE VI WITH REDUCED NUMBER OF HEADINGS[a]

Variety	Succumbed to the disease	Did not succumb to the disease	Totals
I	55 (59.25)	65 (60.75)	120
II	20 (24.7)	30 (25.3)	50
III	37 (34.6)	33 (35.4)	70
IV	46 (39.5)	34 (40.5)	80
Totals	158	162	320

[a] For explanation of the numbers see Table VI.

tributions, but the most important are the binomial, the Poissonian, and the normal. Only these three will be discussed, starting with the binomial distribution because it is historically the first and because the other two developed from it.

If there is a "constant" finite probability p of occurrence of an event A (so that the probability of nonoccurrence is $q = 1 - p$), and if n independent trials have been made to obtain the event (n being a finite integer), the probabilities of obtaining all failures, one success, two successes, three successes, and so on, and finally all n successes will equal, respectively, successive terms of the expanded binomial $(q + p)^n$, which are $q^n, nq^{n-1}p, n(n-1)q^{n-2}p^2/2!, n(n-1)(n-2)q^{n-3}p^3/3!, \ldots, p^n$. Thus the probability that r out of n trials will succeed is

$$p_r = \frac{n!}{(n-r)!r!} p^r q^{n-r} \tag{14}$$

That this is so will be obvious from the following consideration.

The probability of a set of r trials to be all successful, is p^r, and the probability of a set of $n - r$ trials to be all failures is q^{n-r}. Therefore, if r trials are chosen out of n, the probability that all the chosen ones are successful and all the remaining $n - r$ trials are failures is $p^r q^{n-r}$. Now, there are $n!/(n-r)!r!$ ways of chosing r trials out of n (the choices being mutually exclusive), and every time the probability of r chosen trials being successes and the remaining $n - r$ trials being failures is $p^r q^{n-r}$. Thus, the probability of having r successes in n trials without specifying which particular trials should be successful is obtained by adding the probabilities for all possible choices of r trials out of n, thus obtaining Eq. (14).

Equation (14) is, therefore, a probability function of a discontinuous variate r which can take only integral values with the range of variation from zero to n. Equation (14) can thus be considered an example of the general Eq. (9) of Section III.

If there are N sets of n trials, the numbers of sets with 0, 1, 2, 3, . . . , n successes will be expected to be products of multiplication of N by the corresponding probabilities [see Section III, Eq. (8)], i.e., by the successive terms of the expanded binomial $(q + p)^n$. The result-

TABLE VII

An Example of the Binomial Distribution: Numbers of Plants Infected by Insects[a]

Numbers infected in a set of five plants	Terms of the binomial	Values of terms of the binomial	Expected numbers of sets	Observed numbers of sets
0	q^5	0.066	6.6	5
1	$5q^4p$	0.238	23.8	28
2	$10q^3p^2$	0.344	34.4	30
3	$10q^2p^3$	0.249	24.9	28
4	$5qp^4$	0.090	9.0 } 10.3	7 } 9
5	p^5	0.013	1.3	2
Totals		1.000	100.0	100

[a] Total number of plants used: 500. Total number of infected plants: 210. The plants were divided into 100 sets of five. $p = 210/500 = 0.42$; $q = 0.58$.

ing frequency distribution of the N sets of n trials among $n + 1$ classes corresponding to 0, 1, 2, 3, . . . , n successes is called the "binomial distribution." A more general definition is the following: If a variate can take the values 0, 1, 2, 3, . . . , n, and if the relative frequencies with which these values occur equal successive terms of the expanded binomial $(q + p)^n$, the variate is distributed in a binomial distribution.

To take an example, let us consider an experiment to test the efficiency of transmitting a plant virus disease by an insect, as shown in Table VII. The insects were first fed on virus-infected plants and then transferred at random to healthy test plants, one insect being placed on each of 500 plants previously divided into 100 sets of 5 plants, taking care that plants within each set are as uniform as possible, so that we can assume that at least within each set the plants are equally susceptible to infection. Let us assume that 210 plants out of the total of 500 developed the disease. Thus, assuming that all plants were equally susceptible, our estimate of the probability that an insect will transmit the disease to any particular plant is $210/500 = 0.42$. As the numbers from which the estimate is made are rather large, we shall assume that $p = 0.42$ and $q = 0.58$.

The sets of five plants differ in the number of plants that have developed the disease, the number ranging from 0 to 5, and so the sets can be divided into six classes on this basis. The class frequencies will be expected to be proportional to the corresponding probabilities given by the successive terms of the expanded binomial $(0.58 + 0.42)^5$, provided all the plants in all the sets are about equally susceptible to the infection. Table VII shows the values of the terms of the binomial and also the expected and the observed class frequencies. Since the observed frequencies do not differ greatly from those expected, it seems that the distribution of the sets among the six classes is indeed binomial, so the sets of plants did not differ appreciably in susceptibility to the infection. Whether or not the differences between the expected and observed frequencies are greater than can reasonably be expected to have happened by chance can be tested using the χ^2 test, as described in Section V,B.

The two important facts concerning the binomial distribution of numbers of successes in sets on n trials are that the mean value of the number is

$$\mu = pn \tag{15}$$

and its variance is

$$\sigma^2 = pqn \tag{16}$$

These two facts will now be proved, not only because of their intrinsic importance but also because they are going to be used later to prove other facts. The reader need not necessarily follow the proofs, but he should remember the conclusions shown by Eqs. (15) and (16).

The value of the mean follows from the definition of probability. If we have N sets of n trials (N being a large number), so that the total number of trials is Nn, and if M is the number of successes in all the trials, the probability of a success is $p = M/Nn$ [see Eq. (7), Section III], which is the mean number of successes per trial. Therefore, the mean number of successes per set is $\mu = M/N = pn$.

The variance of a variate is, by definition, the mean value of the squares of the deviations of the variate from its mean [see Eq. (2), Section I]. Let r_i be the number of successes in the ith set. The variance of the number is, therefore,

$$\sigma^2 = \frac{1}{N} \sum_{i=1}^{N} (r_i - \mu)^2 = \frac{1}{N} \sum_{i=1}^{N} (r_i^2 - 2r_i\mu + \mu^2)$$

$$= \frac{1}{N} \left[\sum_{i=1}^{N} (r_i^2) - 2\mu \sum_{i=1}^{N} (r_i) + N\mu^2 \right]$$

Since $\sum_{i=1}^{N} (r_i)$ is the total number of successes, which is $M = (M/N)N = \mu N$, we have

$$\sigma^2 = \frac{1}{N} \left[\sum_{i=1}^{N} (r_i^2) - 2N\mu^2 + N\mu^2 \right] = \frac{1}{N} \sum_{i=1}^{N} (r_i^2) - \mu^2 \qquad (17)$$

The value of μ is given by Eq. (15), but we still have to obtain the value of $\sum_{i=1}^{N} (r_i^2)$, which is the sum of squares of the numbers of successes in all N sets. As the number of sets with $r = 0, 1, 2, 3 \cdots$ equals the products of multiplication of N by the successive terms of the expanded binomial $(q + p)^n$, the sum of squares of all the values of r is

$$\sum_{i=1}^{N}(r_i^2) = N[q^n 0^2 + npq^{n-1}1^2 + n(n-1)p^2q^{n-2}2^2/2!$$
$$+ n(n-1)(n-2)p^3q^{n-3}3^2/3! + n(n-1)(n-2)(n-3)p^4q^{n-4}4^2/4!$$
$$\cdots p^n n^2] = N[npq^{n-1} + 2n(n-1)p^2q^{n-2} + 3n(n-1)(n-2)p^3q^{n-3}/2!$$
$$+ 4n(n-1)(n-2)(n-3)p^4q^{n-4}/3! + \cdots n^2 p^n]$$
$$= Nnp[q^{n-1} + 2(n-1)pq^{n-2} + 3(n-1)(n-2)p^2q^{n-3}/2!$$
$$+ 4(n-1)(n-2)(n-3)p^3q^{n-4}/3! + \cdots np^{n-1}]$$
$$= Nnp\{q^{n-1} + (n-1)pq^{n-2} + (n-1)(n-2)p^2q^{n-3}/2!$$
$$+ (n-1)(n-2)(n-3)p^3q^{n-4}/3! \cdots p^{n-1} + (n-1)p[q^{n-2}$$
$$+ (n-2)pq^{n-3} + (n-2)(n-3)p^2q^{n-4}/2!$$
$$+ (n-2)(n-3)(n-4)p^3q^{n-5}/3! + \cdots p^{n-2}]\}$$
$$= Nnp[(q+p)^{n-1} + (n-1)p(q+p)^{n-2}]$$
$$= Nnp[1 + (n-1)p] \quad \text{(because} \quad q + p = 1)$$

Therefore,

$$\frac{1}{N} \sum_{i=1}^{N} (r_i^2) = np[1 + (n-1)p] = npq + n^2p^2$$

Substituting this and also $\mu = pn$ into Eq. (17), we get

$$\sigma^2 = pqn$$

An important conclusion from Eqs. (15) and (16) is that the "relative dispersion", i.e., the ratio of the standard deviation to the mean $\sigma/\mu = (pqn)^{1/2}/pn = (q/pn)^{1/2}$ decreases with the increasing n. Thus, when binomially distributed numbers are small, the relative dispersion is large, and many such numbers must be known to obtain an estimate of the mean with reasonable accuracy. In contrast, when the numbers are large, the relative dispersion may be so small that the knowledge of one number may give an accurate estimate of the mean.

Another important feature of binomially distributed numbers is that their sums are also binomially distributed, provided the value of p is constant throughout. This is obvious from the fact that addition of the numbers is equivalent to the addition of sets of trials simply to obtain larger sets. Thus, with N sets of n trials, adding all the sets will result in a set of Nn trials. In the example of transmission of a plant virus by an insect we have concluded that sets of plants probably do not differ in susceptibility to infection. We can, therefore, consider all 500 plants as one set, and 210 infected plants can be considered as one of a population of binomially distributed numbers with the estimated standard deviation of $(0.42 \times 0.58 \times 500)^{1/2} = 11.04$, about 5% of the number (which means that the relative dispersion is about 0.05). The reasoning would obviously not apply if sets of plants did differ in susceptibility to infection, because the probability of any particular plant becoming infected (p) would then differ from one set to another.

Another example of a binomially distributed quantity, which is particularly important in microbiological work, is the number m of "sterile" tubes out of a total number of tubes, say n, all containing the same amount of a diluted culture of a microorganism. The term "sterile tube" will mean a tube from which a new culture cannot be started, i.e., which does not contain at least one organism. The number m will be expected to be binomially distributed (in a hypothetical population of similar sets of n tubes that would be obtained by repeating the experiment many times) because there is a constant probability, p, that any particular tube will be sterile. The value of p is unknown, but if m tubes out of the total number of n are sterile, m/n is an estimate of p.

The variance of m is $pqn = p(1 - p)n$, so that an estimate of the variance is $(m/n)(1 - m/n)n = m(1 - m/n)$. Thus, an estimate of the variance of the estimate of p (i.e., of m/n) is $(m/n^2)(1 - m/n)$, which will decrease as the number of tubes increases. For example, if $m = 8$ and $n = 20$, the estimate of p is 0.4, and the estimate of its variance is 0.012, so that the standard error is 0.11, which is about 28% of the estimate of p (i.e., the relative dispersion is 0.28). If $m = 40$ and $n = 100$, the estimate of p is also 0.4, but the estimate of its variance is 0.0024, so that the standard error is 0.049, which is 12% of the estimate of p (i.e., the relative dispersion is 0.12).

Ways of finding the limits within which the "true" value of p probably lies will be discussed in Sections V,C and H. The relationship between the value of p and the mean number of organisms per tube will be discussed in the next section.

C. The Poisson Distribution

The Poisson distribution is encountered in virological problems probably more frequently than any other type of frequency distribution. It is a special case of the binomial distribution when the probability (p) of an event occurring is infinitesimally small, but the number of trials (n) so large that the mean number of successes in n trials; i.e., $\mu = pn$, is finite.

For example, if a fluid containing virus particles is irradiated, and if only 1 quantum of radiation energy has been delivered, the probability of a particular virus particle being "hit" by the quantum is the same as that of any other particle, but is infinitesimal. However, when many quanta have been delivered, the mean number of hits per particle may become finite. Every delivered quantum is equivalent to another trial to hit a given particle.

To take another example, let us assume that we take several infinitesimally small samples of the same volume from a source containing virus particles. The probability that a particular particle will occur in any one sample is the same for all samples, but is infinitesimal. However, if the source contains very many particles, the mean number per sample may be finite. Every particle in the source is equivalent to a trial to get a particle into any one sample.

One important feature of the Poissonian distribution can be deduced at once, namely, the fact that the variance of numbers distributed in this fashion equals their mean. This follows from Eqs. (15) and (16). The mean is $\mu = pn$ and the variance is $\sigma^2 = pqn$, but as $q = 1 - p$ virtually equals unity, because p is infinitesimal,

$$\sigma^2 = pn = \mu \qquad (18)$$

The values of p and n may be unknown, but if there is an estimate of μ, automatically there is an estimate of σ^2.

The probabilities of the variate taking the values 0, 1, 2, 3, and so on, will now be derived. The reader need not necessarily follow the derivation, but he should remember the conclusion, which is that the probabilities equal successive terms of the Poisson series shown in Eq. (19).

It was shown (Section IV,B) that when the probability of obtaining an event in a single trial is p, the probabilities of obtaining 0, 1, 2, 3, . . . successes in a set of n trials equal the successive terms of the expansion of the binomial $(q + p)^n$. When the conditions are such that the mean number of successes per set (i.e., pn) is not large, the terms of the expansion corresponding to probabilities of obtaining large numbers are, obviously, infinitesimal, and only the first several terms have finite values. The successive terms are

$$q^n, \quad nq^{n-1}p, \quad n(n-1)q^{n-2}p^2/2!, \quad n(n-1)(n-2)q^{n-3}p^3/3!, \quad \cdots$$

Since n is a very large number, multiplication by $n - a$, where a is a small number, can be substituted by multiplication by n (because the ratio $(n - a)/n$ tends to unity when n tends to infinity). We can also substitute $np = \mu$. The value of q^{-a} can also be substituted by unity when a is small (because the value of q differs from 1 by an infinitesimal value of p). The terms of the expansion will thus become

$$q^n, \quad \mu q^n, \quad \mu^2 q^n/2!, \quad \mu^3 q^n/3!, \quad \cdots$$

However, we cannot substitute 1 for q^n because although q is smaller than 1 only by an infinitesimal value of p, the value of n is assumed to be so large that q^n is appreciably smaller than 1. We must, therefore, obtain the value of q^n.

We can write

$$q^n = (1 - p)^n = \left[\left(1 - \frac{1}{1/p}\right)^{1/p}\right]^{pn}$$

Since p is infinitesimal, and so can be assumed to tend to zero, $1/p$ can be assumed to tend to infinity. We know from elementary algebra that the value of $(1 + 1/x)^x$ tends to $e = 2.718 \cdots$ when x increases. We also know that when x increases $(1 - 1/x)^x \to (1 + 1/x)^{-x} \to e^{-1}$. Therefore,

$$q^n = \left[\left(1 - \frac{1}{1/p}\right)^{1/p}\right]^{pn} = e^{-pn} = e^{-\mu}$$

If we substitute this into the terms of the expansion, they will become

$$e^{-\mu}, \quad \mu e^{-\mu}, \quad \mu^2 e^{-\mu}/2!, \quad \mu^3 e^{-\mu}/3!, \quad \cdots \tag{19}$$

and the succession of these terms is called the "Poisson series" in μ.

Thus, if the mean of the variate is μ, the probabilities of the variate taking the values 0, 1, 2, 3 $\cdots$ equal the successive terms of the Poisson series. Generally, the probability of the variate taking the value of r is

$$p_r = \mu^r e^{-\mu}/r! \tag{20}$$

Equation (20) is, therefore, a probability function for a discontinuous variate that can take only integral values starting from zero, but not having any definite upper limit.

If N values of the variate are taken at random (N being a large number), the numbers of those whose values are 0, 1, 2, 3 $\cdots$ will, therefore, be expected to be products of multiplication of N by the successive terms of the Poisson series [see Section III, Eq. (8)]. The resulting distribution of the N values of the variate among the classes corresponding to the values of 0, 1, 2, 3, . . . is called the "Poisson distribution." The following is a more general definition: If a variate can take the values 0, 1, 2, 3, . . ., and if the relative frequencies with which these values occur equal the successive terms of a Poisson series, the variate is distributed according to the Poisson distribution.

In addition to some characteristic features of its own, the Poisson distribution, being a special case of the binomial distribution, has also all the main features of the binomial distributions (see Section IV,B). Thus, first, the relative dispersions of numbers distributed according to the Poisson distribution decreases with the increasing magnitude of the numbers. Second, the sums of numbers that are distributed according to the Poisson distribution are also distributed according to the Poisson distribution.

Different ways in which the Poisson series can occur in virological problems will be illustrated by three examples.

1. *Example 1*

We have considered the number of virus particles in an infinitesimally small sample, taken from a source containing many particles, as an example of one of a population of numbers distributed according to the Poisson series. Let us assume that each of 200 unit volumes, taken from a diluted preparation of a bacteriophage, has been plated with a suspension of susceptible bacteria, so that each viable phage particle had an equal chance to produce a plaque. Let us assume that 321 plaques have been produced in all the plates, so that the mean number of plaques per plate is $321/200 = 1.605$. If all the manipulations were done accurately, the numbers of plates with plaque numbers 0, 1, 2, 3, . . . will be expected to occur in proportions to the successive terms of the Poisson series with $\mu = 1.605$.

Table VIII shows the values of the first several terms of the Poisson series and also the expected and the observed numbers of plates with 0, 1, 2, 3, . . . plaques. Since the observed numbers do not differ much from those expected, it seems that, indeed, the numbers of plaques on different plates are distributed according to the Poisson series. Whether or not the differences between the expected and the observed frequencies are greater than can reasonably be expected to have happened by chance can be tested using the χ^2 test (see Section V,B).

TABLE VIII

AN EXAMPLE OF THE POISSON DISTRIBUTION: NUMBERS OF PLAQUES PER PLATE FORMED BY A BACTERIOPHAGE[a]

Numbers of plaques in the plates	Terms of the Poisson series	Values of terms of the series	Expected numbers of plates	Observed numbers of plates
0	$e^{-\mu}$	0.201	40.2	45
1	$\mu e^{-\mu}$	0.323	64.6	58
2	$\mu^2 e^{-\mu}/2!$	0.259	51.8	53
3	$\mu^3 e^{-\mu}/3!$	0.139	27.8	28
4	$\mu^4 e^{-\mu}/4!$	0.055	11.0	10
5	$\mu^5 e^{-\mu}/5!$	0.018	3.6 ⎫	3 ⎫
6	$\mu^6 e^{-\mu}/6!$	0.005	1.0 ⎬ 4.8	3 ⎬ 6
7	$\mu^7 e^{-\mu}/7!$	0.001	0.2 ⎭	0 ⎭
8	$\mu^8 e^{-\mu}/8!$	—	—	0
Totals:		1.001	200.2	200

[a] Total number of plates: 200. Total number of plaques: 321. Mean number of plaques per plate: $321/200 = 1.605$.

If it is concluded that the numbers of plaques on different plates are distributed according to the Poisson series, the 321 plaques in all 200 plates can also be considered as one of a hypothetical population of numbers that are distributed according to the Poisson series with the estimated standard deviation of $321^{1/2} = 17.9$, i.e., about 5.5% of the number.

2. Example 2

Let us again assume that a virus is a bacteriophage and that samples of an equal volume are taken from a preparation that is so diluted that some samples have no particles, some have one, some have two, and so on, the numbers of particles in different samples being distributed according to the Poisson series. The samples are added to tubes all containing the same amount of the same liquid culture of susceptible bacteria. We shall assume that phage will multiply whenever at least one phage particle is present in the added sample, and that we have a method of detecting whether or not phage has multiplied. The tubes in which phage has not multiplied were defined in the previous section as sterile tubes.

Since the distribution of numbers of phage particles in the samples is assumed to be Poissonian, the proportion of sterile tubes will be expected to be $P = e^{-\mu}$, which is the first term of the Poisson series in μ, when μ is the mean number of particles per sample [see Eq. (19)].

Thus, if the value of P has been obtained experimentally, the value of μ can then be computed from the equation $P = e^{-\mu}$, so that

$$\mu = -\ln P = \ln 1/P = 2.3 \log 1/P \qquad (21)$$

For example, if the proportion of sterile cultures is $P = 0.25$, this means that the mean number of particles per sample is approximately

$$\mu = 2.3 \log 1/0.25 = 2.3 \log 4.0 = 1.4$$

To test the correctness of the assumption that the phage can multiply from a single particle, use can be made of the fact that the mean number of particles per sample (μ) is proportional to the reciprocal of the dilution factor, so that

$$\mu_i = c/f_i$$

where c is a constant (corresponding to the concentration of the phage in the original preparation) and f_i is the dilution factor. Therefore, the value of P should be a function of the dilution factor, namely, $P_i = e^{-c/f_i}$. Whether this is so or not can be tested experimentally, as discussed in Section VI,A.

We may be interested in the proportion of cultures in which the phage has multiplied from only one particle, which we shall call "pure cultures." The proportion of samples that contain just one particle equals the second term of the Poisson series, namely $\mu e^{-\mu}$. The proportion of samples that contain one or more particles is $1 - e^{-\mu}$. Therefore, the ratio of the pure cultures to the total number of cultures in which the phage has multiplied is

$$R = \mu e^{-\mu}/(1 - e^{-\mu})$$

When, for example, the proportion of sterile tubes is $P = 0.25$, with $\mu = 1.4$, $R = 1.4 \times 0.25/(1 - 0.25) = 0.26$, only one in about four cultures in which phage has multiplied will be expected to be pure. If we want 9 out of 10 cultures to be pure, so that $R = 0.9$, the dilution of the phage preparation must be such that the proportion of sterile tubes is $P = 0.84$, which corresponds to the mean of about 0.174 particles per sample.

3. Example 3

Let us assume that a virus solution is exposed to UV radiation. As already shown, the numbers of quanta of radiation energy that "hit" different virus particles will be expected to be distributed according to the Poisson series. However, only a proportion of these quanta are absorbed by the virus (or by the virus nucleic acid), and only a proportion of those that are absorbed destroy infectivity. Let us assume that there is a constant probability that a quantum that hits a virus particle is absorbed, and another constant probability that inactivation will occur when a quantum is absorbed. If the latter is ϕ, it means that, on average, one out of $1/\phi$ absorbed quanta will inactivate. The probability ϕ is called "quantum efficiency" or "quantum yield" (see Chapter 3 in this volume).

The absorbed quantum that happens to inactivate will for convenience be called "effective." The probability that any particular effective quantum will be absorbed by any particular virus particle is assumed to be the same for all particles, but it is infinitesimal. When very many quanta have been delivered, the mean number of effective quanta absorbed per particle may be finite, and the numbers of such quanta absorbed by different particles will be distributed according to a Poisson series.

Let us assume that the mean number of quanta absorbed per particle is M, and that the quantum efficiency is ϕ. This would mean that the mean number of effective quanta absorbed per particle is ϕM. Proportions of virus particles that have absorbed 0, 1, 2, 3, . . . effective quanta would then equal the successive terms of the Poisson series with $\mu = \phi M$. Thus, the proportion of particles that have not absorbed any effective quanta is $p = e^{-\phi M}$, which is, therefore, the proportion of the original infectivity still remaining after the irradiation. Assuming there are no complicating circumstances, ϕM will be proportional to the dose of supplied radiation energy. If the energy is supplied at a constant rate, $\phi M = kt$, where t is the time of irradiation and k is a constant. Thus the proportion of original infectivity remaining after irradiation for time t should be

$$P = e^{-\phi M} = e^{-kt} \tag{22}$$

This means that the rate of inactivation will be expected to follow what is called "first-order kinetics" (see Chapter 3 in this volume). Plotting log P against t should, therefore, follow a straight line. Whether it does can be tested experimentally. If it does, we can conclude that the above assumptions are compatible with experimental results. For any particular value of P found experimentally, the value of ϕM can be computed using Eq. (22). If, from suitable measurements, the value of M (i.e., the mean number of quanta absorbed per virus particle) can also be computed, the value of ϕ can be obtained.

If inactivation could not be caused by single effective quanta but always by a joint effect of several such quanta, the rate of inactivation would not follow first-order kinetics.

D. The Normal Distribution

The normal distribution is a distribution of a continuous variate. In theory the variate can take any value between $-\infty$ and $+\infty$ which can be taken to mean that there are no exactly specified limits within which the variate can vary. The term "normal" is rather misleading, since it suggests that any other distribution is "abnormal." The term "gaussian" is sometimes used, after Gauss, who did the pioneering work on this type of distribution, but as the term "normal" is used much more, it will also be used here.

The normal distribution is a limit of the binomial distribution when p is finite and n tends to infinity. If x is the number of "successes," the mean value of x (pn) and the variance of x (pqn) are both very large. We assume, however, that each success (with the probability p) results in a very small increment of a measured quantity y, but the number of trials n is so large that the total increments are finite and measurable quantities. If the measured quantities were $y = x/(pqn)^{1/2}$ the variance would be 1; however, the measured quantity may be σ times this value (the value of σ depending on the scale of measurement), so that we may have $y = x\sigma/(pqn)^{1/2}$. The standard deviation of y will then be σ. Because n can theoretically tend to infinity, deviations of the variate y from its mean can vary from $-\infty$ to $+\infty$. In practice they do not, and the range of variation depends on the magnitude of the standard deviation.

The derivation of the normal probability function from the binomial distribution is beyond the scope of this chapter. The probability differential eventually obtained is

$$dp = \frac{1}{\sigma\sqrt{2\pi}} \exp\left[-\frac{1}{2}\left(\frac{y-\mu}{\sigma}\right)^2\right] dy \qquad (23)$$

which is a particular case of the general probability differential given by Eq. (10) of Section III. The probability differential, Eq. (23), satisfies the condition given by Eq. (13) of Section III, because

$$\int dp = \frac{1}{\sigma(2\pi)^{1/2}} \int_{-\infty}^{\infty} \exp\left[-\frac{1}{2}\left(\frac{y-\mu}{\sigma}\right)^2\right] dy = 1 \qquad (24)$$

The probability differential, Eq. (23), is completely specified by the values of the mean (μ) and of the standard deviation (σ). The curve of the normal probability function, shown in Fig. 1, is obtained by plotting values of dp/dy [of Eq. (23)] as ordinates against the values of $y - \mu$ as abscissas, when all the values are in units of standard deviation (so that $\sigma = 1$). (The values of the ordinates can be obtained from a table of ordinates of the normal distribution). The curve is symmetrical around the mean (i.e., at $y - \mu = 0$), and the area under the curve equals 1. At the highest point of the curve the value of the ordinate is about 0.4, and the slope is steepest at points corresponding to the values of $y - \mu$ equal $+1$ and -1.

If Eq. (23) is written in a short form,

$$dp = F(y - \mu)dy$$

the probability of y taking any value between a and b is

$$p = \int_a^b F(y - \mu)dy$$

and the probability of y deviating from μ in either direction by a value greater than r is

$$p = \int_{-\infty}^{\mu-r} F(y - \mu)dy + \int_{\mu+r}^{\infty} F(y - \mu)dy$$

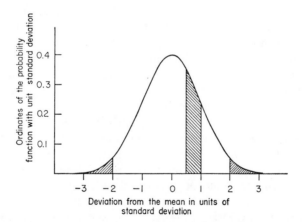

FIG. 1. The probability curve of the normal distribution. The total area under the curve equals unity. The area of the shaded segment between $+0.5$ and $+1.0$ is 0.15. The sum of the areas of the shaded segments to the right of $+2.0$ and to the left of -2.0 is 0.0475. This means that if variates are given in units of standard deviation and if the origin is at the mean, the probability of a variate taking any value between $+0.5$ and $+1.0$ is 0.15, and the probability of a variate deviating from the mean by more than 2.0 in either direction is 0.0475.

Graphically the probabilities of the variate occurring within various limits can be represented by corresponding areas under the curve of the normal probability function, as shown by shaded areas in Fig. 1. The values of the probabilities can be obtained from a table of the normal distribution or from a table of "probits."

A distribution of a continuous variate that is symmetrical need not be normal. Because of the great importance of the normal distribution, we may want to know whether or not a given distribution is normal, and, if it is not, how much it does deviate from the normal. The most elegant method of measuring departure from normality, which is based on the use of the so-called k statistics, is beyond the scope of this chapter, and we shall limit ourselves to a graphic comparison and to the application of the χ^2 test.

Table IX shows the distribution of 1500 lengths (in centimeters) of three kinds of imaginary variable objects (A, B, and C) among classes with intervals of 1 cm, and Fig. 2 shows the distribution of the lengths by means of histograms on which the curve of the normal distribution is superimposed for comparison. (The height of a rectangle equals P/I, where P is the proportion of the values of the variate that belong to a given class and I is the class interval in units of standard deviation.) The mean of all three samples of objects is the same (145.87 cm), but the standard deviations are different (2.61, 2.49, and 3.00), so that the class intervals in units of standard deviation (i.e., reciprocals of the standard deviations) also differ.

A glance at Fig. 2 shows that, although all three distributions are nearly symmetrical, only histogram A follows the course of the curve of the normal distribution reasonably closely, whereas histograms B and C deviate from it quite distinctly: B is too high and too slim, whereas C is too low and too broad.

In addition to observed class frequencies, Table IX also shows the frequencies that would be expected on the assumption of the normal distribution. These were computed by multiplying 1500 by the probabilities for the class intervals obtained from a table of the normal distribution or from a table of probits. The χ^2 test can be applied to see whether the deviations of the observed from the expected frequencies can be expected to have occurred simply by chance. The test will show (see Section V,B) that this is so with respect to A, but not with respect to B and C. Thus, only sample A can be assumed to have been taken from a normally distributed population.

When the values of a variate are divided into classes, the number of classes must be large enough to offer the opportunity of testing whether the pattern of the distribution does follow the shape of the

TABLE IX

COMPARISONS OF CLASS FREQUENCIES OF THREE DIFFERENT SAMPLES WITH THOSE EXPECTED ON THE ASSUMPTION OF THE NORMAL DISTRIBUTION

Center of class interval (cm)	Sample A — Upper limits of class intervals in terms of the standard deviation with the mean at 0	Sample A — Expected	Sample A — Observed	Sample B — Upper limits of class intervals in terms of the standard deviation with the mean at 0	Sample B — Expected	Sample B — Observed	Sample C — Upper limits of class intervals in terms of the standard deviation with the mean at 0	Sample C — Expected	Sample C — Observed	Center of class interval (cm)
154.5	Above +2.7272	4.80 ⎱	1 ⎰{1	Above +2.4613	10.35 ⎱	16 ⎰{1	Above +2.7048	5.10	1	154.5
153.5		⎰	{0		⎱	{0	+2.7048	8.10	1	153.5
152.5	+2.7272	9.45	15		⎰	{15	+2.3720	17.85	15	152.5
151.5	+2.3447	23.10	25	+2.4613	19.20	23	+2.0392	34.95	32	151.5
150.5	+1.9622	48.30	50	+2.0596	43.50	50	+1.7064	61.20	92	150.5
149.5	+1.5797	87.75	75	+1.6579	83.70	65	+1.3736	96.30	119	149.5
148.5	+1.1972	138.00	159	+1.2562	137.85	129	+1.0408	135.75	150	148.5
147.5	+0.8147	187.80	184	+0.8545	193.50	150	+0.7080	171.30	155	147.5
146.5	+0.4322	220.95	208	+0.4528	231.45	269	+0.3752	194.10	160	146.5
145.5	+0.0497	225.30	215	+0.0511	235.95	290	+0.0424	196.65	173	145.5
144.5	−0.3328	198.75	194	−0.3506	205.65	191	−0.2904	178.80	155	144.5
143.5	−0.7153	151.65	167	−0.7523	152.55	143	−0.6232	145.50	148	143.5
142.5	−1.0978	100.05	114	−1.1540	96.45	85	−0.9560	106.20	121	142.5
141.5	−1.4803	57.15	53	−1.5557	52.05	45	−1.2888	69.45	113	141.5
140.5	−1.8628	28.35	20	−1.9574	24.00	23	−1.6216	40.80	50	140.5
139.5	−2.2453	12.15	15		12.30 ⎱	21 ⎰{16	−1.9544	21.30	11	139.5
138.5	Below −2.6278	6.45 ⎱	5 ⎰{4		⎱	{4	−2.2872	10.05	3	138.5
137.5		⎰	{1	Below −2.3591	⎰	{1	Below −2.6200	6.60	1	137.5
Totals		1492.75	1500		1498.50	1500		1500.00	1500	

curve of the normal distribution. When a variate is continuous, the choice of a class interval is arbitrary, and the number of classes can be increased by decreasing the class interval. The number of classes must, however, be kept within limits so that the class frequencies are large enough for any kind of test to be possible, and this depends on the number of values of a variate that are available. The class interval should not be greater than about half of the standard deviation, and preferably smaller. The number of available values of a variate should, therefore, be large enough to make the fulfillment of this requirement possible.

The normal distribution is the most important distribution in statistical practice, first, because continuous variates, whose distributions

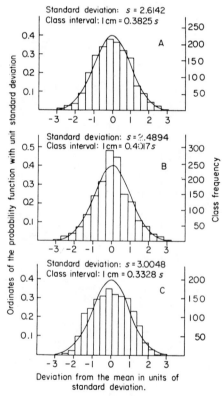

FIG. 2. Comparisons of three histograms with the curve of the normal distribution: A, the distribution pattern follows the course of the curve reasonably closely; B, the distribution pattern is too slim and too high; C, the distribution pattern is too broad and too low.

are approximately normal, are common, and, second, because means of large numbers of values of almost any kind of variate are distributed normally; indeed, distributions of means of only a few values, say about 10, may already resemble the normal distribution, whatever the distribution of the original variate. Even distributions of discontinuous variates, such as the binomial of the Poissonian distributions, which are strongly asymmetrical when the means are small, become symmetrical and resemble the normal distribution when the means are large. When the mean is about 12, the distributions already begin to resemble the normal.

The fact that the mean (or the sum) of many values of a variate is normally distributed, almost irrespective of the kind of distribution of the variate, is called the "central limit theorem," probably the most important theorem in the science of statistics. It can be proved rigorously, but the proof is beyond the scope of this chapter. Let us consider only a simple example: When the variate is the number of dots on a die, the six possible values of the variate are the integers from 1 to 6, and the probability of any one of them occurring is 1/6. The distribution of such a variate is called "rectangular," because the histogram of the distribution follows a horizontal line. However, the distribution of the sum (or the mean) of as few as four values of the variate already approximates the normal distribution fairly closely, and when the number of the values making up the sum (or the mean) is considerably increased, the distribution of the sum (or the mean) will become almost exactly normal.

It needs to be emphasized that although it is frequently stated that measurements of any kind of biological objects are distributed approximately normally, this is wrong. When, for example, weights of some individuals are roughly proportional to the cubes of their heights, the weights and the heights cannot both be normally distributed. If the heights are, the weights are not; the cube roots of the weights would then be normally distributed. Distributions of measurements of some materials, for example, lengths of particles of some viruses, may indeed be very far from normal, being strongly asymmetrical and even having several peaks.

E. BIVARIATE AND MULTIVARIATE DISTRIBUTIONS: REGRESSION AND CORRELATION

In considering the principle of contingency tables, we considered a distribution of objects according to two different kinds of features, namely, the distribution of a number of animals according to varieties and according to the way they reacted to exposure to infection. Both features were qualitative, and the purpose of the test was to see whether susceptibility to infection depends on the variety. However, objects or events may be distributed according to two or more quantitative features that may vary continuously or discontinuously, and so we may have to deal simultaneously with several different variates connected with one another in such a way that particular values of one correspond to particular values of the others, the correspondence being determined by some kind of coincidence. Each of the variates can, nevertheless, be distributed in its own way, and the distribution of all of them is called "multivariate." The problem of dependence of values of one variate on corresponding values of another is, obviously, of basic importance in all kinds of research work, and, consequently, it is an important subject in statistics. The two main methods of dealing with the subject are regression and correlation. It should be emphasized at the start that, if there is a causal relationship between corresponding values of two different variates, a correlation between them may be expected to exist, but the reverse is far from being true. For example, the number of a certain kind of crime committed per year may have increased during recent years, and the number of vacuum cleaners sold per year may also have increased. There may, therefore, be a statistically significant correlation between the two sets of numbers, although there is no causal relationship between them.

Obviously many different values of a variate can correspond to a particular value of another, even when there is a dependence between them. When, for example, one variate is the number of local lesions per leaf of a host plant inoculated with a virus preparation and the other variate is the age of the plant, not all plants of a given age will have exactly the same number of lesions. The numbers may, however, be scattered around a mean that does depend on the age of the plant, and so the mean number of lesions may be expressed as a function of the age of the plant. When the mean value of one variate is expressed as a function of another, the first variate will be called "dependent" and the other "independent." There may, of course, be many different kinds of functional relationships between the mean of one variate and the value of another, or of several other variates, and so the subject is obviously much too complicated to be dealt with here comprehensively. We shall consider briefly only linear bivariate regression and correlation. It should, perhaps, be pointed out that when a relationship between variates is not linear it may still be treated as if it were linear within a narrow range of values of the independent variate.

Let us assume that the relationship between two variates x and y is such that when the value of x is x_i, the expected value of y is

$$Y_i = \alpha + \beta(x_i - \mu) \tag{25}$$

where μ is the mean of all values of x, and α and β are constants called "regression coefficients," whose magnitude depends on the scale of measurements of x and y. Thus, x is an independent and y is a dependent variate, and Eq. (25) is the equation of regression of y on x. Obviously, α equals the mean of Y (and, therefore, the mean of all values of y) and β is the ratio of an increase of Y to an increase of x (which can be either positive or negative). Thus, if y_j and y_i are two values of y which correspond, respectively, to x_j and x_i, $y_j - y_i$ will, on average, equal $\beta(x_j - x_i)$, and so $y_i - \alpha$ (where α is the mean of all values of y) will, on average, equal $\beta(x_i - \mu)$. Consequently, the product $(y_i - \alpha)(x_i - \mu)$ will, on average, equal $\beta(x_i - \mu)^2$. Therefore, the sum of a large number N (assumed to tend to infinity) of the products is

$$\sum_{i=1}^{N} (y_i - \alpha)(x_i - \mu) = \beta \sum_{i=1}^{N} (x_i - \mu)^2$$

so that

$$\beta = \sum_{i=1}^{N} (y_i - \alpha)(x_i - \mu) / \sum_{i=1}^{N} (x_i - \mu)^2 \tag{26}$$

If y and x were independent of each other, any value of y would have an equal chance of being paired with any value of x, and so the average value of $y_j - y_i$, and of $y_i - \alpha$, would be zero, and so the value of β would be zero.

The constants α and β are, as usual, unknown parameters, the estimates of which obtained from a limited number of n pairs of corresponding values of y and x will be designated a and b, respectively. The equation of regression of y on x will then be written

$$Y_i = a + b(x_i - \bar{x}) \tag{27}$$

where $a = \bar{y}$, which is the mean of n values of y, $\bar{x}$ is the mean of n values of x, and b is obtained from the equation

$$b = \sum_{i=1}^{n} (x_i - \bar{x})(y_i - \bar{y}) / \sum_{i=1}^{n} (x_i - \bar{x})^2 \tag{28}$$

The value of the sum of products (of deviations of the corresponding values of y and x from their means) can be easily computed using the identity

$$\sum_{i=1}^{n} (x_i - \bar{x})(y_i - \bar{y}) = \sum_{i=1}^{n} (x_i y_i) - n\bar{x}\bar{y}$$

If a calculating machine is available, the sum of products of the corresponding values of y and x can be accumulated, and the value of $n\bar{x}\bar{y}$ is then deducted.

To take an example, let us consider an experiment shown in Table X, in which 30 plants were divided randomly into three groups of 10, and then all the plants were inoculated with a virus preparation, but one group was inoculated when the plants were at the age of 2 weeks, the other at the age of 3 weeks, and the third at the age of 4 weeks. The purpose of the experiment was to see how the numbers of local lesions per leaf, formed on different plants as a result of inoculation, depend on the age of the plant. A quick inspection of the numbers will show that the numbers tend to become fewer as the age of the plants increases from 2 to 4 weeks.

For reasons explained below, the numbers of lesions were transformed by adding 5 and taking logarithms of the resulting sums. The transformed values were used as the dependent variate y, and the age of plants (in weeks) as the independent variate x. The value of a of Eq. (27) is the mean of all the values of y, which is $\bar{y} = 1.697$. The value of b, computed according to Eq. (28), is $b = -1.6/20 = -0.08$. The mean value of the independent variate is $\bar{x} = 3$, so that the value of y that would be expected to be obtained on a plant of any age within the range 2–4 weeks would be

$$Y_i = 1.70 - 0.08(x_i - 3)$$

where x_i is the age of the plant in weeks. This is the equation of regression of the transformed numbers of lesions on the age of the plant.

In general, regression of y on x is not the same as regression of x on y, since the values of both regression coefficients will differ. For example, the values of a and b of the regression of the age of the plant on the transformed number of lesions are 3 and -2.16, respectively. Often only one of the regressions has any physical meaning. For example, the regression of the transformed number of lesions on the age of the plant shows how the number depends on the age of the plant. The regression of the age of the plant on the transformed number of lesions would show how the age of the plant depends on the number of lesions, which is obviously nonsense. The regression will then have only a conventional meaning of a mathematical definition. However, the regression of the amount of virus that can be isolated from an infected plant on the number of lesions per leaf of the plant,

TABLE X

EFFECT OF AGE OF A PLANT ON SUSCEPTIBILITY TO INFECTION WITH A VIRUS

Numbers of local lesions per leaf shown in parentheses.
Numbers without parentheses are transformed[a] numbers of lesions

Age of plants (weeks)										
2	(46) 1.71	(75) 1.90	(37) 1.62	(105) 2.04	(33) 1.58	(81) 1.93	(55) 1.78	(39) 1.64	(48) 1.72	(58) 1.80
3	(27) 1.51	(55) 1.78	(63) 1.83	(34) 1.59	(48) 1.72	(44) 1.69	(73) 1.89	(25) 1.48	(80) 1.93	(39) 1.64
4	(17) 1.34	(43) 1.68	(28) 1.52	(55) 1.78	(31) 1.56	(35) 1.60	(24) 1.46	(63) 1.83	(47) 1.72	(38) 1.63

a The transformations were made by adding 5 to the numbers of lesions and taking logarithms of the resulting sums.

and vice versa, would both have a physical meaning. In some circumstances, regressions of y on x and of x on y may even be identical.

Another measure of relationship between two variates is the "correlation coefficient." If b_1 and b_2 are the estimates of the coefficients of linear regression of y on x and of x on y, respectively, the geometric mean of the two estimates [i.e., $(b_1 b_2)^{1/2}$] is the correlation coefficient. Thus, the value of the correlation coefficient, r, is given by the formula

$$r = \sum_{i=1}^{n} (x_i - \overline{x})(y_i - \overline{y}) / \left[\sum_{i=1}^{n} (x_i - \overline{x})^2 \times \sum_{i=1}^{n} (y_i - \overline{y})^2 \right]^{1/2} \quad (29)$$

This is, of course, an estimate of the unknown parameter whose value can be designated by the symbol ρ. With regards to the correlation coefficient, the two variates are quite equivalent (i.e., the correlation coefficient between x and y and between y and x is the same). The correlation coefficient does not show how values on one variate depend on those of another, but it shows how closely the corresponding values of the two variates are associated. The value of the correlation coefficient can range between $+1$ and -1. When it is zero, there is no association between corresponding values of the variates at all (complete independence). When it is $+1$ or -1, the value of one variate is completely determined by the value of the other, so that we do not really have two variates but two different measures of the same variate. Applying Eq. (29) to the transformed numbers of lesions and ages of plants (shown in Table X), we get the correlation coefficient

$$r = -1.6/(20 \times 0.7407)^{1/2} = -0.416$$

The problem that may often arise when regression or correlation coefficients have been estimated is whether the estimated values differ significantly from zero or within what limits their "real" values may lie. This subject will be discussed in Section V,D,3. The tests of significance are based on the assumption of the normal distribution of the values of the dependent variable around their expected values. (The problem of distribution of values of the independent variate does not arise. These values may often be deliberately chosen by the experimenter.) To insure this, the values of the dependent variate may have to be transformed, as discussed in Section V,G. For this reason the numbers of local lesions have been transformed, as described above.

A relationship between two variates can also be shown graphically by means of a "dot diagram," which is obtained by plotting the values of one variate against the corresponding values of another.

The distribution of the dots will not only show at a glance whether the values of one variate depend on those of another but will also give an indication whether the dependence is linear or curvilinear and in what range of values of the independent variate the dependence can be assumed linear. The degree of scatter of the dots will give an indication of closeness of the association between corresponding values of two variates. If the dots fall exactly on a line, the value of the correlation coefficient is $+1$ or -1, and this, as explained above, means that we are really not dealing with two different variates.

V. Tests of Significance

The purpose of a test of significance is to find whether or not experimental results are compatible with a certain hypothesis, and/or to find limits within which the "real" value of an estimated quantity may be expected to be with some degree of confidence. If a hypothesis is exact in its prediction, a test of significance will be based on computing the probability of experimental data deviating simply by chance from the value, or the values, predicted by the hypothesis. If the probability is too small to be acceptable, we conclude that the hypothesis is wrong, or that a factor was involved that has not been taken into consideration. If the probability is large enough to be acceptable, we conclude that the data are compatible with the hypothesis, but nothing more. This does not necessarily mean that the hypothesis is right.

It should be pointed out immediately that when we say the probability of experimental data deviating by chance from the values predicted by a hypothesis we do not mean the probability of their deviating exactly as they do. Probability of this may be very small or infinitesimal, even when the deviation is small. We mean the probability of the data deviating as much as they do or more. Also, if a deviation can occur in two directions, we shall be usually concerned with the probability of the data deviating as much as they do or more in both directions.

How small the probability should be to justify the rejection of a hypothesis, or, in other words, what probability should be used for a test of significance, is a matter of individual judgment. It is usually taken as 0.05 (i.e., 5%), but the requirement can be made more rigorous by decreasing this value.

If a hypothsis is not exact in its prediction, the assumption that it is wrong may give an exact prediction. This assumption can then be considered as another hypothesis called the "null hypothesis," and this hypothesis can then be subjected to a test of significance. If we conclude that the data are incompatible with the null hypothesis, we can conclude that they support the original hypothesis.

The following examples may illustrate the principles of these procedures. Let a hypothesis be that the rate of inactivation of a virus by some agent follows a certain course, so that a plot of residual infectivity against the amount of treatment should give a certain line. This is an exact prediction. Results of estimations of infectivity do not, of course, fall exactly on the line, and so the problem may be whether or not the deviations from the line are too great for the hypothesis to be tenable. Thus, we compute the probability of the results deviating from the line as they do or more, only by chance. If the probability is large enough to be acceptable, we conclude that the results are compatible with the hypothesis. We may say that the deviations of estimated from predicted values are not significant. If the probability is too small, we conclude that the results deviate too much and are, therefore, not compatible with the hypothesis. We may then say that the deviations of estimated from predicted values are significant.

An example of a hypothesis that does not give an exact prediction is an assertion that a certain treatment alters infectivity of a virus preparation without specifying the magnitude of the alterations. As the hypothesis does not give an exact prediction, we shall test the null hypothesis, namely, that the treatment has no effect on infectivity, so that infectivity of the treated preparation equals that of an untreated control preparation. This is an exact prediction. Results of estimations of infectivities of the preparations will, however, usually differ, and we shall have to compute the probability of the difference arising simply by chance. If we find that the probability is too small to be acceptable, we conclude that we have "disproved" the null hypothesis. Then we shall say that the difference between the results of estimations of infectivities is significant, and, therefore, the results support the original hypothesis that the treatment affects infectivity.

To find the limits within which the "real" value of an estimated quantity may be, we find the limits for values that differ from the actually obtained estimate so that the probabilities of the differences occurring simply by chance are large enough to be acceptable. The limits are called the "fiducial limits."

A. A Test by Assumption of Random Selection

Some simple problems can be solved exactly in a simple way without any assumptions with regard to frequency distributions and without the use of any statistical tables. This can be done when a problem can be solved by computing the numbers of ways in which a number of objects can be randomly divided into groups. The principle can be best explained with an example.

Let us assume that a vaccine against a virus disease is tested on 20 volunteers when there is nothing to indicate that any of them may be more or less resistant to the disease than any other. We divide the volunteers randomly into two groups of 10, which we shall call groups A and B. Only the members of group A are vaccinated, and then both groups are exposed to infection. Let the numbers of volunteers in groups A and B, who did and did not succumb to the disease, be given in Table XI, which is a 2×2 contingency table. The table shows that all 20 volunteers can also be divided into two classes irrespective of

TABLE XI
THE RESULTS OF TESTING A VACCINE

Class	Result of test	Group A (vaccinated)	Group B (not vaccinated)	Totals
I	Succumbed to the disease	4	8	12
II	Did not succumb to the disease	6	2	8
Totals		10	10	20

whether they belong to group A or B (i.e., irrespective of whether they were vaccinated or not), class I containing 12 individuals who succumbed to the disease and class II containing 8 individuals who did not succumb to the disease.

Not all the individuals who were not vaccinated (group B) succumbed to the disease, and vaccination did not prevent the disease because some members of group A succumbed to it. However, as the proportion of individuals who succumbed to the disease was considerably greater in group B than in group A, we may think that there is a possibility that vaccination has increased resistance, and the problem is whether the results of the test shown in Table XI are sufficient to support this assumption.

The assumption does not give an exact prediction, and we shall, therefore, test the null hypothesis, namely, that vaccination had no effect, i.e., neither increased nor decreased resistance to the disease. According to this hypothesis the distribution of 12 members of class I and of 8 members of class II among groups A and B, as shown in Table XI, is simply a result of a random choice by chance. The problem now is to compute the probability of a random choice being such that at least 6 members of class II are included either in group A or in the group B, which means that 6, 7, or all 8 of the members of class II are included either in group A or in group B. (This will automatically include all the relevant considerations with regard to the members of class I.) If the probability is too small to be acceptable, we shall conclude that the null hypothesis is wrong, and, therefore, that vaccination has increased resistance to the disease.

To compute the probability, we have to compute the number of ways of choosing 10 out of 20 volunteers so that 6, 7, or all 8 of class II are included, and also the total number of all possible ways of choosing 10 out of 20.

TABLE XII

THE NUMBER OF WAYS OF SELECTING

Numbers from class		Numbers of ways of selecting from class		Numbers of ways of selecting from classes
I	II	I	II	I and II
2	8	66	1	66
3	7	220	8	1,760
4	6	495	28	13,860
			Total	15,686

Table XII shows the number of ways of selecting 10 individuals out of 20 so that the indicated numbers from classes I and II occur among the selected 10. In general, the number of ways n objects can be selected out of a total of m objects is $m!/(m-n)!n!$. When all 8 members of class II are to be taken, 2 members of class I must be selected and added to make the total number up to 10. The number of ways of selecting 2 out of 12 is $12 \times 11/2 = 66$. Thus there are 66 ways of selecting 10 out of 20 volunteers so that all 8 of class II are included. To have 7 members of class II included we must select 7 out of 8 members of class II, the number of ways of doing this being 8. To make the number up to 10 we must add 3 members of class I, the number of ways of selecting 3 out of 12 being $12 \times 11 \times 10/3! = 220$. Thus, the total number of ways of selecting 10 out of 20 volunteers so that 7 of class II are included is $8 \times 220 = 1760$. Finally, to have 6 members of class II included we must select 6 out of 8, the number of ways of doing this being $8 \times 7 \times 6 \times 5 \times 4 \times 3/6! = 28$, and we must add 4 members of class I, the number of ways of selecting 4 out of 12 being $12 \times 11 \times 10 \times 9/4! = 495$. Thus, the total number of ways of selecting 10 out of 20 volunteers so that 6 from class II are included is $28 \times 495 = 13{,}860$. Therefore, the total number of ways of selecting 10 out of 20 volunteers so that at least 6 from class II are included is $66 + 1760 + 13{,}860 = 15{,}686$.

This is the number of ways of selecting for group A only or for group B only. The number of ways of selecting 10 out of 20 volunteers so that at least 6 members of class II are included either in group A or in group B is twice that number, and, therefore, is $2 \times 15{,}686 = 31{,}372$. Now, the total number of all possible ways of dividing 20 volunteers into two groups of 10 (i.e., the number of ways of selecting 10 objects out of 20) is $20!/10!10! = 184{,}756$. Therefore, the probability that a random selection of 10 volunteers out of 20 will include at least 6 members of class II either in group A or in group B is $P = 31{,}372/184{,}756 = 0.1698$, which corresponds to an average of about once in six trials. The probability is large enough to be acceptable, and, therefore, the null hypothesis is acceptable. Thus we may come to the conclusion that although the experimental results may be indicative, they cannot be considered sufficient to support the assumption that vaccination has affected resistance to the disease in any way. More tests are needed for a decision to be made.

B. THE χ^2 TEST

The test of significance described above, based on the assumption of random selection, is quite exact and appears simple. However, as Table XI shows, there were only four cells into which all the objects could be divided according to their belonging to one of two groups and also to one of two classes, and the total number of objects was small. If the number of cells and the number of objects were considerably greater, a similar treatment would become prohibitively laborious. The test that can then be applied, and is easily done, is the χ^2 test, although the result is only approximate.

The χ^2 test is generally applicable for comparing numbers of objects actually observed to fall into any number of divisions with the numbers that are expected because of a hypothesis. The term "classes" will be used to mean any such divisions, even though the term "cells" may be for various reasons more appropriate, especially when dealing with contingency tables. Let us assume that M objects are distributed among r classes, so that the numbers of the objects in the classes are m_1, m_2, m_3, ..., m_r. Thus $\sum_{i=1}^{r} (m_i) = M$. Let the corresponding expected numbers be μ_1, μ_2, μ_3, ..., μ_r. This means that also $\sum_{i=1}^{r} (\mu_i) = M$. Let the differences between the corresponding observed and expected numbers be $x_1 = m_1 - \mu_1$, $x_2 = m_2 - \mu_2$, $x_3 = m_3 - \mu_3$, ..., $x_r = m_r - \mu_r$. The value of χ^2 is defined as

$$\chi^2 = \sum_{i=1}^{r} (x_i^2/\mu_i) = x_1^2/\mu_1 + x_2^2/\mu_2 + x_3^2/\mu_3 + \cdots x_r^2/\mu_r \qquad (30)$$

The value of χ^2 obviously increases as deviations of actual from expected numbers increase. The value of χ^2 also depends on the number of classes, for each class contributes a component (x_i^2/μ_i) to the total value of χ^2. The frequency distribution of values of χ^2 depends, therefore, on the number of classes, or, more exactly, on the number of degrees of freedom (see Section I). The problem of computing frequency distribution of the values of χ^2 for different numbers of degrees of freedom is algebraically difficult and complicated and cannot be dealt with here. However, the results of such computations have been tabulated, and so we can easily make use of frequency distributions of values of χ^2 by using one such table.

The principle of the use of frequency distribution of values of χ^2 is as follows. The hypothesis that predicts the expected class frequencies is tested by assuming that the differences between observed and expected class frequencies arise simply by chance. The table of the distribution of the values of χ^2 will then show the probabilities of the value of χ^2 being as great or greater, or as small or smaller, than the value that we have actually obtained. (If the former is P, obviously the latter is $Q = 1 - P$.) If both probabilities are large enough to be acceptable, we conclude that the hypothesis that postulates the expected class frequencies is compatible with the observed data. The hypothesis is suspect when either of the two probabilities is too small to be acceptable. This means that the hypothesis becomes suspect not only when the value of χ^2 is too large, i.e., when observed numbers differ too much from expected numbers, but also when the value of χ^2 is too small, i.e., when the observed numbers are too close to the expected numbers.

A table of distribution of values of χ^2 is used by entering it under the number of degrees of freedom corresponding to our particular problem. It is important, therefore, that the number of degrees of freedom be correctly obtained.

The number of degrees of freedom can here be considered as the number of observed class frequencies that can differ from expected class frequencies independently of other frequencies. If the expected class frequencies were known a priori, all the deviations of the observed from the expected frequencies would be independent of each other (i.e., all could be given arbitrary values without affecting all the other deviations). The number of degrees of freedom would then equal the number of classes. However, expected class frequencies are usually determined by the values of observed frequencies, and this introduces some "constraints," each of which decreases the number of independent deviations by one, and so causes a loss of a degree of freedom. Thus, any s out of a total number r of observed class frequencies may be given arbitrary values, and these may "force" the remaining $r - s$ frequencies to take some values that are functions of the arbitrarily chosen values. Therefore, the value of χ^2, although computed from r deviations of observed from expected class frequencies, is in fact a function of only s independent deviations. Consequently, the number of degrees of freedom (s) is smaller than the number of classes (r). The number of constraints is, therefore, $r - s$. It equals the number of quantities that must be estimated independently of each other from the values of observed frequencies to be used for computation of values of expected frequencies. There is, therefore, a loss of a degree of freedom for estimation of each such quantity. This will be illustrated on examples.

The conditions of applicability of the χ^2 test are that any constraints should be linear and that the expected number in any class should not be smaller than about 5. The linearity of constraints means that "forced" class frequencies should be functions of independent frequencies in the first degree (i.e., in the first power), for otherwise the value of χ^2 may not be convertible into a quadratic function of independent class frequencies, which it must be. The reason for the condition that the smallest expected number in any class should not be less than about 5 is that the theoretical distribution of the values of χ^2 will not be closely realized for very small classes.

1. *Contingency Tables*

Let us take the example of an $m \times n$ contingency table (m columns and n rows) (see Tables VI and VIa). The expected class frequencies (or cell frequencies) are computed from the values of the marginal totals of observed frequencies. Let us alter arbitrarily the values of the deviations of the observed from the expected frequencies. If any of these alterations resulted in an alteration in any of the marginal totals, the values of all the expected class frequencies would be altered, so that the values of all the deviations of observed from expected frequencies would also be altered and so cease to have the assigned arbitrary values (i.e., would cease to be independent). Therefore, only $m - 1$ deviations in any row can be taken arbitrarily, and they will then determine the value the mth deviation must take so that the value of the corresponding right-hand side marginal total remains unaltered. Similarly, only $n - 1$ deviations in any column can be taken arbitrarily, and they will then determine the value the nth deviation must take so that the value of the corresponding bottom marginal total remains unaltered. There are, therefore, $(m - 1)(n - 1)$ degrees of freedom, whereas the number of classes (or cells) is mn.

Another way of reasoning to obtain the number of degrees of freedom is the following. The expected class frequencies are computed from the marginal totals, and the number of the totals estimated independently of each other from the observed frequencies is $m + n - 1$. This is so because if m totals for the columns are first estimates, each estimation is independent of the others, but then only $n - 1$ totals for the rows are estimated independently, the value of the last being determined by the fact that the sum of the totals of the columns must equal the sum of the totals of the rows. The number of independently estimated quantities from which the expected class frequencies are computed, therefore, is $m + n - 1$, and so this is the number of lost degrees of freedom. As the total number of classes is mn, the number of degrees of freedom is $mn - m - n + 1 = (m - 1)(n - 1)$.

Table VI is a 3×4 contingency table, so that the number of degrees of freedom is $2 \times 3 = 6$. The value of χ^2 is 15.3. A table of distribution of values of χ^2 will show that with 6 degrees of freedom the probability of this value of χ^2 being exceeded by chance is only about 0.02 (i.e., 1 in about 50 trials). We can conclude, therefore, that the observed class frequencies deviate from those expected more than could be expected to occur by chance.

Table VIa is a 2×4 contingency table, so that the number of degrees of freedom is $1 \times 3 = 3$. The value of χ^2 is 4.8. A table of distribution of values of χ^2 will show that with 3 degrees of freedom the probability of this value of χ^2 being exceeded by chance is about 0.2 (i.e., 1 in about 5 trials). We can conclude, therefore, that the deviations of the observed from the expected frequencies could have occurred by chance.

2. Binomial and Poissonian Distributions

Let us now consider the χ^2 test for conformity of experimental data with binomial or Poissonian distribution (see Tables VII and VIII). A number of units are distributed among several classes according to the numbers of some "events" that have occurred within the units. (In Table VII, the units are sets of five plants and the event is a plant becoming infected. In Table VIII, the units are plates and the events are plaques formed by phage particles.) Two quantities independently estimated from observed class frequencies are used for computing expected class frequencies: (1) the total number of units in all classes and (2) the mean number of events per unit. There are, therefore, two constraints leading to a loss of 2 degrees of freedom. Thus, when there are r classes, the number of degrees of freedom is $r - 2$.

Table VII compares observed class frequencies with those that would be expected if the distribution were binomial. There are six classes, but the expected frequency of the class of sets of plants, all five of which are infected, is much too small for the χ^2 test to be applicable. We combine, therefore, the classes of sets with four and five plants infected, thus obtaining a new class with expected frequency of 10.3 and with observed frequency of 9. The other classes remain unaltered, so that the number of classes is now 5. There is a loss of 2 degrees of freedom because of the two constraints, so that the number of degrees of freedom is 3. The value of χ^2 is 2.6. A table of distribution of values of χ^2 will show that with 3 degrees of freedom the probability that this value of χ^2 will be exceeded by chance is about 0.45. We conclude, therefore, that the assumption of the binomial distribution is perfectly compatible with the experimental data.

Table VIII compares observed class frequencies with those expected on the assumption of the Poisson distribution. The expected class frequencies of plates with five and of those with more than five plaques are too small for the χ^2 test to be applicable. We combine, therefore, all the classes with five and more plaques per plate, thus obtaining a new class with the expected frequency of 4.8 and the observed frequency of 6. All the other classes remain unaltered, so that now we have six classes. There is a loss of 2 degrees of freedom because of the two constraints, so that the number of degrees of freedom is 4. The value of χ^2 is 1.67. A table of distribution of values of χ^2 will show that with 4 degrees of freedom the probability that this value of χ^2 will be exceeded by chance is about 0.8. This also means that the probability of a value of χ^2 being by chance as small or smaller than that actually obtained is about 0.2. We conclude, therefore, that the assumption of the Poissonian distribution is compatible with the experimental data.

The above method of computing the value of χ^2 to test for conformity with binomial or Poisson distribution requires large numbers of units, so that when these are distributed among several classes, the numbers in the classes are large enough for the χ^2 test to be applicable. The numbers of events within the units, according to which the units are classified, should be rather small, so that the number of classes can be reasonably small. When, however, the units are few, and the events within the units are many, the procedure based on a modified form of χ^2, which is called the "index of dispersion," may be applicable. It is based on numbers of events in different units and not on numbers of units in different classes.

When the distribution is expected to be binomial, the index of dispersion is

$$\chi^2 = \frac{1}{\bar{x}q} \sum_{i=1}^{N} (x_i - \bar{x})^2 \tag{31}$$

where $\bar{x}$ is the mean number of events per unit, x_i is the number of events within a unit, N is the number of units, and $N - 1$ is the number of degrees of freedom. When the distribution is expected to be Poissonian, the index of dispersion is

$$\chi^2 = \frac{1}{\bar{x}} \sum_{i=1}^{N} (x_i - \bar{x})^2 \tag{32}$$

which is really the same as Eq. (31), the apparent difference arising from the fact that in the Poissonian distribution q can be substituted by unity. Both equations can be easily obtained by modifying Eq. (30) to suit particular circumstances.

As an example of the use of the index of dispersion to test for compatibility with the binomial distribution, let us consider the experiment shown in Table VII, modified in such a way that instead of dividing 500 test plants into 100 sets of five, we have divided them into five sets of 100. Let the numbers of infected plants in the five sets be 42, 46, 37, 49, and 36. The total number of infected plants is 210, so that $p = 210/500 = 0.42$ and $q = 0.58$. The mean number of infected plants per set is $\bar{x} = 210/5 = 42$. The value of χ^2, computed according to Eq. (31), is $\chi^2 = 5.17$, the number of degrees of freedom being 4. A table of distribution of values of χ^2 will show that with this number of degrees of freedom the probability of the value of χ^2 being by chance as great or greater than the above value is about 0.27, so that the probability of its being as small or smaller is about 0.73. The experimental results are, therefore, compatible with the assumption of the binomial distribution.

As an example of the use of the index of dispersion to test for compatibility with Poisson distribution, let us consider an experiment of the same type as that described in Table VIII. However, let us assume that only 10 plates were used and that the numbers of plaques in the plates were 21, 18, 23, 19, 24, 21, 14, 27, 17, and 25. Thus the mean number of plaques per plate is $x = 20.9$. The value of χ^2 computed according to Eq. (32) is 6.84, the number of degrees of freedom being 9. A table of distribution of values of χ^2 will show that with this number of degrees of freedom the probability of χ^2 being by chance as great or greater than the above value is about 0.65, so that the probability of

χ^2 being as small or smaller is about 0.35. The experimental results are, therefore, compatible with the assumption of a Poisson distribution.

3. The Normal Distribution

Finally, let us consider application of the χ^2 test for conformity of experimental results with the assumption of the normal distribution. Table IX shows class frequencies that are assumed to have been observed in three different samples and also class frequencies that would be expected on the assumption of the normal distribution.

With the normal distribution there are three constraints that result in a loss of 3 degrees of freedom, because there are three quantities from which the expected class frequencies are computed and which are estimated independently from observed class frequencies: (1) the total number of values of the variate, (2) its mean, and (3) its standard deviation.

A few classes of samples A and B, shown in Table IX, must be pooled to fulfill the condition that expected class frequency of any class should not be smaller than about 5. This decreases the number of classes of sample A from 18 to 16, so that the number of degrees of freedom is 13, and the value of χ^2, computed according to Eq. (30), is 20.897. A table of distribution of values of χ^2 will show that, with 13 degrees of freedom, the probability of the values of χ^2 being as great or greater than the above value is 0.07, which is just acceptable, and so we conclude that the observed class frequencies of sample A are compatible with the assumption of the normal distribution.

The values of χ^2 for samples B and C are 46.62 and 92.93, with 11 and 15 degrees of freedom, respectively. Both values of χ^2 are so large that they are beyond the range usually shown in tables of distribution of χ^2. We conclude, therefore, that the deviations of the observed from the expected class frequencies are much too great for the assumption of the normal distribution of values of samples B and C to be tenable.

C. Tests of Significance of Means and Differences of Means of Large Samples

We shall make use of three facts: (1) that when a sample of values of a variate is large (say about 100 values or so), the estimate of variance can be assumed not to differ appreciably from the "real" variance of the population, (2) that the means of large samples are normally distributed around the mean of the population irrespective of the kind of distribution of the variate (the "central limit theorem," see Section IV,D), and (3) that if the variance of the variate is σ^2, the variance of the mean of a random sample of n values of the variate is σ^2/n, so that the standard error of the mean is $\sigma/(n)^{1/2}$ (see Section I).

Let us take the probability of 0.05 as the level of significance. A table of the normal distribution will show that the probability of a quantity deviating from the mean of its population by at least twice its standard error is about 0.05. Therefore, if the sample mean m differs from any fixed value by at least twice its standard error [i.e., by at least $2\sigma/(n)^{1/2}$], we shall conclude that the difference is significant, which would mean that the fixed value differs from the mean of the population. Consequently, any fixed value differing from the sample mean by less than twice the standard error could be accepted as a possible value of the mean of the population. Thus, the values $m - 2\sigma/n^{1/2}$ and $m + 2\sigma/n^{1/2}$ are the fiducial limits between which the value of the mean of the population probably lies. If the probability of 0.01 is taken as our level of significance, the fiducial limits will be $m - 2.6\sigma/n^{1/2}$ and $m + 2.6\sigma/n^{1/2}$.

Now, let us assume that we have two large samples of n_1 and n_2 values, the sample means being m_1 and m_2, and variances $\sigma_1{}^2$ and $\sigma_2{}^2$, which may or may not be equal. Since means of large samples are normally distributed, differences between their means are also normally distributed. As the variances of the means of the two samples are $\sigma_1{}^2/n_1$ and $\sigma_2{}^2/n_2$, the variance of the differences of the two means is $\sigma_1{}^2/n_1 + \sigma_2{}^2/n_2$, so that the standard error is $(\sigma_1{}^2/n_1 + \sigma_2{}^2/n_2)^{1/2}$. Reasoning as above, and taking the probability of 0.05 as the level of significance, we conclude that the fiducial limits for the difference of the means of the two populations are $m_1 - m_2 - 2(\sigma_1{}^2/n_1 + \sigma_2{}^2/n_2)^{1/2}$ and $m_1 - m_2 + 2(\sigma_1{}^2/n_1 + \sigma_2{}^2/n_2)^{1/2}$. If one of these values is positive and the other negative, the value of zero is included among possible differences between the means of the two populations. In other words, if the absolute value of $m_1 - m_2$ does not exceed $2(\sigma_1{}^2/n_1 + \sigma_2{}^2/n_2)^{1/2}$, the value of $m_1 - m_2$ does not differ significantly from zero.

Let us take the example of the distribution of numbers of plants infected with a virus by an insect in sets of five plants, as shown in Table VII. The variate x is the number of infected plants in a set of five, and we have 100 values of the variate, the mean being $m = 2.10$. As the distribution is binomial, the variance is $p \times q \times n = 0.42 \times 0.58 \times 5 = 1.218$ [see Eq. (16), Section IV,B]. However, we may not know that the distribution is binomial, or we may doubt whether it is exactly binomial, and we can obtain an estimate of the variance using the generally applicable Eq. (4) of Section I:

$$s^2 = \frac{1}{N-1}\sum_{i=1}^{N}(x_i - m)^2 = \frac{1}{N-1}\left[\sum_{i=1}^{N}(x_i^2) - Nm^2\right]$$

$$= \frac{1}{99}(562 - 100 \times 4.41) = 1.22$$

The variance of the mean of 100 values of the variate, therefore, is 0.0122 (see Section I), so that the standard error is 0.11. A conventional way of recording this is by writing the value of the mean as $m = 2.10 \pm 0.11$.

If our level of significance corresponds to the probability of 0.05, the fiducial limits for the mean are $2.10 - 0.22 = 1.88$ and $2.10 + 0.22 = 2.32$. This would mean that the "true" value of the probability that a randomly chosen insect will transmit the virus disease to a plant lies within the limits of 0.38 and 0.46.

Let us assume that another similar experiment was done under the same conditions with another species of insect, the test plants being assigned at random to the two experiments. Let the mean number of infected plants in a set of five plants be 2.60 and the variance 1.25, so that the variance of the mean is 0.0125. The difference between the means of the two experiments is $2.60 - 2.10 = 0.5$, and the variance of the difference is $0.0122 + 0.0125 = 0.0247$, so that the standard error is 0.157. The difference between the two means exceeds its standard error more than 3 times, which is highly significant (corresponding to the probability of less than 0.01; see a table of the normal distribution). We can conclude, therefore, that the two species of insect differ in their ability to transmit the virus disease.

D. The t Test

When samples are small the problem that complicates any test of significance is that an estimate of variance may differ from the "true" variance of the population quite appreciably, the standard error of the variance increasing as the size of the sample decreases. As we do not know the "true" variance and have to use its estimate, we have to make a proper allowance for the variability of the estimate. Thus, if for a given level of significance a variable quantity must exceed its standard error a times to be significant (i.e., to differ significantly from zero), the value of a will increase as the size of the sample decreases. The value of a will, therefore, be expected to be a function of the size of the sample. Actually, it is a function of degrees of freedom.

The main difference between tests of significance with large and

small samples is that whereas with large samples the type of frequency
distribution of the population does not matter much, it is important
with small samples. This is so because, although the distribution of
the means even of small samples may be approximately normal irrespective of the type of distribution of the population, the distribution
of the estimates of the variance, on which tests of significance are
based, depends not only on the number of degrees of freedom but also
on the type of distribution of the population. With large samples the
estimate of variance does not differ appreciably from the "real" variance of the population, and so the problem of distribution of the estimate does not arise. We shall now consider tests of significance with
small samples from normally distributed populations. Algebraic derivations of relevant probability functions and computations of probabilities are far beyond the scope of this chapter. However, results of
the computations are tabulated, and all we need consider is how to use
the tables. The tables with which we are going to deal are those of the
distribution of "Student's ratio" (distribution of t) and of "variance
ratio." The results of tests of significance obtained by the use of these
tables are quite exact when populations are exactly normally distributed. If the distributions are only approximately normal (as they
often are in practice), the results are only approximate. If the distribution of a population definitely deviates from the normal, the tables
can be used legitimately only if the variate can be transformed so that
the distribution of the transformed values is at least approximately
normal.

We shall first consider a few out of many different kinds of problems
that can be solved by application of the distribution of Student's ratio,
i.e., by the so-called t test.

The value of t can be generally defined as the ratio of a variable
quantity, whose mean value is assumed to be zero, to its standard error.
The table of distribution of t shows, for different numbers of degrees
of freedom, the probabilities of t exceeding different values, both positive and negative. (If we are interested only in positive or only in
negative values, the probability must be halved.) The number of degrees of freedom (usually shown in tables under the symbol n, which
should not be confused with the symbol n often used in this article to
designate the number of values of a variate) is that on which the estimate of variance of single values of the variate is based.

1. Significance of the Mean of a Small Sample

Let us assume that the following are the weights (in arbitrary units)
of 10 individuals of a species, randomly taken from a large population:

9.9,   13.4,   11.9,   10.8,   11.1,   10.1,

14.4,   15.5,   11.6,   14.6

The mean value of the sample is, therefore, 12.33, and the number of degrees of freedom for estimation of the variance of the population is 9.

We are interested in finding the fiducial limits for the mean of the population. Let our variable quantity be $m - \mu$, where m is the mean of a sample of 10 values and μ is the mean of the population. The values $m - \mu$ will be assumed to be normally distributed with the mean equal to zero. Now, the estimate of the variance of the population is

$$s^2 = \frac{1}{n-1} \sum_{i=1}^{n} (x_i - m)^2 = \frac{1}{n-1} \left[\sum_{i=1}^{n} (x_i^2) - nm^2 \right]$$

$$= \frac{1}{9} (1556.37 - 10 \times 152.029) = 4.009$$

Thus the variance of the mean, and therefore also of the quantity $m - \mu$ (μ being a fixed value), is 0.4009, so that the standard error is 0.6332. Thus $t = (m - \mu)/0.6332 = (12.33 - \mu)/0.6332$. If we take the probability of 0.05 as our level of significance, we shall find from a table of distribution of t that, when the number of degrees of freedom is 9, t must exceed 2.262 to differ significantly from zero. Therefore, the value of $12.33 - \mu$ must not be greater than $0.6332 \times 2.262 = 1.43$, or smaller than -1.43, to be acceptable. Thus, the fiducial limits for μ are 10.90 and 13.76.

2. Comparison of the Means of Two Small Samples

The problem of whether or not the means of two small samples differ significantly is the commonest problem in most kinds of research work. One sample of values may, for example, be obtained by exposure of some experimental units to a treatment and another by using some other experimental units as controls. The decision whether the treatment had an effect may then depend on finding whether the means of the two samples differ significantly. We shall now approach this problem by a method based on investigating the possibility that the treatment had no effect, so that the two samples are taken at random from the same population and differ only by chance. This will be our null hypothesis. We shall then find the probability of the samples differing as they do or more if the null hypothesis is correct. If the probability appears large enough to be acceptable, we shall conclude that the results of the experiment failed to show that the treatment had an effect.

Let us have two samples of n_1 and n_2 values with the means m_1 and m_2 and the estimates of variance s_1^2 and s_2^2 based on $n_1 - 1$ and $n_2 - 1$

degrees of freedom, respectively. If the samples are taken from the same population, the difference between the means $(m_1 - m_2)$ is a normally distributed quantity with the mean equal to zero, and s_1^2 and s_2^2 are two different estimates of the same variance, so that we can "pool" them to obtain the following estimate of the variance based on $n_1 + n_2 - 2$ degrees of freedom:

$$s^2 = [(n_1 - 1)s_1^2 + (n_2 - 1)s_2^2]/(n_1 + n_2 - 2)$$
$$= \left[\sum_{i=1}^{n_1} (x_i - m_1)^2 + \sum_{i=1}^{n_2} (x_i' - m_2)^2 \right]/(n_1 + n_2 - 2)$$

where x_i is the ith value of the first sample and x_i' is that of the other. Thus, the pooled estimate of the variance of the population (s^2) is obtained by summing the squares of deviations of the sample values from their means and dividing the sum by the total number of degrees of freedom $n_1 + n_2 - 2$.

The pooled estimate of variance s^2 will now be used to obtain the value of t. The estimate of the variance of m_1 is s^2/n_1, that of m_2 is s^2/n_2, and that of $m_1 - m_2$ is, therefore,

$$s^2/n_1 + s^2/n_2 = s^2 \left(\frac{n_1 + n_2}{n_1 n_2} \right)$$

so that the standard error of $m_1 - m_2$ is

$$s \sqrt{\frac{n_1 + n_2}{n_1 n_2}}$$

Thus,

$$t = \frac{m_1 - m_2}{s} \sqrt{\frac{n_1 n_2}{n_1 + n_2}} \qquad (33)$$

The probability of t exceeding various values when the number of degrees of freedom is $n_1 + n_2 - 2$ is found in tables of distribution of t.

The way the pooled estimate of variance is obtained is of basic importance here. It must be obtained as shown above. If it were obtained by summing the squares of the deviations of all $n_1 + n_2$ values of the two samples from their common mean $(n_1 m_1 + n_2 m_2)/(n_1 + n_2)$ and dividing the sum by $n_1 + n_2 - 1$, a more accurate estimate of the variance would be obtained, but it would not be independent of $m_1 - m_2$, whereas the distribution of t is derived on the assumption that the variable quantity, such as $m_1 - m_2$, and the estimate of its variance are independent of each other.

To take an example, let us assume that we have a sample of 10 healthy individuals of a species and another sample of 9 individuals that have been infected with a mild virus disease, but otherwise treated similarly. Both samples were taken at random from a large population. We are interested in whether or not the disease has affected the weight of the individuals. Let the weights (in arbitrary units) be: Healthy: 9.9, 13.4, 11.9, 10.8, 11.1, 10.1, 14.4, 15.5, 11.6, 14.6. The mean: $m_1 = 12.33$. The variance: $s_1^2 = 4.009$. Infected: 10.4, 8.1, 9.5, 8.5, 9.6, 13.1, 13.4, 10.5, 9.7. The mean: $m_2 = 10.31$. The variance: $s_2^2 = 3.410$. The pooled estimate of the variance is

$$s^2 = \frac{1}{n_1 + n_2 - 2} \left[\sum_{i=1}^{n_1} (x_i - m_1)^2 + \sum_{i=1}^{n_2} (x_i' - m_2)^2 \right]$$

$$= \frac{1}{n_1 + n_2 - 2} \left[\sum_{i=1}^{n_1} (x_i^2) - n_1 m_1^2 + \sum_{i=1}^{n_2} (x_i'^2) - n_2 m_2^2 \right]$$

$$= \frac{1}{17} (1556.37 - 10 \times 152.029 + 983.94 - 9 \times 106.296) = 3.727$$

The standard deviation, therefore, is $(3.727)^{1/2} = 1.931$. Thus, substituting in Eq. (33), we have

$$t = \frac{2.02}{1.931} \left(\frac{10 \times 9}{10 + 9} \right)^{1/2} = \frac{2.02}{0.887} = 2.277$$

(The value of 0.887 is the standard error of the difference of the means.)

A table of distribution of t will show that when the number of degrees of freedom is 17, the probability of t taking a value exceeding 2.277 is smaller than 0.05 but greater than 0.02. If we take the probability of 0.05 as our level of significance, we shall conclude that the value of t differs from zero significantly, and so our null hypothesis is probably wrong. This would mean that the virus disease did decrease weight.

Having come to this conclusion, we may now be interested in the fiducial limits for the difference between mean weights of the healthy and diseased population. Let the difference be d, our estimate of which is $m_1 - m_2$. We shall, therefore, assume the quantity $m_1 - m_2 - d$ to be normally distributed, with the mean zero. The value of t is the ratio of $m_1 - m_2 - d$ to its standard error. Since d is a fixed value, the standard error of $m_1 - m_2 - d$ is the same as that of $m_1 - m_2$. We can, therefore, use the standard error found above for $m_1 - m_2$, provided that we can assume that the variance of the population is not affected by the disease, although the mean is. If it were affected, the pooled estimate of variance would have no meaning, and the t test would not be valid.

684 A. KLECZKOWSKI

Assuming that the variance was not affected, we have

$$t = \frac{m_1 - m_2 - d}{0.887} = \frac{2.02 - d}{0.887}$$

Now, taking again the probability of 0.05 as our level of significance, we find from the table that when the number of degrees of freedom is 17 the value of t greater than 2.11 or smaller than -2.11 occurs with the probability of 0.05. Therefore, any value of d will be acceptable that fulfills the following inequality

$$-2.11 < \frac{2.02 - d}{0.887} < 2.11$$

so that

$$0.15 < d < 3.89$$

When two small samples are from populations with different variances, so that the result of pooling the estimates of the variances would be meaningless, a test of significance of the difference between the means of the samples can be made, but the method of doing this is beyond the scope of this article. The variance ratio test (see below) can be used to find whether or not two sampling variances can be assumed to be estimates of the same variance.

3. *Significance of Coefficients of Linear Regression and Correlation*

Tests of significance of estimates of coefficients of linear regression, i.e., of the values a and b of Eq. (27), Section IV,E, will be considered as another example of the application of the t test. Whatever the values of the independent variate (x) are, and these can often be chosen at will, the values of the dependent variate (y) are scattered about their expected values, and we shall need the variance of y to evaluate the significance of our estimates of the regression coefficients. Let the expected value of y, which corresponds to the value of $x = x_i$, be Y_i [given by the regression Eq. (27) of Section IV,E], let the observed value of y be y_i, and let there be n pairs of corresponding values of x and y. The estimate of the variance of y is

$$s^2 = \frac{1}{n-2} \sum_{i=1}^{n} (y_i - Y_i)^2 \tag{34}$$

i.e., the sum of the squares of the deviations of the actual from the expected values of y divided by the number of degrees of freedom, which is $n - 2$ because there is a loss of 1 degree of freedom for estimation of the coefficient a and a loss of another degree of freedom for estimation of the coefficient b of the regression equation.

Let us take the example of the regression of transformed numbers of lesions y on the age at which the plant was inoculated x (see Section IV,E). The expected values of y for plants inoculated at the age of 2, 3, and 4 weeks are 1.78, 1.70, and 1.62, respectively. There were 10 plants inoculated at each of three ages, and so we have three sets of values of $y - Y$ obtained by subtracting actually obtained values of y from those expected. The total number of comparisons between actually obtained values with those expected is 30, and so the number of degrees of freedom is 28. Therefore, the estimate of the variance of y, obtained according to Eq. (34), is $s^2 = 0.6049/28 = 0.0216$, so that the standard deviation is $s = 0.147$.

It should be noted that the deviation of any value of y from the corresponding value of Y, which is the expected value of y for a given value of x, contributes to the estimate of the variance of y. It is assumed, therefore, that the variance of y is the same for all values of x.

The variance of a, which is the mean of all n values of y, is s^2/n, the value of s^2 being obtained from Eq. (34). The standard error of a is, therefore, $s/n^{1/2}$. To find the fiducial limits for α we proceed as described above when significance of the mean of a small sample was discussed. In the example of regression of transformed numbers of lesions on the age of the plant, the value of a is 1.70, and the variance of a is $0.0216/30 = 0.00072$ (based on 28 degrees of freedom), so that the standard error is 0.0268. Using a table of distribution of t, as described above, we find that at the probability level of 0.05 the fiducial limits for α are 1.64 and 1.76.

We shall now consider the test of significance of the value of b. Let us first consider the numerator of the expression that gives the value of b [Eq. (28) of Section IV,E], which is $\sum_{i=1}^{n} [(y_i - \bar{y})(x_i - \bar{x})]$. It can be written in the form $\sum_{i=1}^{n} [y_i(x_i - \bar{x})]$. If the variance of y is s^2, the variance of $y_i \cdot (x_i - \bar{x})$ is $s^2(x_i - \bar{x})^2$ (see Section I), so that the variance of $\sum_{i=1}^{n} [y_i(x_i - \bar{x})]$ is $s^2 \sum_{i=1}^{n} [(x_i - \bar{x})^2]$. To obtain b, we have to divide $\sum_{i=1}^{n} [y_i(x_i - \bar{x})]$ by $\sum_{i=1}^{n} (x_i - \bar{x})^2$. Therefore, to obtain the variance of b we have to divide the variance of $\sum_{i=1}^{n} [y_i(x_i - \bar{x})]$ by $[\sum_{i=1}^{n} (x_i - \bar{x})^2]^2$, thus obtaining

$$\mathrm{var}(b) = s^2 / \sum_{i=1}^{n} (x_i - \bar{x})^2$$

The standard error of b is, therefore, $s/[\sum_{i=1}^{n} (x_i - \bar{x})^2]^{1/2}$. If, by our null hypothesis the value of b is a normally distributed quantity with the mean equal to zero,

$$t = \frac{b}{s}\left[\sum_{i=1}^{n}(x_i - \bar{x})^2\right]^{1/2}$$

with the number of degrees of freedom equal to $n - 2$. If the table of distribution of t shows that for this number of degrees of freedom the probability of t exceeding by chance the value that is actually found is too small to be acceptable, we shall conclude that b differs from zero significantly (i.e., β is not zero). The fiducial limits within which the value of β may lie can be obtained in the usual way when

$$t = \frac{b - \beta}{s}\left[\sum_{i=1}^{n}(x_i - \bar{x})^2\right]^{1/2}$$

It should be noted that it was tacitly assumed that the values of y are distributed normally around their expected values. If this is not true and the distribution is only approximately normal, the results of the t tests are only approximately true.

In the example of regression of transformed numbers of lesions on the age of the plant, the value of b is -0.08, so that $t = -(0.08/0.147)$ $20^{1/2} = -2.43$, which, with 28 degrees of freedom, corresponds to the probability of about 0.02. We conclude, therefore, that b differs significantly from zero. To obtain the fiducial limits for β at the probability level of 0.05, the limits for the value of β must be computed, so that $t = [(-0.08 - \beta)/0.147]20^{1/2} = (-0.08 - \beta) \times 30.4$ is smaller than $+2.048$ and greater than -2.048 (see a table of distribution of t). Thus, the fiducial limits are -0.013 and -0.147.

The t test can also be used to assess the significance of an estimate of the correlation coefficient, the value of t being

$$t = \frac{r}{(1 - r^2)^{1/2}}(n - 2)^{1/2}$$

where r is the estimate of the correlation coefficient [obtained from Eq. (29) of Section IV,E], n is the number of pairs of corresponding values from which the value of r is computed, and $n - 2$ is the number of degrees of freedom. Derivation of the above equation is beyond the scope of this article. The reason for the transformation of r according to the equation is the extreme deviation of the distribution of r from the normal distribution, which makes a direct comparison of the value of r with its standard error a fallacious procedure.

We have obtained (Section IV,E) the value of -0.416 for the correlation coefficient between the transformed numbers of lesions and the age of the plant. The computation was based on 30 pairs of corresponding values of two variates, so the number of degrees of freedom is **28**. Substituting into the above equation, we get

$$t = -\frac{0.416}{(1 - 0.416^2)^{1/2}} 28^{1/2} = -2.42$$

A table of distribution of t will show that, with 28 degrees of freedom, this corresponds to the probability of about 0.02. We conclude, therefore, the value of t differs significantly from zero, and, therefore, the value of r differs significantly from zero. Consequently, there is a correlation between the numbers of lesions (or, more exactly, between the transformed numbers of lesions) and the age of the plant. The minus sign of the correlation coefficient means that as the age increases the numbers of lesions decreases.

An assessment of significance of an estimate of the correlation coefficient can be made even more quickly (without actually computing the value of t) by using a table of values of the correlation coefficient for different levels of significance. Such a table can be found in some textbooks on statistics, and also in Fisher and Yates's "Statistical Tables" and in Pearson and Hartley's "Biometrika Tables." The table must be entered under n, which is the number of degrees of freedom.

E. THE VARIANCE RATIO TEST (R TEST)

To consider the possibility of two small samples having been taken at random from the same population, the significance of the difference between their means was tested by the t test using Eq. (33). The sampling variances were assumed to be two different independent estimates of the same variance, and were pooled. We shall now consider a way of testing whether or not two sampling variances can indeed be two independent estimates of the same variance. This is done by the variance ratio test, which is also called the R test. By comparing the sampling variances, we have, therefore, another way of testing whether or not two samples are from the same normal population, even when the means of the samples may not differ significantly.

Tables of variance ratio show the probability distribution of the ratio of the larger to the smaller estimate of the same variance of a normally distributed population for different numbers of degrees of freedom on which the estimates are based. If the two estimates are s_1^2 and s_2^2, based, respectively, on n_1' and n_2' degrees of freedom, and if $s_1^2 > s_2^2$, then $R = s_1^2/s_2^2$. The value of R that is exceeded by chance with a given probability is shown on the intersection of the column for n_1' degrees of freedom and of the row for n_2' degrees of freedom. There are several tables for several different probabilities. If we find that the probability of R exceeding the value that is actually found is too small to be acceptable, we shall conclude that the two sampling variances are not estimates of the same variance.

In the example of application of the t test to the difference between the means of two small samples, the two sampling variances were 4.009 and 3.410, based on 9 and 8 degrees of freedom, respectively. Thus $R = 1.176$. The tables of variance ratio show that for 9 and 8 degrees of freedom, this corresponds to the probability greater than 0.2. We can conclude, therefore, that the two sampling variances can be estimates of the same variance.

The R test can be applied to many different types of problems, but we shall now consider only one that is analogous to the problem of the difference of the means of two samples, which we have considered above and solved by means of the t test. However, instead of only two samples, we shall now deal simultaneously with any number of samples resulting from subjecting several, say N, groups of experimental units to different treatments, the same number, say n, units being allocated at random to each group (unrestricted randomization, see Section II,A).

As in the problem with only two samples, our null hypothesis is that the treatments have no effect, and so all the samples have been taken at random from the same normal population. The means of the samples are, therefore, normally distributed around the general mean of the population with the variance σ^2/n, if σ^2 is the variance of the population. If m_1, m_2, m_3, . . . , m_N are the means of the N samples, the estimate of the variance of the mean (i.e., the estimate of σ^2/n) is

$$s_m{}^2 = \frac{1}{N-1} \sum_{i=1}^{N} (m_i - \overline{m})^2$$

where $\overline{m}$ is the general mean, so that the estimate of the variance of the population (i.e., the estimate of σ^2) is

$$S_p{}^2 = \frac{n}{N-1} \sum_{i=1}^{N} (m_i - \overline{m})^2 \tag{35}$$

which is based on $N-1$ degrees of freedom.

Another estimate of σ^2 is obtained by pooling the sampling variances obtained separately with each of N samples. Thus, if $s_1{}^2$, $s_2{}^2$, $s_3{}^2$, . . . , $s_N{}^2$ are the sampling variances, the pooled estimate of the variance of the population is

$$s^2 = \frac{1}{N} \sum_{j=1}^{N} (s_j{}^2) = \frac{1}{N(n-1)} \sum_{j=1}^{N} \left[\sum_{i=1}^{n} (x_{ij} - m_j)^2 \right] \tag{36}$$

where x_{ij} is the ith value of the jth sample and m_j is the mean of the jth sample. As each sampling variance is based on $n - 1$ degrees of freedom, the pooled estimate of variance s^2, given by Eq. (36), is based on $N(n - 1)$ degrees of freedom.

The two estimates of variance [$S_p{}^2$ of Eq. (35) and s^2 of Eq. (36)] are independent of each other, and so, if $S_p{}^2 > s^2$, the variance ratio is

$$R = S_p{}^2/s^2$$

the degrees of freedom being $N - 1$ and $N(n - 1)$. If with these degrees of freedom the probability of R exceeding the value that is actually obtained is too small to be acceptable, we shall conclude that our null hypothesis is not true, which would mean that not all the treatments had no effect, i.e., at least one treatment had an effect. We can then evaluate the significance of the difference between the means of any two samples by the t test. Our estimate of the variance of the mean is s^2/n, and, therefore, that of the difference of two means is $2s^2/n$, and so the standard error of the difference is $s(2/n)^{1/2}$. Thus, if m_a and m_b are the means of any two of the N samples,

$$t = \frac{m_a - m_b}{s} \left(\frac{n}{2}\right)^{1/2} \tag{37}$$

the number of degrees of freedom being $N(n - 1)$.

It should be obvious that we can use the R test instead of the t test. When the means of only two samples are compared, the value of $S_p{}^2$ becomes $n[(m_a - \overline{m}_{ab})^2 + (m_b - \overline{m}_{ab})^2]$, where $\overline{m}_{ab}$ is the mean of the two means [i.e., $\overline{m}_{ab} = \frac{1}{2}(m_a + m_b)$]. Thus

$$S_p{}^2 = n[(m_a - \overline{m}_{ab})^2 + (m_b - \overline{m}_{ab})^2] = (n/2)(m_a - m_b)^2$$

which is based on 1 degree of freedom. Therefore, if $S_p{}^2 > s^2$,

$$R = (n/2)[(m_a - m_b)^2/s^2]$$

with 1 and $N(n - 1)$ degrees of freedom. Comparing this with Eq. (37), we see that $R = t^2$. Indeed, a comparison of the tables of distributions of R and t will show that for any given probability the values of R for one and n' degrees of freedom are equal to the squares of the values of t for n' degrees of freedom.

There are also tables of distribution of z, which differ from the tables of distribution of R in that $z = \frac{1}{2}\ln R$.

Examples of application of the R test will be given below.

F. ANALYSIS OF VARIANCE

When an experimental design is such that one or more sources of variation (known or suspected) are eliminated from comparisons of means of several treatments (see Section II,B), a statistical examination of the results must be such that a proper allowance is made for the elimination of the sources of variation. With some experimental designs this can be done by the method called the "analysis of variance." The method is based on a division of the total sum of squares of deviations of all the values of a variate from their mean into several sums of squares that correspond to different sources of variation and a "residual" sum of squares that corresponds to the variation that has not been eliminated. The method can, therefore, be used for estimation of the experimental error. Also the total number of degrees of freedom for deviations of all the values of the variate from their mean is subdivided into several numbers of degrees of freedom corresponding to the different sums of squares. By dividing each sum of squares by the corresponding number of degrees of freedom, the variances are obtained that correspond to different sources of variation and the residual variance, which is our estimate of the experimental error. The residual variance is then used as a standard of comparison for assessing the significance of the other variances (which is done by the variance ratio test), or the significance of a difference between any two means, which can be done either by the variance ratio test or by the t test. The way the divisions of sums of squares and of degrees of freedom are made will be illustrated with examples of analyses of results of experiments designed by unrestricted randomization (see Section II,A), as randomized blocks and as Latin squares (see Section II,B).

The simplest example of analysis of variance is when the only source of variation that is to be eliminated from the estimation of experimental error are differences between results of treatments. This occurs when an experiment is designed by assigning at random n experimental units to each of N treatments (unrestricted randomization). Examination of results of such an experiment by the variance ratio test has already been described (Section V,E). The variance ratio, R, was obtained by dividing the variance $S_p{}^2$ given by Eq. (35) by the variance s^2 given by Eq. (36), the two variances resulting from variation between treatments and within treatments, respectively. The arithmetic work of computing N separate sums of squares to obtain the value of s^2, namely, $\sum_{j=1}^{N}\left[\sum_{i=1}^{n}(x_{ij}-m_j)^2\right]$, can be simplified by application of the principle of the analysis of variance, i.e., by making use of the fact that

$$\sum_{j=1}^{N} \left[\sum_{i=1}^{n} (x_{ij} - \overline{m})^2 \right] = \sum_{j=1}^{N} \left[\sum_{i=1}^{n} (x_{ij} - m_j)^2 \right] + n \sum_{j=1}^{N} (m_j - \overline{m})^2$$

where x_{ij} is the ith value obtained with the jth treatment, m_j is the mean for the jth treatment, and $\overline{m}$ is the mean of all the values of the variate. We usually arrange these sums of squares as shown in Table XIII.

Thus, the "total" sum of squares of deviations of all the values of the variate from their mean $\overline{m}$ is divided into two parts, one resulting from the variation between the treatments and the other (called "within treatments") from other sources of variation. We have, therefore, to compute only two separate sums of squares, namely, between treatments and the total, and then the sum of squares within treatments can be found by subtraction.

TABLE XIII

ANALYSIS OF VARIANCE WHEN AN EXPERIMENT WAS DESIGNED BY RANDOM ASSIGNMENT OF n UNITS TO EACH OF N TREATMENTS

Source of variation	DF	Sums of squares
Between treatments	$N - 1$	$n \sum_{j=1}^{N} (m_j - \overline{m})^2$
Within treatments (error)	$N(n - 1)$	$\sum_{j=1}^{N} \left[\sum_{i=1}^{n} (x_{ij} - m_j)^2 \right]$
Total	$Nn - 1$	$\sum_{j=1}^{N} \left[\sum_{i=1}^{n} (x_{ij} - \overline{m})^2 \right]$

The table also shows that the same principle applies to degrees of freedom (DF): the total number of degrees of freedom for comparisons between all the values of the variate, namely, $Nn - 1$, is divided into two parts: the number of degrees of freedom for comparisons between the treatments, namely, $N - 1$, and the number for comparisons within each of N treatments, namely, $N(n - 1)$, which can, therefore, be obtained from the others by subtraction. Thus, the sum of squares and the number of degrees of freedom within treatments correspond to the residual variation that remains after eliminating the variation between treatments from the total variation and, therefore, represent an estimate of the experimental error.

Dividing the sums of squares by their corresponding degrees of freedom, one obtains the variances that can be compared by the variance ratio test, as described above. It should be noticed that the variance within treatments is what was described above as the pooled estimate

692

A. KLECZKOWSKI

of the variance of the population. It is assumed, therefore, that the variance is not affected by the treatments.

When the experimental design is more complicated than that of unrestricted randomization, analysis of variance is also somewhat more complicated, but the basic principle remains the same. Let us consider results of an experiment designed as randomized blocks (see Section II,B,1). Let us assume that we want to compare infectivities of four differently treated preparations of a plant virus and that we inoculate the preparations, which will be referred to as "treatments," into half leaves of, say, 10 plants, each plant having two suitable leaves, so that there are four units per plant. Each treatment occurs once on each plant (a plant being a block) and half leaves within each plant are assigned to the different treatments at random. Thus a design of randomized blocks is obtained; six such blocks are shown in Table I.

Numbers of lesions formed on the inoculated leaves are a measure of infectivity of the virus preparations, so that our variate could be the number of lesions on each half leaf, but, for reasons that are discussed below, the variate should be a suitably transformed number of lesions (see Section V,G).

Before describing the method of obtaining the residual variance by the procedure of analysis of variance, let us first consider what the residual variance should be. If to compute the variance we took the sum of squares of deviations of all values of the variate from the general mean, all the variation between treatments and between blocks would be included in the estimate of the variance. To exclude these two sources of variation we must take the deviation of any value of the variate not from the general mean but from a value it is expected to have because it belongs to a particular treatment and to a particular block. The expected values are obtained on the assumption that the effects of treatments and of blocks are independent and additive.

Let x_{ij} be the value of the variate that corresponds to the ith treatment and to the jth block, m_{io} the mean of all values with the ith treatment, m_{oj} the mean of all values in the jth block, and $\overline{m}$ the mean of all the values of the variate. If the treatments had no effect, and if there were no variation between the blocks, the expected value for x_{ij} would be $\overline{m}$. However, this is not so, and therefore two adjustments must be made to $\overline{m}$: first by adding $m_{io} - \overline{m}$ to allow for the effect of the ith treatment, and second by adding $m_{oj} - \overline{m}$ to allow for the fact of belonging to the jth block. (Any of these quantities can be either positive or negative.) Thus the expected value is $\overline{m} + m_{io} - \overline{m} + m_{oj} - \overline{m} = m_{io} + m_{oj} - \overline{m}$, and so the deviation of x_{ij} from its expected value is $x_{ij} - m_{io} - m_{oj} + \overline{m}$. If in general, there are k treatments (four in our case) and n blocks (10 in our case), the sum of squares of deviations of all the values of the variate from their expected values is

$$\sum_{j=1}^{n} \left[\sum_{i=1}^{k} (x_{ij} - m_{io} - m_{oj} + \overline{m})^2 \right]$$

This must be divided by the number of degrees of freedom to obtain the estimate of the residual variance. The number of degrees of freedom is the number of independent comparisons between all the actual and expected values of the variate, which is kn, minus one for estimation of $\overline{m}$, minus $k - 1$ for estimation of $k - 1$ values of m_{io} (when $k - 1$ values have been estimated, the kth is obtained automatically because $\sum_{i=1}^{k} (m_{io}) = k\overline{m}$), and minus $n - 1$ for estimation of $n - 1$ values of m_{oj} (because, similarly, $\sum_{j=1}^{n} (m_{oj}) = n\overline{m}$). Thus, the number of degrees of freedom is $kn - 1 - (k - 1) - (n - 1) = kn - k - n + 1 = (k - 1)(n - 1)$.

A direct computation of the sum of squares of deviations of the actual from the expected values of the variate would obviously be rather cumbersome, because each deviation must be taken from a different expected value. The procedure of computing the sum of squares can, however, be greatly simplified by applying the principle of the analysis of variance, i.e., by making use of the fact that

$$\sum_{j=1}^{n} \left[\sum_{i=1}^{k} (x_{ij} - \overline{m})^2 \right] = \sum_{j=1}^{n} \left[\sum_{i=1}^{k} (x_{ij} - m_{io} - m_{oj} + \overline{m})^2 \right]$$
$$+ n \sum_{i=1}^{k} (m_{io} - \overline{m})^2 + k \sum_{j=1}^{n} (m_{oj} - \overline{m})^2$$

These sums of squares are usually arranged as shown in Table XIV.

TABLE XIV

ANALYSIS OF VARIANCE WHEN AN EXPERIMENT WAS DESIGNED AS RANDOMIZED BLOCKS (k TREATMENTS AND n BLOCKS)

Source of variation	DF	Sums of squares
Between treatments	$k - 1$	$n \sum_{i=1}^{k} (m_{io} - \overline{m})^2$
Between blocks	$n - 1$	$k \sum_{j=1}^{n} (m_{oj} - \overline{m})^2$
Residual (error)	$(k - 1)(n - 1)$	$\sum_{j=1}^{n} \left[\sum_{i=1}^{k} (x_{ij} - m_{io} - m_{oj} + \overline{m})^2 \right]$
Total	$kn - 1$	$\sum_{j=1}^{n} \left[\sum_{i=1}^{k} (x_{ij} - \overline{m})^2 \right]$

Thus, to obtain the residual sum of squares we have to compute (1) the total sum of squares of deviations of all the values of the variate from the general mean, (2) those between treatments, and (3) those between blocks (as shown in Table XIV) and subtract (2) and (3) from (1). The same applies to the numbers of degrees of freedom. The sums of squares are divided by the corresponding numbers of degrees of freedom to obtain estimates of variance. Further procedure is as described above. Significance of the variance between treatments or between blocks can be assessed by comparing them with the residual variance using the variance ratio test. Means of any two treatments can be compared also by using the variance ratio test or the t test, as will be explained below. An example of an experiment designed as randomized blocks is given in Section VI,C.

When an experiment is designed as a Latin square (see Section II,B,2), three sources of variation are eliminated from the estimate of the experimental error: variation from differences between (1) rows, (2) columns (whatever the two represent), and (3) treatments. Let us assume that we have an $n \times n$ Latin square, so that there are n rows, n columns, and n treatments. Let x_{ijk} be the value of the variate that corresponds to the ith row, the jth column, and the kth treatment, m_{ioo} the mean of the ith row, m_{ojo} the mean of the jth column, m_{ook} the mean of the kth treatment, and $\overline{m}$ the mean of all the values. Applying the same reasoning as above, and again assuming independence and additivity of effects, the expected value of x_{ijk} is obtained by adding to $\overline{m}$ the following quantities: $m_{ioo} - \overline{m}$, $m_{ojo} - \overline{m}$, and $m_{ook} - \overline{m}$ to allow for the effects of the ith row, the jth column, and the kth treatment, so that the expected value of x_{ijk} is $\overline{m} + m_{ioo} - \overline{m} + m_{ojo} - \overline{m} + m_{ook} - \overline{m} = m_{ioo} + m_{ojo} + m_{ook} - 2\overline{m}$. Thus the deviation of the actual from the expected value of x_{ijk} is $x_{ijk} - m_{ioo} - m_{ojo} - m_{ook} + 2\overline{m}$. Therefore, the residual sum of squares, i.e., the sum of squares of deviations of all actual from expected values, is

$$\sum_{j=1}^{n} \left[\sum_{i=1}^{n} (x_{ijk} - m_{ioo} - m_{ojo} - m_{ook} + 2\overline{m})^2 \right]$$

Note that although k does not occur in the summation symbols, nevertheless all n values of k occur in the sum of squares because combinations of values of i (rows) and j (columns) determine the values of k (treatments). (Table V shows that in any particular Latin square any particular treatment corresponds to intersections of some rows and some columns.)

The number of residual degrees of freedom is obtained in the same way as above, and equals n^2 (the total number of values of the variate), minus one for estimation of $\overline{m}$ and three times minus $n - 1$ for estimation of

$n - 1$ values of m_{ioo}, of m_{ojo}, and of m_{ook} (when $n - 1$ values of any one of them are estimated, the nth value is also estimated because the totals of n values equal $n\overline{m}$). Thus the number of degrees of freedom is $n^2 - 1 - 3(n - 1) = n^2 - 3n + 2 = (n - 1)(n - 2)$.

Again, as before, a direct computation of the residual sum of squares would be extremely cumbersome, and it is greatly simplified by applying the principle of analysis of variance, i.e., by making use of the fact that

$$\sum_{j=1}^{n}\left[\sum_{i=1}^{n}(x_{ijk} - \overline{m})^2\right] = \sum_{j=1}^{n}\left[\sum_{i=1}^{n}(x_{ijk} - m_{ioo} - m_{ojo} - m_{ook} + 2\overline{m})^2\right]$$
$$+ n\sum_{i=1}^{n}(m_{ioo} - \overline{m})^2 + n\sum_{j=1}^{n}(m_{ojo} - \overline{m})^2 + n\sum_{k=1}^{n}(m_{ook} - \overline{m})^2$$

Table XV shows the usual tabular arrangement. The total sum of squares and those between rows, columns, and treatments can be easily computed, and the residual can then be obtained by subtraction. The same applies to the degrees of freedom. Further procedure is the same as described above.

The significance of the difference between means of any two treatments in an experiment of any of the types considered above can be assessed by the t test. The sampling variance of any of the means is s^2/n, where s^2 is the residual variance based, say, on N degrees of freedom, and n is the number of replications of each treatment. Therefore,

TABLE XV

ANALYSIS OF VARIANCE WHEN AN EXPERIMENT WAS DESIGNED AS AN
$n \times n$ LATIN SQUARE

Source of variation	DF	Sums of squares
Between treatments	$n - 1$	$n\sum_{k=1}^{n}(m_{ook} - \overline{m})^2$
Between rows	$n - 1$	$n\sum_{i=1}^{n}(m_{ioo} - \overline{m})^2$
Between columns	$n - 1$	$n\sum_{j=1}^{n}(m_{ojo} - \overline{m})^2$
Residual (error)	$(n - 1)(n - 2)$	$\sum_{j=1}^{n}\left[\sum_{i=1}^{n}(x_{ijk} - m_{ioo} - m_{ojo} - m_{ook} + 2\overline{m})^2\right]$
Total	$n^2 - 1$	$\sum_{j=1}^{n}\left[\sum_{i=1}^{n}(x_{ijk} - \overline{m})^2\right]$

the variance of the difference of any two means, say $m_1 - m_2$, is $2s^2/n$, so that the standard error is $s(2/n)^{1/2}$. Therefore

$$t = \frac{m_1 - m_2}{s} \left(\frac{n}{2}\right)^{1/2}$$

with the number of degrees of freedom equal to N. It is obvious, therefore, that we have assumed that all the means have the same standard error, although some means may differ considerably from some others. Therefore, the variate must be such that the variance is independent of the mean. This is another condition of applicability of analysis of variance in addition to independence and additivity of effects of treatments and other sources of variation that have been eliminated by a particular experimental design.

When an experiment is factorial (see Section II,D), tests of significance of the results can be made by the same procedure. For example, a $2 \times 2 \times 2$ factorial experiment, which is the only kind of factorial experiment described in this chapter (Section II,D), has eight treatments. These can be arranged in any type of experimental design with, say, n replications of each treatment. Let us assume that some sources of variation have been eliminated as a result of an experimental design and that analysis of variance has been applied when the residual variance was found to be s^2, based on N degrees of freedom. If we want to assess the significance, for example, of a main effect or of a total interaction, each of which is given by the sum of the means of all eight treatments, four of which are taken with the positive sign and the other four with the negative sign, and the sum is divided by four, the estimated variance is $8s^2/4^2n = s^2/2n$, so that the standard error is $s/(2n)^{1/2}$. Thus, the significance of the main effect or of the interaction can be assessed by the t test, when t equals the value of the main effect or of the interaction divided by $s/(2n)^{1/2}$, the number of degrees of freedom being N.

G. Transformation of the Variate

The distributions of values of t and of the variance ratio have been derived on the assumption of the normal distribution of the variate; therefore, the t test or the variance ratio test give exact solutions of the problems of statistical significance only when the variate is normally distributed. However, variates that are exactly normally distributed are rare in nature, so that the tests can be expected to give solutions that are only approximately true. Obviously, when a distribution deviates widely from the normal, for example, when instead of following a curve similar to that shown in Fig. 1 it follows a curve that is

U-shaped or J-shaped, or is extremely skewed, or has several peaks, or when the distribution is rectangular, the t test or the R test would lead to false conclusions. Even when the distribution of a variate does not belong to any of such extreme examples of deviation from normality, it may still differ too much from the normal for these tests to give even approximately true solutions, but no generally applicable, quick, and easy methods are available to test whether this is so. Samples of values whose frequency distributions are shown in Figs. 2B and C could be easily shown to belong to populations whose distributions do deviate from the normal, but this does not mean that the t test or the R test are definitely not applicable to these samples, even approximately. In practice, when there are no indications that samples of values may be taken from populations whose distributions deviate widely from the normal, tests of significance based on the assumption of the normal distribution are usually made.

When it is quite obvious that values of a variate are not distributed normally, and when it is also obvious that they can be easily transformed into values that are, such a transformation should be made. It may, for example, be noticed, or deduced theoretically, that logarithms of some values are distributed approximately normally, and then the logarithms should be used instead of the original values when tests of significance based on the assumption of the normal distribution are to be made.

If analysis of variance is to be applied, two other conditions must be fulfilled by the variate, at least approximately: (1) effects of factors contributing to variation must be additive and (2) the variance must be independent of the mean. As shown above, these conditions are basic. If original values of a variate do not fulfill the conditions, they must, therefore, be transformed so that the transformed values do. If no suitable transformation can be found, analysis of variance must not be applied, which also means that experiments designed to eliminate some sources of variation from comparisons between means of treatments will not achieve this purpose quite satisfactorily. This does not necessarily mean that such designs should not be used, but it does mean that the results cannot be properly examined statistically.

Let us take the example of the numbers of local lesions formed by plant viruses on inoculated leaves of a host plant. Let us assume that two different virus preparations formed 3 and 20 lesions per leaf on a plant. We know from experience that if the first preparation forms, say, 15 lesions per leaf on a more susceptible plant, the second will be expected to form not about 32 (which it would if the effect of greater susceptibility were additive), but about 100. Thus the effect of greater susceptibility seems roughly equivalent to multiplication by a factor, or at least approximately so. Therefore, the transformation of the numbers of lesions into logarithms will be expected to make the effect additive. Actually, to fulfill also the condition of independence of the variance from the mean, a transformation must be made that is slightly more complicated than simply taking a logarithm.

If the variance of a population depends on its mean (μ), and if we can express the variance as a function of the mean, say $f(\mu)$, the transformation that will be expected to equalize the variance, making it equal 1 (approximately), is

$$y = \int_a^x dz/[f(z)]^{1/2} \tag{38}$$

where x is the original value and a is an arbitrary constant. That this is so can be shown as follows: Let $x_i = \bar{x} + \Delta x_i$, where x_i is a particular value of x and $\bar{x}$ is the mean value of x. Thus the variance of x is the mean value of $(\Delta x)^2$, which equals $f(\bar{x})$. Therefore, the variance of $x/[f(\bar{x})]^{1/2}$, which is the mean value of $(\Delta x)^2/f(\bar{x})$, equals 1 (see Section I). By a suitable choice of the value of the arbitrary constant a in Eq. (38), the mean value of y, say $\bar{y}$, can be made to correspond to the mean value of x (i.e., $\bar{x}$). Let $y_i = \bar{y} + \Delta y_i$. Therefore,

$$\Delta y_i = \int_{\bar{x}}^{\bar{x}+\Delta x_i} dz/[f(z)]^{1/2} = \frac{\Delta x_i}{[f(x_i')]^{1/2}}$$

the value of x_i' being somewhere between $\bar{x}$ and $\bar{x} + \Delta x_i$. Therefore, the variance of y, which is the mean value of $(\Delta y_i)^2$, and this is the mean value of $(\Delta x_i)^2/f(x_i')$, is approximately 1.

We shall now consider a few important applications of Eq. (38). Let us assume that a variate x is such that its standard deviation (σ) is proportional to the mean. Thus $\sigma = \lambda\mu$, where λ is a constant. Therefore, $\sigma^2 = f(\mu) = \lambda^2\mu^2$. Substituting this into Eq. (38), we get

$$y' = \int_a^x dz/\lambda z = \frac{1}{\lambda} \ln x + C$$

where C is an arbitrary constant. The variance of the values of y' will be expected to equal about 1. Taking C as zero and changing the scale, we can change the above transformation into

$$y = \log x$$

when $y = 0.4343\lambda y'$ (because $\log x = 0.4343 \ln x$). The variance of the values of y will, therefore, be expected to be about $(0.4343\lambda)^2 = 0.189\lambda^2$ (see Section I).

Therefore, whenever there is in indication that standard errors of populations vary and are more or less proportional to the means, the logarithmic transformation can be applied to equalize the variance. The value of λ need not be known. The estimate of variance of the transformed values is obtained by the usual procedure. This may have to be done even with the kind of data that are normally used without any transformation when differences between means of treatments are relatively small. When the differences happen to be exceptionally large, the standard deviations may then differ appreciably, and the data may then have to be transformed into logarithms.

Numbers of local lesions formed by plant viruses on inoculated leaves or half leaves (whichever is used as a unit) are not normally distributed, the distribution being skew (with a peak to the left of the mean and a tail on the right-hand side), and their standard deviation increases with the increasing mean. When the means are not smaller than about 10 per unit, we can assume that the dependence of the standard deviation s on the mean m is linear and can be expressed as

$$s = b(m + c) \tag{39}$$

where b is the coefficient of linear regression of s on m and c is a constant resulting from the fact that the regression line does not pass through the origin but intersects the horizontal axis on its negative side. The value of c is the distance between the point of intersection and the origin.

Substituting this into Eq. (38), we get the transformation where C

$$y' = \int^x \frac{dz}{b(z + c)} = \frac{1}{b} \ln (x + c) + C$$

is an arbitrary constant. Instead of using this, we can use a simpler transformation

$$y = \log (x + c) \tag{40}$$

which will be expected to equalize the variance, making its value be about $0.189b^2$.

In practice, the value of c can be obtained by plotting standard deviations of numbers of lesions x (i.e., of untransformed numbers of lesions) computed separately for each treatment (inoculum) against the mean numbers of lesions for the treatments and passing roughly a regression line through the points thus obtained. Usually there is no need for great accuracy in estimation of the value of c, and the use of any value within a wide range gives satisfactory results. As the choice of a value of c is, therefore, to a large extent arbitrary and need not even be based on the data of the experiment whose results are actually analyzed, there is no loss of a degree of freedom because of the use of c. The range within which the values of c are most frequently found is 5–15, and so any value within this range can be used if no data are available from which even a rough estimate can be made. However, in some problems it may be essential that the value of c be obtained as accurately as possible. It should then be obtained from the results of the experiment that is actually examined.

It may be thought at first that the value of c, if obtained as described above from standard deviations of numbers of lesions obtained with different treatments, may be affected by the contribution of variation from other sources (such as blocks, leaf positions, and so on) that have been taken into account in an experimental design, because the standard deviations include all this variation. However, this will affect only the slope of the regression line but not its point of intersection with the horizontal axis. This is so because effects of the sources of variation on numbers of lesions are not additive but roughly equivalent to multiplication by some factors (see above). When an experimental design is such that the same factors are equally involved with regard to lesions produced by all treatments, standard deviations of numbers of lesions produced with different treatments will be expected to equal standard deviations that would have been obtained if the other sources of variation did not exist, all multiplied by the same quantity. Thus only the slope of the regression line is affected by the sources of variation. This can be proved, but the proof would be somewhat lengthy, and so cannot be given here.

The standard deviation of the numbers of lesions can be considered to be a linear function of the mean given by Eq. (39) only when the mean is not smaller than about 10. As the mean becomes smaller, the value of the standard deviation deviates appreciably from the straight line (39) and approaches zero as the mean approaches zero. It may, therefore, follow a curve that resembles the hyperbola

$$s = b[(m + c)^2 - c^2]^{1/2}$$

Assuming that the hyperbola does indeed show the relationship between the standard deviation and the mean, a transformation that will be expected to equalize the variance is

$$y' = \int_a^x \frac{dz}{b[(z + c)^2 - c^2]^{1/2}} = \frac{1}{b} \ln [x + c + (x^2 + 2cx)^{1/2}] + C$$

where C is an arbitrary constant. In practice, the transformation

$$y = \log \{\tfrac{1}{2}[x + c + (x^2 + 2cx)^{1/2}]\} \tag{41}$$

is more convenient and is recommended. As x increases, the value of y given by Eq. (41) approaches that given by Eq. (40), so that for sufficiently large values of x the value of y can be computed more simply using Eq. (40) than using Eq. (41). The variance of y will be expected to be approximately $0.189b^2$. The use of the transformation by Eq. (41) was found in practice to equalize the variance for all values of the mean number of lesions down to about 1.5, but it ceases to be effective when the mean is smaller than that. The transformation by Eq. (41) is, therefore, more general than by Eq. (40) which is effective when the mean number of lesions is not smaller than about 10. However, the transformation by Eq. (41) is more laborious than by Eq. (40) which is simply read from a logarithmic table or from a slide rule. To make the transformation by Eq. (41) as quick in use as by Eq. (40), Table XVI is provided. Since only two first decimal figures need be used, the table gives the values of the transform by Eq. (41) for several different values of the constant c only as far as two first decimal figures of the transform by Eq. (41) differ from those by Eq. (40). For all larger values of x the transformation by Eq. (40) gives the same results as that by Eq. (41) and so can be used instead of Eq. (41).

The values obtained by the transformation according to Eqs. (40) or (41) not only have the standard deviation independent of the mean but they are distributed approximately normally. It needs emphasizing that the transformation $y = \log x$, if used instead of the above transformations, would "overcorrect": the standard deviation of the transformed values would decrease with the increasing mean, and the distribution would be skew.

The other two important applications of transformations based on Eq. (38) that we shall consider are when the distribution of a variate is binomial or Poissonian. When the distribution is binomial (see Section IV, B), the variate being the number of successes in a set of n trials, the mean number of successes is $\overline{m} = pn$, where p is the probability of a success in a single trial, and the variance is $(\overline{s})^2 = pqn = \overline{m}q$, where $q = 1 - p$ is the probability of a failure in a single trial. However, the variate that is customarily used is not the number of successes in a set of n trials but the proportion of successes, i.e., the number of successes divided by n. Let the proportion be x. The mean value of x is $m = \overline{m}/n = p$, and the variance is $s^2 = (\overline{s})^2/n^2 = pq/n = p(1 - p)/n = m(1 - m)/n = f(m)$. Substituting this into Eq. (38), we obtain the transformation

$$y' = \int_a^x \frac{dz}{[z(1 - z)/n]^{1/2}} = 2(n)^{1/2} \sin^{-1}(x)^{1/2} + C$$

TABLE XVI

The Values of $y = \log \frac{1}{2}[x + c + (x^2 + 2cx)^{1/2}]$[a]

x	y	x	y	x	y	x	y	x	y	x	y	x	y	x	y
c = 3		c = 5		c = 6		c = 10		c = 10		c = 15		c = 20		c = 20	
0	0.18	6	1.02	21	1.43	0	0.70	43	1.72	33	1.67	7	1.35	50	1.84
1	0.52	7	1.06	22	1.44	1	0.89	44	1.73	34	1.68	8	1.38	51	1.84
2	0.65	8	1.10	23	1.46	2	0.97	45	1.74	85	1.69	9	1.40	52	1.85
3	0.75	9	1.13	24	1.47	3	1.03	46	1.75	36	1.70	10	1.42	53	1.86
4	0.82	10	1.16	25	1.49	4	1.08	47	1.75	37	1.71	11	1.44	54	1.86
5	0.89	11	1.19	26	1.50	5	1.12	48	1.76	38	1.72	12	1.46	55	1.87
6	0.94	12	1.22	27	1.52	6	1.15	49	1.77	39	1.72	13	1.47	56	1.87
7	0.99	13	1.25	28	1.53	7	1.19			40	1.73	14	1.49	57	1.88
8	1.03	14	1.27			8	1.22	c = 15		41	1.74	15	1.50	58	1.89
9	1.07	15	1.29	c = 7		9	1.25	0	0.88	42	1.75	16	1.52	59	1.89
10	1.11	16	1.32			10	1.27	1	1.03	43	1.76	17	1.53	60	1.90
11	1.14	17	1.34	0	0.54	11	1.30	2	1.10	44	1.76	18	1.55	61	1.90
12	1.17	18	1.36	1	0.77	12	1.32	3	1.15	45	1.77	19	1.56	62	1.91
13	1.20	19	1.38	2	0.87	13	1.34	4	1.19	46	1.78	20	1.57	63	1.91
		20	1.39	3	0.93	14	1.36	5	1.22	47	1.79	21	1.59	64	1.92
c = 4		21	1.41	4	0.99	15	1.38	6	1.25	48	1.79	22	1.60	65	1.92
		22	1.43	5	1.40	16	1.40	7	1.28	49	1.80	23	1.61	66	1.93
0	0.30	23	1.44	6	1.08	17	1.42	8	1.31	50	1.81	24	1.62	67	1.93
1	0.60	24	1.46	7	1.12	18	1.43	9	1.33	51	1.81	25	1.63	68	1.94
2	0.72			8	1.15	19	1.45	10	1.35	52	1.82	26	1.64	69	1.94
3	0.80	c = 6		9	1.18	20	1.47	11	1.37	53	1.83	27	1.65	70	1.95
4	0.87			10	1.21	21	1.48	12	1.39	54	1.83	28	1.66	71	1.95
5	0.93	0	0.48	11	1.24	22	1.49	13	1.41	55	1.84	29	1.67	72	1.96
6	0.98	1	0.72	12	1.26	23	1.51	14	1.43	56	1.85	30	1.68	73	1.96
7	1.03	2	0.82	13	1.29	24	1.52	15	1.45	57	1.85	31	1.69	74	1.97
8	1.07	3	0.89	14	1.31	25	1.54	16	1.46	58	1.86	32	1.70	75	1.97
9	1.10	4	0.95	15	1.33	26	1.55	17	1.48	59	1.87	33	1.71	76	1.98
10	1.14	5	1.00	16	1.35	27	1.56	18	1.49	60	1.87	34	1.72	77	1.98
11	1.17	6	1.05	17	1.37	28	1.57	19	1.51	61	1.88	35	1.73	78	1.99
12	1.20	7	1.09	18	1.39	29	1.58	20	1.52	62	1.88	36	1.73	79	1.99
13	1.22	8	1.13	19	1.41	30	1.60	21	1.54	63	1.89	37	1.74	80	2.00
14	1.25	9	1.16	20	1.42	31	1.61	22	1.55	64	1.89	38	1.75	81	2.00
15	1.27	10	1.19	21	1.44	32	1.62	23	1.56	65	1.90	39	1.76	82	2.01
16	1.30	11	1.22	22	1.46	33	1.63	24	1.57			40	1.77	83	2.01
		12	1.24	23	1.47	34	1.64	25	1.59	c = 20		41	1.77	84	2.01
c = 5		13	1.27	24	1.49	35	1.65	26	1.60	0	1.00	42	1.78	85	2.02
		14	1.29	25	1.50	36	1.66	27	1.61	1	1.14	43	1.79	86	2.02
0	0.40	15	1.31	26	1.51	37	1.67	28	1.62	2	1.19	44	1.80	87	2.03
1	0.67	16	1.33	27	1.53	38	1.68	29	1.63	3	1.24	45	1.80	88	2.03
2	0.78	17	1.35	28	1.54	89	1.69	30	1.64	4	1.27	46	1.81	89	2.03
3	0.85	18	1.37	29	1.55	40	1.70	31	1.65	5	1.30	47	1.82	90	2.04
4	0.92	19	1.39	30	1.57	41	1.70	32	1.66	6	1.33	48	1.82	91	2.04
5	0.97	20	1.41	31	1.58	42	1.71					49	1.83	92	2.05

[a] For values of x higher than those given in this table $y = \log(x + c)$.

where C is an arbitrary constant. The transformation that is used in practice is

$$y = \sin^{-1} (x)^{1/2} \tag{42}$$

which is obtained from the previous one by taking C as zero and by a change of scale, so that $y = y'/2(n)^{1/2}$. Therefore, the variance of y is $1/4n$.

The value of y, given by Eq. (42), is in radians. It is, however, customary, to express its value in degrees (usually called "angular degrees"). This means that both sides of Eq. (42) are multiplied by $360/2\pi$. Thus, the variance of y translated into degrees is about $(1/4n) \times (180/\pi)^2 = 821/n$. The transformation according to Eq. (42), but expressed in degrees, is called the "angular transformation," and the values of the degrees corresponding to different values of x are tabulated. They can be found in tables of angular transformation that give transformations of values of x expressed as percentages $(p\%)$ or as fractions.

When the distribution of a variate is Poissonian (see Section IV,C), the variance σ^2 equals the mean μ, so that $\sigma^2 = f(\mu) = \mu$. Substituting this into Eq. (38), we get the transformation

$$y' = \int_a^x \frac{dz}{(z)^{1/2}} = 2(x)^{1/2} + C$$

where C is an arbitrary constant. In practice, the transformation

$$y = x^{1/2} \tag{43}$$

is used, which is obtained from the previous one by taking C as zero and by a change of scale so that $y = \frac{1}{2}y'$. Thus the variance of y is about $\frac{1}{4}$.

H. SIGNIFICANCE OF A SINGLE NUMBER FROM A POPULATION WHOSE DISTRIBUTION IS BINOMIAL OR POISSONIAN

The significance of any such number can be assessed quite exactly. Let us first deal with a number from a population whose distribution is binomial. Let the number be a occasions when an event has occurred out of a total of N trials. If the probability of the occurrence of the event in any trial is constant, the distribution of the numbers of occurrences in sets of N trials is binomial. Our estimate of the probability is a/N, and our problem is to find the limits within which the "real" probability may be. The lower limit $p_1 (< a/N)$ will be such that if the probability were actually p_1, an observed number of occurrences as great or greater than a out of N trials would occur by chance only with a relative frequency of P. (The value of P is chosen according to what we shall consider as our level of significance. The term "relative frequency" is used here rather than "probability" to avoid the confusion with the probability of occurrence of the event in any trial.) Similarly, the upper limit $p_2 (> a/N)$ will be such that if the probability were actually p_2, an observed number of occurrences as few or fewer than a out of N trials would occur by chance only with a relative frequency of P.

The solution of the problem is simple in principle, and we shall consider it using a numerical example. Let us choose $P = 0.025$ as our level of significance. This means that the total frequency for both lower and upper limit is 0.05. Let us assume that six events have been obtained in 60 trials. Our estimate of the probability of occurrences of the event in any trial is, therefore, $6/60 = 0.1$, From what was considered in Section IV,B, it is obvious that to find the value of p_1 it is necessary to equate 1 minus the sum of the first six terms of the expanded binomial $(q - p)^{60}$ to 0.025, and to solve the equation for p. To find the value of p_2, we have to equate the sum of the first seven terms of the expanded binomial to 0.025, and also solve the equation for p.

We can solve the equations by successive approximations, finding that $p_1 = 0.038$ and $p_2 = 0.205$. Thus, if we find that 6 out of 60 insects have transmitted a virus, our estimate of the probability of transmission by an insect is 0.1, and we shall conclude that the limits within which the "real" probability is are 0.038 and 0.205. If 6 out of 60 tubes to each of which the same amount of a dilute suspension of some microorganisms was added are found to be sterile (see Section IV,B), we shall conclude that the proportion of sterile tubes can be expected to be anything between 0.038 and 0.205. Therefore, if sterility means the absence of microorganisms, the estimated mean number of the organisms per volume added to each tube is $-2.3 \log 0.1 = 2.3$ [see Eq. (21) of Section IV,C], and the limits within which the "real" value of the mean is are $-2.3 \log 0.038 = 3.27$ and $-2.3 \log 0.205 = 1.58$.

However, solutions of the equations by successive approximations can be extremely laborious. Fortunately, this is unnecessary and the values of p_1 and p_2 can be found rapidly using a table that gives limits of the expectation for binomial and Poisson distributions. Fisher and Yates's "Statistical Tables" (1963) contains such a table. The table does not show the values of p_1 and p_2, but the limits of expectation of the number of occurrences, which are p_1N and p_2N for various values of a and N and for three different values of P (namely, 0.005, 0.025, and 0.1).

Let us now consider a number from a population whose distribution is Poissonian. Let the number be a. The problem is to find the limits within which the mean of the population can be expected to be. The lower limit, $m_1(<a)$, will be such that if the mean were actually m_1, an observed number as great or greater than a would occur only by chance with a relative frequency of P. Similarly, the upper limit, $m_2(>a)$, is such that if the mean were really m_2, an observed number as small or smaller than a would occur by chance only with a relative frequency of P.

To take a concrete example, let us again take 0.025 as the value of P, and let us assume that we have observed nine plaques formed by a unit volume of a diluted preparation of a bacteriophage added to one Petri dish, or distributed among several Petri dishes, containing agar medium and a suspension of susceptible bacteria. Our estimate of the concentration of the bacteriophage in the diluted preparation is, therefore, nine plaque-forming particles per unit volume. To find the value of m_1, it is obvious from Section IV,C that we have to equate one minus the sum of the first 9 terms of the Poisson series in μ to 0.025 and solve the equation for μ. Similarly, to find the value of m_2, we have to equate the sum of the first 10 terms of the Poisson series in μ to 0.025 and solve the equation for μ. We can solve the equations by successive approximations, finding that $m_1 = 4.12$ and $m_2 = 17.08$. However, the values of m_1 and m_2 can be found rapidly from the same table as above if we look for values that correspond to a with $N = \infty$ $(a/N = 0)$.

VI. Estimation of Virus Concentration

A. ESTIMATION BY THE DILUTION METHOD

We have already considered estimation of the concentration of microorganisms by the dilution method from the number a of sterile tubes out of a total number N of tubes to each of which the same volume of a diluted preparation of the organisms has been added (see Section V,H). However, when we do not know beforehand what dilution should be used so that a proportion of the tubes will be sterile, we make several different dilutions, each b times more dilute than the preceding one, and add the same volume from each dilution to a set of n tubes. As a result, we may have several sets of n tubes in which different proportions of the tubes are sterile. This gives us the opportunity of testing the assumption on which our estimation of the concentration is based, namely, that the presence of at least one organism in a tube is sufficient to recognize the tube as fertile. The test will be considered later, and we shall start with estimation of the concentration, taking the assumption for granted.

When we have several sets of n tubes, each inoculated with a different dilution of the material under test, we could, of course, choose only one set and estimate the concentration from it as described above. If we do this, we should choose a set in which the proportion of sterile tubes is the nearest to 20% (which would correspond to 1.6 organisms per tube), for at this proportion the estimate of the concentration will be more accurate than at any other (see below). However, if we use only one set, we lose all the information supplied by the other sets. We shall now consider estimation of the concentration using all this information. Before doing this, it should be emphasized that the procedure for estimating the concentration separately from each set and then taking the mean value would be entirely wrong because of great differences in the precision of the estimations. However, it would not be wrong to take a weighted mean, as will be described below.

The concentration can be estimated rapidly from the total number of fertile tubes at all dilutions using a table of densities of organisms estimated by the dilution method, which is included in Fisher and Yates's "Statistical Tables" (1963). A lengthy description of the way the table should be used is given in the Introduction to this source and need not be repeated here. The variance of the estimate can be obtained from the formula given in the Introduction and in the table itself. The method uses somewhat less than 90% of the information contained in the experimental results.

We shall now consider another method of estimation based on solving the equation of "maximum likelihood." This is the most accurate method using 100% of the information contained in experimental results, but it is laborious, since it involves solving an equation by successive approximations. We shall consider the theoretical background only partially, mainly to demonstrate the use of the principle of maximum likelihood, and we shall derive the equation for the estimate of the concentration and also the variance of the estimate. The reader need not necessarily follow the theoretical considerations and the derivations.

Let the concentration of a preparation be λ organisms per unit volume, and let the unit volume of each of m different dilutions of the preparation be added to one of m sets of n tubes. Let z_1, z_2, z_3, . . . , z_m be the dilutions and r_1, r_2, r_3, . . . , r_m, respectively, the number of fertile tubes in the sets of n tubes. When the dilution is z_i, the mean number of organisms per unit volume is $z_i\lambda$, so that the probability of a tube being sterile is $q_i = e^{-z_i\lambda}$ and of being fertile $p_i = 1 - e^{-z_i\lambda}$ (see Section IV,C). The convention of designating parameters by Greek letters and corresponding statistics by corresponding Latin letters will, for convenience, be abandoned in this Section.

Since the distribution of r for any particular dilution is binomial, the probability of r taking the value of r_i when the dilution is z_i is given by Eq. (14) of Section IV,B and is

$$f_i = \frac{n!}{(n - r_i)!r_i!} \, p_i{}^{r_i}q_i{}^{(n-r_i)}$$

Since the values of r observed at different dilutions can vary by chance independently of each other, the probability that they all have the actually observed values equals the product of probabilities of obtaining the actually observed results at each of the dilutions (see Section III), and therefore is

$$\phi = \prod_{i=1}^{m} (f_i) = \prod_{i=1}^{m} \left[\frac{n!}{(n - r_i)!r_i!} \, p_i{}^{r_i}q_i{}^{(n-r_i)} \right] \tag{44}$$

where the symbol $\prod_{i=1}^{m}$ stands for the product of all values of f_i whose subscript i takes all the values from 1 to m.

Estimation of λ by the method of maximum likelihood is based on finding the value of λ, which gives ϕ a maximum value. This is done by solving for λ the equation

$$\frac{\partial}{\partial \lambda} \ln \phi = \sum_{i=1}^{m} \left[\frac{r_i - n(1 - e^{-z_i\lambda})}{1 - e^{-z_i\lambda}} \, z_i \right] = 0 \tag{45}$$

which can be done by successive approximations, as will be demonstrated below on a numerical example.

A statistic that is obtained by the method of maximum likelihood is consistent and sufficient, i.e., includes the whole of the relevant information contained in the data. It can be proved, although the proof is beyond the scope of this section, that a statistic obtained by any other method that is also consistent and sufficient must be identical with that obtained by the method of maximum likelihood. Values of statistics obtained from a large amount of data are normally distributed around the corresponding parameters (the central limit theorem, Section IV,D). Therefore, if λ is an estimate of the parameter λ_o, and the variance of the estimate is σ^2, the probability function of λ is

$$\phi' = C \exp \left[-\frac{1}{2}\left(\frac{\lambda - \lambda_o}{\sigma}\right)^2 \right] \tag{46}$$

where C is a constant [see Eq. (23) Section IV,D]. The fact of which we are going to make use is that

$$\frac{\partial^2}{\partial\lambda^2} \ln \phi' = -\frac{1}{\sigma^2}$$

A probability function of λ is also given by the value of ϕ of Eq. (44), which is a function of experimental data. Thus, to obtain an estimate of σ^2 from experimental results, we use ϕ of Eq. (44) and assume that the value that $(\partial^2)/(\partial\lambda^2) \ln \phi$ will, on average, be expected to have equals $-1/\sigma^2$. Therefore,

$$-\frac{1}{\sigma^2} = E\left(\frac{\partial^2}{\partial\lambda^2} \ln \phi\right) = -E\left[\sum_{i=1}^{m}\left(\frac{z_i^2 r_i q_i}{p_i^2}\right)\right] = -\sum_{i=1}^{m}\left(\frac{z_i^2 n q_i}{p_i}\right)$$

The symbol E stands for "expectation," i.e., what follows the symbol takes the value that it would, on average, be expected to have. We have made use of the fact that r_i will, on average, equal $p_i n$. It follows that the variance of the estimate of λ is

$$\sigma^2 = \frac{1}{n\sum_{i=1}^{m}[z_i^2 e^{-z_i\lambda}/(1 - e^{-z_i\lambda})]} \qquad (47)$$

When only one dilution, z, is used, Eq. (45) becomes $r/n = 1 - e^{-z\lambda}$, so that the estimate of λ is

$$\lambda = \frac{1}{z} \ln 1/(1 - r/n) \qquad (48)$$

and Eq. (47) for the variance of the estimate of λ becomes

$$\sigma^2 = \frac{e^{z\lambda} - 1}{z^2 n} \qquad (49)$$

Thus, if we put $M = z\lambda$, so that M is the estimate of the mean number of organisms per tube, the variance of M will be $\sigma^2 = (e^M - 1)/n$. Therefore, the relative dispersion of M (i.e, the ratio of the standard error of M to M) is

$$(1/M)[(e^M - 1)/n]^{1/2} = [(e^M - 1)/M^2 n]^{1/2}$$

To find the value of M at which the relative dispersion is the smallest, i.e., the estimate of M that is the most accurate, we must find the value of M at which $(e^M - 1)/M^2$ is a minimum. This is done by solving the equation

$$\frac{d}{dM}(e^M - 1)/M^2 = \frac{e^M(M - 2) + 2}{M^3} = 0$$

so that $e^M = 2/(2 - M)$. Therefore, the most accurate estimate of M is obtained when $M = 1.594$, i.e., when the proportion of sterile tubes is $e^{-1.594} = 0.203$.

Let us consider an example of application of Eqs. (45) and (47). Table XVII shows the result of an experiment in which several dilutions of a preparation of a bacteriophage were made, and then 1 ml of each dilution was added to each of 100 tubes containing 10 ml of a liquid culture of susceptible bacteria. The tubes were incubated for 24 hours and the tubes counted in which bacteria had lysed. In all these tubes the phage had obviously multiplied, but the phage may also

TABLE XVII

RESULTS OF INOCULATING LIQUID BACTERIAL CULTURES WITH A BACTERIOPHAGE PREPARATION AT DIFFERENT DILUTIONS[a]

Dilution (z)	Observed numbers of tubes				
	Lysed	Nonlysed, phage present	Total numbers of fertile tubes (r)	Expected numbers of fertile tubes	χ^2
1/8	89	0	89	90.28	0.1867
1/16	65	0	65	68.83	0.6837
1/32	44	3	47	44.17	0.3248
1/64	29	3	32	25.28	2.3907
1/128	10	2	12	13.56	0.2077
					3.7936

[a] The total of 100 tubes were inoculated with each dilution of the bacteriophage.

have multiplied in some of the tubes that had not lysed, so that the tubes were tested for the presence of phage by inoculating fresh bacterial cultures with samples from them. When there was no lysis, it was concluded that no phage was present, and when lysis was observed, it was concluded that phage was present in the tubes. The numbers of these tubes were added to those in which lysis had occurred in the first instance, so giving the total numbers of fertile tubes.

With dilutions lower than those shown in Table XVII, all 100 inoculated cultures had lysed. We do not have to consider those, because they do not contribute to estimation of phage concentration.

To obtain an estimate of the number of phage particles per milliliter of the original preparation by the method of maximum likelihood, we substitute the data shown in Table XVII into Eq. (45), thus obtaining

$$\frac{89 - 100\{1 - \exp[-(1/8)\lambda]\}}{1 - \exp[-(1/8)\lambda]}\frac{1}{8} + \frac{65 - 100\{1 - \exp[-(1/16)\lambda]\}}{1 - \exp[-(1/16)\lambda]}\frac{1}{16}$$

$$+ \frac{47 - 100\{1 - \exp[-(1/32)\lambda]\}}{1 - \exp[-(1/32)\lambda]}\frac{1}{32}$$

$$+ \frac{32 - 100\{1 - \exp[-(1/64)\lambda]\}}{1 - \exp[-(1/64)\lambda]}\frac{1}{64}$$

$$+ \frac{12 - 100\{1 - \exp[-(1/128)\lambda]\}}{1 - \exp[-(1/128)\lambda]}\frac{1}{128} = 0 \qquad (50)$$

We solve this equation for λ by successive approximations, i.e., by giving different values to λ and computing the values of the left-hand side of the equation, until the value of λ is found for which the left-hand side of the equation equals zero. The procedure is laborious, but skill can be soon acquired. With a table of exponential functions or of natural logarithms and a calculating machine the whole operation takes a few hours.

To make the first guess about the value of λ, one of the terms of the equation can be equated to zero and the resulting equation solved for λ. Let it be the first term. Thus, we solve for λ the equation

$$89 - 100[1 - \exp(-\tfrac{1}{8}\lambda)] = 0$$

thus getting $\lambda = 17.66$. Substituting this into Eq. (50), we get the value of $+0.6250$. Using $\lambda = 18.7$, we get the value of -0.0259. Thus λ is greater than 17.7 and smaller than 18.7. Several successive trials may, for example, give the following results

λ	Value of the equation
17.66	+0.6250
18.64	+0.0072
18.65	+0.0006
18.66	−0.0048
18.70	−0.0259

We can accept 18.65 as our estimate of λ. The value of the standard error we shall compute presently will show that any further elaboration would be superfluous.

The variance of our estimate of λ is obtained by substituting our data and the value $\lambda = 18.65$ into Eq. (47). The value of the denominator is

$$100[(1/8)^2 0.0972/0.9028 + (1/16)^2 0.3117/0.6883 + (1/32)^2 0.5583/0.4417$$
$$+ (1/64)^2 0.7472/0.2528 + (1/128)^2 0.8644/0.1356] = 0.58$$

Thus $\sigma^2 = 1/0.58 = 1.72$, so that the standard error is $\sigma = 1.31$.

Estimates of λ, based on as large amount of data as in Table XVII, can be assumed to be normally distributed, and the estimate of variance, as obtained above, can be assumed not to differ appreciably from the "true" value. Taking the probability of 0.05 as our level of significance (see Section V,C), we see, therefore, that the fiducial limits of λ can be taken as $18.65 - 2\sigma$ and $18.65 + 2\sigma$, i.e., 16.0 and 21.3.

As an alternative to solving Eq. (45), we can solve Eqs. (48) and (49) separately for each dilution, thus getting five estimates of the concentration, say $\lambda_1, \lambda_2, \ldots, \lambda_5$ (which are 17.66, 16.80, 20.32, 24.69, and 16.37), from Eq. (48) and variances of the estimates, say $\sigma_1^2, \sigma_2^2, \ldots, \sigma_5^2$ (which are 5.181, 4.754, 9.083, 19.292, and 22.282), from Eq. (49). Then we compute the weighted mean of the estimates of the concentration, which is

$$\lambda_w = \frac{\sum_{i=1}^{5} [(1/\sigma_i^2)\lambda_i]}{\sum_{i=1}^{5} (1/\sigma_i^2)} = 18.63$$

and the variance of the weighted mean is

$$\sigma^2 = \frac{1}{\sum_{i=1}^{5} (1/\sigma_i^2)} = 1.64$$

so that the standard error is 1.28. The fiducial limits of λ, therefore, are 15.8 and 20.9 (if the probability of 0.05 is taken as our level of significance).

This is a much quicker, though less accurate, method of estimating the concentration than solving Eq. (45), and for most practical purposes it can be considered good enough.

If we wish to test our basic assumption that a tube was classified as fertile when at least one phage particle was present, we compute the numbers of tubes that would be expected to be fertile if the assumption were correct and compare the expected numbers with those actually observed. Using the value of λ obtained by the method of maximum likelihood (i.e., 18.65), the expected number of fertile tubes at a dilution z_i is

$$Y_i = 100[1 - \exp(-18.65z_i)] \tag{51}$$

Whether the deviations of the observed from the expected numbers could have occurred merely by chance can then be tested by the χ^2 test. The 100 tubes used for each dilution of the phage preparation can be divided into two classes, fertile and sterile. The expected class frequencies are Y_i and $100 - Y_i$ [the value of Y_i is given by Eq. (51)].

If r_i is the observed number of fertile tubes with the dilution z_i, the component of the χ^2 contributed by the result obtained at the dilution z_i is

$$\chi_i{}^2 = \frac{(r_i - Y_i)^2}{Y_i} + \frac{[(100 - r_i) - (100 - Y_i)]^2}{100 - Y_i}$$

$$= \frac{(r_i - Y_i)^2}{Y_i} + \frac{(r_i - Y_i)^2}{100 - Y_i}$$

so that the total value of χ^2 is

$$\chi^2 = \sum_{i=1}^{5} (\chi_i{}^2) = \sum_{i=1}^{5} \left[\frac{(r_i - Y_i)^2}{Y_i} + \frac{(r_i - Y_i)^2}{100 - Y_i} \right]$$

The number of degrees of freedom is 5 (one for each dilution) minus 1 lost for estimation of λ (which has been estimated from results obtained with all the dilutions). A condition of applicability of the χ^2 test is that the values of Y_i and of $100 - Y_i$ should not be smaller than about 5. The value of χ^2 obtained with the results shown in Table XVII is 3.7936. A table of the distribution of values of χ^2 will show that with 4 degrees of freedom the probability of obtaining the value of χ^2 as great or greater than the above value is about 0.44, which means that the assumption that phage multiplied when at least one phage particle was present is compatible with the experimental results. If at least two had to be present, the expected number of fertile tubes would, at a dilution z_i, be

$$Y_i = 100(1 - e^{-z_i\lambda} - z_i\lambda e^{-z_i\lambda}) \tag{52}$$

(see Section IV,C). It can be verified that no value of λ will make the expected numbers, computed according to Eq. (52), fit the actually observed numbers r shown in Table XVII. (The χ^2 test will always show that deviations of observed from expected numbers are too great to have occurred simply by chance.) We shall, therefore, conclude that the hypothesis that at least two phage particles are needed for multiplication to occur is incompatible with the experimental results. A hypothesis that at least three or more particles are needed will lead to a still greater divergence of observed from expected values.

A possibility remains that although any particle can multiply, not every one does. There may be a constant probability, say ρ, that a particle will succeed in starting to multiply. We can then write $\rho\mu = \lambda$, where μ is the real concentration that is greater than the value of λ estimated by the dilution method, if $\rho < 1.0$. Results of estimation of concentration by the dilution method alone cannot supply any information concerning the value of ρ. Results of some other method of estimation of the concentration (such as a direct count) may show that the concentration, μ, is greater than λ, which would mean that $\rho = \lambda/\mu$.

Whether the value of ρ is likely to be 1 can sometimes be postulated *a priori*. For example, when concentration of bacteria is estimated by the dilution method, the value of ρ can be expected to be 1, because any viable bacterial cell will be expected to multiply in a suitable medium. When we deal with a bacteriophage, the value of ρ may perhaps be smaller than 1, since some phage particles may possibly fail to attach themselves to the bacteria in a suitable manner. When infectivity of differently diluted virus preparations must be tested by inoculating animals or plants, the value of ρ not only may be smaller than 1 but it may not even be constant. If so, the value of $\lambda(= \rho\mu)$ will also vary from one inoculation to another, which will upset all the foundations of the method of estimation of virus concentration described above, so that a different method is required. A method frequently used in animal virology is based on inoculating groups of animals with different doses of a virus preparation and observing the response, such as the percentage of mortality, time when symptoms appear, and so on. This involves considerations of dose–response relationships and probit analysis, which are beyond the scope of this chapter. The reader is referred to Finney's "Probit analysis" (1952) and "Statistical Method in Biological Assay" (1964) (see also Stairs, 1965).

B. ESTIMATION BY PLAQUE COUNT

This method is used mainly with bacteriophages, but it recently has also been used with some animal viruses. The principle of the method is that every viable virus particle forms a plaque, or there is a constant probability that a viable particle will form a plaque. We shall assume that the probability is unity. If there is a reason to think that the probability is ρ (smaller than unity), the estimate of virus concentration and its standard error, must be divided by ρ.

The method is based on making several progressively increasing dilutions (usually with a factor of 10) of a virus preparation and adding a unit volume of each dilution to each of n plates together with, or already containing, a suitable agar (or other solidifying) medium and a suspension or a layer of susceptible cells. Plaques, which form during a suitable period of incubation, are counted on plates in which the dilution of virus preparation was such that conveniently countable numbers formed.

The fact that at each dilution the distribution of numbers of plaques formed on different plates is Poissonian has already been discussed (Section IV,C). Thus, if at a dilution of $1/a$ the mean number of plaques per plate is m, the variance of m is m/n. Thus, the estimate of virus concentration in the original preparation is am particles per unit volume, and a^2m/n is the variance of the estimate, so that the standard error is $a(m/n)^{1/2}$. Fiducial limits of m can be obtained exactly by the method described above (Section V,H).

If conveniently countable numbers of plaques formed at two different dilutions, say at dilutions $1/a_1$ and $1/a_2$, the mean numbers of plaques per plate being m_1 and m_2, the two estimates of virus concentration in the original preparation are a_1m_1 and a_2m_2, and the variances of the estimates are $a_1{}^2m_1/n$ and $a_2{}^2m_2/n$. The weighted mean of the two estimates, therefore, is

$$\bar{M} = \frac{na_1m_1/a_1{}^2m_1 + na_2m_2/a_2{}^2m_2}{n/a_1{}^2m_1 + n/a_2{}^2m_2} = \frac{1/a_1 + 1/a_2}{1/a_1{}^2m_1 + 1/a_2{}^2m_2} \tag{53}$$

and the variance of the mean is

$$\sigma^2 = \frac{1}{n(1/a_1{}^2m_1 + 1/a_2{}^2m_2)} \tag{54}$$

A more accurate method of estimation is based on solving the equation of maximum likelihood, whose principle was discussed above. When using this method, we shall also make use of the fact that sums of numbers distributed according to a Poisson series are also distributed according to a Poisson series (see Section IV,C).

Let us assume that countable numbers of plaques were formed at N different dilutions of a virus preparation. Let the dilutions be $1/a_1$, $1/a_2$, $1/a_3$, . . . , $1/a_N$, and let the corresponding total numbers of plaques formed on n plates be r_1, r_2, r_3, . . . , r_N. Let λ be the concentration of virus particles in the preparation. Thus the expected number of particles on n plates to which the preparation was added at a dilution of $1/a_i$ is $n\lambda/a_i$. Consequently, according to Eq. (20) of Section IV,C, the probability that the number of plaques is the observed number r_i is

$$p_i = \frac{1}{r_i!} (n\lambda/a_i)^{r_i} \exp(-n\lambda/a_i)$$

Since numbers of plaques formed at N different dilutions are independent of each other, the probability of obtaining all N actually observed numbers is the product of probabilities for different dilutions, which is

$$\phi = \prod_{i=1}^{N} (p_i) = \prod_{i=1}^{N} \left[\frac{1}{r_i!} (n\lambda/a_i)^{r_i} \exp(-n\lambda/a_i) \right]$$

The estimate of λ is obtained by maximizing the value of ϕ, which is done by solving the equation

$$\frac{\partial}{\partial\lambda} \ln \phi = \frac{1}{\lambda} \sum_{i=1}^{N} (r_i) - n \sum_{i=1}^{N} 1/a_i = 0$$

so that

$$\lambda = \frac{\displaystyle\sum_{i=1}^{N} (r_i)}{\displaystyle n \sum_{i=1}^{N} (1/a_i)} \tag{55}$$

As explained above, the variance (σ^2) of an estimate of λ by the method of maximum likelihood is obtained from the equation

$$-\frac{1}{\sigma^2} = E\left(\frac{\partial^2}{\partial\lambda^2} \ln \phi\right) = -E\left[\frac{1}{\lambda^2} \sum_{i=1}^{N} (r_i)\right]$$

$$= -\frac{n}{\lambda} \sum_{i=1}^{N} (1/a_i)$$

We have made use of the fact that the expected value of $\sum_{i=}^{N} (r_i)$ is $n\lambda \sum_{i=1}^{N} (1/a_i)$ [see Eq. (55)]. Thus the variance of the estimate of λ is

$$\sigma^2 = \frac{\lambda}{\displaystyle n \sum_{=1}^{N} (1/a_i)} \tag{56}$$

To take a numerical example, let us assume that five plates were used for each dilution of a preparation of a bacteriophage and that countable plaques were formed at dilutions $1/a_1 = 10^{-9}$ and $1/a_2 = 10^{-10}$ when total numbers of plaques on five plates were respectively, $r_1 = 425$ and $r_2 = 56$, so that the means per plate were $m_1 = 85$ and $m_2 = 11.2$.

The estimate of phage concentration by Eq. (53) is

$$\overline{M} = \frac{10^{-9} + 10^{-10}}{10^{-18}/85 + 10^{-20}/11.2} = 86.9 \times 10^{9}$$

and the variance of the estimate according to Eq. (54) is

$$\mathrm{var}(\overline{M}) = \frac{1}{5(10^{-18}/85 + 10^{-20}/11.2)} = 15.8 \times 10^{18}$$

so that the standard error is 3.97×10^9.

According to Eq. (55), the estimate of phage concentration is

$$\lambda = \frac{425 + 56}{5(10^{-9} + 10^{-10})} = 87.5 \times 10^9$$

and the variance of the estimate according to Eq. (56) is

$$\mathrm{var}(\lambda) = \frac{87.5 \times 10^9}{5(10^{-9} + 10^{-10})} = 15.9 \times 10^{18}$$

so that the standard error is 3.99×10^9. Therefore, the fiducial limits for phage concentration for probability level of about 0.05, are 79.5×10^9 and 96.5×10^9.

C. ESTIMATION BY THE LOCAL LESION METHOD

This method is used mainly with plant viruses to compare the concentration of active virus in an unknown preparation with that of a standard preparation; we shall deal only with the application of the method to plant viruses that form local lesions on leaves of a host plant. The method is based on making different progressively increasing dilutions of the standard and of the unknown and inoculating several leaves or half leaves (whichever is used as an experimental unit) with each dilution, usually by rubbing the leaf surface with the forefinger or with some other suitable implement previously dipped in the inoculum. The experimental design should be such that major sources of variation are eliminated from the experimental error (see Section II). The numbers of lesions formed by different inocula increase with the increasing virus concentration, though the increase may not be linear.

The number of lesions may, of course, depend not only on virus concentration but also on the concentration of any material that may inhibit or enhance infectivity of the virus. When an inhibitor is present in an inoculum, the number of lesions may sometimes even increase with increasing dilution. We shall assume that no materials that inhibit or enhance infectivity are present, at least not at concentrations at which they affect infectivity.

As local lesion tests can be done quickly and inexpensively, and as a statistical treatment of results of a single test takes more time than doing several tests, an economical procedure would be estimating virus concentration from results of several experiments in a rough way by graphic interpolation or some other suitable quick procedure and then using the results as different values of a variate that can then be subjected to a simple statistical treatment (see Section II,C). However, we may want to, or have to, estimate virus concentration from results of a single experiment by a suitable statistical treatment and to assess the precision of the estimate. A method of doing this will be described.

The theoretical aspect of the relationship between the numbers of lesions and virus concentrations is still a matter of speculation and we need not be concerned with it. All we have to know is that although the relationship between numbers of lesions and virus concentrations in general is not linear, there is usually a limited range of concentrations within which the relationship is linear, or nearly so. A dilution curve obtained by plotting numbers of lesions against virus concentration is almost horizontal at high virus concentrations, then begins to curve, and becomes progressively steeper as the concentration decreases; finally, as the concentration decreases still further, the line becomes straight, i.e., the relationship between the numbers of lesions and virus concentrations becomes linear, or nearly so. The method of estimation of concentration discussed below is based on the assumption that there is such a range of linearity and that at least some of the concentrations of the standard and of the unknown are within the range. Whether or not these requirements have been fulfilled in a particular experiment should be ascertained by inspection of the mean numbers of lesions per leaf obtained with differently diluted virus preparations. If the range of linearity has obviously not been covered, and if this appears to be so because virus concentrations were too high, another experiment should be made using more dilute inocula.

As explained above (Section V,G), the numbers of lesions obtained on individual leaves should be transformed according to Eq. (40) or (41) of Section V,G. The statistical method of assaying concentration of virus preparations given below is based on the use of the transformation according to Eq. (41), which is more generally applicable, and some inocula may give too few lesions for the transformation according to Eq. (40) to be effective in equalizing the variance.

When an experiment for assaying virus concentration is designed it is advisable to cover a rather wide range of virus concentrations, even though only some of them may fall within the range of linearity. This will enable us not only to locate the range of linearity but also to find the value of the constant of transformation c to be used for results of this particular experiment. Inoculation with each inoculum is to be considered as a treatment when an experimental design is considered that will eliminate major known sources of variation from the experimental error (see Section II).

Irrespective of how many treatments fall within the range of linearity, to obtain the value of the residual variance s^2 (see Section V,F), all the numbers of lesions on individual leaves obtained with all treatments must be transformed and all the transformed values used in the analysis suitable for a particular experimental design. It is essential that none of the treatments produces on average fewer than about 1.5 lesions per leaf (or half leaf), because with fewer lesions the transformation cannot be expected to equalize the variance.

Let us consider an example with two dilutions of the standard and one dilution of the unknown giving numbers of lesions within the range where linearity can be assumed. Let X_1 and X_2 be the mean number of lesions obtained with the standard diluted $1/a_1$ and $1/a_2$, respectively, and X_3 the mean number of lesions obtained with the unknown diluted $1/a_3$. Let the original concentrations of the standard and of the unknown be v and w, respectively. We want to estimate the value of the ratio w/v. If we disregarded X_2, our estimate of w/v would simply be X_3a_3/X_1a_1, and if we disregarded X_1, it would be X_3a_3/X_2a_2. The two estimates would probably differ, and taking the arithmetic mean would be wrong because of a difference in precision. The precision of each estimate would still have to be assessed, for which there is no easy method. We shall, therefore, approach the problem differently by assessing the precision of an estimate of log w/v.

If the variance of the transformed numbers is s^2 (which is the residual variance obtained in the analysis of variance when it is applicable), the variance of the mean of the transformed numbers obtained with any of the treatments is s^2/n (n being the number of replications of each treatment). This means that if X is the mean number of lesions obtained with a given treatment, the variance of the transform

$$Y = \log \tfrac{1}{2}[X + c + (X^2 + 2cX)^{1/2}]$$

is s^2/n. If, instead of this transformation, we use the transformation $Z = \log X$, the variance of Z will be

$$\mathrm{var}(Z) = (1 + 2c/X)s^2/n \tag{57}$$

(This can be deduced from the considerations concerning the application of Eq. (38) of Section V,G to make the variance independent of the mean.)

Since the values of X are assumed to be proportional to virus concentrations, the expected values of X_1, X_2, and X_3 are, respectively, Kv/a_1, Kv/a_2, and Kw/a_3, where K is a constant whose value we do not have to know, since it will cancel out in further procedure.

We have, therefore, two independent estimates of the value of $\log Kv$: first, $Z_1' = \log a_1 X_1 = \log X_1 + \log a_1 = Z_1 + \log a_1$, whose variance is $\mathrm{var}(Z_1') = \mathrm{var}(Z_1) = s^2(1 + 2c/X_1)/n$, and second, $Z_2' = \log a_2 X_2 = \log X_2 + \log a_2 = Z_2 + \log a_2$, whose variance is $\mathrm{var}(Z_2') = \mathrm{var}(Z_2) = s^2(1 + 2c/X_2)/n$.

Our final estimate of the value of $\log Kv$ is the weighted mean of Z_1' and Z_2', which is

$$\bar{Z}_v = \frac{Z_1'/\mathrm{var}(Z_1') + Z_2'/\mathrm{var}(Z_2')}{1/\mathrm{var}(Z_1') + 1/\mathrm{var}(Z_2')} = \frac{Z_1'/(1 + 2c/X_1) + Z_2'/(1 + 2c/X_2)}{1/(1 + 2c/X_1) + 1/(1 + 2c/X_2)}$$

and the variance of $\bar{Z}_v$ is

$$\mathrm{var}(\bar{Z}_v) = \frac{1}{1/\mathrm{var}(Z_1') + 1/\mathrm{var}(Z_2')} = \frac{s^2}{n} \frac{1}{1/(1 + 2c/X_1) + 1/(1 + 2c/X_2)}$$

We have only one estimate of the value of $\log Kw$, namely, $\bar{Z}_w = \log a_3 X_3 = \log X_3 + \log a_3 = Z_3 + \log a_3$, whose variance is $\mathrm{var}(\bar{Z}_w) = \mathrm{var}(Z_3) = s^2(1 + 2c/X_3)/n$.

Since $\log Kw - \log Kv = \log w/v$, our estimate of $\log w/v$ is $\bar{Z}_w - \bar{Z}_v$, so that we can write

$$\log w/v = \bar{Z}_w - \bar{Z}_v$$

and the variance of the estimate of $\log w/v$ is

$$S^2 = \mathrm{var}(\bar{Z}_v) + \mathrm{var}(\bar{Z}_w)$$

$$= \frac{s^2}{n} \left[\frac{1}{1/(1 + 2c/X_1) + 1/(1 + 2c/X_2)} + (1 + 2c/X_3) \right]$$

The fiducial limits for the value of $\log w/v$ can be obtained as described above (Section V,D) using a table of distribution of t. Thus, we find from the table that for N degrees of freedom (on which the value of s^2 is based) and for a level of significance corresponding to a certain probability, the value of the standard error S must be exceeded, say, r times. Hence the fiducial limits are $\bar{Z}_w - \bar{Z}_v - rS$ and $\bar{Z}_w - \bar{Z}_v + rS$.

If the above procedure has been understood, it can be easily modified when the numbers of treatments that fall within the range of linearity are other than two dilutions of the standard and one dilution of the unknown.

The mean numbers of lesions obtained with different treatments that enter the calculations described above could simply be their arithmetic means, but individual numbers of lesions are values from populations with different variances. For example, a number of lesions on a more susceptible leaf belongs to a population of numbers with a greater variance than that of a smaller number of lesions formed with the same treatment on a less susceptible leaf. Consequently, the two numbers will have different weights. In addition to this, the principle of additivity of effects of sources of variation to be eliminated by an experimental design does not apply to numbers of lesions (see Section V,G). Thus, using arithmetic means of numbers of lesions may be good enough to obtain rough estimates, but if more accurate results are required, a more correct procedure must be adopted based on the use of estimates of means of numbers of lesions obtained by a procedure that can be termed "detransformation."

Let Y be the mean of transformed numbers of lesions obtained with a given treatment. Since the transformed numbers have the same variance s^2, they all have the same weight. Also, the principle of additivity of effects of sources of variation to be eliminated by experimental designs is applicable to the transformed numbers. An estimate of the mean number of lesions, say X, is obtained from Y by "detransformation" according to the equation

$$X = [(2A - c)^2 + 5.29s^2c^2]/4A = A - c + c^2(5.29s^2 + 1)/4A \quad (58)$$

where s^2 is the variance (obtained by the analysis of variance or another suitable procedure), c is the constant of transformation of numbers of lesions, and A is obtained from the equation $\log A = Y + 1.15s^2$. A derivation of Eq. (58) is beyond the scope of this chapter. It can be found in the original paper by Kleczkowski (1955).

To take a concrete example, let us consider actually obtained results of a comparison of infectivity of an unknown preparation of tobacco mosaic virus with that of a standard. The standard was used at five different dilutions: (1) 1/100, (2) 1/300, (3) 1/900, (4) 1/2700, and (5) 1/8100, and the unknown at three different dilutions: (6) 1/300, (7) 1/900, and (8) 1/2700. There were, therefore, eight different treatments. The test plant was *Nicotiana tabacum* L. var Xanthi. Each plant had four inoculable leaves, and eight plants were used. Half leaf was used as the experimental unit, so that there were eight units per plant. The design was such that each treatment occurred once on each plant, and the positions of treatments within plants were randomized, the restriction of randomization being that each treatment occurred an equal number of times (twice) on each leaf position on the stem.

The source of variation from differences between plants and between leaf positions was thus eliminated from the experimental error.

The results are shown in Table XVIII. The numbers in brackets are numbers of local lesions on individual leaves. To find the value constant of transformation, standard deviations of the numbers of lesions were computed separately for each treatment whose mean was not smaller than about 10. The following results were obtained:

Treatment	1	2	3	4	6
Mean	118.5	95.0	41.5	9.75	10.9
Standard deviation	55.0	34.2	21.2	7.2	5.4

The standard deviations were plotted against the means, and a regression line was fitted by eye, which intersected the axis of abscissas approximately at a point corresponding to the value of -5. Thus, the numbers of lesions were transformed according to Eq. (41) of Section V,G using 5 as the value of the constant c. (This point was discussed in Section V,G.) The transformed numbers, shown in Table XVIII without brackets, were used for the analysis of variance shown in Table XIX. The totals for leaf postions were 19.73, 19.79, 20.05, and 23.18. The residual variance based on 46 degrees of freedom is $s^2 = 0.023$.

The estimates of mean numbers of lesions per half leaf for the eight treatments, obtained according to Eq. (58), are $X_1 = 114.0$, $X_2 = 96.0$, $X_3 = 39.3$, $X_4 = 9.4$, $X_5 = 3.7$, $X_6 = 10.5$, $X_7 = 4.5$, and $X_8 = 1.7$. (They happen not to differ much from the arithmetic means.) Inspecting these numbers, or plotting their values against virus concentrations, will lead to the conclusion that except for X_1 they all fall within the range in which linearity can be assumed. Thus, four dilutions of the standard and three of the unknown can be assumed to be within the range of linearity and so can be used to estimate the concentration of the unknown.

Four independent estimates of the value of log Kv and their variances are:

$Z_2' = \log 96.0 + \log\ \ 300 = 4.46$

$$\mathrm{var}(Z_2') = 0.0029(1 + 10/96)\ \ = 0.0032$$

$Z_3' = \log 39.3 + \log\ \ 900 = 4.55$

$$\mathrm{var}(Z_3') = 0.0029(1 + 10/39.3) = 0.0036$$

$Z_4' = \log\ \ 9.4 + \log 2700 = 4.40$

$$\mathrm{var}(Z_4') = 0.0029(1 + 10/9.4)\ \ = 0.0060$$

$Z_5' = \log\ \ 3.7 + \log 8100 = 4.48$

$$\mathrm{var}(Z_5') = 0.0029(1 + 10/3.7)\ \ = 0.0107$$

The weighted mean of the above values of Z is

TABLE XVIII

An Experiment for Estimation of Concentration of Tobacco Mosaic Virus[a]

Treatment No.	Plant No.								Totals	Means
	1	2	3	4	5	6	7	8		
1	(131) 2.13	(66) 1.85	(90) 1.98	(200) 2.31	(50) 1.74	(162) 2.22	(79) 1.92	(170) 2.24	(948) 16.39	(118.5) 2.0488
2	(70) 1.88	(147) 2.18	(76) 1.91	(105) 2.04	(61) 1.82	(87) 1.96	(62) 1.83	(152) 2.20	(760) 15.82	(95.0) 1.9775
3	(40) 1.65	(16) 1.32	(48) 1.72	(58) 1.80	(71) 1.88	(18) 1.36	(21) 1.41	(60) 1.81	(332) 12.95	(41.5) 1.6188
4	(4) 0.92	(5) 0.97	(11) 1.19	(12) 1.22	(7) 1.06	(5) 0.97	(8) 1.10	(26) 1.49	(78) 8.92	(9.75) 1.1150
5	(0) 0.40	(3) 0.85	(3) 0.85	(6) 1.02	(2) 0.78	(9) 1.13	(2) 0.78	(8) 1.10	(33) 6.91	(4.125) 0.8638
6	(8) 1.10	(13) 1.25	(8) 1.10	(1) 0.67	(9) 1.13	(16) 1.32	(16) 1.32	(16) 1.32	(87) 9.21	(10.9) 1.1513
7	(2) 0.78	(2) 0.78	(6) 1.02	(6) 1.02	(6) 1.02	(4) 0.92	(2) 0.78	(5) 0.97	(33) 7.29	(4.125) 0.9113
8	(0) 0.40	(0) 0.40	(1) 0.67	(6) 1.02	(4) 0.92	(1) 0.67	(0) 0.40	(2) 0.78	(14) 5.26	(1.75) 0.6575
Totals	9.26	9.60	10.44	11.10	10.35	10.55	9.54	11.91	82.75	

[a] The numbers in parentheses are the numbers of lesions x, and the numbers not in parentheses are obtained by the transformation $y = \log \frac{1}{2}[x + c + (x^2 + 2cx)^{1/2}]$, the value of the constant c being 5.

$$\bar{Z}_v = \frac{4.46/0.0032 + 4.55/0.0036 + 4.40/0.006 + 4.48/0.0107}{1/0.0032 + 1/0.0036 + 1/0.006 + 1/0.0107} = 4.48$$

and the variance of $\bar{Z}_v$ is

$$\text{var}(\bar{Z}_v) = \frac{1}{1/0.0032 + 1/0.0036 + 1/0.006 + 1/0.0107} = 0.0012$$

Three independent estimates of the value of log Kw and their variances are:

$$Z_6' = \log 10.5 + \log\ 300 = 3.50$$
$$\text{var}(Z_6') = 0.0029(1 + 10/10.5) = 0.0057$$
$$Z_7' = \log\ 4.5 + \log\ 900 = 3.61$$
$$\text{var}(Z_7') = 0.0029(1 + 10/4.5)\ = 0.0093$$
$$Z_8' = \log\ 1.7 + \log 2700 = 3.66$$
$$\text{var}(Z_8') = 0.0029(1 + 10/1.7)\ = 0.0200$$

The weighted mean of the above values of Z is

$$\bar{Z}_w = \frac{3.5/0.0057 + 3.61/0.0093 + 3.66/0.02}{1/0.0057 + 1/0.0093 + 1/0.0200} = 3.55$$

and the variance of $\bar{Z}_w$ is

$$\text{var}(\bar{Z}_w) = \frac{1}{1/0.0057 + 1/0.0093 + 1/0.020} = 0.0030$$

Our estimate of the value of log w/v is

$$\log w/v = \bar{Z}_w - \bar{Z}_v = 3.55 - 4.48 = -0.93 = \bar{1}.07$$

so that $w = 0.12v$.

The variance of the estimate of log w/v is

$$\text{var}(\bar{Z}_w - \bar{Z}_v) = \text{var}(\bar{Z}_w) + \text{var}(\bar{Z}_v) = 0.0012 + 0.003 = 0.0042$$

so that the standard error is 0.0648. Taking the probability of 0.05 as our level of significance, the factor r for 46 degrees of freedom, obtained from a table of distribution of t, is 2.01, so that the fiducial limits for log w/v are $-0.93 - 0.13 = -1.06 = \bar{2}.94$, and $-0.93 + 0.13 = -0.80 = \bar{1}.20$. The value of w is, therefore, between $0.09v$ and $0.16v$, so it can be about 25% smaller, or 33% greater, than the estimated value of $0.12v$. Had greater accuracy been required, more replications (plants) should have been used. The use of plants less variable in susceptibility to infection would also increase precision.

TABLE XIX
Analysis of Variance

Source of variation	Degrees of freedom	Sums of squares	Mean square (variance)
Treatments	7	15.4515	—
Plants	7	0.6813	0.0973
Leaf positions	3	0.5213	0.1737
Residual (error)	46	1.0572	0.023
Total	63	17.7113	

Another statistical method of estimation of the logarithm of the ratio of activities of two virus preparations has been described by Price and Spencer (1943). It is based on the assumption that over a range of concentration the logarithm of the number of lesions is directly proportional to virus concentration. Thus, the relationship between numbers of lesions and virus concentration need not necessarily be linear. The fault of the method is that it is based on the transformation of numbers of lesions into logarithms and on the assumption that this will equalize the variance and make the distribution approximately normal. That this is not so was discussed in Section V,G.

Appendix

Simple Derivations of Some Properties of the Mean and of the Variance

1. *Change of Origin*

If each value of a variate is increased or decreased by adding or subtracting a constant, the mean is similarly increased or decreased, whereas the variance remains unchanged.

Proof: Let the original values be $x_1, x_2, x_3, \ldots$, so that the mean is

$$\mu = \frac{1}{N} \sum_{i=1}^{N} (x_i)$$

when N is large. Let the new values be $(x_1 + d)$, $(x_2 + d)$, $(x_3 + d)$ . . . . The new mean will then be

$$\mu' = \frac{1}{N} \sum_{i=1}^{N} (x_i + d) = \frac{1}{N} \sum_{i=1}^{N} (x_i) + d = \mu + d$$

The variance of the new values [by Eq. (2) of Section I] is

$$\sigma^2 = \frac{1}{N} \sum_{i=1}^{N} \left[(x_i + d) - (\mu + d) \right]^2 = \frac{1}{N} \sum_{i=1}^{N} (x_i - \mu)^2$$

which is the variance of the original values.

2. *Change of Scale*

When all values of a variate are multiplied by a, the mean and the standard deviation are multiplied by a, and the variance by a^2.

Proof: When the values of a variate are multiplied by a, so that they become ax_1, ax_2, ax_3, . . . , the mean will become

$$\frac{1}{N} \sum_{i=1}^{N} (ax_i) = a \frac{1}{N} \sum_{i=1}^{N} (x_i)$$

which is a times the mean of the original values.

If μ is the mean of the original values, the variance of the new values is (when N is large)

$$\sigma^2 = \frac{1}{N} \sum_{i=1}^{N} (ax_i - a\mu)^2 = a^2 \frac{1}{N} \sum_{i=1}^{N} (x_i - \mu)^2$$

which is a^2 times the variance of the original values.

As the standard deviation is the square root of the variance, obviously the standard deviation of the new values is a times the standard deviation of the original values.

3. *The Mean of Products of Two Independent Variates Equals the Product of Their Means*

Proof: Let the values of one variate be x_1, x_2, x_3 $\cdots$ and of the other y_1, y_2, y_3 $\cdots$ and let their means be μ and v. If the variates are independent of each other, any value of x has an equal chance of being paired with any value of y. Thus, the sum of N products of any particular value of x, say x_i, with each of N values of y, is the product of x_i with the sum of a *random sample* of N values of y, which is $x_i \sum_{j=1}^{N} (y_j)$, and therefore the mean of the products is

$$\frac{1}{N} x_i \sum_{j=1}^{N} (y_j) = x_i v$$

when N is large. Thus the sum of N products of x_i with each of N randomly taken values of y is $N x_i v$. Therefore the sum of KN products of each of K randomly taken value of x with each of N randomly taken values of y is $N v \sum_{i=1}^{K} (x_i)$ and so the mean of all the products is

$$\frac{1}{KN}\left[N\nu\sum_{i=1}^{K}(x_i)\right] = \nu\frac{1}{K}\sum_{i=1}^{K}(x_i) = \nu\mu$$

when K is large.

It can be proved in exactly the same way that the mean of products of two independently and randomly taken values of the same variate equals the square of the mean of the variate.

It should be noticed that the assumption that the values of two variates are independent of each other is an essential part of the reasoning. The conclusion does not, therefore, apply to the cases when there is a correlation between values of two variates.

4. The Mean of the Sum (or Difference) of Two Independent Variates Equals the Sum (or Difference) of Their Means

Proof: Let again the variates be x and y, and their means μ and ν. As the variates are independent of each other, any value of one has an equal chance of being added to (or subtracted from) any value of the other. Therefore the sum of N sums (or differences) of a particular value of x, say x_i, and each of N randomly taken values of y is

$$\sum_{j=1}^{N}(x_i \pm y_j) = Nx_i \pm \sum_{j=1}^{N}(y_j) = Nx_i \pm N\left[\frac{1}{N}\sum_{j=1}^{N}(y_j)\right] = Nx_i \pm N\nu$$

Therefore the sum of KN sums (or differences) of K randomly taken values of x and each of N randomly taken values of y is

$$\sum_{i=1}^{K}(Nx_i \pm N\nu) = N\sum_{i=1}^{K}(x_i) \pm KN\nu$$

so that the mean of the sum is

$$\frac{1}{KN}\left[N\sum_{i=1}^{K}(x_i) \pm KN\nu\right] = \frac{1}{K}\sum_{i=1}^{K}(x_i) \pm \nu = \mu \pm \nu$$

5. The Arithmetic Mean of a Small Sample Is a Consistent Estimate of the Mean of the Population

Proof: Let the mean of a random sample of a small number n of values of a variate x be

$$m = \frac{1}{n}\sum_{i=1}^{n}(x_i)$$

Let the procedure of taking a random sample of n values be repeated K times (K being large), and let the mean of jth sample be

$$m_j = \frac{1}{n}\sum_{i=1}^{n}(x_{ij})$$

where x_{ij} is the ith value of x in the jth sample. The mean of K sample means is

$$\frac{1}{K}\sum_{j=1}^{K}(m_j) = \frac{1}{K}\sum_{j=1}^{K}\left[\frac{1}{n}\sum_{i=1}^{n}(x_{ij})\right] = \frac{1}{Kn}\sum_{h=1}^{Kn}(x_h)$$

which is the mean of the population because Kn is a large number.

6. *The Sampling Variance Given by Eq. (4) of Section I Is a Consistent Estimate of the Variance of the Population*

Proof: Let the values of a variate x be x_1, x_2, x_3 $\cdots$ and let μ be the mean of the population. Let μ be subtracted from each value of the variate (which, as shown above, does not affect the value of the variance) and let the new values be ϵ_1, ϵ_2, ϵ_3 $\cdots$ (so that $\epsilon_1 = x_1 - \mu$, $\epsilon_2 = x_2 - \mu$, $\epsilon_3 = x_3 - \mu$ $\cdots$). The mean of the population of the new values is, therefore, zero. Thus

$$\frac{1}{N}\sum_{i=1}^{N}(\epsilon_i) = 0$$

when N is large, but not necessarily so when N is small. In other words, the mean of a small sample of values of ϵ may differ from zero.

The variance of the population [by Eq. (2) of Section I] is

$$\sigma^2 = \frac{1}{N}\sum_{i=1}^{N}(\epsilon_i^2)$$

when N is large.

Let us define z^2 as

$$z^2 = \frac{1}{n}\sum_{i=1}^{n}(x_i - m)^2$$

where n is small and m is the mean of a random sample of n values of x. Now,

$$z^2 = \frac{1}{n}\sum_{i=1}^{n}(x_i - m)^2 = \frac{1}{n}\sum_{i=1}^{n}[(x_i - \mu) - (m - \mu)]^2$$

$$= \frac{1}{n}\sum_{i=1}^{n}\left[\epsilon_i - \frac{1}{n}\sum_{j=1}^{n}(\epsilon_j)\right]^2$$

$$= \frac{1}{n}\sum_{i=1}^{n}\left\{\epsilon_i^2 - 2\frac{1}{n}\epsilon_i\sum_{j=1}^{n}(\epsilon_j) + \frac{1}{n^2}\left[\sum_{j=1}^{n}(\epsilon_j)\right]^2\right\}$$

$$= \frac{1}{n}\sum_{i=1}^{n} (\epsilon_i^2) - 2\frac{1}{n^2}\left[\sum_{i=1}^{n}(\epsilon_i)\right]^2 + \frac{1}{n^2}\left[\sum_{j=1}^{n}(\epsilon_j)\right]^2$$

$$= \frac{1}{n}\sum_{i=1}^{n}(\epsilon_i^2) - \frac{1}{n^2}\left[\sum_{i=1}^{n}(\epsilon_i)\right]^2$$

$$= \frac{1}{n}\sum_{i=1}^{n}(\epsilon_i^2) - \frac{1}{n^2}\sum_{i=1}^{n}(\epsilon_i^2) - \frac{1}{n}\sum_{i=1}^{n}(\epsilon_i\omega_i)$$

$$= \frac{1}{n}\frac{n-1}{n}\sum_{i=1}^{n}(\epsilon_i^2) - \frac{1}{n}\sum_{i=1}^{n}(\epsilon_i\omega_i)$$

where

$$\omega_i = \frac{1}{n}\left[\sum_{j=1}^{n}(\epsilon_j) - \epsilon_i\right]$$

The values of ϵ and of ω are independent of each other because ϵ_i is one of a random sample of n values of ϵ and ω_i is $1/n$th of the sum of the other independently taken $n - 1$ values. As the mean of a large number of randomly taken values of ϵ and of ω is zero, the mean of their products is also zero (see above). Therefore, the mean of a large number of independently obtained values of $1/n\sum_{i=1}^{n}(\epsilon_i\omega_i)$ is zero. Consequently, the mean of a large number, K, of independently obtained values of z^2 is

$$\overline{(z^2)} = \frac{n-1}{n}\frac{1}{Kn}\sum_{i=1}^{Kn}(\epsilon_i^2) = \frac{n-1}{n}\sigma^2$$

Therefore, a consistent estimate of σ^2 from a small sample is

$$s^2 = \frac{n}{n-1}z^2 = \frac{1}{n-1}\sum_{i=1}^{n}(x_i - m)^2$$

7. *If the Variance of a Variate Is* σ^2, *the Variance of the Mean of* n *Randomly Taken Values of the Variate Is* σ^2/n

Proof: Let m be the mean of n randomly taken values of x, and μ the mean of the population. Let d^2 be the square of the deviation of m from μ. Using the same symbols as immediately above, we have

$$d^2 = (m - \mu)^2 = \left[\frac{1}{n}\sum_{i=1}^{n}(x_i) - \mu\right]^2 = \left[\frac{1}{n}\sum_{i=1}^{n}(x_i - \mu)\right]^2$$

$$= \left[\frac{1}{n}\sum_{i=1}^{n}(\epsilon_i)\right]^2 = \frac{1}{n^2}\sum_{i=1}^{n}(\epsilon_i^2) + \frac{1}{n}\sum_{i=1}^{n}(\epsilon_i\omega_i)$$

Now, the variance of the mean is the mean of a large number of independently obtained values of d^2. As explained above, the mean of a large number of independently obtained values of $1/n \sum_{i=1}^{n} (\epsilon_i \omega_i)$ is zero. Therefore, the mean of a large number, K, of independently obtained values of d^2 is

$$\overline{(d^2)} = \frac{1}{Kn^2} \sum_{i=1}^{Kn} (\epsilon_i^2) = \frac{1}{n} \frac{1}{Kn} \sum_{i=1}^{Kn} (x_i - \mu)^2 = \frac{1}{n} \sigma^2$$

The standard deviation of the mean of n values of a variate, i.e., $\sigma/n^{1/2}$ or $s/n^{1/2}$ (when s^2 is a sampling variance), is usually called *the standard error of the mean*. The standard deviation of any statistic is usually called its standard error.

8. *The Variance of the Sum or Difference of Two Independent Variates Is the Sum of Their Variances*

Proof: Let the variates be x and y, their means μ and ν and their variances σ_x^2 and σ_y^2. Let $\epsilon_i = x_i - \mu$ and $\xi_i = y_i - \nu$, so that the means of large random samples of ϵ and of ξ are both zero. Since the variates are independent of each other, any value of one has an equal chance of being paired with any value of the other, and the mean of $x \pm y$ is $\mu \pm \nu$ (see above).

Thus, when N is large, the variance of $x \pm y$ is (by Eq. (2) of Section I)

$$\sigma^2 = \frac{1}{N} \sum_{i=1}^{N} [(x_i \pm y_i) - (\mu \pm \nu)]^2 = \frac{1}{N} \sum_{i=1}^{N} (\epsilon_i \pm \xi_i)^2$$

$$= \frac{1}{N} \sum_{i=1}^{N} (\epsilon_i^2 + \xi_i^2 \pm 2\epsilon_i\xi_i)$$

$$= \frac{1}{N} \sum_{i=1}^{N} (\epsilon_i^2) + \frac{1}{N} \sum_{i=1}^{N} (\xi_i^2) \pm \frac{2}{N} \sum_{i=1}^{N} (\epsilon_i\xi_i)$$

Since the values of ϵ and ξ are independent of each other, and since their means are zero, the mean of their product is also zero (see above), so that

$$\frac{2}{N} \sum_{i=1}^{N} (\epsilon_i\xi_i) = 0$$

Therefore

$$\sigma^2 = \frac{1}{N} \sum_{i=1}^{N} (\epsilon_i^2) + \frac{1}{N} \sum_{i=1}^{N} (\xi_i^2) = \sigma_x^2 + \sigma_y^2$$

730 A. KLECZKOWSKI

9. *Universality of All the Above Properties of Means and Variances*

All the above properties of means and variances were proved without making any assumptions with respect to the type of frequency distribution of the variate, and, therefore, apply to any type of distribution.

REFERENCES

Aitken, A. C. (1945). "Statistical Mathematics," 4th ed. Oliver & Boyd, Edinburgh and London.
Cochran, W. G., and Cox, G. M. (1950). "Experimental Design," Wiley, New York.
Finney, D. J. (1952). "Probit Analysis," 2nd ed. Cambridge Univ. Press, London and New York.
Finney, D. J. (1964). "Statistical Method in Biological Assay," 2nd ed. Griffin, London.
Fisher, R. A. (1958). "Statistical Methods for Research Workers," 13th ed. Oliver & Boyd, Edinburgh and London.
Fisher, R. A. (1960). "The Design of Experiments," 7th ed. Oliver & Boyd, Edinburgh and London.
Fisher, R. A., and Yates, F. (1963). "Statistical Tables for Biological, Agricultural and Medical Research," 6th ed. Oliver & Boyd, Edinburgh and London.
Goulden, C. H. (1952). "Methods of Statistical Analysis," 2nd ed. Wiley, New York.
Haldane, J. B. S. (1939). *J. Hyg.* **39**, 289–293.
Kempthorne, O. (1952). "The Design and Analysis of Experiments." Wiley, New York.
Kendall, M. G., and Stuart, A. (1958–1961). "The Advanced Theory of Statistics." Griffin, London.
Kleczkowski, A. (1949). *Ann. Appl. Biol.* **36**, 139–152.
Kleczkowski, A. (1955). *J. Gen. Microbiol.* **13**, 91–98.
Moran, P. (1954). *J. Hyg.* **52**, 189–193.
Pearson, E. S., and Hartley, H. O. (1954). "Biometrika Tables for Statisticians." Cambridge Univ. Press, London and New York.
Price, W. C., and Spencer, E. L. (1943). *Am. J. Botany* **30**, 720–735.
Quenouille, M. H. (1953). "The Design and Analysis of Experiment." Griffin, London.
Snedecor, G. W. (1946). "Statistical Methods," 4th ed. Iowa State College Press, Ames, Iowa.
Stairs, G. R. (1965). *J. Invertebrate Pathol.* **7**, 5–9.
Stevens, W. L. (1958). *J. Roy. Statist. Soc.* **B20**, 205–214.
Yule, G. U., and Kendall, M. G. (1940). "An Introduction to the Theory of Statistics," 12th ed. Griffin, London.

AUTHOR INDEX

Numbers in italics refer to the pages on which the complete references are listed.

A

Abbott, V., 588, *591*
Abdulmur, S., 187, *208*
Abercrombie, M., 335, *348*
Abinanti, F. R., 381, *459, 464*
Acton, J., 47, *49*
Adams, J. N., 321, *349*
Adams, M. H., 72, *91*, 180, 200, 203, *205*
Agnew, B., 560, *561*
Agol, V. I., 80, *91*
Aitken, A. C., *730*
Aleksandrov, N. I., 441, *458*
Alexander, E. R., 383, *460*
Alexander, H. E., 186, *209*
Alexander, P., 151, *205*
Alford, R. H., 383, 392, *461*
Allen, A. O., 146, *205, 209*
Allen, R., 76, *91*
Allison, A. C., 7, *48*, 161, *205*
Allner, K., 534, *563*
Alper, T., 153, *207*
Amano, T., 571, 581, *592*
Amati, P., 307, 309, *319*, 581, 587, *591*
Ames, B. N., 37, *50*, 588, *592*
Amos, H., 88, *91*
Anderson, D. R., 536, 537, 538, 540, 554, *561, 562*
Anderson, S. A., 382, *460, 463*
Andjaparidze, O. G., 389, *463*
Andrewes, C. H., 376, *463*, 594, 598, *612*
Andrews, P., 39, 40, *48*
Apelgot, S., 144, *205*
Appleyard, R. K., 314, 316, *320*, 321, 348, *348*
Arber, W., 299, 301, *319*, 321, *348*
Armand, N. deSanctis, 263, *278*
Armitage, P., 262, *278*

B

Armstrong, D., 328, 339, *349*, 536, 541, 554, 555, *562, 563*
Armstrong, J. A., 595, *612*
Arrobio, J. O., 388, *461*
Artenstein, M. S., 4, *51*, 385, 388, *458, 459, 462*
Atchison, R. W., 348, *348*
Aulisio, C. G., 390, *459*
Aurelian, L., 4, 7, 9, 10, *48*
Aurisicchio, S., 161, *205*

B

Babos, P., 346, *348*
Bachrach, H. L., 197, 200, 203, 204, *205*, 353, 354, 355, 356, 357, 358, 359, 360, 362, 363, 364, 366, 367, *368, 369*
Bader, J. P., 4, 7, 11, 22, 46, *48*, 87, *91*, 595, *612*
Bailey, J. S., 534, *562*
Bailey, M. L., 377, *463*
Balbinder, E., 302, *319*
Bald, J. G., 347, *348*
Balduzzi, P., 535, 552, 556, *562*
Baluda, M., 4, *48*
Bancroft, J. B., 516, 522, 527, 528, *529*
Banks, P. A., 383, 392, *461*
Barber, T. L., 536, 538, *562*
Barricelli, N. A., 164, *205*
Barile, M. F., 531, 532, 533, 534, 536, 537, 538, 541, 542, 546, 553, *561, 562, 564*
Barnett, L., 185, *205*
Baron, L. S., 534, *563*
Baron, S., 3, 8, 9, 10, 13, 19, 25, 26, 27, 44, 47, *48, 50*, 381, *459, 464*
Barrett, C. D., Jr., 377, 392, *459*
Barrett, N., 172, *208*
Barry, G. T., 588, *591*

731

Barry, R. D., 595, *612*
Basilico, C., 160, 174, 176, *205*
Batanova, T. B., 383, *463*
Bauer, D. J., 236, 237, 247, 248, 249, 251, 252, *277*
Baum, S. G., 382, *462*
Bawden, F. C., 344, *348, 349*
Beals, T. F., 608, *613*
Beard, D., 378, *459*
Beard, J. W., 378, *459*
Beardmore, W. B., 381, *459*
Beineke, B., 154, 168, *206*
Bell, E. J., 390, *462*
Bell, J. A., 377, 382, *459*
Bellanti, J. A., 388, 389, *458, 459, 463*
Bellett, A. J. D., 4, *49*
Belyavin, G., 66, 67, *91*
Benda, G. T. A., 89, *91*
Benenson, A. S., 390, *459*
Benesi, E., 433, 434, 435, *462*
Benjamin, T. L., 174, 176, *205*
Benzer, S., 164, 165, 185, *205*, 288, *319*
Bercks, R., 500, *501*
Berger, J. E., 503, *529*
Berger, R., 122, *138*
Berman, S., 378, 390, *459, 462*
Bernheim, B. C., 4, 7, *51*, 440, *461*
Bernkopf, H., 262, *277*
Berry, G. P., 161, *209*
Berwald, Y., 12, *51*
Best, R. J., 492, 493, *501*
Biddle, F., 66, 67, *91*
Binn, L. N., 373, 390, *459, 461, 462*
Birk, Y., 2, *51*
Black, F. L., 200, *205*
Black, J., 374, *460, 461, 462, 463*
Black, P. H., 48, *51*
Blaškovič, D., 213, 214, 215, 238, 239, 240, 242, 243, 244, 246, 247, 272, 273, 275, 276, *278*
Boand, A. V., 381, *464*
Bockrath, R. C., 145, *206*
Bodey, G. P., 542, 546, *562*
Bodian, D., 380, *459*
Bodo, G., 38, *50*
Boedtker, H., 155, *206*
Boesche, P., 483, *489*
Boichuk, L. M., 383, *463*
Boisen, M., 380, *460*
Bondaletova, I. N., 389, *463*

Bonifas, V. H., 86, 87, *92*, 533, 536, 547, 551, 552, *562, 564*
Borecky, L., 13, *50*
Bowen, E. J., 123, *138*
Boyce, R. P., 166, *205*
Bradley, D. E., 610, *612*
Brand, O. M., 80, 84, *91*
Brandenberg, E., 346, *350*
Brandes, J., 597, *612*
Brandon, F. M., 377, 392, *459*
Brandt, C. D., 368, *368*
Brasch, A., 178, *209*
Breed, R. S., 531, *562*
Breese, S. S., Jr., 197, 200, 203, 204, *205*, 353, 359, 360, 362, 363, 364, 366, *368, 369*
Breinig, M. K., 7, 11, *50*
Brenner, S., 85, *92*, 185, *205*
Brezina, R., 258, 259, *277*
Brightman, I. J., 388, *460*
Brindle, S. A., 556, *564*
Brooks, K., 316, 318, *319*
Brown, A., 531, 541, 542, 546, 551, 552, 555, 556, 558, *562, 563*
Brown, D. M., 194, *205*
Brown, T. M., 534, 544, 547, 548, 549, 550, *562*
Brownell, G. L., 146, *207*
Brownlee, K. A., 234, 261, *277*
Brownstein, B., 533, *562*
Bryan, J. A., 383, *460*
Bryan, W. G., 160, 176, *205*
Bryan, W. R., 451, *463, 483, 489*
Buchan, A., 11, 19, 44, *48*
Buchanan, J. M., 178, *206*
Buckler, C. E., 8, 9, 13, 25, 27, 44, *48*
Buddingh, G. J., 378, *460*
Buescher, E. L., 4, *51*, 382, 385, 388, *458, 459, 462, 463*
Bulgakov, N., 155, *208*
Bullis, C., 533, 534, 536, 541, 545, *563*
Burgi, E., 160, 161, *205, 207*
Burke, D. C., 10, 11, 19, 21, 30, 41, 44, *48, 50*, 161, *205*
Burnet, F. M., 61, *91*, 594, *612*
Burov, S. A., 441, *463*
Burruss, H. W., 375, *460*
Butel, J. S., 203, *208*
Butler, M., 533, 536, *562*
Buynak, E. B., 387, *459, 460, 463, 464*

Buzzell, A., 61, 66, *91*, 152, 155, *205*
Bystryakova, L. V., 383, *463*

C

Cabasso, V. J., 381, 389, *459*
Cadman, C. H., 346, *349*
Calafiore, D. C., 383, *460*
Calef, E., 294, 295, 304, *319*
Callis, J. J., 197, 200, 203, 204, *205,* 353, 354, 359, 364, *368*
Calman, D., 483, *489*
Calvert, J. G., 125, *138*
Campbell, A., 288, 302, 310, 318, *319*, 321, *349*
Campbell, W. E., Jr., 534, *563*
Canchola, J. G., 388, *461*
Cantell, K., 8, 12, 14, 18, *48, 49*
Carey, W. B., 534, *563*
Carmack, C., 191, 193, 194, 195, 196, 201, *206*
Carmichael, L. E., 554, *562*
Carrier, W. L., 166, *208*
Carski, T. R., 531, 533, 536, 539, 541, 544, 555, *562*
Carter, G. R., 534, *562*
Carter, J. E., 263, *278*
Carver, D. A., 4, *50*
Casals, J., 72, *91*
Casey, H. L., 383, *460*
Casey, M. J., 382, *461*
Caspar, D. L. D., 173, 184, 185, *205, 207*
Castagnoli, C., 161, *205*
Casto, B. C., 348, *348*
Cate, T. R., 383, 436, *459*
Chadwick, D. L., 381, *461*
Chalkina, O. M., 388, 441, *463*
Chamailland, L., 175, 176, *207*
Chamberland, 374, *462*
Champe, S. P., 185, *205*
Chang, A. Y., 346, *349*
Chang, I., 390, *460*
Chanock, R. M., **382**, 383, 388, 389, 436, *459, 460, 461, 463, 532, 535, 563, 564*
Chany, C., 7, 30, *49*
Chapman, W. G., 355, *369*
Charbonneau, R. J., 535, 552, 556, *562*
Chargaff, E., 195, *209*
Charlesby, A., 151, *205*
Charlwood, P. A., 37, *51*

Charney, J., 366, 367, *368, 369*
Chase, M., 173, *207*
Chassary, A., 440, *461*
Chenault, S., 47, *49*
Cherry, W. B., 201, *205*
Chevallier, M. R., 587, *592*
Choppin, P. W., 6, *49*
Chrambach, A., 35, *50*
Chu, C. M., 74, *91*
Chu, L. W., 383, 436, *459*
Chumakova, M. Y., 80, *91*
Clark, H. W., 534, 544, *562*
Clark, J. M., Jr., 346, *349*
Clark, W. A., 492, *501*
Clavero, G., 379, *459*
Cline, J. C., 3, 14, *50*
Clowes, R. C., 577, 578, 581, 591, *591, 592*
Clyde, W. A., Jr., 532, *562*
Cochran, W. G., 631, *730*
Cockburn, T. A., 383, *460*
Cogniaux-Le Clerc, J., 41, *49*
Cohen, A., 66, *91*
Cohen, G. H., 393, *459*
Cohen, R. A., 257, 260, 272, 273, *278*
Cohen, S. S., 178, *206*
Cole, G., 390, *459*
Collier, L. H., 531, *562*
Colón, J. I., 80, 84, *91*
Conwell, D. P., 374, *460, 463*
Cook, M. K., 533, *564*
Cooper, P. D., 4, *49, 51,* 89, 91, 596, *612*
Cords, C. E., 4, *49*
Coriell, L. L., 531, 532, 533, 534, 538, 559, 560, *562*
Cornfeld, D., 367, *369*
Cortini, G., 161, *205*
Costlow, R. D., 80, 84, *91*
Cotton, I. M., 152, *205*
Couch, J. W., 382, *463*
Couch, R. B., 436, *459*
Courington, D., 348, *349*
Cowdry, E. V., 601, *612*
Cowles, P., 201, *206*
Cox, A., 527, *529*
Cox, G. M., 631, *730*
Cox, H. R., 374, 379, 381, *459, 461, 463*
Cox, L. M., 383, *460*
Cox, R. A., 14, *50*
Craigie, J., 379, *459*
Cramer, R., 351, 352, *369*

Crawford, E. M., 160, 175, *205,* 607, *612*
Crawford, L. V., 160, 175, *205,* 607, *612*
Crick, F. H. C., 184, *205*
Crittenden, L. B., 340, *349*
Crothers, D. M., 187, *205*
Crowell, R. L., 4, *49*
Crowley, A. M., 383, *460*
Crowther, J. A., 148, *206*
Cruickshank, J. G., 595, *612*
Culbertson, C. G., 200, *208,* 348, *349,* 375, *462*

D

Dahl, D., 295, *319*
Dalldorf, G., 608, *612*
Dal Prato, A., 353, *369*
Darnell, J. E., Jr., 89, *91*
Darwish, M., 378, *459*
Davenport, F. M., 377, 392, *459, 460*
Dawe, C. J., 451, *463*
Dean, D. J., 389, *459*
DeBoer, C. J., 353, 354, *368*
Deeks, D., 603, *613*
Defendi, V., 541, *563*
de Harven, E., 598, *612*
Del Campillo-Campbell, A., 309, *319*
De Leva, A. M., 525, *529*
Del Guidice, R. A., 544, *562*
Delihas, N., 175, 177, 178, *206*
De Maeyer, E., 7, 45, *49*
De Maeyer, J., 45, *49*
DeMargerie, H., 581, 584, *592*
DeMeio, J. L., 388, *459, 461*
Demerseman, P., 142, *207*
Denhardt, G. H., 304, *320*
de Rosier, D. J., 527, *529*
DeSanctis, A. M., 388, *459*
Dessauer, F., 148, *206*
DeWitt, W., 575, *591*
Diamond, E. L., 380, *460*
Dickinson, L., 285, *278*
Dienes, L., 534, 543, *562*
DiMarzio, E. A., 187, *206*
Di Mayorca, G., 160, 174, 176, *205*
Dimond, A. E., 155, 173, 200, *208*
Dinter, Z., 6, 7, *49*
Dirksen, M. L., 178, *206*
Di Stefano, H. S., 331, 333, 348, *349*
Dixon, C. B., 30, 31, 33, 34, 35, 38, *51*

Dolphin, G. W., 146, *206*
Donini, P., 161, *205*
Donnelley, M., 389, *459*
Donovan, A., 375, *460*
Doty, P., 187, 189, 191, 195, *206, 208*
Dougherty, R. M., 325, 331, 333, 348, *349*
Douglas, A., 389, *459*
Dove, W. F., 288, 295, 296, 297, *319*
Drake, M. E., 464, *464*
Drees, O., 483, *489*
Drew, R., 173, *206*
DuBuy, H. G., 8, *48,* 493, *501*
Duesberg, P. H., 160, *206*
Duffy, C. E., 378, *462*
Dulbecco, R., 22, *49,* 116, *138,* 191, *206,* 271, *277*
Dulworth, W. G., 388, *461*
Dykstra, T. P., 493, *501*

E

Eagle, H., 86, *91,* 547, *562*
Earle, W. R., 451, *463*
Eaton, M. D., 532, 533, 534, 535, *562*
Ebisuzaki, K., 175, 177, 178, *206*
Eddy, B. E., 380, *459*
Edgar, R. S., 304, *320*
Edmondson, W. P., 383, 436, *459*
Edwards, G. A., 554, *562*
Eggers, H. J., 601, *612, 613*
Eigelsbach, H. T., 541, *563*
Eignes, J., 195, *206*
Ekert, B., 142, *607*
Eldjarn, L., 151, *206*
Elsner, V., 531, 542, 546, 551, 552, 555, 558, *563*
Emma, V., 161, *205*
Enders, J. F., 7, 11, 12, *49, 50,* 379, 380, 383, 384, 386, *459, 461, 462, 463,* 594, *612*
Enger, M. D., 155, 160, *208*
Engle, C., 272, 273, *278*
Epstein, R. H., 164, *206*
Ertel, I. J., 533, 534, 536, 541, 545, *563*
Evans, W. M., 389, *459*
Eveland, W. C., 537, 542, 546, *562*
Everhart, D. L., 588, *591*
Exner, F. M., 142, *208*
Eylar, O. R., 390, *464*
Eyring, H., 181, *206*

sberg, H. S., 69, 74, 76, *91, 92*
rardi, A. J., 380, *460,* 532, 533, 534, 541, *563*
lasgow, L. A., 2, 7, 13, 45, *49, 50*
lasstone, S., 181, *206*
ochenour, R. B., 390, *459*
Goebel, W. F., 69, 72, *91,* 588, *591, 592,*
Gold, E., 6, 8, *49*
Goldé, A., 176, *207,* 325, 334, *349*
Gonzales, P., 533, *563*
Goodgal, S., 312, *319*
Goodpasture, E. W., 378, *460*
Gordon, I., 47, *49*
Gordon, M. P., 193, *206*
Gordy, W., 153, *206*
Gori, G. B., 552, 555, *563*
Gotlieb-Stematsky, T., 355, *369*
Gottschalk, A., 66, *91*
Goulden, C. H., *730*
Gowen, J. W., *206*
Grabowsky, M. W., 542, 546, *562*
Graham, A. F., 155, *208,* 533, *562*
Graham, M. G., 588, *591*
Gratia, A., 565, *592*
Grayston, J. T., 390, *460*
Graziosi, F., 161, *205*
Greaves, R. I. N.. 493, 494, *501*
Greeley, L. W., 492, 494, 495, *501*
Greene, E. L., 76, *92*
Gregg, N. C., 58, *91*
Greiff, D., 486, 488, *489*
Greig, A. S., 534, *562*
Gresser, I., 12, *49*
Guerin, M. M., 432, *462*
Guild, W. R., 189, *206*
Guild, W. P., 143, 146, 149, *208*
Guinee, V. F., 383, *460*
Gundelfinger, B. F., 383, 436, *459*
Guss, M. C., 541, *563*
Guthrie, G. S., 191, *208*

H

Habel, K., 7, 13, *49,* 58, 77, 78, 86, *91, 92,* 451, *463,*
Hacker, C., 552, *562*
Hagen, U., 164, *207*
Hahn, E., 533, *562*
Hakala, M. T., 533, *563*
Haldane, J. B. S., *730*

Hallum, J. V., 13, 30, 31, 38, *49*
Hamblet, F. E., 353, 354, *368*
Hammon, W. McD., 348, *348,* 378, *459*
Hamparian, V. V., 601, *612*
Hampel, B., 263, *278*
Hamre, D., 234, 261, *277*
Hanafusa, H., 322, 323, 324, 325, 327, 329, 331, 332, 333, 334, 336, 338, 339, 340, 341, 342, 343, 344, *349*
Hanafusa, T., 322, 323, 324, 325, 327, 329, 331, 332, 334, 336, 339, 342, 343, *349*
Hanaoka, M., 581, *592*
Hanel, E., 560, *564*
Hanig, M., 61, 66, *91*
Hantover, M. J., 382, *459*
Hare, R., 376, *461*
Hargett, M. V., 375, *460*
Harpaz, I., 2, *51*
Harriman, P. D., 163, 177, *207*
Harris, L., 125, *138*
Harrison, B. D., 346, *349*
Harrison, G. R., 97, *138*
Harrison, V. R., 390, *459, 462*
Hart, R. G., 173, *207*
Hartley, H. O., *730*
Hartley, J. W., 603, *612*
Hartman, F. W., 432, *460, 461*
Hatchard, C. G., 126, *138*
Hatten, B. A., 534, *563*
Hattman, S., 85, *91*
Havens, M. L., 381, *464*
Hayashi, M., 193, *207*
Hayashi, M. N., 193, *207*
Hayflick, L., 451, 454, *460, 462,* 531, 532, 533, 534, 535, 536, 538, 539, 540, 541, 542, 543, 545, 548, 549, 552, 554, 560, *562, 563*
Hearn, H. J. Jr., 531, 542, 546, 551, 552, 555, 558, *563*
Heaysman, J. E. M., 335, *348*
Hebert, T. T., 493, 499, *501*
Heineberg, H., 6, 8, *49*
Helinsky, D. R., 575, *591*
Heller, E., 7, 11, 15, 41, *49*
Hemphill, F. M., 380, *460*
Henderson, D. A., 383, *460*
Henle, G., 3, *49,* 87, *91,* 541, *562,*
Henle, W., 3, 11, 15, *49, 51,* 87, *91,* 262, *277*
Henmi, M., 76, *92*

F

Faber, J. E., 533, 534, *563*
Fabisch, P., 84, *92*
Fabricant, J., 536, 538, 554, *562*
Fagraeus, A., 381, *460*
Falcoff, E., 7, *49*
Falkow, S., 535, *563, 564*
Fantes, K. H., 33, 34, *49*
Farr, A. L., 364, *369*
Fauconnier, B., 7, *49*
Fazekas de St. Groth, S., 389, *459*
Feldman, H. A., 598, *612*
Feltz, W. R., 534, *562*
Fenwick, M. L., 89, *91*
Fermi, C., 374, *459*
Fernandes, M. V., 375, *464*
Ferris, W. R., 347, *350*
Field, A. K., 48, *50*
Fiers, W., 191, 192, *206*
Finch, J. T., 529, 597, *612*
Finkelstein, H., 378, *459*
Finkelstein, R. A., 76, *91*
Finney, D. J., 230, *277*, 713, *730*
Finter, N. B., 8, 19, 44, 48, *49*, 262, *277*
Fischer-Fantuzzi, L., 294, 304, *319*
Fischinger, P. J., 6, 7, *50*
Fisher, R. A., 220, 228, *278*, 704, 706, *730*
Fisher, W. P., 366, *368*
Flaks, J. G., 178, *206*
Flosdorf, E. W., 482, *489*
Fluke, D. J., 148, 154, 159, 160, 168, 173, 176, *206*
Fogh, H., 533, 537, 544, *562*
Fogh, J., 533, 537, 544, 552, 554, *562*
Folkers, K., 265, *278*
Fonseca da Cunha, J., 375, *460*
Font, W. F., 383, *460*
Force, E. E., 595, *612*
Forro, F., Jr., 159, 173, 174, 176, *206, 208*
Foster, R. A. C., 180, *206*
Fowler, R. C., 534, 544, *562*
Fox, G., 560, *562*
Fox, J. P., 374, 375, 379, *460, 463*
Fox, M., 166, *206*
Francis, T., Jr., 376, 380, 388, *460*
Franklin, N. C., 288, 295, 296, 297, 319
Franklin, R. E., 173, *206*
Fredericq, P., 565, 566, 567, 570, 571, 578, 580, *591*
Freifelder, D., 163, *206*

Fremont, J. C., 383,
French, C. S., 97, *138*
Freundt, E. A., 532, 5
Frey, S., 525, *529*
Fridborg, E., 345, *349*
Friedemann, A. B., 178,
Friedman, M., 201, *206*
Friedman, R. M., 10, 11, 1.
Friend, C., 535, 552, *562*, 59
Fuerst, C. R., 159, 163,
315, 319, *319, 321, 349*
Fukasawa, T., 85, *91*
Fulton, F., 262, *278*
Funk, F., 145, *206*

G

Gabliks, J., 272, 273, *278*
Gaffney, E. V., 533, *563*
Gafford, L. G., 533, *564*
Gajewska, E., 201, *206*
Gall, J. G., 529, *529*
Gallian, M. J., 368, *369*
Gallus, H. P. C., 492, *501*
Gapochko, K. G., 441, *458*
Garber, E. B., 147, *208*
Gard, S., 199, *206*, 234, *278*, 381, *460*, 594, *612*
Garen, A., 161, *206*
Garin, N. S., 441, *458*
Gauld, R. L., 382, *460, 463*
Gauntt, C. J., 21, *49*
Gefen, N. E., 441, *458*
Gelfand, H. M., 374, *460*
Gellert, M., 167, *206*
Genig, V. A., 390, *460, 464*
Gentry, G. A., 533, *564*
Germer, W. D., 75, *91*
Gest, H., 144, 159, *207*
Gesteland, R. F., 155, *206*
Ghendon, I. Z., 381, *460*
Gibbs, C. J., Jr., 390, *459*
Gibbs, J. H., 187, *206*
Gieskin, R. F., 541, *563*
Gifford, G. E., 9, 11, 19, 21, 23, 24, 25, *49, 50*
Ginoza, W., 142, 148, 151, 152, 155, 156, 157, 158, 159, 160, 161, 164, 165, 167, 177, 187, 188, 189, 190, 191, 192, 193, 194, 195, 196, 201, *206, 209*

Hennessen, H., 375, *462*

Hennessy, A. V., 377, 392, *459, 460*

Henry, C., 75, *91*

Herderscheê, D., 531, 552, 559, *563*

Hermodsson, S., 7, 9, 10, 11, 20, *49*

Herrmann, E. C., Jr., 257, 260, 272, 273, *278*

Hershey, A. D., 144, 159, 160, 161, 163, 173, *207, 208*

Hess, W. R., 203, 204, *205,* 353, 354, 359, 364, *368*

Hetrick, F., 378, *462*

Hiatt, C. W., 199, *207*

Hidaka, Z., 493, *501*

Hieninson, M. A., 389, *463*

Hill, N. O., *613*

Hilleman, M. R., 7, 13, 15, 27, 29, 30, 31, 32, 33, 34, 35, 38, 48, *50,* 366, 367, *369,* 380, 382, 386, 387, 388, 436, 437, 438, *459, 460, 461, 462, 463, 464,* 532, 533, 534, 541, *563,* 601, *612*

Hills, G. J., 513, 514, 516, 519, 521, 522, 525, 526, 527, 528, 529, *529*

Hine, G. J., 146, *207*

Hinsdill, R. D., 588, *592*

Hirst, G. K., 3, *51, 78, 91,* 376, *460,* 594, *612*

Hitchborn, J. H., 519, 521, 525, *529*

Hjertén, S., 345, *349*

Ho, M., 2, 3, 6, 7, 8, 9, 11, 25, 26, 29, 41, 42, 43, 45, *49, 50*

Höglund, S., 345, *349*

Hoelle, C. J., 191, 193, 194, 195, 196, 201, *206*

Hoggan, M. D., 348, *349*

Holland, I. B., 590, *592*

Holland, J. F., 533, *563*

Holland, J. J., 4, *49*

Hollings, M., 493, *501*

Holloway, A., 384, *459*

Holmes, B., 152, 155, *207*

Holmes, F. O., 594, *612*

Holmes, K. C., *529*

Holmgren, N. B., 534, *563*

Holt, A. S., 97, *138*

Holweck, F., 149, *207*

Hook, A. E., 200, *209,* 381, 435, *459, 464*

Hopps, H. E., 4, 7, *51,* 385, *462*

Horne, R. W., 184, 185, *205, 207,* 594, 595, 597, *612*

Hornibrook, J. W., 58, *91*

Horoszewicz, J. S., 533, *563*

Horsfall, F. L., Jr., 63, 69, 74, *91, 92,* 265, *278*

Horstmann, D. M., 598, *612*

Hosley, R. J., 381, *464*

Hostetler, D. D., 440, *461*

Hotchkiss, R. D., 187, 188, 190, *208*

Hottle, G. A., 381, *459, 464*

Hotz, G., 151, 160, 161, *207*

Howard-Flanders, P., 153, 166, *205, 207*

Howarth, S., 578, *592*

Howe, H. A., 380, *459*

Hradečná, Z., 168, *207*

Huang, A. S., 5, 9, 12, 15, 41, 44, *50, 51, 52*

Huang, N., 367, *369*

Huber, M., 383, 392, *461*

Huber, W., 178, *209*

Huebner, R. J., 328, 339, *349, 350,* 382, 383, 436, 451, *459, 460, 461, 463*

Huff, J. W., 193, *206*

Hull, R. N., 348, *349,* 390, *461*

Human, M. L., 85, *91*

Hummeler, K., 536, 539, 540, 554, 555, *563*

Hutchinson, F., 143, 146, 149, 158, 160, 171, 174, *206, 207, 208*

Hyatt, D. F., 9, 20, *52*

Hybner, C. J., 535, *564*

I

Ichter, J. T., 367, *369*

Idoine, J. B., 80, 84, *91*

Ikic, D., 375, *462*

Ilyin, N. A., 441, *463*

Ingraham, L., 160, *207*

Isaacs, A., 2, 3, 6, 10, 11, 12, 14, 16, 19, 20, 26, 30, *50*

Ishizaki, R., 339, 340, 341, 343, *350*

Ivánovics, G., 566, *592*

Ives, D. R., 595, *612*

J

Jackson, E. B., 373, *461*

Jacob, F., 285, 286, 300, 301, 312, 315, 319, *319,* 321, 348, *349,* 567, 574, 585, *592*

Jacobs, J. P., 533, *564*

Jagger, J., 122, *138,* 176, *207*

Jamison, R. M., 348, *349*

Jansz, H. S., 163, 192, *207, 208*

Jenner, E., 372, *461*
Jensen, F., 380, *461*
Jensen, K. E., 368, *368,* 388, *461*
Jerne, H. K., *209*
Jervis, G. A., 381, *461*
Jesaitis, M. A., 72, *91*
Johns, H. E., 146, *207*
Johnson, F. H., 180, *206*
Johnson, H. N., 389, *461*
Johnson, I. S., 348, *349*
Johnson, M. L., 8, *48*
Johnson, T. C., 4, 5, 6, 7, *50*
Joklik, W. G., 89, *91*
Joklik, W. K., 48, *50*
Jordan, E., 304, *319*
Jordan, L. E., 348, *349*
Josse, J., 165, *207*
Jovin, T., 35, *50*
Jungwirth, C., 38, *50*

K

Kaesburg, P., 155, 160, *208*
Kaiser, A. D., 285, 286, 289, *319*
Kalinkina, A. G., 389, *463*
Kamen, M. D., 144, 159, *207*
Kaminsky, J., 125, *138*
Kaplan, C., 197, *207,* 373, *461*
Kaplan, M. M., 594, *612*
Karakajumcan, M. K., 389, *463*
Karzon, D. T., 75, *91,* 383, *460*
Kasel, J. A., 383, 392, *461*
Kasha, M., 95, *138*
Kassanis, B., 133, 134, *138,* 344, 345, 346,
    348, 349
Kato, Y., 581, *592*
Katz, S. L., 383, 384, *459, 461*
Kauzman, W., 186, *207*
Kay, W. W., 435, *464*
Kayajanian, G., 290, *319*
Keene, J. P., 147, *207*
Kellenberger, G., 299, 301, 304, *319, 320,*
    321, *348*
Kempe, C. H., 383, *461*
Kempf, J., 176, *207*
Kempner, E. S., 173, *207*
Kempthorne, O., *730*
Kendall, M. G., *730*
Kennedy, J. W., 144, 159, *207*
Kenny, G. E., 531, 533, 536, 552, 556, 559
    563, 564

Kessel, J. F., 380, *461*
Ketler, A., 601, *612*
Khoobyarian, N., 6, 7, *50*
Kilbourne, E. D., 14, 45, 50, *51*
Kilham, L., 608, *612*
Kim, H. W., 388, *461*
Kirchstein, R. I., 13, *48*
Kirk, B. E., 381, *464*
Kirkham, W. R., 10, *49*
Kirschstein, R. L., 381, 385, *459, 462, 464*
Kiseleva, I. S., 389, *463*
Kissling, R. E., 375, *461*
Kitaoka, M., 76, *92*
Kleczkowski, A., 93, 133, 134, *138,* 720,
    730
Kleczkowski, J., 133, *138*
Klein, M., 57, *91*
Kleineberger-Nobel, E., 532, 538, *563*
Kleinschmidt, W. J., 3, 14, *50, 51*
Klimovickaja, V. I., 389, *463*
Klosterman, H. J., 493, *501*
Klug, A., 184, 185, *205, 207,* 503, 527, *529,*
    597, *612*
Klyachko, N. S., 387, *463*
Knight, V., 383, 392, 436, *459, 461*
Koch, G., 197, 199, 202, *207*
Köhler, E., 346, *349*
Koerner, J. F., 178, *206*
Kohiyama, M., 587, *592*
Kono, Y., 8, 42, 43, *50*
Konrad, M. W., *207*
Koprowski, H., 374, 375, 380, 381, 389,
    460, 461, 464
Kordová, N., 258, 259, *277*
Korn, D., *209*
Kornberg, A., 165, *207*
Kornberg, S. R., 165, *207*
Korns, R. F., 380, *460*
Kossobudzki, S. L., 375, *460*
Kozinski, A. W., 166, *207*
Kraemer, P. M., 532, 541, *563*
Kraft, L., 200, *207*
Kreuz, L. E., 36, 37, 38, *50*
Krieg, D. R., 164, 177, *207*
Kriegshaber, M. R., 389, *463*
Kroeger, A., 176, *207*
Krueger, A. P., 180, *207*
Kucera, S. L., 257, 260, 272, 273, *278*
Kupsky, C., 200, *209*

L

Labusquiere, R., 440, *461*
Lacassagne, A., 160, *209*
Lackman, D. B., 390, *462*
Lackovič, V., 13, *50*
Laidlaw, P. P., 376, *463,* 547, *563*
Laidler, K. J., 181, *206*
Lambin, P., 440, *461*
Lampson, G. P., 7, 13, 15, 27, 29, 30, 31, 32, 33, 34, 35, 38, 48, *50*
Lane, D., 188, *208*
Lang, D. J., 436, *459*
Langmuir, A. D., 380, *462*
Larke, R. P. B., 8, *50*
Larson, V. M., 532, 533, 534, 541, *563*
Latarjet, R., 122, *138,* 142, 144, 154, 160, 167, 174, 175, 176, 178, *205, 207,* 325, *349*
Lauffer, M. A., 152, 155, 200, 202, *205, 207*
Laughton, N., 534, *564*
Laurent, A. M., 377, *463*
Lavallé, R., 574, *592*
Lawson, L. A., 533, *564*
Lea, D. E., 141, 143, 146, 149, 152, 154, 155, 156, 159, 160, 161, 169, *207*
Leach, R. H., 533, 536, *562*
Leagus, M. B., 436, *461*
Lease, G. O., 377, 392, *459*
LeBouvier, G. L., 367, *369*
Lederberg, E. M., 288, *320*
Lederberg, J., 288, *319, 320*
Lee, D. Y., 552, 555, *563*
Lehrich, J. R., 383, 392, *461*
Leidy, G., 186, *209*
Lelliott, R. A., 493, *501*
Lemcke, R. M., 532, 535, 538, 539, *563*
Lennette, E. H., 54, *91,* 488, *489*
Leonidova, S. L., 389, *463*
Lerman, L. S., 187, 188, *207*
Leslie, J., 482, *489*
Levcenko, E. N., 389, *463*
Levine, S., 47, *50*
Levinson, H. S., 147, *208*
Levy, A. H., 9, 19, 20, 35, 36, 37, 38, 41, *49, 50, 52*
Levy, H. B., 26, 47, *50*
Lewis, M. J., 572, *592*
Ley, A. C., 373, *461*
Lichtienstein, J., 178, *206*
Lieberman, M., 262, *277*

Liebhaber, H., 78, 79, 80, 83, *91, 92*
Liljas, A., 345, *349*
Lindberg, B. K. S., 345, *349*
Lindenmann, J., 2, 10, 11, 19, 20, 21, 23, 24, 25, 26, 30, *50*
Link, F., 213, 214, 215, 217, 218, 219, 222, 223, 224, 230, 233, 238, 239, 240, 242, 243, 244, 246, 247, 258, *278*
Lipschitz, R., 195, *209*
Lipson, H., 504, 510, 511, 527, *529*
Littlefield, J. W., 161, *209*
Liu, O. C., 262, 263, *277, 278*
Lloyd, W., 375, *461*
Lockart, R. Z., Jr., 7, 10, 11, 12, 18, 19, 21, 22, 47, *49, 50, 51*
Lockingen, L. S., 152, *205*
LoGrippo, G. A., 432, 435, *460, 461*
Loofbourow, J. R., 96, *138*
Loosli, C. G., 382, *459*
Lorenz, E., 160, 176, *205*
Lorenz, R. J., 271, *278*
Love, J. W. P., 383, 436, *459*
Lowenthal, J. P., 378, 390, *459, 462*
Lowry, O. H., 364, *369*
Ludwig, W., 383, 436, *459*
Lunan, K. D., 161, *208*
Lunceford, C. D., 542, *564*
Luria, S. E., 85, *91,* 142, *208,* 321, *349,* 591, *592*
Luzyanina, T. Ya., 387, *461, 463*
Luzzati, D., 587, *592*
Lwoff, A., 321, *349,* 594, 595, 597, *612*
Lynn, R. J., 540, *563*

M

McCarthy, K., 75, *91*
McCaughery, W. F., 347, *350*
McClelland, L., 376, *461*
McCloskey, R. V., 13, *48*
McCloy, E. W., 164, *209*
McCrea, J. F., 174, 175, *208*
MacFarlane, J. O., 381, *464*
McGee, Z. A., 532, 535, *563, 564*
Machlowitz, R. A., 366, 367, *368, 369,* 388, *462*
McKerlie, M. L., 26, *48*
McKinney, H. H., 492, 494, 495, 501, *501*
McLaren, A. D., 93, 99, 134, *138*
McLaren, L. C., 4, 5, 6, 7, *50*

McLean, I. Wm., Jr., 200, *209*, 377, 381, 435, *459*, *461*, *464*
MacLeod, R., 513, *529*
Macpherson, I., 533, 534, 536, 544, 556, 557, *563*
Macpherson, I. A., 355, *369*, 533, 534, *563*
Madoff, S., 534, *562*
Maeda, A., 588, 589, 590, 591, *592*
Magill, T. P., 376, *461*
Malizia, W. F., 531, 534, 536, *562*
Maloney, J. B., 483, *489*
Malsberger, R. G., 263, *278*
Manaker, R. A., 554, *562*
Mandel, B., 68, 69, *91*
Manson, L. A., 541, *563*
Maramorosch, K., 604, *613*
Marchenko, A. T., 381, *460*
Marcus, P. I., 4, 48, *50*, 88, *91, 92*
Marennikova, S. S., 389, *463*
Markham, F. S., 381, *459*
Markham, R., 152, 155, *207*, 345, *349, 350*, 513, 516, 522, 525, 526, 527, 528, 529, *529*
Marmur, J., 187, 188, 189, 191, 195, *206, 208*
Martin, R. G., 37, *50*, 588, *592*
Mascoli, C. C., 436, *461*
Mason, P. J., 33, 34, *49*
Matheka, H. D., 366, *369*, 598, *613*
Matsuda, S., 378, *461*
Matsushiro, A., 321, *349*
Mattern, C. F. T., 525, *529*
Mauer, M. E., 483, *489*
Mayor, H. D., 348, *349*, 596, 604, *613*
Mayr-Harting, A., 585, 589, *592*
Medearis, D. N., Jr., 6, *51*
Melnick, J. L., 203, *209*, 348, *349*, 488, *489*, 601, *613*
Mendelson, J., 45, *50*
Merigan, T. C., 8, 14, 18, 26, 27, 29, 30, 31, 33, 34, 35, 38, 48, *48, 50, 51*
Meryman, H. T., 492, *501*
Meselson, M., 36, *51*, 302, 303, 307, 309, *319, 320*
Metzgar, D. P., 388, 438, *464*
Meyer, H. M., Jr., 4, 7, *51*, 385, 386, 440, *461, 462*
Meyer, K. F., 381, *461*
Micklem, L. R., 373, *461*
Mikutskaya, B. A., 387, *461, 463*

Miller, O. T., 560, *564*
Miller, R. C., 160, 164, 165, 189, 191, 192, 201, *206*
Miller, V. K., 180, *206*
Milovanovic, M. V., 383, 384, *459, 461, 462*
Mitra, S., 155, 160, *208*
Mitus, A., 383, *462*
Miyama, A., 571, 581, *592*
Mohler, N. M., 96, *138*
Moloney, J. B., 160, 176, *205*
Monk, M., 577, *592*
Mood, M. T., 483, *489*
Moorhead, P. S., 380, 454, *460, 461*
Moran, P., *730*
Morenne, P., 122, *138*
Morgan, H. R., 87, *91*
Morgan, I. M., 75, *91*, 380, *459*
Morioka, Y., 76, *92*
Morrison, J. M., 41, *48*
Morse, M. L., 288, *320*
Morton, H. E., 531, 532, 534, 540, *563, 564*
Moses, M. J., 381, *459*
Mowat, G., 355, *369*
Moyer, A. W., 381, *459*
Mtvarelidze, A. A., 389, *463*
Mucnik, L. S., 389, *463*
Mudd, S., 482, *489*
Müller, A., 160, 161, *207*
Murphy, E. B., 3, 14, *50*
Murphy, W. H., 533, 534, 536, 541, 545, *563*
Murray, E. G. D., 531, *562*
Muschel, L. H., 534, *563*
Mussgay, M., 359, *369*

N

Nagler, C., 191, *208*
Nakamura, M., 590, *592*
Nakano, M., 76, *92*
Napier, J. A., 380, *460*
Nardelli, L., 353, *369*
Nardone, R. M., 533, *563*
Nash, J. C., 390, *461*
Nathanson, N., 380, *462*
Naughton, M. A., 35, *50*
Nave, F., 383, *460*
Neal, A. L., 368, *368*
Neimark, H. C., 532, 535, *563*

Nelson, D. J., 374, 381, *461*
Nelson, J. B., 535, 552, *562*
Nelson, T. L., 381, *461*
Nemes, M. M., 7, 13, 15, 27, 29, 30, 31, 32, 33, 34, 35, 38, 48, *50*
Neurath, A. R., 392, *462*
Neva, F. A., 4, 7, *51*, 385, *464*
Newland, S. E., 66, *91*
Nitz, R. E., 382, *463*
Nixon, H. L., 344, 345, *349*
Nocard, E., 531, *563*
Nomura, M., 567, 572, 585, 587, 588, 589, 590, 591, *592*
Nomura, S., 76, 78, *92*
Norman, A., 151, 155, 160, *206*
Norton, T. W., 381, *461*
Noyes, W. F., 516, *529*

O

O'Connell, R. C., 533, 534, *563*
Officer, J. E., 531, 541, 542, 546, 551, 552, 555, 556, 558, *562, 563*
Ogawa, H., 581, *592*
Ohoki, M., 571, 587, 588, *592*
Okazaki, W., 340, *349*
Okuyan, M., 328, 339, *349*
Olin, G., 381, *460*
Olitzky, P. K., 72, *91*
Olivier, L. J., 608, *612*
O'Neill, C., 33, 34, *49*
Oppenheimer, F., 433, 434, 435, *462*
Ormsbee, R. A., 390, *462*
Osborn, J., 6, *51*
Oster, G., 99, 113, 134, *138*, 503, *529*
Owens, R. E., 368, *368*
Oxelfelt, P., 345, *349*
Oxman, M. N., 48, *51*
Ozeki, H., 574, 575, 576, 577, 578, 580, 581, 584, 590, *591, 592*

P

Paiqen, K.. 302, 303, *320*
Pait, C. F., 380, *461*
Panina, G., 353, *369*
Panos, T. C., 386, *462*
Papavassiliou, J., 571, *592*
Paranchych, W., 155, *208*
Park, B. H., 72, *91*

Parker, C. A., 126, *138*
Parkes, A. S., 488, *489*
Parkman, P. D., 4, 7, *51*, 385, 386, *462*
Parrott, R. H., 388, *461*
Pasteur, L., 374, *462*
Paton, G. R., 533, *564*
Patty, R. E., 197, 200, 203, 204, *205*, 353, 354, 359, 364, *368*
Patuleia, M. C., 535, 552, *562*
Paucker, K., 11, 12, 15, 18, 28, *48, 51*
Paul, J. R., 381, *462*
Payne, F. E., 608, *613*
Pearson, E. S., *730*
Pease, P. E., 534, *564*
Peck, F. B., Jr., 375, 390, *461, 462*
Peck, J. L., Jr., 378, *462*
Peebles, T. C., 383, *459*
Peeler, B. E., 388, *461*
Pene, J. J., 532, *563*
Penna, H. A., 375, *460*
Peoples, D. M., 534, *564*
Pepper, D. S., 67, *91*
Peradze, T. V., 383, *463*
Pereira, H. G., 600, 602, *613*
Perez, Gallardo F., 379, *459*
Perkins, F. T., 451, *462*, 533, *564*
Perlman, D., 556, *564*
Perlman, P. L., 272, 273, *278*
Person, S,. 145, *206*
Peterson, D. R., 383, *460*
Petralli, J. K., 8, *51*
Philipson, L., 6, 7, 20, *49*, 345, *349*
Phillips, A. W., 38, *51*
Phillips, G. B., 560, *564*
Pihl, A., 151, *206*
Pillemer, L., 76, *92*
Pirie, N. W., 344, *348, 349*
Pohjanpelto, P., 4, *51*
Pokorny, B. A., 45, *50*
Polatnick, J., 355, 356, 357, 358, *369*
Pollard, E. C., 141, 143, 145, 146, 149, 155, 159, 169, 170, 171, 172, 173, 176, 180, 200, 201, 202, 205, *206, 207, 208, 209*, 430, *462*, 488, *489*
Polley, J. R., 432, *462*
Pollock, M. E., 531, 533, 536, 552, 556, 559, *563, 564*
Polson, A., 603, *613*
Ponten, J. A., 380, *461*
Potash, L., 388, *462, 464*

Pouwels, P. H., 163, 192, *207*, *208*
Powell, H. M., 200, *208*, 374, *462*
Powelson, D. M., 533, *564*
Preston, R. E., 608, *613*
Price, W. C., 200, 202, 203, *207*, *208*, 724, *730*
Pristasová, N., 274, *278*
Pruden, B., 153, *206*
Purcell, R. H., 383, 388, 389, 436, *459*, *463*

Q

Quenouille, M. H., *730*
Quersin-Thiry, L., 58, *91*

R

Rabidean, G. S., 97, *138*
Rabson, A. S., 10, *49*
Racker, E., 68, *91*
Rada, B., 238, 239, 240, 242, 243, 244, 246, 247, 272, 273, 275, 276, *278*
Ragetli, H. W. J., 90, *91*
Randall, C. C., 533, *564*
Randall, R., 390, *459*, *462*
Randall, R. J., 364, *369*
Rapp, F., 203, *208*, 348, *349*
Rasmussen, R., 325, 333, *349*
Ratcliff, G. A., 9, 20, *52*
Rathbun, M. L., 383, *460*
Ráthová, V., 217, 218, 219, 222, 223, 224, *278*
Raus, J., 213, 214, 215, 217, 218, 219, 222, 223, 224, *278*
Rauth, A. M., 148, 150, 158, *208*
Ravdin, R., 380, *461*
Ravkina, L. I., 389, *463*
Reamer, R., 340, *349*
Reaume, M., 180, 200, 201, *208*
Rechen, H. J. L., 125, *138*
Reczko, E., 597, 607, *613*
Reddi, K. K., 116, *138*
Rees, M. W., 185, *205*
Reese, D. R., 375, *461*
Reese, M., 345, *349*, *350*
Reeves, P. R., 566, 588, 590, *592*
Regamey, R. H., 375, *462*
Reich, P. R., 535, *564*
Reichmann, M. E., 345, 346, *349*, *350*

Reimer, C. B., 348, *349*
Reinhard, K., 451, *463*
Reinhart, H., 436, *461*
Reinicke, V., 45, *51*
Reynolds, B. L., 590, *592*
Ricci, N. I., 375, *461*
Rice, S. A., 187, *208*
Richardson, C. C., 167, *209*
Riggs, D. B., 531, 534, 536, 542, 546, *562*
Rights, F. L., 88, *92*
Rightsel, W., 486, 488, *489*
Riley, H. D., Jr., 367, *369*
Robbins, E., 88, *91*
Robbins, F. C., 6, 8, *49*, 379, 380, *459*, *462*
Robillard, N. F., 544, *562*
Robinson, D., 378, *462*
Robinson, H. L., 348, *350*
Robinson, L. B., 531, *564*
Robinson, T. A., 374, *463*
Robinson, W. S., 160, *206*
Robson, M., 189, *206*
Roca-Garcia, M., 381, *459*
Roger, M., 187, 188, 190, *208*
Rogers, N. G., 440, *461*
Rogul, M., 532, 535, *563*, *564*
Roizman, B., 4, 7, 9, 10, *48*, *51*, 531, *564*
Rojhel, V. M., 389, *463*
Roller, A., 166, *208*
Rope, E. Z., 381, *464*
Rose, J. A., 535, *564*
Rosebrough, N. J., 364, *369*
Rosenzweig, E. C., 390, *464*
Rotem, Z., 12, 14, 37, *50*, *51*
Rothblat, G. H., 531, *564*
Rous, P., 322, *350*
Rouse, H. C., 86, 87, *92*, 533, 536, *564*
Roux, 374, *462*
Roux, E. R., 531, *563*
Rowe, W. P., 382, *460*, *462*, 603, *612*
Rubin, B. A., 382, *461*
Rubin, H., 4, *51*, 58, 59, *92*, 322, 323, 324, 327, 328, 329, 330, 332, 333, 334, 339, 340, 341, 342, 343, *349*, *350*
Rubinstein, I., 161, 163, *208*
Ruchman, I., 378, *462*
Ruegsegger, J. M., 374, 381, *459*, *462*, *463*
Russell, W., 533, *563*
Ruthig, D. W., 383, *460*
Ruys, A. C., 531, 552, 559, *563*
Rytel, M. W., 14, 45, *51*

S

Sabin, A. B., 378, 381, *462*, 532, *564*
Sachs, L., 12, *51*
Sadler, P. W., 236, 237, *277*
Sänger, H. L., 346, *350*
Sagik, B. P., 85, *92*
Sagin, J. F., 366, *369*
Saksela, E., 380, *461*
Salaman, M. H., 161, 169, *207*
Salb, J. M., 48, *50*, 88, *92*
Salita, T. V., 389, *463*
Salk, J. E., 377, 380, *462*, *463*
Santero, G., 353, *369*
Sarber, R. W., 381, *459*
Sarma, P. S., 328, 339, *349*, *350*
Sauerbier, W., 154, 167, *208*
Schachman, H. K., 160, 186, *208*
Schaffer, F. L., 367, *369*
Schakir, R., 8, *49*
Schambra, F. E., 146, 160, 174, *208*
Scherp, H. W., 451, *463*
Schildkraut, C., 195, *206*
Schimke, R. T., 532, 533, 536, 538, 541, *562*, *564*
Schlesinger, R. W., 2, 3, *51*, 81, 86, 87, *92*, 533, 536, *564*
Schmidt, N. J., 54, *91*
Schmidt, N. S., 488, *489*
Schneider, W. C., 364, *369*
Scholes, G., 142, 151, 152, *208*
Schonne, E., 31, *51*
Schuler, E. E., 488, *489*
Schulze, I. T., 81, 82, 83, *92*
Schuster, H., 160, *208*
Schwab, M. P., 374, *463*
Schwarz, H. A., 147, *209*
Schwerdt, C. E., 367, *368*, *369*
Seeds, W. E., 503, *529*
Sehgal, O. P., 346, 347, *350*
Sela, I., 2, *51*
Semple, D., 374, *463*
Sergeyev, V. M., 441, *458*
Sertic, V., 155, *208*
Setlow, R. B., 143, 146, 149, 154, 156, 166, *208*
Seto, Y., 595, *613*
Shapiro, H. S., 195, *209*
Sharpless, G. R., 374, 389, *459*, *462*, *463*
Shedlovsky, A., 85, *92*

Shein, H. M., 380, *463*
Shepard, M. C., 531, 533, 542, 555, 558, *562*, *564*
Sherwood, R. W., 382, *463*
Shikina, E. S., 383, *463*
Shilo, R., 355, *369*
Shockell, L. F., 482, *489*
Shope, R. E., 14, *51*
Shugar, D., 93, *138*, 201, *206*
Sibley, W. A., 8, *52*
Siegel, A., 346, 347, *350*, 526, *529*
Silber, G., 494, 495, *501*
Silver, S., 575, *592*
Silverberg, R. J., 58, *91*
Simard, R. G., 125, *138*
Siminovitch, L., 321, *349*, 585, *592*
Simpson, J. A., 148, 150, 158, *208*
Sinanoglu, O., 187, *208*
Sinsheimer, R. L., 155, 160, 161, 191, 192, *206*, *208*
Skoda, J., 272, 275, *278*
Skurska, Z., 11, 15, *51*
Slotnick, V. B., 380, *460*
Smadel, J. E., 373, 379, 440, 451, *461*, *463*
Smart, K. M., 45, *50*, *51*
Šmejkal, F., 234, 248, 250, *278*
Smirnov, M. S., 441, *458*
Smith, A. V., 488, *489*
Smith, C. B., 388, 389, *463*
Smith, H. H., 375, *464*
Smith, K. D., 348, *349*
Smith, K. M., 152, 155, 159, 160, *207*, 609, *613*
Smith, K. O., 191, *208*
Smith, N. R., 531, *562*
Smith, P. F., 532, 334, 539, *564*
Smith, S. M., 576, 577, 578, 580, *592*
Smith, T. J., 6, 7, 8, 9, 12, 13, 14, 15, 29, 38, 42, *51*
Smith, W., 376, *463*, 598, *613*
Smorodintsev, A. A., 378, 383, 387, 388, 441, *461*, *463*
Sneath, P. H. A., 594, *612*, *613*
Snedecor, G. W., *730*
Snellbaker, L. F., 47, *50*
Snipes, W., 153, *206*
Snyder, J., 542, 546, *562*
Snyder, R. M., 9, 20, *52*

Somerson, N. L., 532, 533, 535, 541, *562, 564*

Sonnabend, J. A., 47, *49*

Šorm, F., 234, 248, 250, 272, 275, *278*

Southam, C. M., 76, *92*

Spencer, E. L., 724, *730*

Spicer, D. S., 366, *369*

Spicer, S. S., 84, *92*

Spiegelman, S., 193, *207,* 346, *349*

Squire, R. A., 554, *562*

Sreevalsan, T., 22, *51*

Stacey, K. A., 113, *138*

Stanbridge, E., 533, 534, 535, 536, 545, 549, 560, *563*

Stahl, F. W., 36, *51,* 168, *208,* 316, *320*

Stairs, G. R., 713, *730*

Stallones, R. A., 382, *460, 463*

Stanček, D., 270, 271, 272, *278*

Stanley, W. M., 174, *208,* 368, *369,* 376, *463*

Starman, B., 191, *208*

Stearns, A. E., 184, 186, 201, *209*

Stebbins, M. R., 389, *459*

Steinberg, C., 316, *320*

Steinberger, A., 88, *92*

Stent, G. S., 144, 159, 160, 162, 163, 177, 178, *207, 209*

Stevens, W. L., *730*

Stevenson, D., 47, *49*

Stewart, R. C., 595, *612*

Stim, T. B., 438, *464*

Stinebring, W. R., 3, 8, 9, 13, 30, 31, 38, 42, 44, *49, 51, 52,* 531, 554, *563*

Stocker, B. A. D., 572, 576, 577, 578, 580, 581, 584, *592*

Stoker, M., 355, *369*

Stokes, A. R., 503, *529*

Stokes, J., Jr., 387, 388, 436, *460, 461, 462, 463, 464*

Strandberg, B., 345, *349*

Streisinger, G., 185, *205,* 304, *320*

Streissle, G., 604, *613*

Strickland, A. G. R., 22, *49*

Strizova, V., 454, *464*

Stuart, A., *730*

Stuart-Harris, C. H., 235, *278*

Studier, F. W., 164, *209*

Sueoka, N., 187, *206*

Sukkonen, J. J., 8, 14, *49*

Sulkin, S. E., 76, *91,* 534, *563*

Sutton, R. N. P., 27, *51*

Svedmyr, A., 381, *460*

Svet-Moldavskaja, I. A., 389, *463*

Svet-Moldavsky, G. Ja., 389, *463*

Sweet, B. H., 380, 388, 390, *460, 462, 463, 464*

Swift, H. F., 547, 548, 549, 550, *562*

Symonds, N., 164, *209*

Symons, R., 345, *349*

Syverton, J. T., 161, *209,* 531, 552, 556, *564*

Szántó, J., 274, *278*

T

Takebe, H., 152, 168, *209*

Takemori, N., 76, 78, *92*

Takemoto, K. K., 58, 77, 78, 79, 80, 83, 84, *91, 92,* 525, *529*

Tallent, G., 390, *462*

Tamm, C., 195, *209*

Tamm, I., 63, *92,* 265, 267, 268, 269, *278,* 601, *612, 613*

Taube, S. E., 3, 42, 44, *52*

Taylor, A. R., 381, 433, 434, 435, *459, 462, 464*

Taylor, C. A., 504, 510, 511, 527, *529*

Taylor, D. W., 164, *209*

Taylor, J., 46, *51*

Taylor-Robinson, D., 532, *564*

Temin, H. M., 322, 334, *350,* 595, *613*

Tessman, I., 160, 162, *209*

Tessman, E. S., 160, 162, *209*

Theiler, M., 375, 376, *461, 464,* 598, *613*

Thomas, R., 303, *320*

Thomas, R. E., 383, *460*

Thompson, W. R., 389, *459*

Thuillier, 374, *462*

Tigertt, W. D., 378, *462*

Till, J. E., 176, *209*

Timian, R. G., 493, *501*

Timm, E. A., 200, *209,* 381, 435, *464*

Ting, R. C., 321, *349*

Todd, A. R., 194, *205*

Todd, J., 533, *563*

Tolchinsky, E., 380, *460*

Toler, R. W., 493, 499, *501*

Tolmach, L. J., 187, 188, *207*

Tomaru, K., 493, *501*

Tomassani, N., 536, 539, 540, 554, 555, 563
Toolan, H. W., 608, *613*
Tournier, P., 594, 595, 597, *612*
Towle, L. R., 439, *464*
Toyoshima, S., 595, *613*
Traub, F. D., 178, *209*
Trautman, R., 353, 359, 360, 362, 363, 364, 366, *368, 369*
Treadwell, P. E., 533, 536, *564*
Trkula, A., 155, *205*
Trlifajova, J., 454, *464*
Tully, J. G., 534, *564*
Turner, H. C., 328, 339, *349, 350*
Tyrrell, D. A. J., 27, *51*
Tytell, A. A., 7, 13, 15, 27, 29, 30, 31, 32, 33, 34, 35, 38, 48, *50*, 366, 367, *369*, 388, 438, *462, 464*

U

Ubertini, B., 353, *369*
Ueda, T., 595, *613*
Unanov, S. S., 389, *463*
Ungar, J., 375, *462*
Uroma, E., 8, 14, *49*
Utz, J. P., 73, *92*

V

Valentine, R. C., 600, *613*
Valle, M., 8, 14, *49*
van der Veen, J., 382, *464*
Van Frank, R. M., 381, *464*
Van Hoosier, G. L., Jr., 381, *459, 464*
van Rhijn, G. R., 531, 552, 559, *563*
van Rotterdam, C., 163, *207*
Vanselow, A. P., 364, *369*
Vargosko, A. J., 388, *461*
Vessey, K. B., 161, 167, 177, 191, 193, 194, 195, 196, 201, *206*
Vieu, J. F., 566, *592*
Vilček, J., 7, 8, 11, 33, *51, 52*, 270, 271, 272, *278*
Vilches, A., 3, *51*
Vinograd, J., 36, *51*, 160, 189, 192, *209*
Vinson, T. O., 383, *460*
Vogt, M., 22, *49*, 191, *206*, 271, *277*
Vogt, P. K., 323, 324, 325, 327, 328, 330, 331, 333, 338, 339, 340, 341, 342, 343, 348, *349, 350*

Voight, R. B., 380, *460*
Volkova, O. F., 389, *463*

W

Wagner, R. R., 2, 3, 5, 7, 8, 9, 10, 12, 13, 14, 15, 16, 18, 19, 20, 22, 26, 27, 29, 32, 34, 35, 38, 41, 42, 44, 45, *49, 50, 51, 52*
Wallace, R. E., 552, *564*
Wallis, C., 203, *208*, 488, *489*, 601, *613*
Wallis, L. C., 203, *209*
Wang, S. P., 390, *460*
Wang, S. S., 598, *612*
Ward, J. F., 142, 151, 152, *208*
Ward, R., 378, *462*
Ward, T. G., 390, *461*
Warfield, M. S., 382, *460, 463*
Warren, J., 368, *369*, 378, *462*
Warren, S. L., 161, *209*
Watanabe, T., 577, *592*
Waterson, A. P., 607, *613*
Watson, D. W., 201, *205*
Watson, J. D., 159, 161, 168, 177, 184, *205, 209*
Watson, R. F., 547, 548, 549, 550, *562*
Webster, R. G., 377, 392, *459*
Wedgewood, R. J., 76, *92*
Wedum, A. G., 560, *564*
Weibel, R. E., 387, 388, 436, *460, 461, 462, 463, 464*
Weigle, J. J., 293, 299, 301, 302, 303, *319, 320*, 321, *348*
Weihl, C., 367, *369*
Weil, R., 160, 189, 191, 192, *209*
Weinberger, H. J., 534, *562*
Weintraub, M., 90, *91*
Weiss, B., 167, *209*
Weiss, J. J., 142, 146, 151, 152, *208, 209*
Weiss, R., 348, *350*
Weissbach, A., *209*
Weissman, S. M., 535, *564*
Weller, T. H., 4, 7, *51*, 379, 380, 385, *459, 462, 464*
Wenner, H. A., 380, *460*
Werner, J. H., 382, *460*
Wesslen, T., 373, 381, *460, 464*
Wetter, C., 597, *612*
Wheelock, E. F., 3, 13, 29, *52*
White, C. L., 483, *489*

Whitfield, J. F., 314, 316, *320*
Whitman, J. E., Jr., 387, *460, 464*
Whitman, L., 75, *92*
Whitmore, G. F., 155, *209*
Whittler, R. G., 532, 535, *563*
Wiberg, J. S., 178, *206*
Wichelhausen, R. H., 531, *564*
Wiener, F. P., 263, *278*
Wiktor, T. J., 375, 389, *464*
Wilbur, W. R., 8, *51*
Wilcox, W. C., 393, *459*
Wildy, P., 184, *207,* 596, *613*
Wilkins, M. H. F., 503, *529*
Williams, R. C., 160, *208*
Winget, C. A., 30, 31, 33, 34, 35, 38, *51*
Wingo, S. T., 383, *460*
Winkelstein, W., 383, *460*
Winkler, U., 154, *209*
Wisseman, C. L., 390, *464*
Wittler, R. G., 533, 534, 535, *563, 564*
Wittman, G., 598, *613*
Woese, C. R., 197, 200, 203, *209*
Wollman, E., 160, *209,* 321, 348, *349*
Wollman, E. L., 300, 301, 315, 319, *319*
   321, *349,* 567, 585, *592*
Wood, R. D., 38, *51*
Woodhour, A. F., 388, 438, *462, 464*
Woodruff, A. M., 378, *460*

Woolridge, R. L., 390, *460*
Wright, H. F., 348, *349*

Y

Yaguchi, R., 537, 542, 546, *562*
Yanofsky, C., 288, 295, 296, 297, *319*
Yates, F., 220, 228, *278,* 704, 706, *730*
Yen, C. H., 390, *460*
Yershov, F. I., 25, *52*
Youngner, J. S., 3, 8, 9, 13, 30, 31, 38,
   42, 44, *49, 51, 52,* 75, *91,* 197, 200, *209*
Yule, G. U., *730*

Z

Zaitlin, M., 346, 347, *350*
Zamenhof, S., 186, *209*
Zarafonetis, C. J. D., 533, 534, 536, 541,
   545, *563*
Z'drodovskii, P. F., 390, *464*
Žemla, J., 33, *52*
Zhdanov, V. M., 25, *52,* 377, 441, *462, 464,*
   594, *613*
Zichichi, M. L., 304, *320*
Zimm, B. H., 187, 188, 189, 190, *205, 206*
Zimmer, K. G., 141, 142, 149, *209*
Zimmerman, S. B., 165, *207*
Zinder, N. D., 161, *206,* 288, 294, *320*
Zwillenberg, L. D., 547, *564*

Subject Index

A

α-Particles, properties, 145–147

Absorbance of spectrophotometes, calculation, 102–112

definition, 101

Absorption cross section, definition, 104

Acetone powders of plant viruses, 499–500

Acetoxycycloheximide, as interferon-formation inhibitor, 45

Acridine dyes, effect on *col* factors, 581

Actinometry, 122-129

malachite green leukocyanide in, 125–126

potassium ferrioxalate in, 126–129

uranyl oxalate in, 123–125

Actinomycin, as interferon formation inhibitor, 44, 46–47

Adeno-associated viruses, 348

Adenovirus type 2, interferon induction by, 7

Adenovirus type 3, in respiratory tract disease, 382

Adenovirus type 4, in respiratory tract disease, 382

vaccine, 454

Adenovirus type 5, structure, 184–185

Adenovirus type 7, in respiratory tract disease, 382

SV40 genome incorporation into, 382

Adenovirus type V, DNA content of, 161

ionizing radiation effects on, molecular weight by, 161

Adenoviruses, classification methods, 595, 597, 599, 600, 603, 605, 608

defective variant, 348

inhibitors of, 86–87

interferon induction by, 6, 7

nucleic acid, heat sensitivity, 202

preparation, large-scale, 368

satellite viruses of, DNA of, 608

structure, 184, 185

vaccines for, 380, 389, 392

formulations, 438

killed-virus type, 402, 403, 405, 407–408, 413, 414

potency, 413

preparation, 382–383

standards, 383, 402, 403

SV 40 contamination, 382, 392

tests, 414

Adjuvant 65, *see* Peanut oil adjuvant

Adjuvants, for vaccines, 415, 436–439

Aerosols, for mass immunization, 440–443

African horse sickness virus, classification, 603

Alfalfa mosaic virus, preservation of, 494–496, 498

thermal inactivation of, 200, 202

Aluminum adjuvants for virus vaccines, 415, 436–437

p-Aminobenzolaldehyd-3-thiosemicarbazone, as antiviral agent, assay, 261

Analysis of variance, 690–696

Animal viruses, freeze-drying of, 488–489

glycerol storage and shipping of, 484–485

pure, quantity preparation of, 351–369

refrigeration of, 485–486

safety measures for at Plum Island Disease Laboratory, 465–480

storage and preservation of, 481–489

principles, 482–484

thermal inactivation, 200

Animals, in animal-pathogen research, 476–478

Anthrax, mass immunization for, 441

Antibiotics, bactericidal, *see* Colicines

Mycoplasma treatment by 556–558

Antibody, as viral inhibitors, 55–59

Antiviral agents, testing for, 211–278
 animal experiments, 215–255
 egg experiments, 255–274
 experimental design, 224–255
 multiple-dose experiments, 240–251
 single-dose experiments, 225–240
 therapeutic index, 251–255
 in tissue cultures, 263–274
1-β-D-Arabinofuranosylcytosine · HCl, as antiviral agent, assay, 235
Arboviruses, classification, 598, 599, 600, 601, 602, 604, 609
 Group A type, inhibitors, 80–81
 Group B type, inhibitors, 82–84
 inhibitors of, 72–74, 75–76, 80–84
 interferon induction by, 6, 7, 11, 15
 as vaccine contaminants, 456
 vaccines for, 378, 389–390
 contamination, 391
Arlacel A, see Mannide monooleate
Arrhenius equation, 180
Assay, of plant viruses, plants for, 500
 statistical methods of, 615–730
Aureomycin, in Mycoplasma control, 560
 in vaccine production, 444
Autopsy rooms, for animal-pathogen laboratories, 478
Avian contaminants of vaccines, 456–457
Avian leukosis virus, cellular antibody from, 59
 as RSV helper virus, 341, 342
 as vaccine contaminant, 392, 422–423, 447, 456, 457
Avian myeloblastosis virus, as RSV helper virus, 341
Avian orphan virus (GAL), in chickens, 456
6-Azauracirliboside, as antiviral agent, assay, 248–250, 258–260

B

β-rays, properties, 144–145
B virus (of monkeys), as vaccine contaminant, 455
 vaccine development, 390
Bacteria, nucelic acids, ionizing radiation effects on, 144–145
 preservation of, 482

Bactericidal antibiotics, see Colicines
Bacteriophage 22, DNA content of, 161
 ionizing radiation effects on, molecular weight by, 160
Bacteriophage BM, DNA content of, 161
 ionizing radiation effects on, molecular weight by, 161
Bacteriophage K, ionizing radiation effects on, size and shape by, 169
 thermal inactivation, 180
Bacteriophage λ, DNA content of, 161
 ionizing radiation effects on, inactivation, 168
 molecular weight by, 161
 mutation studies on, 282–290, 292–295, 298, 299
 complementation in, 311
 defective-particle isolation, 301–305
 of physiological block, 312–319
Bacteriophage M1, thermal inactivation, 201
Bacteriophage M3, thermal inactivation, 201
Bacteriophage M5, thermal inactivation, 201
Bacteriophage P2, mutation, 284
Bacteriophage P22, in Colicine studies, 579
 ionizing radiation effects on, 152–153
Bacteriophage R17, ionizing radiation effects on, molecular weight by, 154 160
 physicochemical properties, 155
 RNA, content of, 161
 thermal inactivation, 196, 201
Bacteriophage S13, DNA content of, 160
 ionizing radiation effects on, molecular weight by, 160
Bacteriophage ϕX174, classification, 597, 605
 DNA, content of, 160
 thermal inactivation, 189, 191–193, 195, 201
 ionizing radiation effects on, inactivation, 146, 162–165
 molecular weight by, 154–160
 size and shape from, 174
 as standard, 148

physicochemical properties, 155
structure, 184
Bacteriophage T1, DNA, content of, 160
  radiation effects on, 159, 162
  ionizing radiation effects on, inactiva-
      tion, 146, 175, 177
    molecular weight by, 160
    repair, 154
    size and shape from, 173, 174
    as standard, 146, 148
  mutation in, 295
  thermal inactivation, 180, 200, 201, 202,
      204
Bacteriophage T2, DNA content of, 161
  inhibitors of, 58, 85
  ionizing radiation effects on, inactiva-
      tion, 165, 177
    molecular weight by, 160–162
  optical diffraction studies on, 518
  thermal inactivation, 180, 200, 201, 204
  UV radiation of, 116
Bacteriophage T3, thermal inactivation,
    180, 200
Bacteriophage T4, DNA, content of, 161
  ionizing radiation effects on inactiva-
      tion, 162–168, 175, 177, 178
    molecular weight by, 161
  mutation, 284, 304
  thermal inactivation, 180, 200
  UV inactivation, 177
  v-gene, for UV-damage repair, 153
Bacteriophage T5, thermal inactivation,
    180, 200, 203
Bacteriophage, T7, ionizing radiation ef-
    fects on,
    inactivation, 163–164, 167
  thermal inactivation, 180, 200, 201, 204
Bacteriophages, classification methods,
    597, 605, 610, 611
  defective, see Defective bacteriophages
  estimation of concentration of, 709
  inhibitors of, 57, 72, 76
  ionizing radiation effects on, 144, 145
  morphology, 596–597
  plaque count of, 713–716
    Poisson distribution of, 653
  structure, 185
  thermal inactivation of, 180, .200–201
  UV in activation of, 116, 133

Barley stripe mosaic virus, preservation,
    492, 493, 496
Bayol F, as vaccine adjuvant, 438
Bean pod mottle virus, preservation, 498
Bean (southern) mosaic virus, preserva-
    tion, 498
  thermal inactivation, 202
Bean yellow mosaic virus, preservation,
    498
Bean viruses, preservation, 495, 498
Beer-Lambert law, 103
Bethe-Bloch equation, 170
Binomial distribution, 645–650
  of tests of significance, 674–677
Blue tongue virus, classification, 603
Bovine contaminants, of vaccines, 456–
    457
Bovine diarrhea virus, classification, 607
Brome mosaic virus, preservation, 496
Brucella, mass immunization for, 441
Brucella abortus virus, interferon induc-
    tion by, 8
Bunyamwera virus, classification, 600
  interferon bioassay by, 19
Burkitt's lymphoma virus, in resistance
    to myxoviruses, 87
Bushy stunt virus, ionizing radiation ef-
    fects on, 161
  RNA content of, 160

C

Calcium-45, use in radiation biology, 144
Calf kidney culture, preparation, 353–
    354
Calf lymph smallpox, vaccine, 456
Canine contaminants of vaccines, 456–
    457
Canine distemper virus, classification,
    603, 607
  as vaccine contaminant, 456
Canine hepatitis virus, structure, 184
  as vaccine contaminant, 456
Canine renal tissue cultures, for virus-
    vaccine preparation, 404
  purity test, 410–411
Caprochlorone, as antiviral agent, assay,
    263

Capsomeres, 184–185
  definition and number, 576, 597
Carbon-14, use in radiation biology, 144
Carcinogenesis, by vaccines, possibility, 457–458
Carcinogenic hydrocarbons, as interferon-formation inhibitors, 45
Carnation, virus inhibitor in, 90
Cell cultures, in vaccine preparation, 379–385
  contamination, 453–454, 531–564
Certrifilmer, in virus inactivation, 433, 434
Cesium chloride solution, for density-gradient certrifugation, 361
Cherry (sour) necrotic ringspot virus, preservation, 499
Chicken embryo lethal orphan virus, 456
Chick embryo tissue cultures, for virus-vaccine preparation, 403–404
  contamination, 452–453
  purity test, 410
Chikungunya virus, interferon induction by, 7, 8, 16
  bioassay by, 19
Chlamydozoäceae, non-virus characteristic, 595, 610
Chloracetyl urea, as antiviral agent, assay, 276
Chloramphenicol, in Mycoplasma control, 557
7-Chlortetracycline, in Mycoplasma control, 557
Cholera, mass immunization for, 439
Chorioallantoic membrane, in antiviral agent testing, 256, 265–267
Chu inhibitors of myxoviruses, 74–75
Cobalt-60, use in radiation biology, 143, 144, 156
Col factors, 566–567
  elimination of, 580–581
  genetic transfer of, 574–581
    by cell-to-cell conjugation, 575–576
    by high-frequency colicinogeny transfer, 576–577
    by other factors, 578
    phage-mediated transduction of, 578–580
Colds, rhinoviruses as cause, 387

Colicines, 565–592
  bacterial strains resistant to, 569–570
  demonstration on agar plates, 567–569
  detection of colicinogenic strains, 567–581
  isolation, 587–588
  lacunae assay, 582–584
  mode of action, 588–591
  molecular weight determination of, 588
  production of, 581–588
    induction, 587
  titration of 582, 585–586
    killing particles, 585–586
    punch-hole assay, 585
    spot test, 585
  type identification, 570–572
Colicinogenic bacteria, separation from noncolicinogenic cells, 572–574
Colorimeters, in virus-inactivation studies, 101–102
Contingency tables, 642–644
Copper sulfate, as antiviral agent, assay, 248
Cortisone, as interferon-formation inhibitor, 45
Cowpea chlorotic mottle virus, optical diffraction studies, 522, 528
Cowpox virus, antiviral agents for, assay, 252
  classification, 600
  in smallpox resistance, 372
Cox vaccine for typhus, 379
Coziella burneti, antiviral agents for, assay, 258
Coxsackie B virus, interferon induction by, 6, 8
Coxsackieviruses, inhibition of, 58
Cucumber green mottle mosaic virus, preservation, 499
Cucumber mosaic virus, preservation, 492, 494, 497
Cycloheximide, as interferon-formation inhibitor, 44–45
Cyclotron bombardment chamber, 170
Cysteamine, as protectant in radiobiology, 151
Cysteine, effect on interferons, 31
  as protectant in radiobiology, 151

d-Cytidine monophosphate hydroxy-methylase, in phage, radiation inactivation, 175, 177
d-Cytidylicdesaminase, in phage, radiation inactivation, 175

D

D₃₇ dose, in radiobiology, 150
Defective bacteriophages, 279–320
  complementation in, 311–315
  isolation of deletion mutants, 288–297
  isolation of point mutants, 282–288
  killing and lysis of cells, 318
  localization of defect, 305–311
  media for transduction studies, 291
  physiological block in, 312–319
Defective viruses, 321–350
  detection and properties, 297–305
  separation of defective particles, 301–305
Dehydration of plant viruses *in situ*, 494–499
6-Demethyl-7-chlortetracycline, in Mycoplasma control, 557
Dengue virus, inhibitors of, 81–83
  vaccine for, 378, 389–390
Density-gradient flotation, in virus purification, 363
Density-gradient certrifugation, in virus purification, 361–363
Deoxyribonucleic acid, *see* DNA
Deoxyviruses, classification methods, 596
Dermacentor andersoni, in spotted-fever vaccine preparation, 379
Dermovaccinia, antiviral agents for, assay, 248–250
5,6-Dichloro-1-β-D-ribofuranosylbenzimidàzole, as antiviral agent, assay, 266–267, 269
Dilution method, virus concentration by, 705–713
2,5-Dimethylbenzimidazole, as antiviral agent, assay, 268
DNA viruses, classification, 605, 607–608
Deuteron(s), distribution of ionizations and excitations around, 172
  properties, 145–146
Dienes stain, 547

DNA, circular type, thermal inactivation, 191–193
  ionizing radiation effects on, 142, 144, 152–153, 159–169
  thermostability of, 186–193, 198, 201
Dosimetry, in ionizing radiation of viruses, 146–148
  biological type, 148
  Fricke type, 146–147
  sodium cacodyte type, 147
Drakeol 6VR, as vaccine adjuvant, 438
Dry Ice, in virus preservation, 486–487
Duboscq colorimeter, 101–102
Dust vaccines, 441
Dyne, definition, 119

E

Eagle's solution, modified, 356
Eastern equine encephalitis virus, inhibitors, 81
  interferon induction by, 7
  bioassay by, 19, 20
  vaccine, 378, 389
Eaton agent, *see* Mycoplasma pneumoniae
ECHO virus 11, interference to, by rubella virus, 4
ECHO viruses, classification methods, 600
  inactivation, 57
Ectromelia virus, classification, 600
Edmonston strain of measles virus, vaccine from, 383–385
EEL photoelectric colorimeter, 102
Egg albumin, thermal inactivation, 203–204
Eggs, use in antiviral agent tests, 255–274
Einstein (energy unit), definition, 119, 120
Electron microscopy, optical diffraction methods in, *see* Optical diffractometer
Electron volt, definition, 119, 120
Encephalitis viruses, inhibitors of, 72
  vaccines for, 378
Encephalomyocarditis virus, antiviral agents for, assay, 270–272
  classification, 601

inhibitors of, 78–80
interferon bioassay by, 19, 20
preservation, 483
Enders' measles virus vaccine, 383, 384
Endotoxin, interferon induction by, 8, 13
biosynthesis, 42–43
Energy radiation, units for, 118–120
Enteric coated capsules of vaccine, 436
Enteroviruses, in respiratory tract disease, 387
thermal inactivation, 203
Envelopes, in viruses, 598
Enzymes, UV inactivation, 99
Episomes, 566
Equine encephalitis virus, interference to, by influenza virus, 3
vaccine for, 378
Erg, definition, 119
Erythromycin, in Mycoplasma control, 557
Escherichia coli, colicinogenic strains, 569, 571, 572, 574, 578–581
strain ∅, in colicine tests, 569, 589–590
Escherichia freundii, colicinogenic strain, 571
Experimental design, 615–730
factorial exepriments, 635–638
Latin squares, 631–634
quantities computed from data, 634–635
randomization, 626–627
variation elimination, 627–634
randomized blocks, 627–631

F

Factorial experiments, 635–638
Far East encephalitis virus, inhibitors of, 72
Fermi vaccine for rabies, 374
Ferrioxalate actinometer, 122
(*See also* Potassium ferrioxalate actionometer)
Ferrous–ferric sulfute system dosimetry, 146–147
Filters, for UV radiation, 94–96
Fluorodinitrobenzene, effect, on interferons, 31
p-Fluorophenylalanine, as interferon-formation inhibitor, 44, 47

Foamy viruses, as vaccine contaminants, 456
Foot-and-mouth disease virus,
assay, 352
concentration and purification, 359–363
by density-gradient centrifugation, 361–363
by density-gradient flotation, 363
interferon induction by, 6, 7
occurrence in Western Hemisphere, 465
precautions against in U.S.A., 465
preparation in quantity, 352–366
purity and viral parameters, 364–366
stability, 358–359
thermal inactivation, 197, 200, 203
Formaldehyde, use in virus inactivation, 430–432
Fowl leukosis virus, as vaccine contaminant, 391
Fowl sarcoma virus, classification methods, 595
Fowl tumor viruses, classification, 598, 603, 607
Fowlpox virus, classification, 598, 602
Francis inhibitors, *see* α-(Neuraminic acid) inhibitors of myxoviruses
Freeze-drying, of viruses, 482, 483–484
animal, 488–489
plant, 492–494
Freezing, of animal viruses, 486–487
of plant viruses, 492
Frequency distribution(s), binomial distribution, 645–650
contingency tables, 642–644
statistical definition, 620
Freund's mineral adjuvants, for vaccines, 437–438
Fricke dosimetry, 146–147
Friend virus, ionizing radiation inactivation of, 176
Fusidic acid, in Mycoplasma control, 557

G

γ-inhibitor, as antiviral agent, assay, 213–214, 238, 246–247

γ-Rays,
properties, 143–144
Genetron, dissociation of antigen-antibody complex by, 57
Gentamicin, in Mycoplasma control, 557
Glucosol solution, 262, 265
Glutathione, as protectant in radiobiology, 151, 158
Glycerol storage of animal viruses, 484–485
of plant viruses, 500–501
Guinea pig contaminants of vaccines, 456–457
Guanidine, in interferon production, 45
in virus classification, 601

H

Heat, virus inactivation by, see Thermal inactivation of viruses
Helenine, as interferon-inducing factor, 48
Hemadsorption viruses, as vaccine contaminants, 456
Hemoglobin, thermal inactivation, 201
Hemophilus influenzae, DNA, thermal stability, 186
Herpes simplex virus, antiviral agents for assay, 235, 237
interferon induction by, 7, 10
structure, 184
Herpes viruses, classification methods, 597, 602, 605, 608
inhibitors of, 76, 84, 88
interference by, 4
interferon induction by, 7
nuclear inclusions of, 602
Human virus vaccines, preparation, 371–464
Human wart virus, optical diffraction studies, 516
Hyaluronidase, effect on α-(neuraminic acid) inhibitors, 63
Hydrocortisone, as interferon-formation inhibitor, 45
Hydrogen-3, use in radiation biology, 144, 145
2(α-Hydroxybenzyl) benzimidazole, in virus classification, 601

5-Hydroxytetracycline, in Mycoplasma control, 557
Hygromycin B, in Mycoplasma control, 557
Hypospray Jet-Injector, 439–442

I

Immunization, mass methods of, 439–443
by aerosols, 440–443
by jet guns, 439–440
Inclusion bodies, use in virus classification, 601
Infectious bronchitis virus, classification, 607
Infectious laryngotracheitis virus, in chickens, 456
Influenza A virus, radiation inactivation of, 176
Influenza viruses, antiviral agents for, 212
assay, 213, 217, 222–223, 229, 238–246, 262–263, 266
classification methods, 595, 596, 607
DNA, thermal stability, 186–187
inhibitors of, 66–67, 73, 75, 84
interference by, to equine encephalitis virus, 3
interferon for, 2, 3
interferon induction by, 8, 10, 11, 13, 14–15
bioassay by, 19, 21
mass immunization for, 441
vaccine, 389
contamination, 392
formulations, 438
preparation, 368, 376–377, 378
Interference, in animal virus-cell systems, 3–5
auto-, type, 3
heterologous type, 3
homologous type, 3
Interferon(s), 1–52
adsorption of, 27
in animal virus-cell systems, 152
antigenicity of, 28
bioassay, 17–25
cell system for, 18–19
indicator virus, 19–20

precision, 18
sensitivity, 18
titration methods, 20–25
biosynthesis, 40–45
  in animals, 44
  endotoxin-induced types, 42–43
  inhibitors, 44
  model systems, 43–45
  of virus-induced types, 41–42
centrifugation, 35–38
  equilibrium sedimentation, 36
  zonal-rate type, 36–38
chromatography of, 33–34
  on CMC, 33–34
  on CM-Sephadex, 34
definition, 2–3
effect on T antigen formation, 48
  on viral RNA synthesis, 47
electrophoresis, 34–35
enzyme effect on, 30
heat effects on, 29
in heterologous interference, 3
identification by biological tests, 25–28
from leukocytes, 12–13
molecular sieve filtration, 38–40
oxidation-reducing agents effect on, 30–31
pH effects on, 28–29
physical and chemical effects on, 28–31
physical properties, 31–40
precipitation, 32–33
  by, acetone and alcohol, 33
  by acid, 32–33
  by ammonium sulfate, 32
  by zinc acetate, 33
production 5–17, 48
  in animals, 13–14
  bacteria effects on, 3
  choice of virus, 6–11
  inactivated virus and, 10
  inducible cells, 11–13
  inducing agents, 14
  multiplicity factor in, 9
  reinduction, 11
  strain variation in, 10
purification, 31–40, 48
species specificity, 27
storage, 31

study methods, 45–48
UV irradiation of, 29–30
viruses inducing, choice, 6–11
Ionizing radiation, effects on living systems, 140
  indirect, 151–153
  free radicals from, 151–153
  inactivation of viruses by, 139–209
    D_{3t} dose, 150
    dosimetry, 146–148
    molecular weight from, 154–174
    nucleic acid role in, 140–142
    phosphate effects on, 151–152
    radiation types, 143–146
    selective, 174–179
    target theory, 148–174
  protective agents against, 151
  types, 143–146
Iridescent insect viruses, classification methods, 605
Isatin β-thiosemicarbazone, as antiviral agent, assay, 237, 251, 252

J

Japanese B encephalitis virus, inhibitors of, 72
  vaccine, 389
    preparation, 378
Jet guns, for for mass immunization, 439–440
Joule, definition, 119

K

K virus, classification, 603
Kanamycin, in Mycoplasma control, 557, 559
Klebsiella, colicinogenic strains of, 574

L

Laboratory design, for animal-pathogen research, 472–476
Lacunae assay for colicines, 582–584
Lambert's law, 112
Lamps, for UV radiation, 94–96
Laser, in optical diffractometer, 504–506, 508
Latent rat virus, classification, 605, 608

Latin squares, in experimental design, 631–634

LCM, as vaccine contaminants, 456

Lecithinlike viral-inhibitor, 72–74

Lee virus, antiviral agents for, assay, 267–269

Lemon balm extract, as antiviral agent, assay, 257, 260, 272, 273

Leukemia agent, as possible vaccine contaminant, 457

Leukosis viruses, classification methods, 603, 607

Lily-fleck corn virus, presentation, 492, 497

Linear energy transfer (LET) of charged particles, 145

Lipid inhibitors of viruses, 72–74

Lymphoma agent, as possible vaccine contaminant, 457

Lyophilization, see Freeze-drying

Lysozyme, in phage, UV inactivation, 177

M

Malachite green leukocyanide actinometer, 125–126

Mannide monooleate, use in virus vaccines, 437

MC 2343, as antiviral agent, assay, 261

Measels virus, classification, 602, 603
  interferon induction by, 7, 8
  mass immunization, for, 440
  thermal inactivation, 200
  vaccine, 378, 380, 389
    clinical trials, 428
    formulations, 436
    from killed virus, 383–384, 402, 403, 408, 413, 414–415
    live-virus type, 384–385, 416–417, 418–419, 420–421, 422, 423, 426
    potency, 413
    preparation, 383–385, 454
    standards, 383–385, 402
    tests, 414–415
  variants of, 384

Megacines, 565

β-Mercaptoethanol, effect on interferons, 30, 31

Mercury lamps, for UV radiation, 95–96

Metaphase arrest, in viral inhibition, 88

7-Methylisatin β-thiosemicarbazone, as antiviral agent, assay, 236–238

N-Methyl-N'-nitro-N-nitrosoguanidine, effect on col factors, 581

Δ', 17α-Methyltestosterone, as interferon-formation inhibitor, 45

Mice, in antiviral agent assay, 213 ff.
  for virus-vaccine production, tests on 412

Microbiological safety program at Plum Island Animal Disease Laboratory, 466–472

Microwatt, definition, 119

Milliwatt, definition, 119

Mitomycin c, in colicine preparation, 588

Molecular weight of viruses, by target theory, 154–174

Monkey B virus, vaccine development, 390

Monkey kidney tissue, for tissue culture of viruses, 403, 417–418
  contamination, 452, 455–456
  purity test, 409–410

Monochromators, for UV radiation, 97–98

Mouse cytomegalovirus, interferon, failure to induce, 6, 9

Mouse leukemia virus, classification, 597

Mucoid inhibitors, of bacteriophages, 72
  of mumps virus, 69, 72
  of pneumonia virus of mice, 69, 72

Mucopolysaccharides, as virus inhibitor, 68–69

Mumps virus, classification methods, 596, 607
  inhibitor of, 69, 72
  vaccine development, 378, 386–387, 389
  formulations, 436

Murine leukosis viruses, as vaccine contaminants, 391

Murray Valley encephalitis virus, inhibitors for, 84

M. tuberculosis, in virus vaccines, 437

Mycoplasma, antibiotic treatment of, 556–558
  antiserum treatment of, 558–559
  artifacts and controls, 547–552

bacteria L forms and, 532, 534–535
cell-culture contamination by, 531–564
  cultivation, 541–542
  detection 535–541
  elimination, 552–559
  identification, 542–544
  prevention and control, 559
  sources, 533–535
  subculture of, 545
  "fried egg" type, 545, 547
  media for, 545–547
  properties, 532–533
Mycoplasma pneumoniae, isolation, 539
  test for in vaccines, 409
  Streptococcus MG and, 535
  vaccine development, 387
Myxomatosis virus, classification, 602
Myxovirus Yucaipa, in chickens, 456
Myxoviruses, antiviral agents for, assay, 265, 267–268
  Burkitt's lymphoma and resistance to, 87
  classification method, 596, 601, 604, 606, 607
  β-inhibitors of, 74–75
  interferon induction by, 6, 7, 10
  bioassay by, 19, 20
  α-(neuraminic acid) inhibitors of, 61–66
  γ-(neuraminic acid) inhibitors of, 66–67
  thermal inactivation, 203

N

Necropsy rooms, for animal-pathogen laboratories, 478
Neomycin, in Mycoplasma control, 557
  in vaccine production, 444–445
α-(Neuraminic acid) inhibitors of myxoviruses, 61–66
  characterization, 61–63
  purification, 63–66
γ-(Neuraminic acid) inhibitors of myxoviruses, 66–67
  neuraminidase effect on, 66–67
  purification of, 67
Neuraminidase, effect on γ-inhibitors of myxoviruses, 66–67

Neurovaccinia virus, antiviral agents for, assay, 236–238, 248–251, 252
Newcastle disease virus, antiviral agents for, assay, 257, 260, 273–275
  classification methods, 596, 607
  inhibition of, 58, 73, 76
  interference to, by rubella virus, 3–4
  interferon induction by, 7, 8, 9–19, 25
  biosynthesis, 41–45
  ionizing radiation effects on, 160
  RNA, content of, 160
  thermal inactivation, 197, 200, 203
Nitrogen (liquid), in virus preservation, 487, 492
Nothoscordum mosaic virus, preservation, 497
Novobiocin, in Mycoplasma control, 557
Nuclear polyhedrosis viruses, classification methods, 605, 609
Nucleic acid (viral), interferon and, 14
  ionizing radiation effects on, 140–142, 154–174
  thermostability of, 186–196, 202
Nucleocapsid, definition, 596

O

Oat mosaic virus, preservation, 493, 497, 500
Oil adjuvants, for virus vaccines, 437–439
Oils, as adjuvants for vaccines, 437–439
Oncogeny potential of vaccine contaminants, 457–458
Optical density, of spectrophotometers, definition, 101
Optical diffractometer, 503–529
  apparatus, 504–507
  experimental procedure, 510–511
  laser for, 504–506, 508
  optical-system alignment, 507
  use, 511–527
Orf virus, classification, 598

P

Papillomaviruses, *see* Papovaviruses
Papovaviruses, classification methods, 597, 603, 605, 607–608
  interferon induction by, 7

Paracoli, colicinogenic strains, 571
Parainfluenza viruses, classification methods, 596, 607
  interferon induction by, 7, 8, 10, 11
  in respiratory tract disease, 387–389
  vaccine development, 388–389
Paramyxoviruses, classification, 606, 607
Paromomycin, in Mycoplasma control, 557
Pea streak virus, preservation, 498
Pea viruses, preservation, 495, 498
Peanut oil adjuvant, for vaccines, 438–439
Penicillin, in Mycoplasma control, 560
Pepsin, thermal inactivation, 201
Phage, *see* Bacteriophages
Penanthroline, reagent for actinometry, 127
Phenyl isothiocyanate, effect on interferons, 31
Phosphate ions, effects on virus irradiation, 151–152, 158
Phosphorus-32, use in radiation biology, 144, 145
Phosphorus-33, use in radiation biology, 145
Photoelectric cells, in UV radiation measurement, 122
Picornaviruses, classification methods, 601, 604, 606
  interferon induction by, 6, 7, 11
Plant, age and virus susceptibility, 665
Plant viruses, acetone powders of, 499–500
  assay of, plants for, 500
  chemical dehydration *in situ,* 494–499
  classification methods, 596, 597, 600, 606, 609, 611
  elongated types, 606
  defective, 344–348
  freeze-drying of, 492–494
  freezing of, 492
  glycerine storage of, 500–501
  inhibitors of, 89–90
  preservation and storage of, 491–501
  thermal inactivation, 200
Plaque-inhibition assay, of interferon, 22–25
Plasmids, 566

Platinum phthalocyanine, electron micrography, 511–512, 522, 527
Pleuropneumonia-like organisms, *see* Mycoplasma
Plum Island Animal Disease Laboratory, 465–480
  animal facilities, 476–478
  animal supply, 476
  laboratory design, 472–476
  laboratory techniques in, 478–480
  microbiological safety program at, 466–472
  pathogen-containment methods at, 465–480
  necropsy facilities, 478
  operational procedures, 474–475
  sewage and air control, 475–476
  traffic control, 473–474
Pneumoccocus, DNA of, thermal inactivation, 188–189, 190
Pneumonia virus of mice, inhibitors of, 69, 72
Poisson distribution, 650–656
  of tests of significance, 674–677
Poliovirus(es), glutamine requirement of, 86
  inhibition of, 58, 76–78, 80, 89
  interference by, 4, 5, 6
  interferon induction by, 7, 11
  preparation in quantity, 366–368
  structure, 184
  thermal inactivation, 197, 200, 202
  vaccine(s), 389
    clinical trials, 427–428
    contamination, 380, 391, 455
    formulations, 436, 438
    killed-virus type, 402, 404–405, 413–414
    live-virus type, 416–423, 425–427
    oral, 381–382
    potency, 413, 425
    preparation, 380–382, 454
    Sabin type, 381
    Salk type, 380
    standards, 382, 402
    SV40 in, 380, 391
    tests, 413–414
Polyomavirus, classification, 597, 603, 607
  DNA, content of, 160
    thermal inactivation, 189, 192, 202

interferon induction by, 7, 10
ionizing radiation effect on,
  inactivation, 176, 178
  molecular weight by, 160
structure, 184
tubular particle, optical diffraction
  studies, 525
UV inactivation, 176
Positive ions, properties, 145
Potassium ferrioxalate actinometer,
  126–129
  procedure for use, 127–129
  reagents for, 126–127
Potato Canada streak virus, preservation of, 493
Potato vein-banding mosaic virus, preservation of, 493
Potato X virus, absorption spectrum,
  105, 106
  preservation, 497, 499
Potato Y virus, preservation, 497
Powassan virus, interferon induction by,
  8
Power, radiation, units for, 119
Poxviruses, antiviral agents for, assay,
  252
  classification methods, 595, 597, 598,
    608
  interferon induction by, 7
Probability, in statistical analysis, 638–
  642
Properdin, as viral inhibitor, 76
β-Propiolactone, use in virus inactivation, 432–433
1-Propylisatin β-thiosemicarbazone, as
  antiviral agent, assay, 236
Protein, denaturation, 186
Proteus, colicinogenic strains of, 574,
  575
Proteus X19, Rickettsia prowazeki and,
  535
Protons, properties, 145–146
Providencia, colicinogenic strains of, 574
Psittacosis virus, amino acids in synthesis of, 87
  inhibitors of, 73
  vaccine for, 378
Puromycin, as interferon-formation inhibitor, 44–45
Pyocines, 565

Q

Q fever agent, vaccine development, 390
Quantum, definition, 119, 120
Quantum efficiency, in UV inactivation
  of viruses, 133

R

Rabbit kidney vacuolating virus, classi-
  fication, 603
Rabbit myxoma virus, classification, 598
Rabbit pox virus, antiviral agents for,
  assay, 253
Rabbits, for virus-vaccine production,
  tests, 411–412
Rabies virus, classification, 606
  preservation, 482
  vaccine, 389
    formulations, 436
    preparation, 374–375, 378, 389
    subunit type, 392–393
Radiation, ionizing, see Ionizing radiation
  UV see Ultraviolet radiation
Randomization, in experimental design,
  626–627
Rattle virus, optical diffraction studies
  on, 521
Rayleigh's law, 115
Receptor-destroying enzyme, effect, on
  α-(neuraminic acid) inhibitors, 62–
  63
Refrigeration of animal viruses, 485–486
Reoviruses, classification methods, 597,
  603, 606
  in respiratory tract diseases, 307
Respiratory syncytial viruses, in respiratory disease, 387, 388
  vaccine development, 388–389
Respiratory tract diseases, adenoviruses
  as causes of, 382
  vaccine development, 388–389
  viruses causing, 387–388
Respiratory virus complex, vaccine development, 387–389
  problems, 387
Rhinoviruses, classification methods, 601
  in respiratory tract diseases, 387
  vaccine, 454

Rhizobium bacteriophage, UV inactivation of, 133
Ribonuclease, thermal inactivation, 201
Ribonucleic acid, *see* RNA
Riboviruses, classification methods, 596
Rickettsia, as bacteria, 610
Rickettsia prowazeki, Proteus X19 and, 535
vaccine from, 379
Rickettsia rickettsia, vaccine from, 379
Rickettsial agents, vaccines for, 378, 379, 389–390
Rift Valley fever virus, classification, 602
vaccine development, 390
Rinderpest virus, classification, 603, 607
RNA, hydrolysis of, 195
ionizing radiation effects on, 154–155
thermostability, 193–196, 201
mRNA, 173
RNA viruses, classification, 604, 606–607
Rocky Mountain Spotted Fever Rickettsia, vaccine, 379
Rodent leukemia viruses, classification, 603
Rous associated virus, RSV and, 323–324
Rous inhibitory factor (RIF), interference by, 4
Rous sarcoma virus, defective, 322–332, 348
antigenic specificity, 339–340
cytological methods, 330–331
demonstration of, 326–332
experiments, 332–344
host range, 340–342
properties of, 338–344
recognition, 322–326
helper virus for, 327–328
ionizing radiation effects, on inactivation, 176
molecular weight by, 159, 160
inhibition of, 58–59, 76
interferon induction by, 7, 11
bioassay by, 22
preservation, 483
RNA, content of, 160
Rubella virus, detection, 447
interference by, ECHO virus 11, 4

to Newcastle disease virus, 3–4
interferon induction by, 7
vaccine development, 385–386, 389, 454
formulations, 436
Russian encephalitis virus, antiviral-agent assay, 270
inhibitors of, 72
interferon induction by, 11
vaccine, 378, 389
preparation, 378

S

Sabin oral poliovirus vaccine, 381–382
Sabouraud medium, for virus vaccine, 399–400
Salk vaccine for poliovirus, development, 380
poliovirus preparation for, 366–368
Salmonella spp., colicinogenic strains, 574, 576
Salmonella typhimurium, colicigenic, strain, 568, 572, 575, 576, 578, 579, 580, 584, 587
Sarcoma agent, as possible vaccine contaminant, 457
Scatter of radiation, calculation of, 113–118
definition, 112–113
Scattering constant, 115
Scrapie virus, classification, 601
Selenium photocells for UV radiation measurement, 122
Semliki Forest virus, antiviral agents for, assay, 257, 273
interferon bioassay by, 19, 46
Semple vaccine for rabies, 374
Sendai virus, interferon bioassay by, 19
Serratia, colicinogenic strains of, 574–581
Serum albumin, thermal inactivation, 201
Sewage, from animal-pathogen laboratories, disposal of, 475–476
Shigella spp., colicinogenic strains, 574
Shigella boydii, colicinogenic strain, 571
Shigella dispar, colicinogenic strain, 571
Shigella sonnei, colicinogenic strain, 571, 572, 575, 576, 587

Shope papilloma virus, DNA content of, 161
  ionizing radiation effects on, molecular weight by, 161
Sigma virus of *Drosophila,* classification, 606
Significance, tests of, 667–705
  analysis of variance, 690–696
  coefficients of linear regression and correlation, 684–687
  of means and differences, 677–679
  R test, 687–689
  random selection in, 668–671
  of a single number, 703–705
  t test, 679–687
  transformation of the variate, 696–703
Simian contaminants of vaccines, 455–456
Simian virus 5, interferon induction by, 6
  in man, 456
Simian virus 40, classification, 607
  incorporation into adenovirus, 599
  interferon effects on, 48
  as vaccine contaminant, 380, 382, 391, 455–456
Sindbis virus, interferon induction by, 7, 8, 12
  bioassay by, 19
Smallpox, vaccine for, *see* Vaccinia virus, vaccine preparation
Specification, statistical definition, 620
Spotted fever virus, vaccine, 378
S. lactis phage, thermal inactivation, 201
Sodium acetate, as radiosensitivity potentiator, 152
Sodium cacodylate dosimetry, 147
Sodium chloride, as radiosensitivity potentiator, 152
Sodium periodate, effect on interferons, 31
Sodium thioglycollate, effect on interferons, 31
Southern bean mosaic virus, *see* Bean (southern) mosaic virus
Spectrophotometers, in virus-inactivation studies, 100–101
Spinach, virus inhibitor in, 89–90
Spiramycin, in Mycoplasma control, 557

Standard deviation, statistical definition, 620
Standard errors, statistical definition, 621
Staphylococcus phage K, ionizing radiation effects on, size and shape by, 174
  thermal inactivation of, 180
Statistical methods of assay, 615–730
  binomial distribution, 644–650
  bivariate and multivariate distributions, 661–667
  definitions, 617–638
  frequency distributions in, 642–667
  normal distribution, 656–661
  Poisson distribution, 650–656
  probability, 638–642
  summation symbol, 616–617
  sums of squares in, 624
  tests of significance in, 667–705
  virus concentration estimation, 705–730
Statolon, interferon induction by, 14
Steroid hormones, as interferon-formation inhibitor, 45
St. Louis encephalitis virus, inhibitors of, 72, 84
Streptomycin, in Mycoplasma control, 560
Student's ratio, in statistics, 680
Sugarcane mosaic virus, preservation, 492, 497
Sulfhydryl compounds, as protectants in radiobiology, 151, 158
Sulfur-35, use in radiation biology, 142
Summation symbol, 616–617
Sums of squares, 624
SV40 virus, *see* Simian virus 40
Swine fever virus, classification, 607

T

T(transmissible interfering factor), 4–5
Target theory in virus irradiation, 148–174
  action probability of a hit, 151
  anoxic effect, 153
  host-cell reactivation, 153–154
  indirect effects, 151–153
  methods and application, 149–154

molecular weight from, 154–174

size and shape from, 169–174

Tetracycline, in Mycoplasma control, 557

Theiler's virus (GD VII), mucopolysaccharide inhibitor of, 68–69

action, 68–69

properties, 68

purification, 68, 70–71

Therapeutic index, in antiviral agent assay, 251–255

Thermal inactivation of viruses, 139, 180–205

in dry or wet heat, 204

kinetic analysis, 196–199

reaction rate theory, 181–184

virus structure and, 184–196

Thermopiles, for radiation measurement, 120–122

Thioglycollate medium, for virus vaccine, 399–400

Thymidine, radiation effects on, 153

Tick-borne virus, see Russian tick-borne virus

Ticks, in spotted-fever vaccine preparation, 379

Tipula iridescent virus, classification, 597

Tissue cultures, for virus propagation, 403–404

contamination, 451–453

Tobacco etch virus, preservation, 494, 497

Tobacco mosaic virus, A protein, optical micrography, 513

concentration, statistical estimation, 722

defective variant, 346–347

diffraction studies, 503

interferon-like inhibitor for, 2

ionizing radiation effects on, inactivation, 146, 152

molecular weight by, 154–157

as standard, 148

physicochemical properties, 154–155

PM 2 strain, optical diffraction studies, 526

preservation, 491

structure, 184

thermal inactivation, 200–204

RNA of, content, 160

radiation effects on, 155, 160

thermal inactivation, 193–196, 201

UV radiation inactivation by, 133, 134, 174

scatter by, 113–114, 116

Tobacco necrosis virus, ionizing radiation effects on, molecular weight by, 160

preservation, 494

RNA content of, 160

satellite, 344–346

thermal inactivation, 200, 202

UV inactivation of, 133

Tobacco rattle virus, defective variant, 346–347

Tobacco ringspot virus, inhibition of, 89–90

ionizing radiation effects on, molecular weight by, 160

preservation, 492, 497, 499

RNA content of, 160

thermal inactivation, 200

Tobacco streak virus, 492, 497, 498

Tomato spotted wilt virus, preservation, 492, 493

Trachoma virus, vaccine development, 390

formulation, 438

Transmissible interfering factor (T), 4–5

Transmittance of spectrophotometers, calculation, 103

definition, 101

Trifluorotrichloroethane, see Genetron

Trypsin, effect on α-(neuraminic acid) inhibitors, 62

in interferon identification, 30

Tumor viruses, classification methods, 603

Turbidity, in UV radiation studies, 113

Turnip yellow mosaic virus, optical diffraction studies on, 519, 523

tubular inclusions, optical diffraction studies, 523–524

Tylosin, in Mycoplasma control, 557, 560

Typhoid virus, mass immunization, 440

Typhus, strain E, 379

vaccine, 378

preparation, 379

U

Ultraviolet radiation, virus inactivation by, 93–138
  action spectra, 137–138
  calculations, 102–118
  energy absorption, 99–118
  exposure methods, 98–99
  radiation measurement, 118–129
  radiation sources, 94–98
  rate measurement, 99, 129–138
  scatter of radiation energy, 112–118
  terminology, 102–118
  for vaccines, 433–434
  (see also Actinometry)
Uranyl oxalate actinometer, 123–125
  solution for, 123
Urea, effect on interferons, 30, 31
Urethan, as antiviral agent, assay, 223–224, 240–246
Urine, inhibitor precipitation from, 63–66

V

Vaccination, history of, 372
Vaccines (human viral),
  cell-culture technology, 379–385
  contaminants, 454–458
  experimental type, 385–390, 443–451
    clinicals trials in man, 449
    production, 443–446
    requirements, 450–451
    testing, 447–448
  formulations of, 435–439
    adjuvants, 415, 436–439
    aqueous, 435–436
    enteric coated capsules, 436
    lyophilized, 436
  future developments, 390–393
  historical development, 373–393
  inactivation methods, 430–435
    combination, 434–435
    β-propiolactone, 432–433
    formaldehyde, 430–432
    UV irradiation, 433–434
  killed-virus type manufacturing standards, 402–416
    adjuvants, 415

clarification, 404–405
  dosage and labeling, 415
  extraneous protein, 415
  inactivation, 405
  potency, 413
  preservatives, 408
  residual live virus, 406–408
  testing, 409–413
  tissue culture for, 403–404
  virus strains, 402–403
  killed vs. live type, 429–430
  live-virus type manufacturing standards, 416–429
    production, 416–421
    testing, 421–426
    virus propagation, 419
  manufacturing standards, 393–402
    animals, 396–397
    equipment, 396
    records, 397
    retention samples, 397
    work areas, 394–396
  mass immunization by, 439–443
  pre-cell culture technology, 373–379
  product standards, cultures, 401
    dating and storage, 401–402
    general safety, 399
    ingredients, 401
    labels, 398
    potency, 398–399
    purity and identity, 400
    release protocols, 400–401
    release requirements, 398
    sterility, 399–400
  special problems in, 451–458
    adventitious agents, 454–458
    propagation system, 451–454
  tests on, statistical significance, 669
Vaccinia virus, antiviral agents for, assay, 234, 257, 261, 273, 275, 276
  classification, 598, 600
  DNA, content of, 161
  inhibitor of, 76, 88
  interferon induction by, 7
    bioassay by, 19
  ionizing radiation effects on, molecular weight by, 161
    size and shape by, 169
  mass immunization for, 440
  preservation, 481

thermal inactivation of, 197
vaccination, history, 372
vaccine, 389
  contamination, 391, 456, 457
  formulations, 436
  preparation, 373, 378
Variable, statistical definition, 618–619
Variola virus, classification, 600
  inhibitors of, 75
Venezuelan equine encephalomyelitis virus, inhibitors of, 81
  vaccine, 378
Vesicular stomatis virus, classification, 597, 602–603, 606
  interferon, failure to induce, 9
  as interferon-bioassay indicator, 20, 23, 27–28
Vinblastine, metaphase arrest by, 88
Viral inhibitor(s), 53–92
  antibody, to host cell, 58–59
  to virus, 55–57
  β-inhibitors of myxoviruses, 74–76
  in bovine serum, 76–77
  classification, 60
  in equine serum, 77–78
  heat-labile, 74–76
  heat-stable, 76–78
  host-induced modification of, 85–86
  inapparent and latent infections, 87
  lipid type, 72–74
  metaphase arrest as, 88
  methods for study, 53–92
  mucopolysaccharide type, 68–69
  mycoplasms contamination of tissue culture cells, 86–87
  α-(neuraminic acid) type, 61–66
  γ-(neuraminic acid) type, 66–67
  nonspecific, 60–90
  in the overlay plating agar, 78–84
  phosphatase content and, 88
  properdin as, 76
  tissue cultures from immune animals, 88–89
  virus–cell interaction and, 89
Virus classification, 593–613
  criteria for, 594
  envelopes in, 598
  hemagglutinins in, 599
  at lower levels, characteristics, 599
    antigenic structure, 599–600

    biological behavior, 602–603
    inclusion-body formation, 601–602
    site of growth, 600–601
    stability, 601
    tropisms, pathology, and symptomatology, 603
  of major groups, criteria, 595–599
    chemical composition, 595–596
    genetic characters, 599
    morphology, 596–599
    nomenclature, 603–610
  projections in, 599
  simple tests for, 612
Viruses, classification of, see Virus classification
  defective, see Defective viruses
  DNA-containing, detection, 595–596, 605, 607, 608
  electron micrography, 515
  estimation of concentration, statistical, 705–730
    by dilution method, 705–713
    by local lesion method, 716–724
    by plaque count, 713–716
  inhibitors of, see Viral inhibitors
  ionizing radiation in activation of, 139–209
  molecular weight of by target theory, 154–174
  optical diffraction studies, 511–529
  plant, see Plant viruses
  plant susceptibility to, age and, 665
  preparation, large-scale, 352–368
  preservation and storage, 481–501
  prophyalctic and therapeutic agents for, see Antiviral agents
  RNA-containing, detection, 595–596, 604, 606–607, 609
  size and shape, from target theory, 169–174
  structure of, 184–196
  thermal inactivation of, 139, 180–205
  UV inactivation of, 93–138
  vaccine, see Vaccines

W

Wart viruses, classification methods 607–608

Watt, definition, 119

West Nile virus, interferon induction by, 8

Western equine encephalomyelitis virus, inhibitors of, 81
  interferon induction by, 7, 11
    bioassay by, 22
  vaccine, 389

Wheat mosaic virus, preservation, 497

Wheat streak mosaic virus, preservation, 497

Wheel of microbiological safety, 467

White cowpox virus, antiviral agents for, assay, 252

Wound tumor virus, classification, 606

X

X-rays, properties, 143–144

χ_2 test, 671–677

Y

Yellow fever virus, interferon induction by, 8
  mass immunization for, 440
  vaccine, 389
  contamination, 391, 457
    formulations, 436
    for neurotropic strain, 376
    preparation, 375–376, 378
    standards, 376
    for strain 17D, 375–376